LONG + LIVE + MATH

High School Math Solution
Integrated Math II

Student Edition
Volume 2

Sandy Bartle Finocchi and Amy Jones Lewis

with Josh Fisher, Janet Sinopoli, and Victoria Fisher

501 Grant St., Suite 1075
Pittsburgh, PA 15219
Phone 888.851.7094
Customer Service Phone 412.690.2444
Fax 412.690.2444

www.carnegielearning.com

Cover Design by Anne Milliron

ISBN: 978-1-60972-414-6
Student Edition, Volume 2

Printed in the United States of America
2 3 4 5 6 7 8 9 B&B 21 20

LONG + LIVE + MATH

ACKNOWLEDGMENTS

High School Math Solution Authors

- Sandy Bartle Finocchi, Senior Academic Officer
- Amy Jones Lewis, Director of Instructional Design
- Josh Fisher, Instructional Designer
- Victoria Fisher, Instructional Designer
- Janet Sinopoli, Instructional Designer

Foundational Authors

- William S. Hadley, Co-Founder
- David Dengler
- Mary Lou Metz

Vendors

- Lumina Datamatics, Ltd.
- Mathematical Expressions, LLC

Images

www.pixabay.com

Special Thanks

- Alison Huettner for project management and editorial review.
- Jacyln Snyder for her contributions to the Teacher's Implementation Guide facilitation notes.
- Harry Lynch for his contributions and review of the Statistics and Probability strand.
- The members of Carnegie Learning Cognitive Scientist Team—Brendon Towle, John Connelly, Bob Hausmann, Chas Murray, and Martina Pavelko—for their insight in learning science and collaboration on MATHia® Software.
- John Jorgenson, Chief Marketing Officer, for all his insight and messaging.
- Carnegie Learning Education Services Team for content review and providing customer feedback.
- The entire Carnegie Learning staff for their hard work and dedication to transforming math education.
- The families of the authoring team for their continued support.

Mathematics is so much more than memorizing rules. It is learning to reason, to make connections, and to make sense of the world. We believe in Learning by Doing(TM)—you need to actively engage with the content if you are to benefi t from it. The lessons were designed to take you from your intuitive understanding of the world and build on your prior experiences to then learn new concepts. My hope is that these instructional materials help you build a deep understanding of math.

Sandy Bartle Finocchi, Senior Academic Officer

You have been learning math for a very long time—both in school and in your interactions in the world. You know a lot of math! In this course, there's nothing brand new. It all builds on what you already know. So, as you approach each activity, use all of your knowledge to solve problems, to ask questions, to fix mistakes, and to think creatively.

Amy Jones Lewis, Director of Instructional Design

At Carnegie Learning we have created an organization whose mission and culture is defined by your success. Our passion is creating products that make sense of the world of mathematics and ignite a passion in you. Our hope is that you will enjoy our resources as much as we enjoyed creating them.

Barry Malkin, CEO, Carnegie Learning

TABLE OF CONTENTS

Volume 1 Student Edition

Module 1: Reasoning with Shapes

Module 2: Investigating Proportionality

Topic 1: Similarity

Topic 2: Trigonometry

Topic 3: Circles and Volume

Volume 2 Student Edition

Module 3: Exploring Functions

Topic 1: Functions Derived from Linear Relationships

Topic 2: Exponentials

Topic 3: Introduction to Quadratic Functions

Module 4: Seeing Structure

Topic 1: Solving Quadratic Equations

Topic 2: Applications of Quadratic Equations

Topic 3: Circles on a Coordinate Plane

Module 5: Making Informed Decisions

Topic 1: Independence and Conditional Probability

Topic 2: Computing Probabilities

MODULE 3

EXPLORING FUNCTIONS

The lessons in this module build on what you already know about functions. In this module, you will explore functions that are derived from linear functions. You will then deepen your understanding of exponential functions and learn a new rule of exponents. Finally, you will learn the key characteristics of a new function type—quadratic functions. You will discover that the different function transformations affect all function types the same way.

TOPIC 1

Functions Derived from Linear Relationships

Absolute value functions are V-shaped, like this skein of geese. (Did you know that a group of geese is called a skein *in the sky, but a* gaggle *on the ground?)*

Module 3: Exploring Functions

TOPIC 1: FUNCTIONS DERIVED FROM LINEAR RELATIONSHIPS

Students begin this topic with a reminder about absolute value. They calculate the absolute value of given values before considering the linear absolute value function. Students first graph the function $f(x) = x$, and then graph $f(x) = |x|$ discussing how the graph changed. The process is repeated for $f(x) = |-x|$. Students explore transformations of the function, and they graph and analyze linear piecewise functions based on their intuition about given real-world scenarios. At the end of the topic, students derive inverses of linear functions.

Where have we been?

Students enter this topic with a wide range of experiences with linear functions. They have written and graphed linear relationships in middle school and in previous topics of this course. Students have also transformed linear functions, focusing primarily on vertical dilations, vertical translations, and reflections.

Where are we going?

Although derived from linear relationships, linear absolute value functions, linear piecewise functions, and step functions are more complex than the linear functions students have dealt with previously. They share enough characteristics with linear functions to be familiar to students, but they also serve as a bridge to the nonlinear functions students will study later in this course: exponential functions and quadratic functions.

Linear Absolute Value Function

The coordinate plane shows the graph of the linear absolute value function $f(x) = -2|x - 1| + 4$.

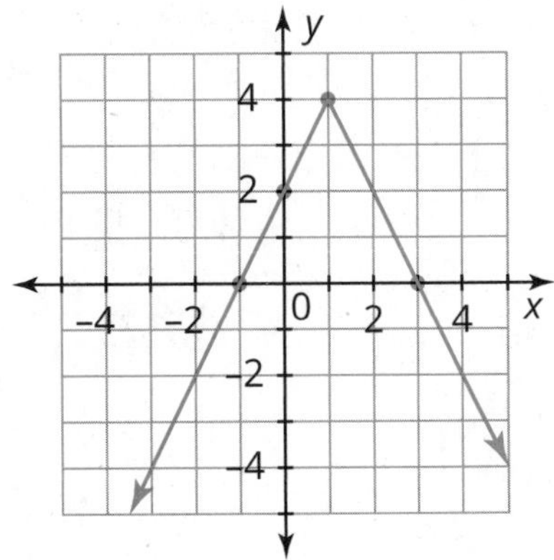

The graph increases to a vertex and then decreases and is symmetric across a vertical line through the vertex.

Error, Error!

In the real world, absolute values are often used to describe measurement errors or tolerance levels in manufacturing. This is particularly important when controlling waste produced in the manufacturing process.

For example, if a company uses a machine to fill a cereal box with cereal, it wants to make sure that the machine is operating within tolerance. This means that the machine may overfill some boxes and underfill others, but the overfill and underfill should be within a certain distance from a specified value.

For that calculation, absolute value functions are used:
$|\textit{machine amount} - \textit{expected amount}\ | \leq \textit{tolerance}.$

Talking Points

It can be helpful to understand different kinds of functions for college admissions tests.

Here is an example of a sample question:

Which of the following is the graph of $f(x) = |x - 4|$?

(A)

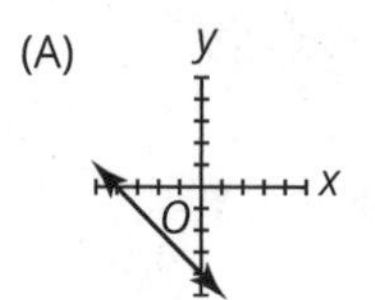

(B)

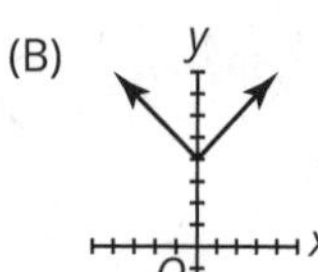

(C)

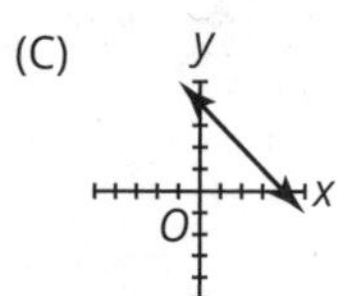

(D)

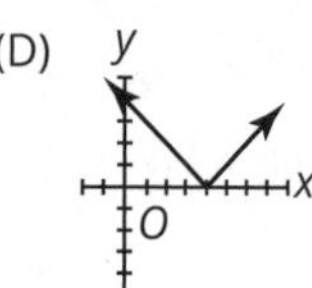

(E)

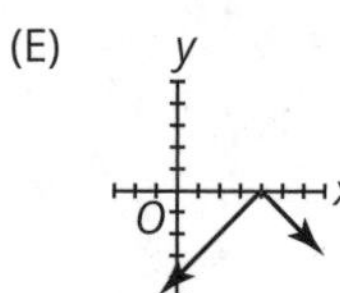

To solve this problem, you need to know about absolute value functions. Choice D is the correct graph of the function.

Key Terms

absolute value
The absolute value of a number is its distance from zero on the number line.

line of reflection
A line of reflection is the line that the graph is reflected across.

piecewise function
A piecewise function is a function that can be represented by more than one function, each of which corresponds to a part of the domain.

step function
A step function is a piecewise function on a given interval whose pieces are discontinuous constant functions.

inverse function
The inverse function takes the output value, performs some operation(s) on this value, and arrives back at the original function's input value.

1

Putting the V in Absolute Value

Defining Absolute Value Functions and Transformations

Warm Up

The graph of $f(x) = x$ is shown. Graph each transformation.

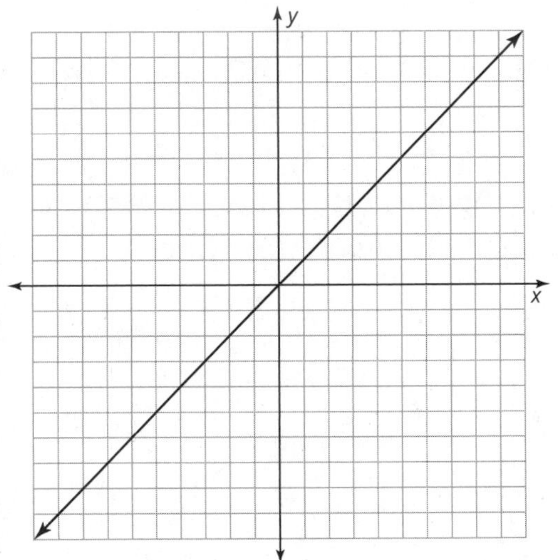

1. $g(x) = f(x) + 5$
2. $h(x) = 2 \cdot f(x) - 3$
3. $j(x) = \frac{1}{2} \cdot f(x) - 1$

Learning Goals

- Experiment with transformations of absolute value functions using technology.
- Graph absolute value functions and transformations of absolute value functions.
- Determine the effect of replacing the basic absolute value function $f(x) = |x|$ with $f(x) + D$, $Af(x)$, and $f(x - C)$ for different values of A, C, and D.
- Distinguish between function transformations that occur outside the function and inside the argument of the function.

Key Terms

- absolute value
- reflection
- line of reflection
- argument of a function

You know how to transform linear functions. How can you define absolute value functions and show transformations of this function type?

GETTING STARTED

Distance Is Always Positive

Absolute value is indicated with vertical bars: $|-4|$ is read as "the absolute value of -4."

The **absolute value** of a number is its distance from zero on the number line.

1. Follow your teacher's instructions to model each absolute value expression on the *x*-axis of a classroom coordinate plane. Rewrite each expression without the absolute value symbol.

a. $|-2|$

b. $|2|$

c. $|1 - 2|$

d. $|-3 - (-5)|$

e. $|-2 \cdot 3|$

f. $|0 \cdot 4|$

g. $\left|\frac{12}{-3}\right|$

h. $|8 \div (-4)|$

2. Write your observations about the absolute value expressions you and your classmates modeled on the number line.

3. Provide counterexamples to show why Sonja's statement is incorrect.

Sonja
Absolute values are always positive. So, $|a| = -a$ is not possible.

ACTIVITY
1.1

Graphs of Absolute Value Functions

Follow your teacher's instructions to model the function $f(x) = x$ on the classroom coordinate plane with your classmates.

1. Record the coordinates of the plotted points for $f(x) = x$ in the table.

x	y	
	$f(x) = x$	$f(x) = \|x\|$
−9		
−6		
−4		
−1		
0		
3		
5		
8		

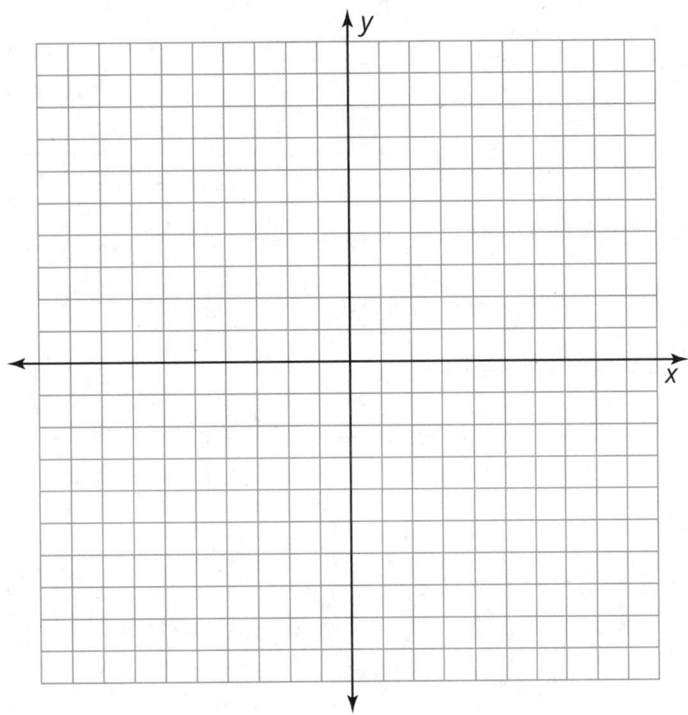

2. Change all the plotted points to model the function $f(x) = |x|$. In the table, record the coordinates of the new points for $f(x) = |x|$.

3. Describe how the points move from the graph of $f(x) = x$ to the graph of $f(x) = |x|$.

4. Graph the function $f(x) = |x|$. Describe the characteristics of the function that you notice.

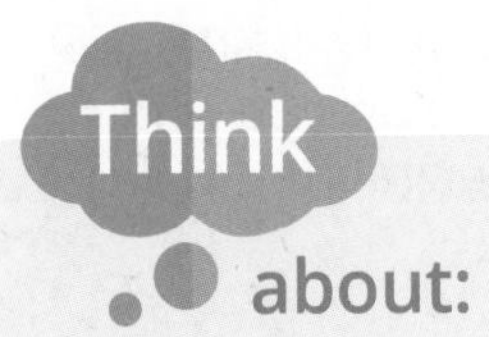

What are the domain and range?

Next, consider the function $f(x) = -x$. Model this function on the classroom coordinate plane with your classmates.

5. Record the coordinates of the plotted points for $f(x) = -x$ in the table.

x	y	
	$f(x) = -x$	$f(x) = \|-x\|$
-9		
-6		
-4		
-1		
0		
3		
5		
8		

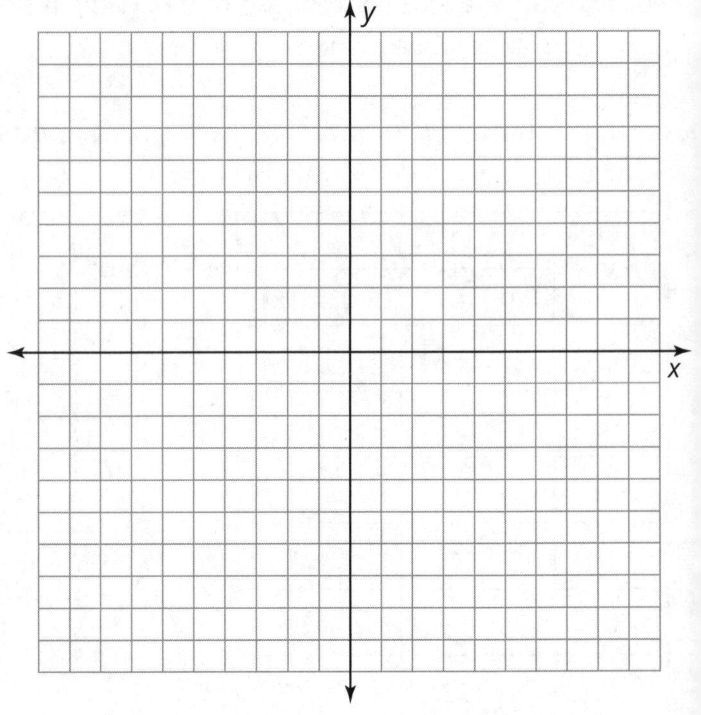

6. Change all the plotted points to model the function $f(x) = |-x|$. In the table, record the coordinates of the new points for $f(x) = |-x|$.

7. Describe how the points move from the graph of $f(x) = -x$ to the graph of $f(x) = |-x|$.

Use a straightedge to be precise when you graph.

8. Graph the function $f(x) = |-x|$. Compare this function with the function $f(x) = |x|$.

ACTIVITY 1.2

Transformations Inside and Outside the Function

Consider the three absolute value functions shown.

$g(x) = |x|$ $c(x) = |x| + 3$ $d(x) = |x| - 3$

1. Use technology to graph each function. Then, sketch and label the graph of each function.

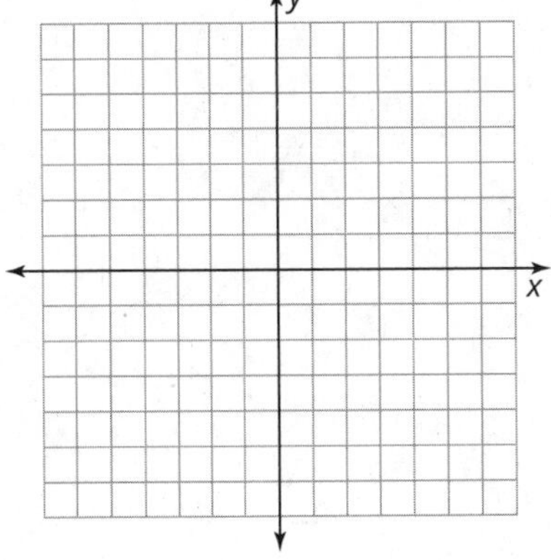

2. Write the functions $c(x)$ and $d(x)$ in terms of the basic function $g(x)$. Then describe the transformations of each function.

3. Describe the similarities and differences between the three graphs. How do these similarities and differences relate to the equations of the functions $g(x)$, $c(x)$, and $d(x)$?

Recall that a function $t(x)$ of the form $t(x) = f(x) + D$ is a vertical translation of the function $f(x)$. The value $|D|$ describes how many units up or down th graph of the original function is translated.

4. Describe each graph in relation to the basic function $g(x) = |x|$. Then use coordinate notation to represent the vertical translation.

a. $f(x) = g(x) + D$ when $D > 0$

b. $f(x) = g(x) + D$ when $D < 0$

c. Each point (x, y) on the graph of $g(x)$ becomes the point ____________ on $f(x)$.

Consider these absolute value functions.

$g(x) = |x|$ $\qquad$ $k(x) = \frac{1}{2}|x|$

$j(x) = 2|x|$ $\qquad$ $p(x) = -|x|$

5. Use technology to graph each function. Then, sketch and label the graph of each function.

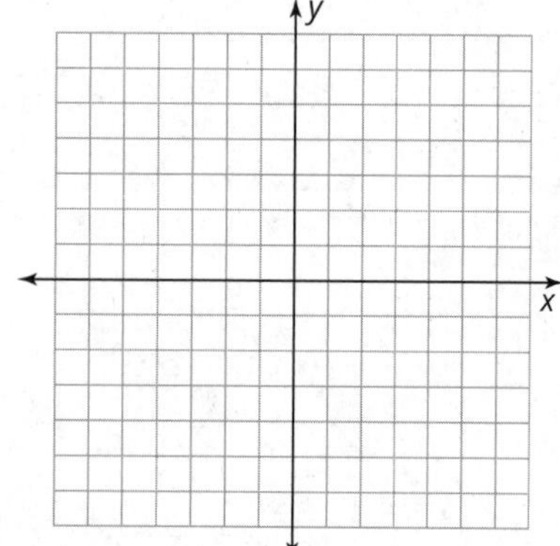

6. Write the functions $j(x)$, $k(x)$, and $p(x)$ in terms of the basic function $g(x)$. Then describe the transformations of each function.

NOTES

ecall that a function $t(x)$ of the form $t(x) = A \cdot f(x)$ is a vertical dilation of ne function $f(x)$. The A-value describes the vertical dilation of the graph of ne original function.

Describe each graph in relation to the basic function $g(x) = |x|$. Then use coordinate notation to represent the vertical translation.

a. $f(x) = A \cdot g(x)$ **when** $A > 1$

b. $f(x) = A \cdot g(x)$ **when** $A < 0$

c. $f(x) = A \cdot g(x)$ **when** $0 < A < 1$

d. Each point (x, y) on the graph of $g(x)$ becomes the point _______________ on $f(x)$.

A **reflection** of a graph is the mirror image of the graph about a line of reflection.

A **line of reflection** is the line that the graph is reflected across. A horizontal line of reflection affects the y-coordinates.

You know that changing the A-value of a function to its opposite reflects the function across a horizontal line. But the *line of reflection* for the function might be different depending on how you write the transformation and the order the transformations are applied.

8. **Josh and Vicki each sketched a graph of the function $b(x) = -|x| - 3$ using different strategies. Write the step-by-step reasoning used by each student.**

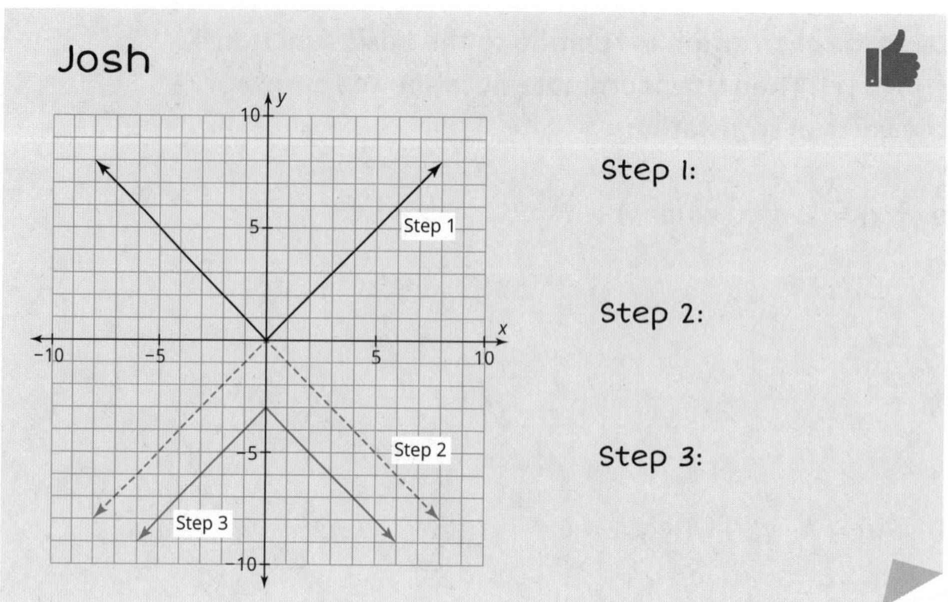

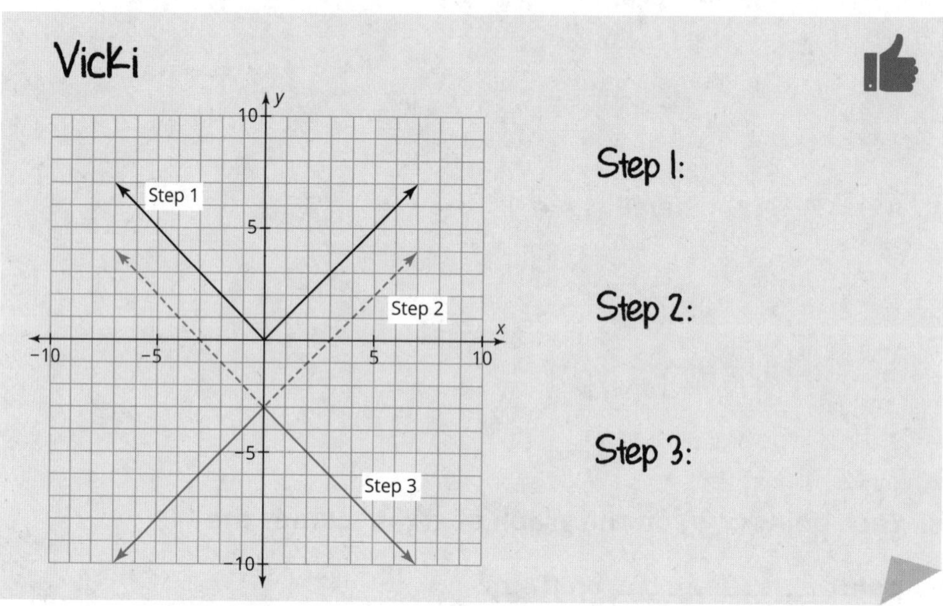

9. **Explain how changing the order of the transformations affects the line of reflection.**

iven the function $f(x) = |x|$. Use the coordinate plane shown to answer uestions 10 through 14.

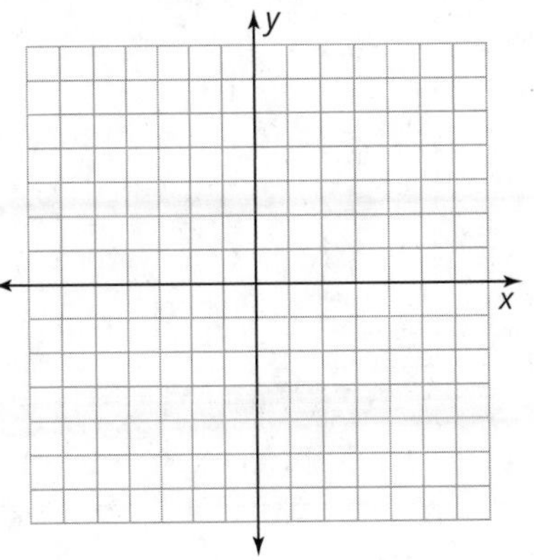

0. Consider the function $a(x) = 2f(x) + 1$.

a. Use coordinate notation to describe how each point (x, y) on the graph of $f(x)$ becomes a point on the graph of $a(x)$.

b. Graph and label $a(x)$ on the coordinate plane shown.

1. Consider the function $b(x) = -2f(x) + 1$.

a. Use coordinate notation to describe how each point (x, y) on the graph of $f(x)$ becomes a point on the graph of $b(x)$.

b. Graph and label $b(x)$ on the same coordinate plane shown.

2. Describe the graph of $b(x)$ in terms of $a(x)$.

3. Consider the function $-a(x)$.

a. Use coordinate notation to describe how each point (x, y) on the graph of $a(x)$ becomes a point on the graph of $-a(x)$.

b. Graph and label $-a(x)$ on the coordinate plane shown.

14. Describe the graph of $-a(x)$ in terms of $a(x)$.

Consider these absolute value functions.

$g(x) = |x|$ $m(x) = |x - 2|$ $n(x) = |x + 2|$

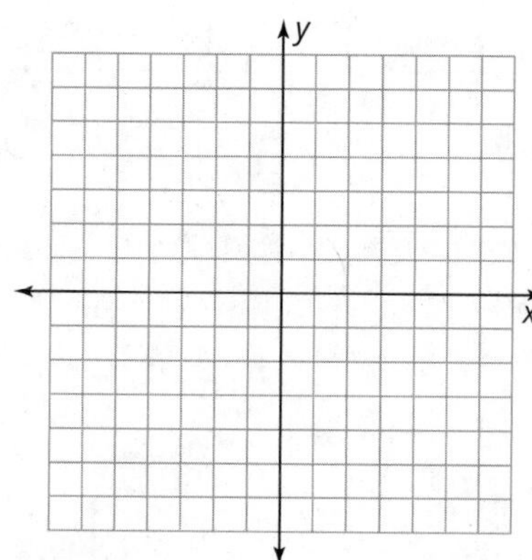

15. Use technology to graph each function. Then, sketch and label the graph of each function. Describe how $m(x)$ and $n(x)$ relate to $g(x)$.

The expression $x + C$ is the same as $x - (-C)$.

A function $t(x)$ of the form $t(x) = f(x - C)$ is a horizontal translation of the function $f(x)$. The value $|C|$ describes the number of units the graph of $f(x)$ is translated right or left. If $C > 0$, the graph is translated to the right. If $C < 0$, the graph is translated to the left.

16. Write the functions $m(x)$ and $n(x)$ in terms of the basic function $g(x)$. Describe how changing the C-value in the functions $m(x)$ and $n(x)$ horizontally translated the function $g(x)$.

17. Use coordinate notation to show how each point (x, y) on the graph of $g(x)$ becomes a point on a graph that has been horizontally translated.

ACTIVITY 1.3

Combining Transformations of Absolute Value Functions

When a function is transformed by changing the *A*- or *D*-values or both, these changes are said to occur "outside the function." These values affect the output to a function, *y*. When the *C*-value is changed, this changes the *argument of the function*. A change to the argument of a function is said to happen "inside the function." These values affect the input to a function, *x*.

The **argument of a function** is the expression inside the parentheses.

For $y = f(x - C)$ the expression $x - C$ is the argument of the function.

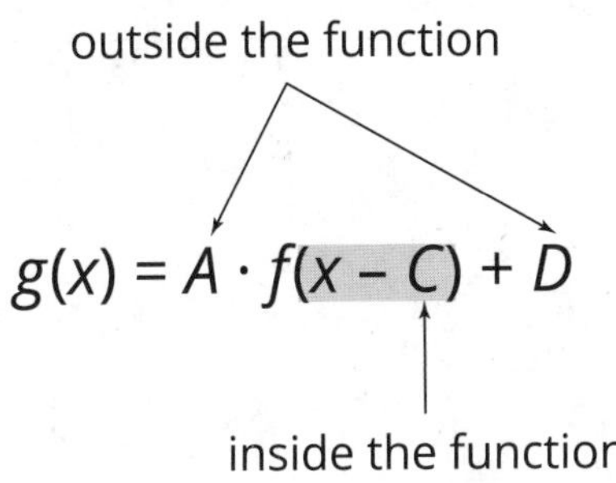

1. **Use coordinate notation to describe how each point (x, y) on the graph of $f(x)$ becomes a point on the graph of $g(x)$.**

The ordered pair $(x, |x|)$ describes any point on the graph of the basic absolute value function $f(x) = |x|$. For a transformation of the function, any point on the graph of the new function can be written as $(x + C, A|x + C| + D)$.

2. **Given the basic absolute value function $f(x) = |x|$. Consider each transformation. Describe how the transformations affected $f(x)$. Then use coordinate notation to describe how each point (x, y) on the graph of $f(x)$ becomes a point on the graph of the transformed function. Finally, sketch a graph of each new function.**

a. $m(x) = 2f(x - 1)$

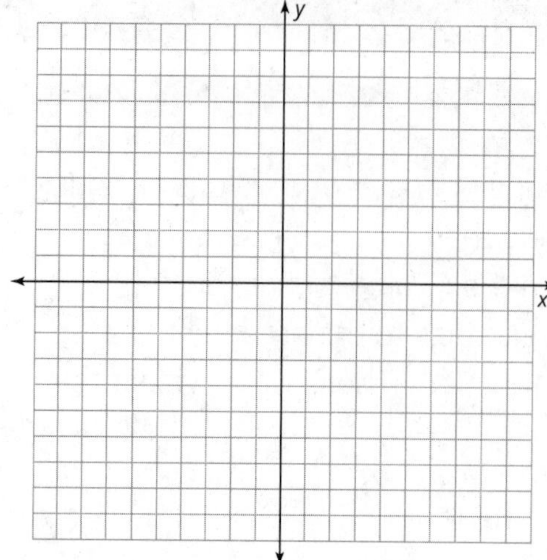

b. $r(x) = \frac{1}{2}f(x + 2) - 2$

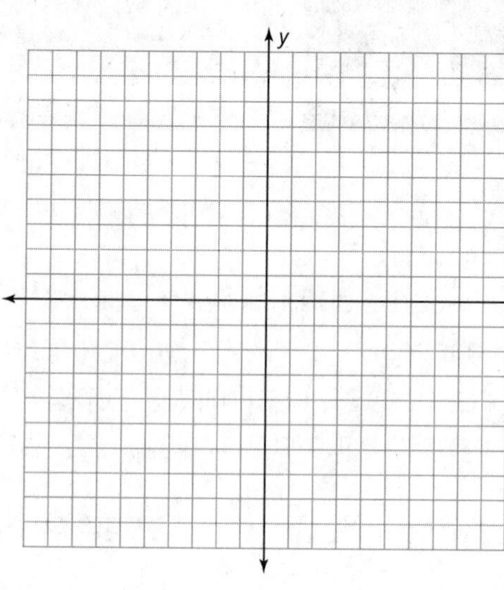

c. $w(x) = 2f(x + 3) + 1$

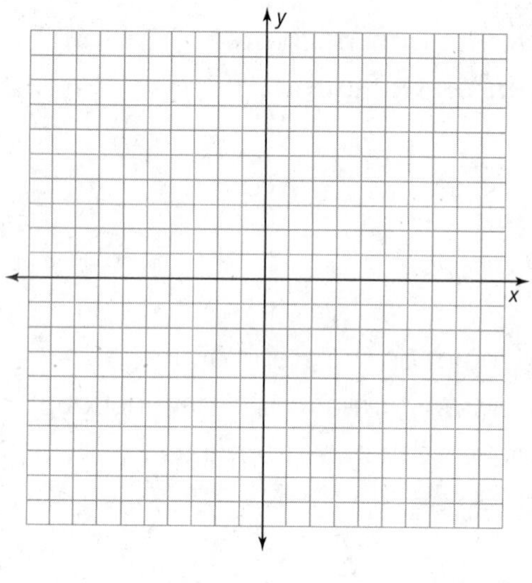

d. $v(x) = -2f(x + 3) + 1$

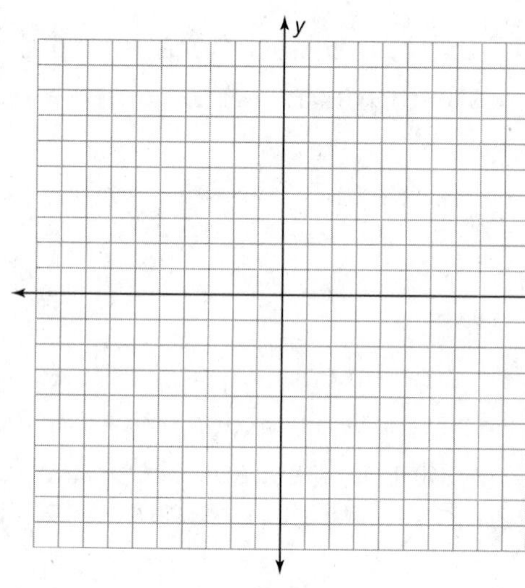

3. Graph $-w(x)$ on the same coordinate plane as $w(x)$ in Question 2 part (c). Describe the similarities and differences between the graph of $v(x)$ and the graph of $-w(x)$.

ACTIVITY 1.4

Writing Equations in Transformation Form

1. Consider the function, $f(x) = |x|$. Write the function in transformation function form in terms of the transformations described, then write an equivalent equation.

Transformation	Transformation Function Form	Equation
a. Reflection across the x-axis		
b. Horizontal translation of 2 units to the left and a vertical translation of 3 units up		
c. Vertical stretch of 2 units and a reflection across the line $y = 0$		
d. Vertical dilation of 2 units and a reflection across the line $y = 3$		
e. Horizontal translation of 3 units to the right, a vertical translation down 2 units, and a vertical dilation of $\frac{1}{2}$		
f. Vertical compression by a factor of 4		
g. Vertical stretch by a factor of 4		

NOTES

TALK the TALK 

A, C, and D

The function $f(x) = A|x - C| + D$ is graphed with varying values for A, C, and D.

1. **Match the given values of A, C, and D with the graph of the function with corresponding values. Explain your reasoning.**

   a. $A = 1$, $C = 0$, and $D > 0$

   b. $A = 1$, $C = 0$, and $D < 0$

   c. $A > 1$, $C > 0$, and $D > 0$

   d. $0 < A < 1$, $C < 0$, and $D < 0$

Graph A

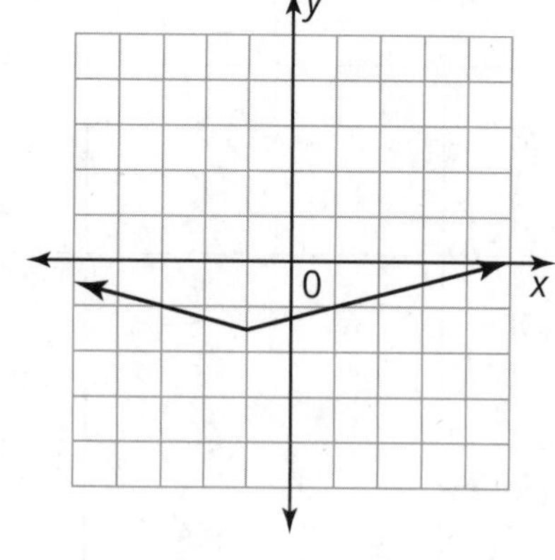

Graph B

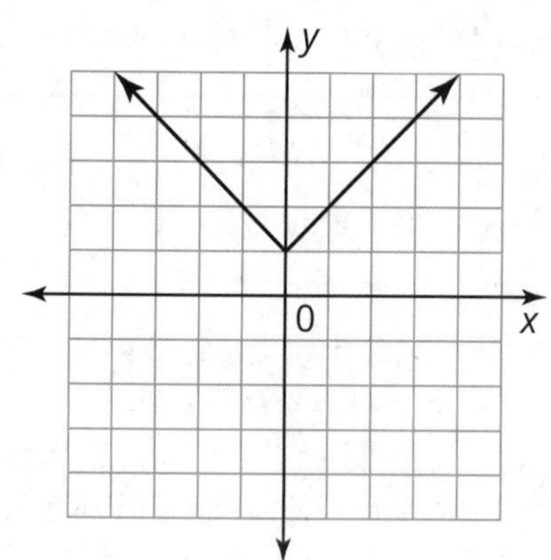

Graph C

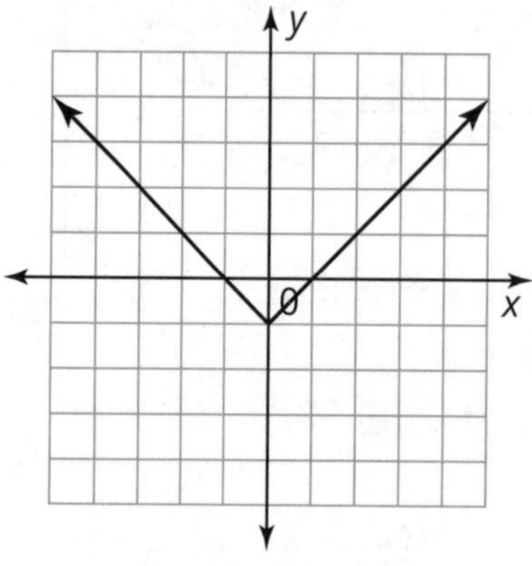

Graph D

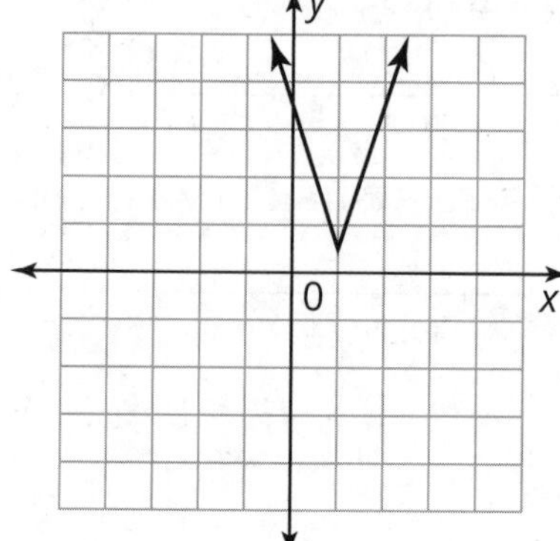

NOTES

2. Complete the table by describing the graph of each function as a transformation of the basic function $f(x) = |x|$. Write the ordered pair that describes any point on the graph of the transformed function.

Function Form	Equation Information	Description of Transformation
$f(x) = |x| + D$	$D < 0$	
	$D > 0$	
$f(x) = A|x|$	$A < 0$	
	$0 < A < 1$	
	$A > 1$	
$f(x) = |x - C|$	$C < 0$	
	$C > 0$	

NOTES

3. **Determine whether each statement is true or false. If the statement is false, rewrite the statement as true.**

   a. **In the transformation function form $g(x) = Af(x - C) + D$, the A-value vertically stretches or compresses $f(x)$, the C-value translates $f(x)$ horizontally, and the D-value translates the function $f(x)$ vertically.**

   b. **Key characteristics of the basic absolute value function include a domain and range of real numbers.**

   c. **The domain of absolute value functions is not affected by translations or dilations.**

   d. **Vertical translations do not affect the range of absolute value functions.**

   e. **Horizontal translations do not affect the range of absolute value functions.**

   f. **Vertical dilations do not affect the range of absolute value functions.**

Assignment

Write

Given a basic function $y = f(x)$ and a function written in transformation form $g(x) = A \cdot f(x-C) + D$, describe how the transformations that are inside a function affect a graph differently than those on the outside of the function.

Remember

The basic absolute value function is $f(x) = |x|$.

The transformed function $y = f(x) + D$ shows a vertical translation of the function.

The transformed function $y = Af(x)$ shows a vertical dilation of the function when $A > 0$ and when $A < 0$ it shows a vertical dilation and reflection across the x-axis.

The transformed function $y = f(x - C)$ shows a horizontal translation of the function.

Practice

Given the basic function $f(x) = |x|$. Consider each transformation. Describe how the transformations affected $f(x)$. Then use coordinate notation to describe how each point (x, y) on the graph of $f(x)$ becomes a point on the graph the transformed function. Finally, sketch a graph of each new function.

1. $g(x) = \frac{1}{3}f(x) - 2$
2. $j(x) = 2f(x + 1) + 4$
3. $m(x) = -\frac{1}{2}f(x - 3) - 1$
4. $p(x) = -f(x + 4) + 3$

Stretch

The function $g(x)$ shown is a transformation of $f(x) = |x|$.

Write the function $g(x)$ in terms of $f(x)$.

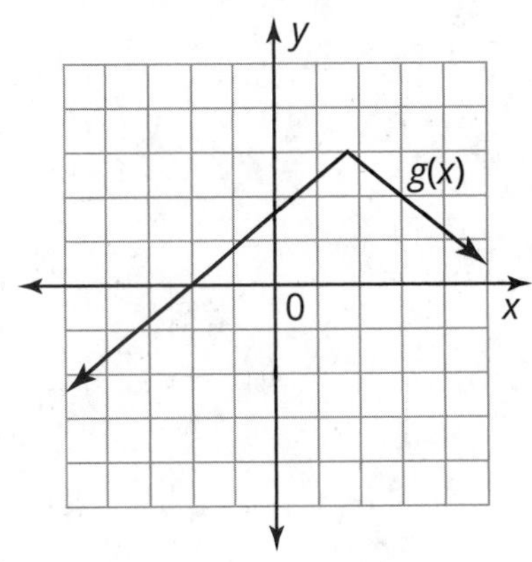

Review

1. The TransAmerica Pyramid is the second highest building in San Francisco. It is shaped like a pyramid with a square base. The side length of the base is 175 feet, and the building is 853 feet tall. What is the volume of the TransAmerica Pyramid?
2. A perfume manufacturer is considering new bottles for one of their perfumes. The bottles are cylinder-shaped with a diameter of 9 centimeters and a height of 10 centimeters. How much perfume will the bottle hold? Use 3.14 for π and round your answer to the nearest tenth if necessary.
3. In circle M shown, the length of $\overset{\frown}{PW}$ is 18π centimeters and $m\angle PRW$ is 56°. Determine the length of the diameter of circle M. Round your answer to the nearest hundredth.

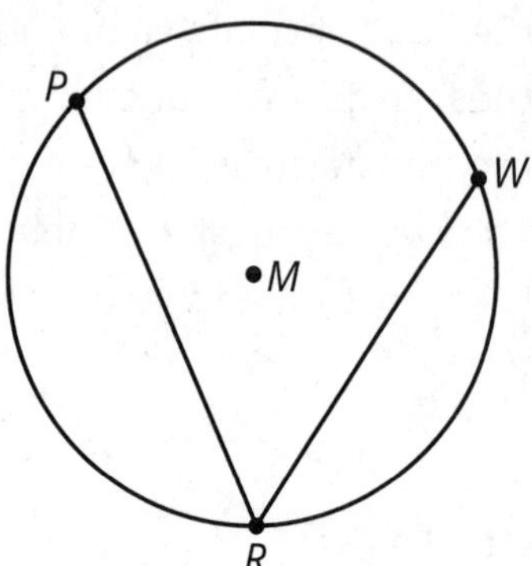

4. The measure of a central angle is 65°. The length of the radius is 25 cm. Determine the length of the arc intercepted by the central angle.
5. Write the equation of a line that passes through the point (−4, 3) and is parallel to the line $3x - 4y = 8$.
6. Write the equation of a line that passes through the point (−7, 11) and is perpendicular to the line $3x + 15y = -20$.

2

Play Ball!

Absolute Value Equations and Inequalities

Warm Up

Evaluate each expression.

1. $|9 + (-4)|$

2. $|-1 - 5|$

3. $|4 \times (-6)|$

4. $|0 \div (-2)|$

Learning Goals

- Understand and solve absolute value equations.
- Solve and graph linear absolute value inequalities on number lines.
- Graph absolute value functions and use the graph to determine solutions.

Key Terms

- linear absolute value equation
- linear absolute value inequality
- equivalent compound inequality

You know what the graphs of absolute value functions look like. How can you use what you know about graphs and linear equations to solve absolute value equations and inequalities?

GETTING STARTED

Opposites Attract? Absolutely!

You can solve many absolute value equations using inspection.

1. Graph the solution set of each equation on the number line given.

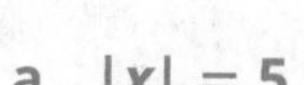

a. $|x| = 5$

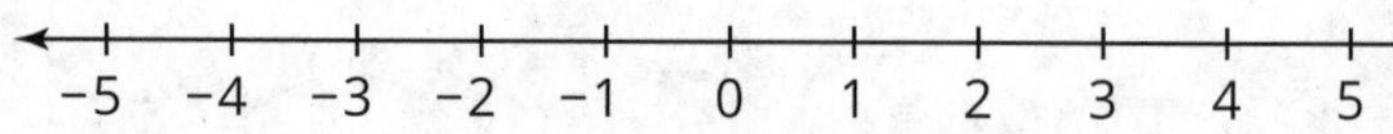

b. $|x| = 2$

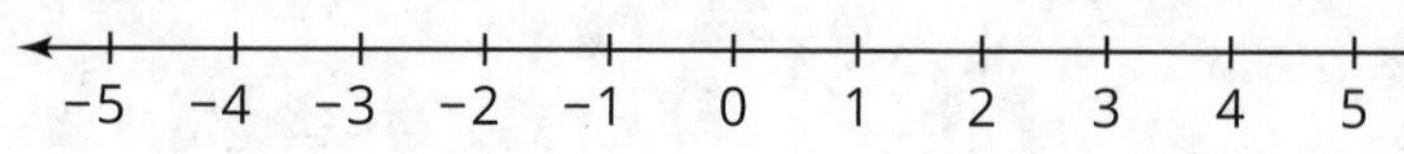

c. $|x| = -3$

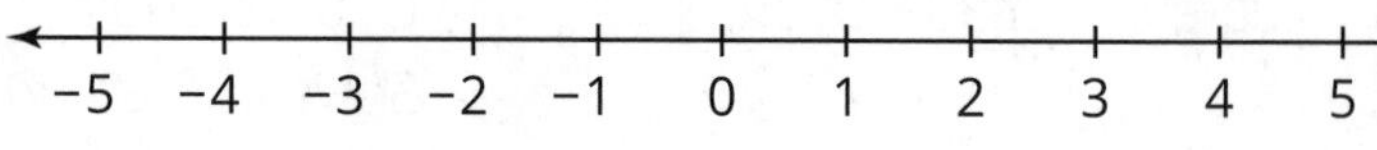

d. $|x| = 0$

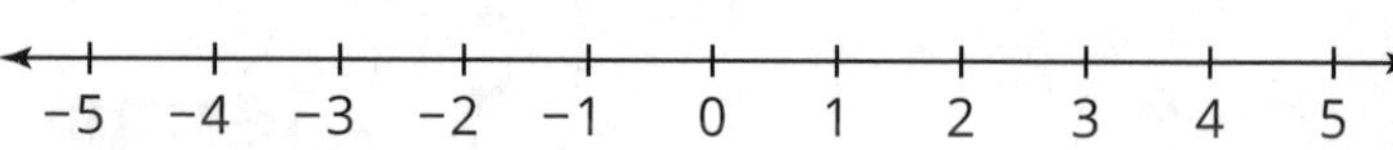

2. Write the absolute value equation for each solution set graphed.

a.

−5 −4 −3 −2 −1 0 1 2 3 4 5

b.

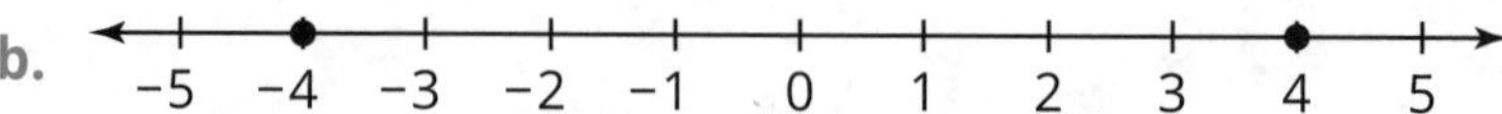

ACTIVITY
2.1

Creating an Absolute Value Function from a Situation

ne official rules of baseball state that all baseballs used during rofessional games must be within a specified range of weights. The aseball manufacturer sets the target weight of the balls at 145.045 grams n its machines.

Sketch a graph that models the relationship between a manufactured baseball's weight, *x*, and its distance from the target weight, *y*. Explain how you constructed your sketch. Then write an absolute value equation to represent the situation and the graph.

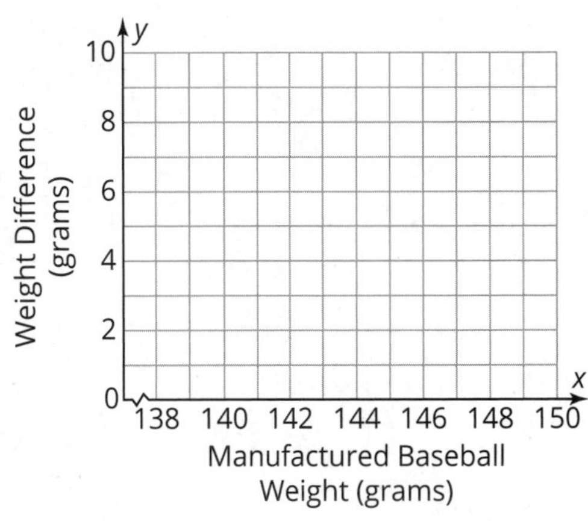

The specified weight allows for a difference of 3.295 grams in the actual weight of a ball and the target weight. Since the weight must be within a distance of 3.295 grams from the target weight, $y = 3.295$.

a. **Graph the equation $y = 3.295$ on the coordinate plane in Question 1.**

b. **What two equations can you write, without absolute values, to show the least acceptable weight and the greatest acceptable weight of a baseball? Explain your reasoning.**

c. **Use the graph to write the solutions to the equations you wrote in part (b). Show your work.**

How is the function transformed from the basic function $f(x) = |x|$?

ACTIVITY
2.2

Solving Absolute Value Equations

The two equations you wrote can be represented by the **linear absolute value equation** $|w - 145.045| = 3.295$. To solve any absolute value equation, recall the definition of absolute value.

Worked Example

Consider this linear absolute value equation.

$$|a| = 6$$

There are two points that are 6 units away from zero on the number line: one to the right of zero, and one to the left of zero.

$$+(a) = 6 \quad \text{or} \quad -(a) = 6$$

$$a = 6 \quad \text{or} \quad a = -6$$

Now consider the case where $a = x - 1$.

$$|x - 1| = 6$$

If you know that $|a| = 6$ can be written as two separate equations, you can rewrite any absolute value equation.

$$+(a) = 6 \quad \text{or} \quad -(a) = 6$$

$$+(x - 1) = 6 \quad \text{or} \quad -(x - 1) = 6$$

1. **How do you know the expressions $+(a)$ and $-(a)$ represent opposite distances?**

2. **Martina and Bob continued to solve the linear absolute value equation $|x - 1| = 6$ in different ways. Compare their strategies and then determine the solutions to the equation.**

Martina

$(x - 1) = 6$ or $(x - 1) = -6$

Bob

$x - 1 = 6$ or $-x + 1 = 6$

Solve each linear absolute value equation. Show your work.

a. $|x + 7| = 3$

b. $|x - 9| = 12$

c. $|3x + 7| = -8$

d. $|2x + 3| = 0$

yourself:

Before you solve each equation, think about the number of solutions each equation may have. You may be able to save yourself some work—and time!

Artie, Donald, Cho, and Steve each solved the equation $|x| - 4 = 5$.

Artie 

$|x| - 4 = 5$

$(x) - 4 = 5$ $\quad$ $-(x) - 4 = 5$

$(x) = 9$ $\quad$ $-x = 9$

$x = -9$

Donald

$|x| - 4 = 5$

$|x| = 9$

$(x) = 9$ $\quad$ $-(x) = 9$

$x = -9$

Cho 

$|x| - 4 = 5$

$(x) - 4 = 5$ $\quad$ $-[(x) - 4] = 5$

$x - 4 = 5$ $\quad$ $-x + 4 = 5$

$x = 9$ $\quad$ $-x = 1$

$x = -1$

Steve

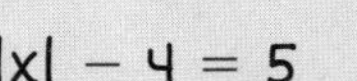

$|x| - 4 = 5$

$(x) - 4 = 5$ $\quad$ $-(x) - 4 = -5$

$x = 9$ $\quad$ $-x - 4 = -5$

$-x = -1$

$x = 1$

a. **Explain how Cho and Steve incorrectly rewrote the absolute value equation as two separate equations.**

b. **Explain the difference in the strategies that Artie and Donald used.**

Consider isolating the absolute value part of the equation before you rewrite it as two equations.

5. Solve each linear absolute value equation.

a. $|x| + 16 = 32$

b. $23 = |x - 8| + 6$

c. $3|x - 2| = 12$

d. $35 = 5|x + 6| - 10$

ACTIVITY

2.3 Absolute Value Inequalities

ou determined the linear absolute value equation $|w - 145.045| = 3.295$ identify the most and least a baseball could weigh and still be within the pecifications. The manufacturer wants to determine all of the acceptable eights that the baseball could be and still fit within the specifications. ou can write a **linear absolute value inequality** to represent this roblem situation.

. Write a linear absolute value inequality to represent all baseball weights that are within the specifications.

. Use the graph to determine whether the weight of each given baseball is acceptable. Substitute each value in the inequality to verify your answer.

a. 147 grams

b. 140.8 grams

c. 148.34 grams

d. 141.75 grams

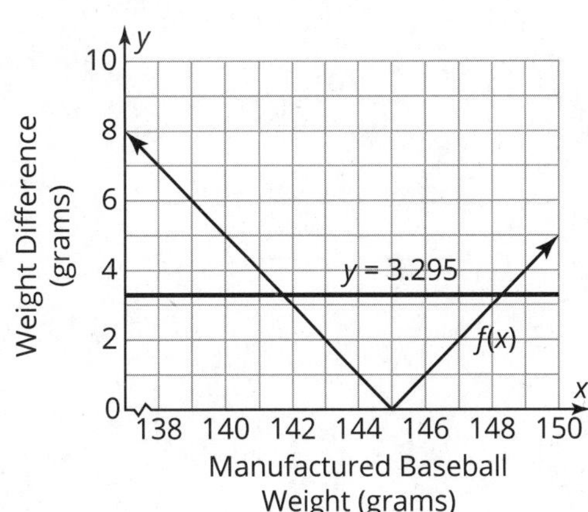

3. **Use the graph on the coordinate plane to graph the inequality o the number line showing all the acceptable weights. Explain the process you used.**

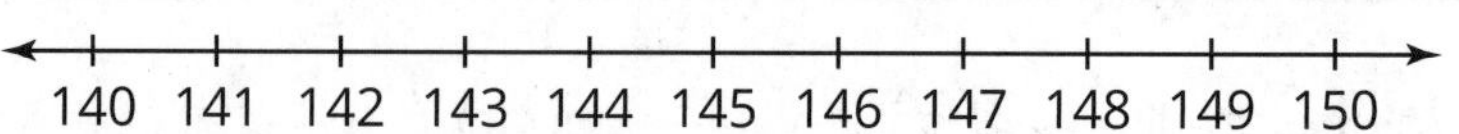

4. **Complete the inequality to describe all the acceptable weights, where *w* is the baseball's weight.**

$\_\_\_\_\_\_\_\_\_\_ \leq w \leq \_\_\_\_\_\_\_\_\_\_$

5. **Raymond has the job of disposing of all baseballs that are not within the acceptable weight limits.**

   a. **Write an absolute value inequality to represent the weights c baseballs that Raymond can dispose of.**

   b. **Graph the inequality on the number line. Explain the process you used.**

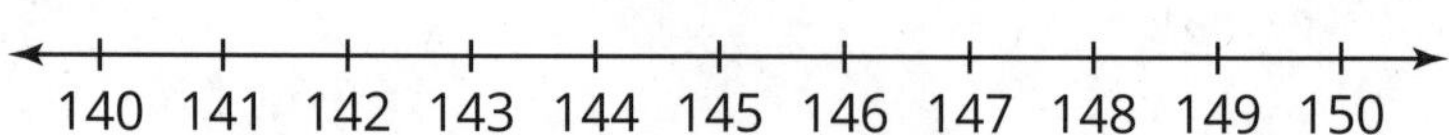

ACTIVITY
2.4

Solving Problems with Absolute Value Functions

Little League Baseball, the diameter of the ball is slightly smaller than that a professional baseball.

For Little League baseballs, the manufacturer sets the target diameter to be 7.47 centimeters. The specified diameter allows for a difference of 1.27 centimeters.

a. Sketch the graph of the linear absolute value function, *f*(*d*), on the coordinate plane.

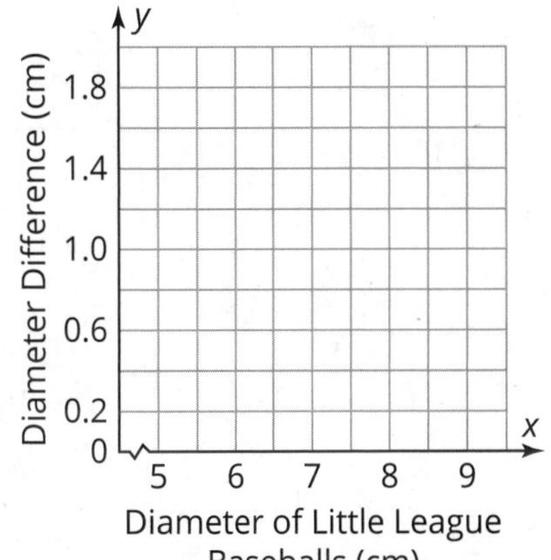

b. Use your graph to estimate the diameters of all the Little League baseballs that fit within the specifications. Explain how you determined your answer.

c. Algebraically determine the diameters of all the baseballs that fit within the specification. Write your answer as an inequality.

The manufacturer knows that the closer the diameter of the baseball is to the target, the more likely it is to be sold. The manufacturer decides to keep only the baseballs that are less than 0.75 centimeter from the target diameter.

a. Algebraically determine which baseballs will not fall within the new specified limits and will not be kept. Write your answer as an inequality.

b. How can you use your graph to determine whether you are correct?

ACTIVITY **2.5**

Absolute Value and Compound Inequalities

Absolute value inequalities can take four different forms, as shown in the table. To solve a linear absolute value inequality, you can first write it as an **equivalent compound inequality**.

Notice that the equivalent compound inequalities do not contain absolute values.

Absolute Value Inequality	Equivalent Compound Inequality
$\|ax + b\| < c$	$-c < ax + b < c$
$\|ax + b\| \le c$	$-c \le ax + b \le c$
$\|ax + b\| > c$	$ax + b < -c$ or $ax + b > c$
$\|ax + b\| \ge c$	$ax + b \le -c$ or $ax + b \ge c$

1. **Solve the linear absolute value inequality by rewriting it as an equivalent compound inequality. Then graph your solution on the number line.**

   a. $|x + 3| < 4$

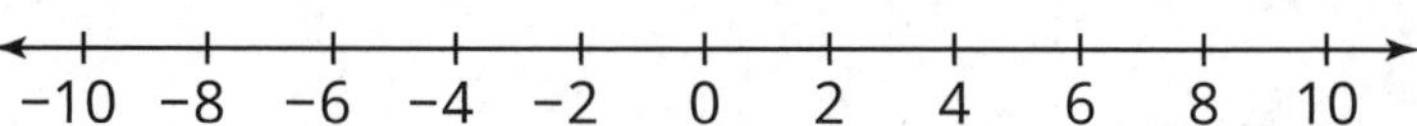

   b. $6 \le |2x - 4|$

As a final step, don't forget to check your solution.

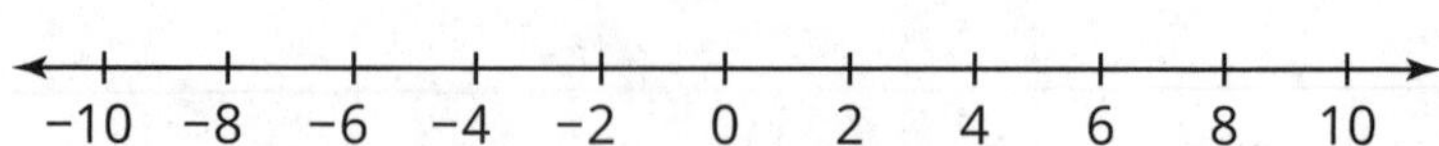

c. $|-5x + 8| + 2 < 25$

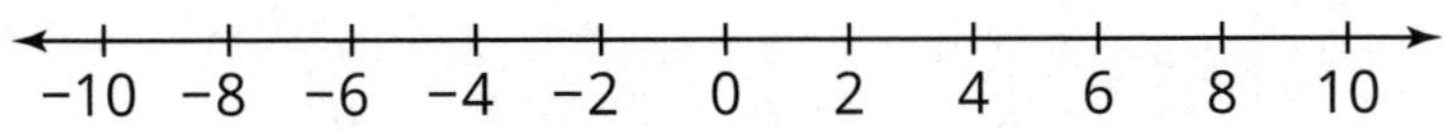

d. $|x + 5| > -1$

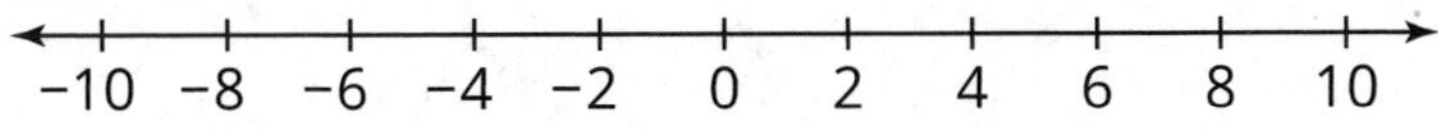

e. $|x + 5| < -1$

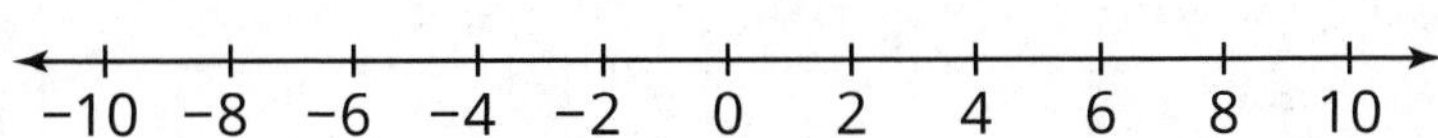

NOTES

TALK the TALK 

Seeing Double

Consider the situation from the first activity: a baseball manufacturer sets the target weight of the baseballs at 145.045 grams. The specified weight allows for a certain distance, y, between the actual weight and the target weight.

1. **Suppose this distance between the target weight and the actual weight is cut in half. Describe how this represents a transformation of the original function. Sketch a graph of the new function and write the new equation.**

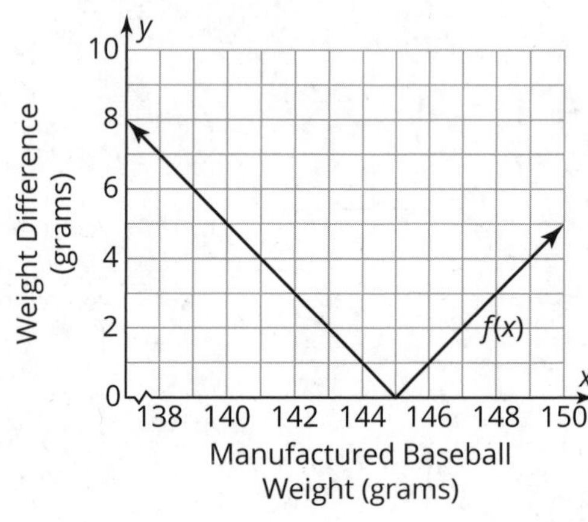

2. **Describe why you can rewrite an absolute value equation as two separate equations.**

Assignment

Write

Describe the similarities and differences between solving a linear absolute value equation and a linear absolute value inequality.

Remember

You can rewrite any absolute value equation as two equations to solve. If $|x| = c$, where c is any real number, then $+(x) = c$ or $-(x) = c$.

Absolute value inequalities can take four different forms. To solve a linear absolute value inequality, you can first write it as an equivalent compound inequality.

Absolute Value Inequality	Equivalent Compound Inequality
$\|ax + b\| < c$	$-c < ax + b < c$
$\|ax + b\| \leq c$	$-c \leq ax + b \leq c$
$\|ax + b\| > c$	$ax + b < -c$ or $ax + b > c$
$\|ax + b\| \geq c$	$ax + b \leq -c$ or $ax + b \geq c$

Practice

1. The Billingsly Cookie Company is trying to come up with a cookie that is low in fat but still has good taste. The company decides on a target fat content of 5 grams per cookie. In order to be labeled low-fat, a difference of 1.8 grams per cookie is acceptable.
   a. Write an expression that represents the difference between the fat in a cookie from the new recipe and the target fat content. Use f to represent the amount of fat in a cookie from the new recipe.
   b. Write an absolute value inequality to represent the restrictions on the difference in the amount of fat.
   c. One of the bakers creates a cookie recipe that has 6.5 grams of fat per cookie. Is this recipe acceptable? Explain your reasoning.
   d. Another baker comes up with a cookie recipe that has 2.9 grams of fat per cookie. Is this recipe acceptable? Explain your reasoning
   e. Algebraically determine the greatest and least number of grams of fat a cookie can contain and still fall within the required specifications. Write your answer as an inequality.
   f. Sketch the graph of the absolute value inequality from part (b).
2. Solve each absolute value equation or inequality.
   a. $|x| + 8 = 15$
   b. $|x + 5| = -15$
   c. $|x + 4| \leq 9$
   d. $|3x - 1| > 14$
   e. $|x - 9| > -1$

Stretch

John, Rasheed, and Jeorge are different ages. Rasheed is six less than twice John's age. Jeorge's age is nine more than half of John's age. The difference between Rasheed and Jeorge's ages is no more than nine years.

1. Write an expression that represents the difference between Rasheed and Jeorge's ages.
2. Write an absolute value inequality to represent the maximum difference in their ages.
3. Determine whether it is possible for John to be twenty years old. Explain your reasoning.
4. Algebraically determine the greatest and least age John can be so that the difference between Rasheed and Jeorge's ages is no more than nine years.

Review

1. Given the function $f(x) = |x|$. Sketch a graph of each new function.

   a. $g(x) = -|x + 1| - 3$

   b. $h(x) = \frac{3}{4}|x - 2| + 1$

2. The tower on Philadelphia City Hall has 4 clocks. Each clock face measures 26 feet in diameter. Determine the area of the sector formed by the minute hand and the hour hand on one of the clocks when the time is 8:00.
3. Solve for a in the equation $\frac{a - b}{12} = 11 - 6a$.

3

I Graph in Pieces

Linear Piecewise Functions

Warm Up

A graph that represents the amount of water in a bathtub is shown.

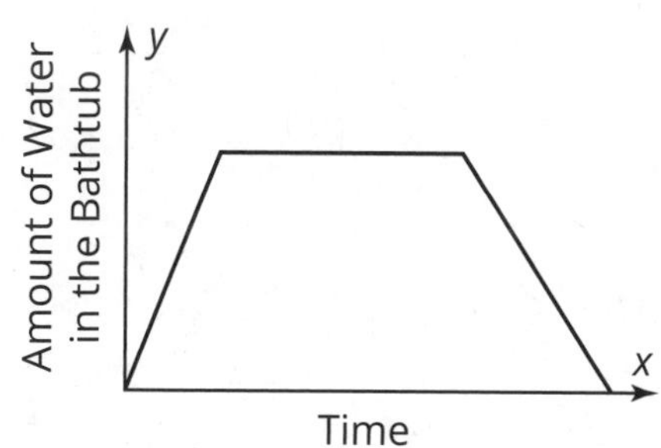

1. Is the relation a function? Why or why not?

2. Describe the problem situation in each of the 3 pieces of the graph.

3. Did the bathtub fill or drain faster? How do you know?

Learning Goals

- Create graphs of linear piecewise functions.
- Write linear piecewise functions from scenarios, tables, and graphs.
- Interpret or write a scenario for a piecewise graph.
- Use technology to graph and evaluate linear piecewise functions.
- Compare a linear absolute value function to a linear piecewise function.

Key Terms

- piecewise function
- linear piecewise function

You explored the graphs of absolute value functions. What other functions involve graphs composed of more than one line or line segment?

Just Playing Some B-Ball

Your teacher is going to read a scenario line by line.

1. **As each line is read, graph that piece of the scenario.**

Label your axes!

Reflect on your process and the mathematics by responding to these questions.

2. **Will everyone in class have the exact same graph? Explain your reasoning.**

3. **What clues from the scenario did you use to decide how steep to make each line segment?**

4. **How did you determine the length of each line segment?**

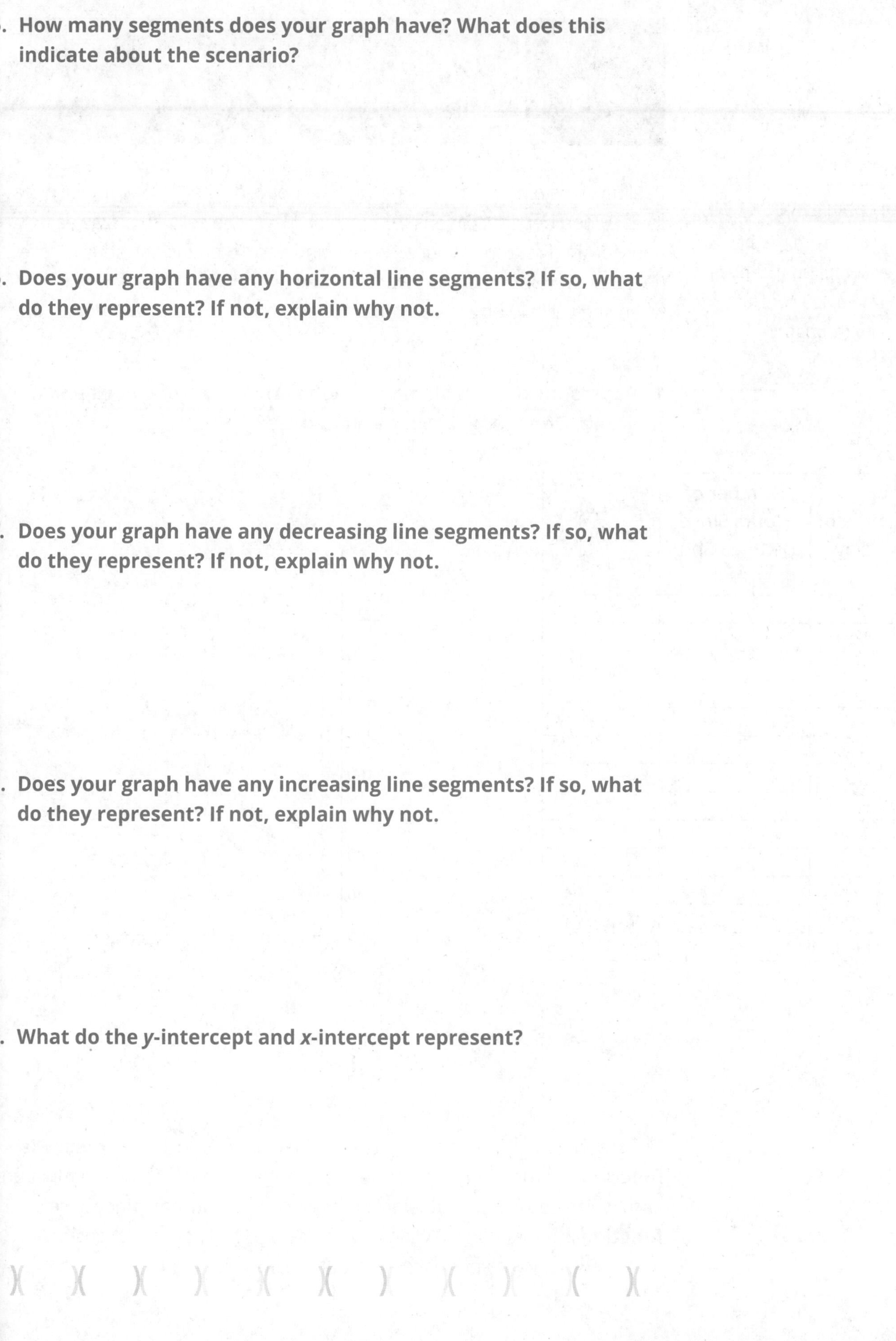

5. **How many segments does your graph have? What does this indicate about the scenario?**

6. **Does your graph have any horizontal line segments? If so, what do they represent? If not, explain why not.**

7. **Does your graph have any decreasing line segments? If so, what do they represent? If not, explain why not.**

8. **Does your graph have any increasing line segments? If so, what do they represent? If not, explain why not.**

9. **What do the *y*-intercept and *x*-intercept represent?**

ACTIVITY **3.1**

Developing a Piecewise Function from a Scenario

To model this problem, make the assumption that pizza is sold at a constant rate throughout each hour.

Paulina owns a popular pizza parlor. She noticed a daily trend in her pizza sales. When her shop opens for lunch at 11 AM, she sells 30 pizzas each hour for the first three hours. Sales dwindle to 10 pizzas per hour for the next 3 hours. Business picks up from 5 PM until closing time at 11 PM, when she sells 40 pizzas each hour for all 6 hours.

1. **Represent this problem situation with a table of values and a graph. Don't forget to label your axes.**

Time of Day	Number of Hours Since the Pizza Shop Opened	Total Number of Pizzas Sold
11 AM	0	0
12 PM		
1 PM		
2 PM		
3 PM		
4 PM		
5 PM		
6 PM		
7 PM		
8 PM		
9 PM		
10 PM		
11 PM		

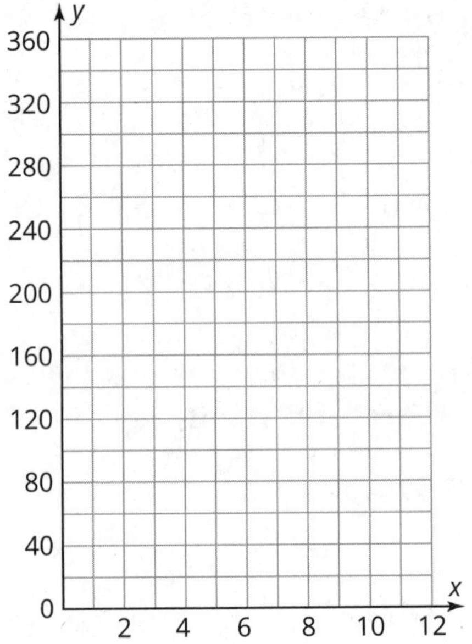

The graph that you created represents a piecewise function. A **piecewise function** is a function that can be represented by more than one function, each which corresponds to a part of the domain. A **linear piecewise function** is a function that can be represented by linear functions only, each of which corresponds to a part of the domain.

Use the graph and table to answer each question.

a. Identify the domain of this problem situation.

b. How many pieces make up this function? What is the domain of each piece?

Determine the equation that represents each piece of the function for each given time period. Show your work.

a. from 0 to 3 hours

b. from more than 3 hours to 6 hours

c. from more than 6 hours to 12 hours

To write a piecewise function, you must write the equation followed by its domain for each piece of the function. Complete the function by transferring the information from Question 3 into the proper format. Define your variables.

$$f(x) = \begin{cases} \_\_\_\_\_\_\_\_\_\_ & \_\_\_\_\_\_\_\_\_\_ \\ \_\_\_\_\_\_\_\_\_\_ & \_\_\_\_\_\_\_\_\_\_ \\ \_\_\_\_\_\_\_\_\_\_ & \_\_\_\_\_\_\_\_\_\_ \end{cases}$$

5. **What piece should be used to determine the *y*-intercept of the function? Explain your reasoning.**

6. **Use technology to graph your function. Then answer each question and identify the piece of the function you used. Explain your reasoning.**

   a. **At what time of day will the pizza shop sell its 300th pizza?**

   b. **At what time of day will the pizza shop sell its 150th pizza?**

   c. **At what time of day will the pizza shop sell its 70th pizza?**

ACTIVITY 3.2

Interpreting the Graph of a Piecewise Function

The graph shows the percent of the charge remaining on a cell phone battery over time.

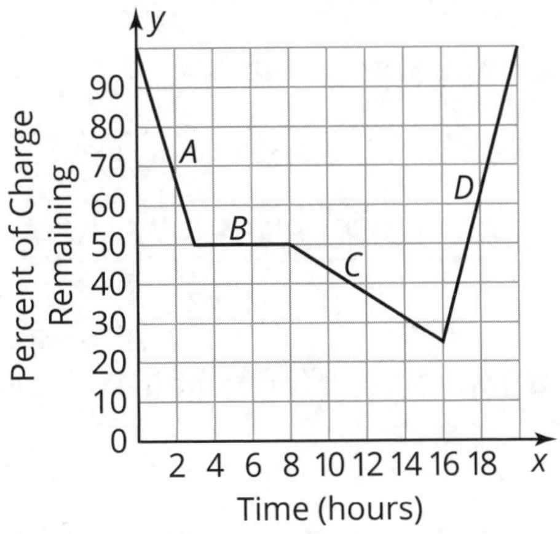

1. Describe the type of function shown in the graph.

2. Write a possible scenario that models the graph.

3. Explain how you know the graph represents a function in terms of this problem situation. Then, write a function $f(x)$ to model the graph. Define your variables.

4. Determine the slope, x-intercept(s), and y-intercept. Explain what each means in terms of this problem situation.

5. **Determine which piece(s) of the graph can be described by each statement.**

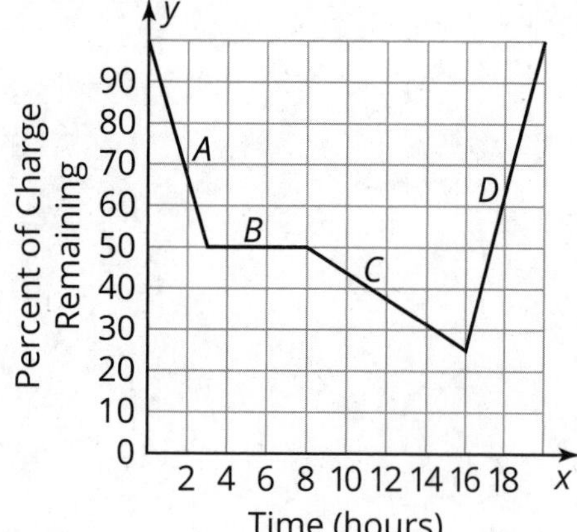

   a. **The cell phone was not in use.**

   b. **The cell phone battery was recharging.**

   c. **The cell phone was in use.**

   d. **The cell phone battery was fully charged.**

   e. **The cell phone battery was half-charged.**

6. **Determine whether each statement is true or false. If it is false, explain why it is false.**

   a. **The cell phone battery died after 20 hours.**

   b. **The cell phone battery lost 25% of its charge during an 8-hour period.**

   c. **The cell phone was used the most between the 16th and 20th hours.**

   d. **The cell phone battery was charged twice.**

   e. **After the first 3 hours, the battery had half the charge it began with.**

Write a scenario to model your own cell phone use during a typical day. Give your scenario to your partner and have them graph it while you graph your partner's scenario. Then, work together to determine the equation of each piecewise function.

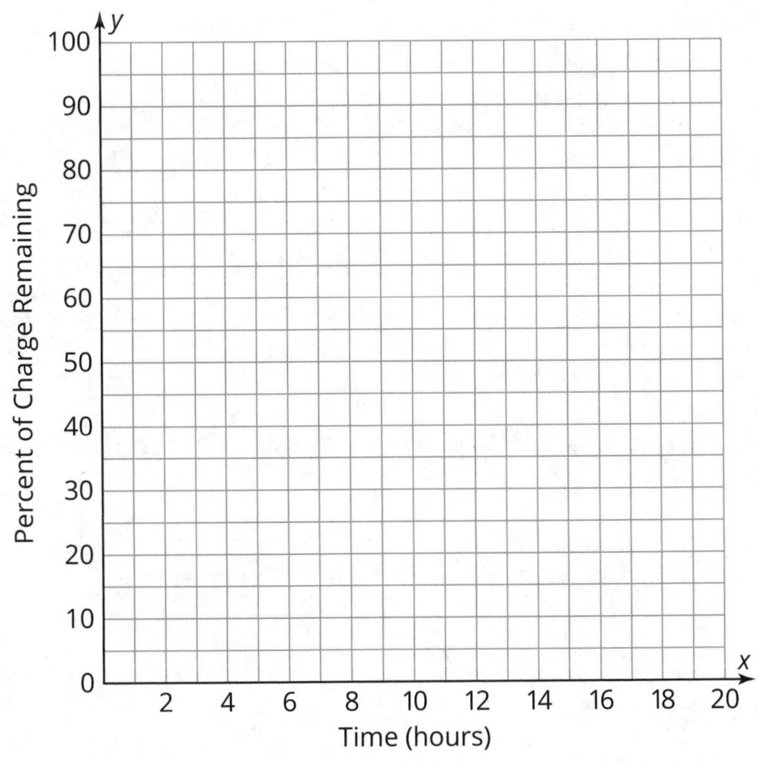

ACTIVITY

3.3 Transformations of Piecewise Functions

You can use what you know about transformations to transform any function, including a piecewise function. A transformed function is often written using the prime symbol (′).

For example, a transformation of the function $f(x)$ is written as $f'(x)$.

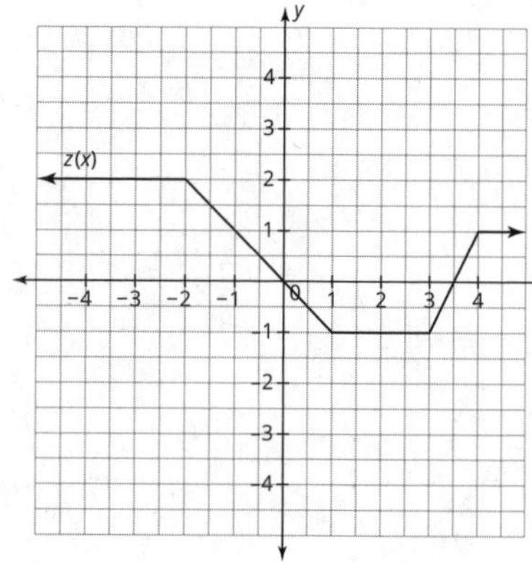

1. The graph of a function $z(x)$ is shown. Sketch the graphs of $z'(x)$ and $z''(x)$.

a. $z'(x) = z(x) + 3$

b. $z''(x) = z(x) - 4$

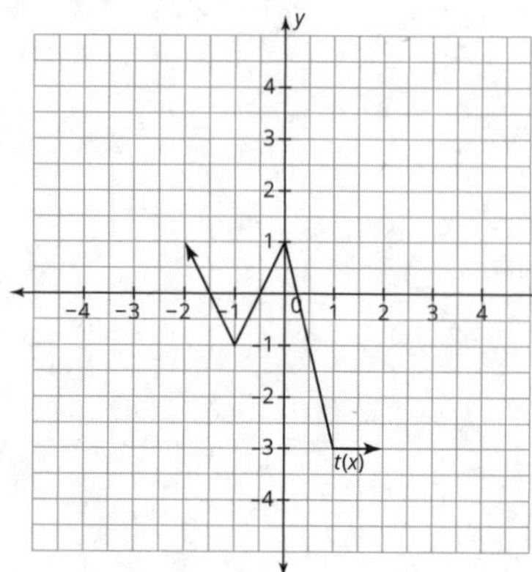

2. The graph of a function $t(x)$ is shown. Sketch the graphs of $t'(x)$ and $t''(x)$.

a. $t'(x) = t(x + 3)$

b. $t''(x) = t(x - 1)$

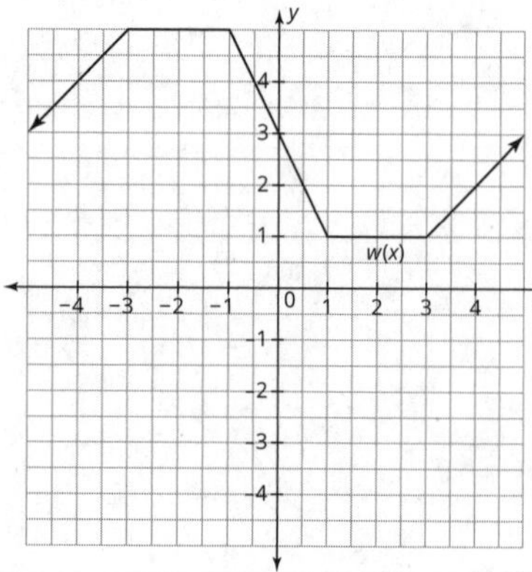

3. The graph of a function $w(x)$ is shown. Sketch the graphs of $w'(x)$ and $w''(x)$.

a. $w'(x) = -w(x)$

b. $w''(x) = w(-x)$

ACTIVITY

3.4

A Special Type of Piecewise Function

Consider the graph of $f(x) = |x|$.

1. Explain how the graph also represents a linear piecewise function.

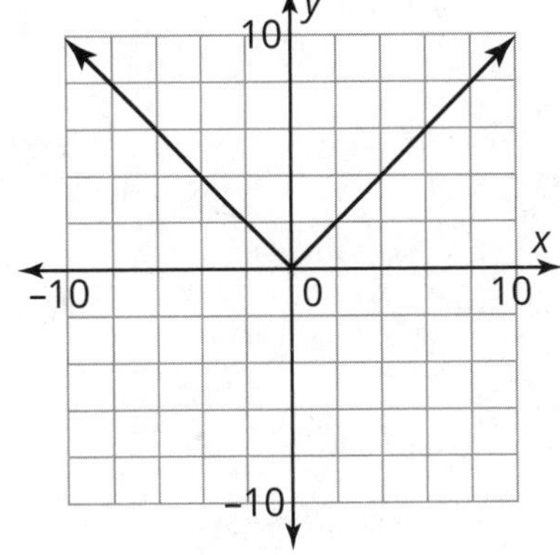

2. Write a linear piecewise function to represent the graph.

3. How is the symmetry of the absolute value function reflected in the equivalent linear piecewise function?

Consider this linear piecewise function.

$$g(x) = \begin{cases} x + 50, & -50 \leq x \leq 0 \\ -x + 50, & 0 < x \leq 50 \end{cases}$$

4. Sketch a graph of this function.

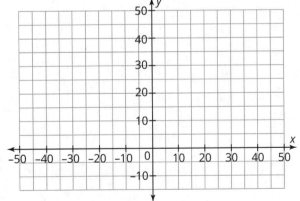

5. Explain how the graph also represents a linear absolute value function.

6. Write $g(x)$ as a linear absolute value function.

NOTES

TALK the TALK 

Piecing It All Together

1. **Write a piecewise function to model each absolute value function.**

a. 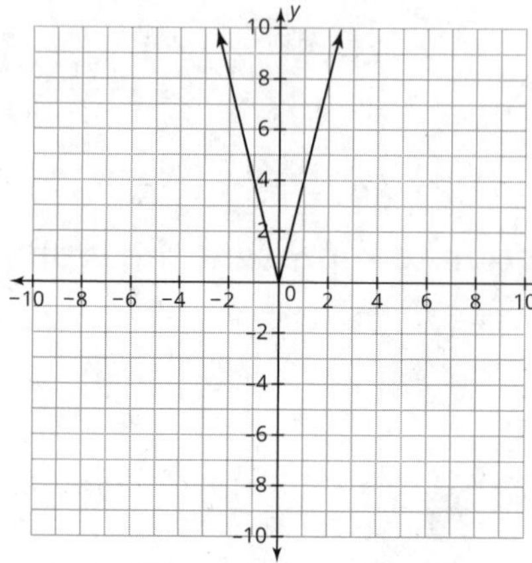

b. 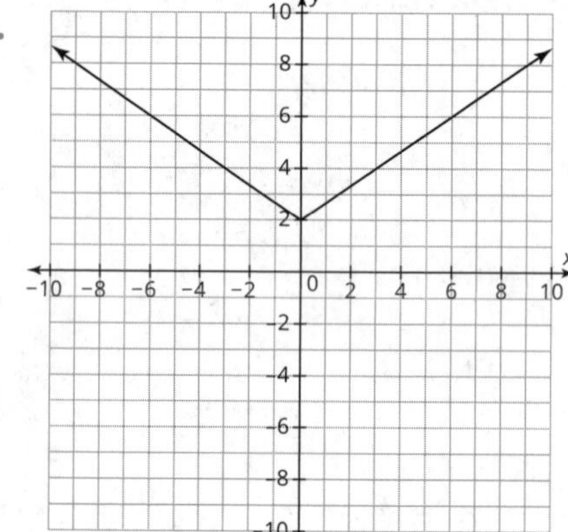

c. 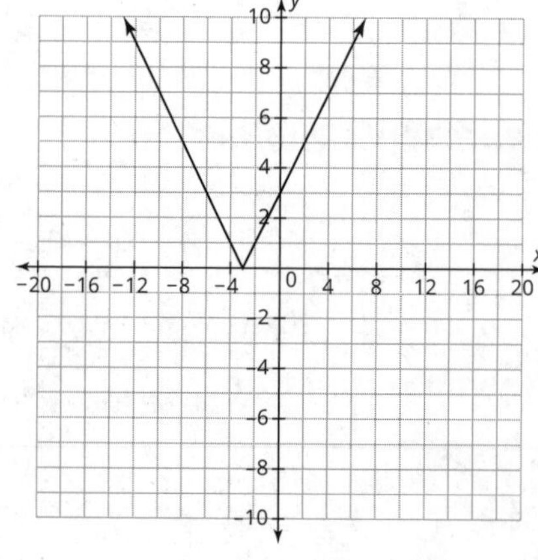

Assignment

Write

Explain the basic absolute value function using the definition of a linear piecewise function.

Remember

A linear piecewise function is a function that can be represented by linear functions, each of which corresponds to a part of the domain. To write a linear piecewise function, you must write the linear equation and domain for each part of the function.

Practice

1. Jin fills up a 510-gallon pool in the backyard for her children. She fills it with the garden hose at a rate of 17 gallons per minute. After it is filled, she lets it sit for 30 minutes in order to let the water temperature rise. The children then get in and have fun for an hour. The pool loses about $\frac{1}{2}$ gallon of water each minute due to their splashing and playing. At the end of the hour, they tear the pool while getting out, which causes a leak. The pool then begins to lose water at a rate of 2 gallons per minute.
   a. Complete the table to show the amount of water in the pool after each minute.
   b. Create a graph to model the problem situation. Include when the pool will be empty.
   c. Write a piecewise function that models this problem situation. Explain your reasoning for each piece of the function.
   d. Identify the *x*- and *y*-intercept. Explain what they mean in terms of the problem situation.
   e. Determine when the pool will have 470 gallons of water in it. Identify the piece(s) of function you used. Explain your reasoning.

Time (minutes)	Amount of Water (gallons)
0	
5	
20	
30	
45	
60	
80	
100	
120	
150	
200	

2. Jin asks her children to pay her back for the damaged pool. They must give her $15 per week. Together they have $165 in a savings account.
   a. Write a function to represent the amount of money they have after *x* weeks. Describe the domain and range of this function in terms of the problem situation.
   b. To rebuild their account, the children will receive a combined $15 per week in allowances. They start saving the week after their account is depleted and save for another 11 weeks. What are the domain and range of this function and what do they mean in terms of the problem situation? Write a function to represent this part of the graph.
   c. Graph the equations on the same grid. Is the graph continuous or discrete? Explain your reasoning.
   d. Write a function to represent the entire graph.

Stretch

The graphs of two linear piecewise functions are shown.

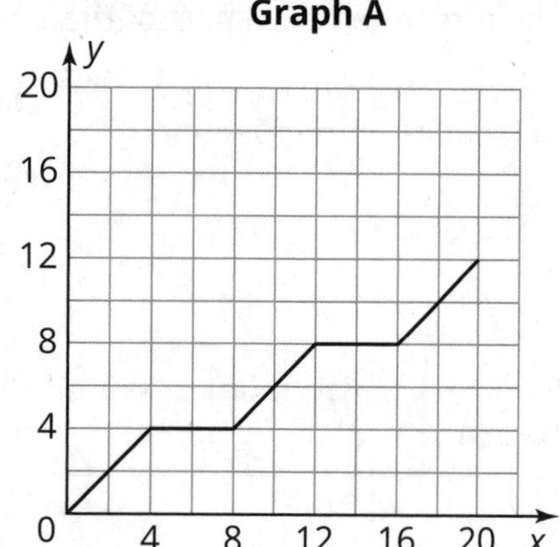

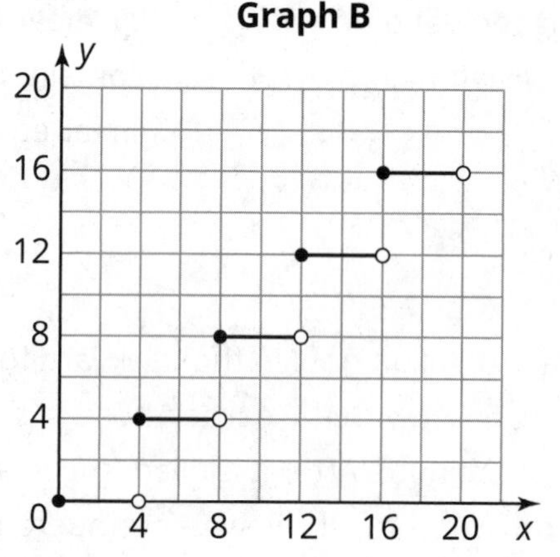

1. Describe the similarities and differences in the two graphs.
2. Determine the value of $f(x)$ for each graph when $x = 8$.
3. Determine the value of $f(x)$ for each graph when $x = 18$.
4. Write the piecewise functions for each graph.

Review

1. The Me-OW Company sells cat food in bags labeled 13 *pounds*. The quality control manager is in charge of making sure the bags get filled properly. To be labeled 13 *pounds*, a difference of no more than 0.15 pound is acceptable.
   a. Write an absolute value inequality to represent the restrictions on the difference in the weight of the bag.
   b. Determine the greatest and least amount of cat food a bag can contain and still fall within the required specifications. Write your answer as an inequality.

2. Leonore is making a quilt with circles stitched together. The circles all have a diameter of 16 inches. In order for the quilt to have straight edges, she must cut off the portion of the circular fabric that is shaded in the diagram for the border pieces. The measure of the central angle is 105°. How much surface area of the border pieces will she lose when she removes this part of the fabric piece? Use 3.14 for π and round your answer to the nearest hundredth if necessary.

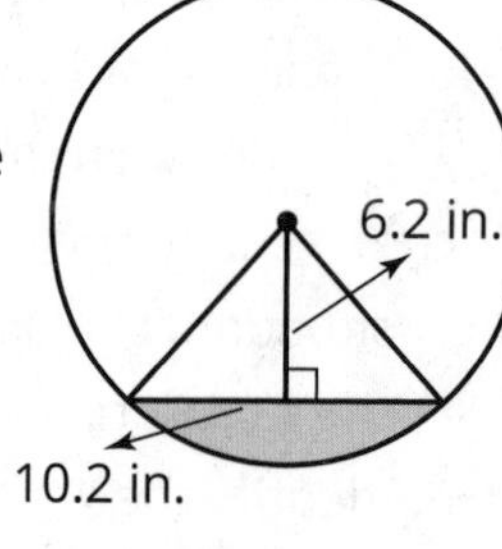

3. Use a trigonometric ratio to solve for the value of x. Round your answer to the nearest tenth.

a.

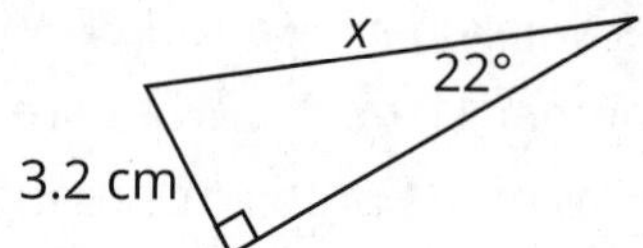

b.

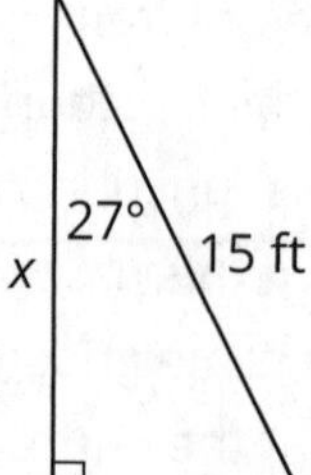

4

Step By Step

Step Functions

Warm Up

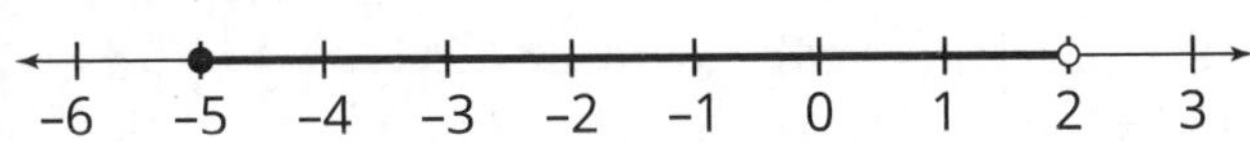

1. What is the significance of the open and closed endpoints in this graph?

Learning Goals

- Write and graph step functions from problem situations.
- Interpret the graphs and function notation representing step functions.
- Use technology to graph a step function.

Key Terms

- discontinuous graph
- step function
- greatest integer function (floor function)
- least integer function (ceiling function)

You have seen the absolute value function as an example of a linear piecewise function. What are other special cases of linear piecewise functions?

A High-Five for Height

At Adventure Village, there are minimum height requirements to determine if children can safely enjoy the rides.

- There are 22 rides any child can ride regardless of their height, although an adult must accompany the child for some rides.
- There are 10 additional rides that a child must be at least 36 inches tall to ride.
- There are 12 additional rides that a child must be at least 46 inches tall to ride.

1. Identify the independent and dependent quantities in this scenario.

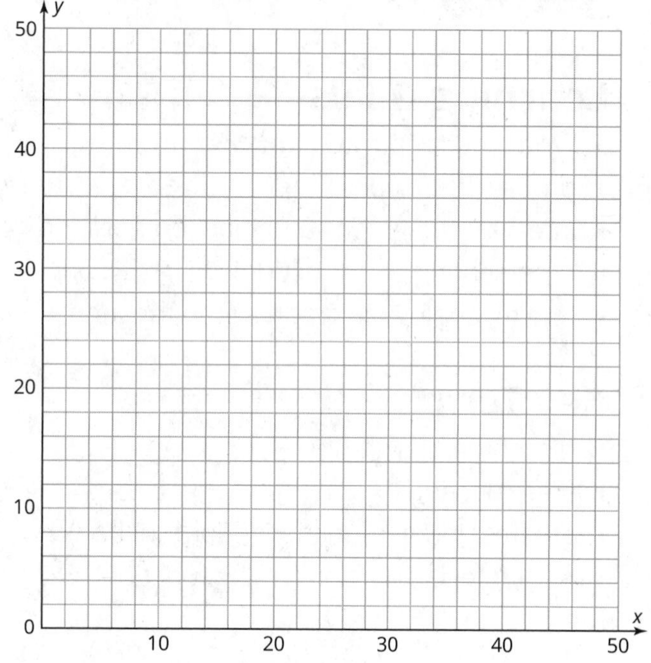

2. Use the scenario to graph the function. Label the axes.

3. Determine the number of rides a child is eligible to ride for each height.

a. 36 inches

b. $45\frac{15}{16}$ inches

c. 46 inches

4. How is this graph similar to the graphs in the previous lesson? How is it different?

ACTIVITY

4.1

Introducing Step Functions

Taking 10,000 steps per day is a popular fitness goal for individuals striving for a more active lifestyle. Jason has a fitness tracker, and developed a program where he plans to increase the number of steps he takes each day until he reaches his goal of 10,000 steps per day. Jason set a daily step goal for each week, Sunday through Saturday. He recorded his plan in the graph shown.

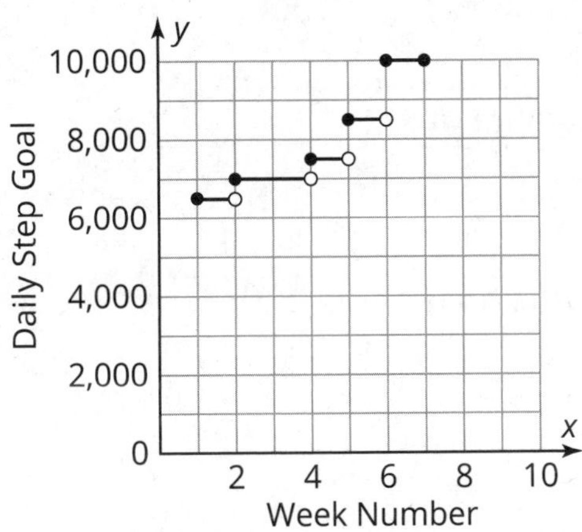

1. Use the graph and scenario to answer each question.

a. When does Jason plan to reach his goal of 10,000 steps per day?

b. Why does the graph start at $x = 1$?

c. On what day(s) is Jason's goal to walk 8000 steps?

d. Why do you think one piece of the graph has closed circles on both of its ends?

2. Consider the graph at $x = 2$.

   a. What is $f(2)$?

   b. Explain what is happening in the scenario right before $x = 2$.

3. Consider the graph at $f(x) = 7000$.

   a. What is the value of x?

   b. Explain what is happening in the scenario when $f(x) = 7000$.

4. Write a piecewise function to represent this graph and scenario.

This graph and the piecewise graph in the previous activity are neither discrete nor continuous. They are *discontinuous.* A **discontinuous graph** is a graph that is continuous for some values of the domain with at least one disjoint area between consecutive x-values.

. **Consider the examples of discontinuous graphs. Which graph(s) represent functions? Use the definition of *function* to justify your response.**

Graph A

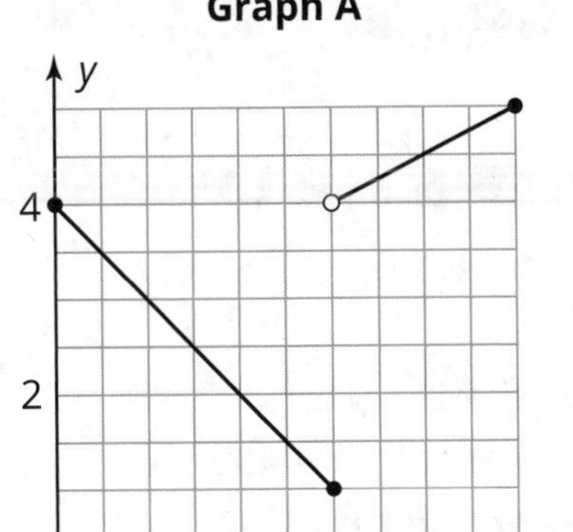

Graph B

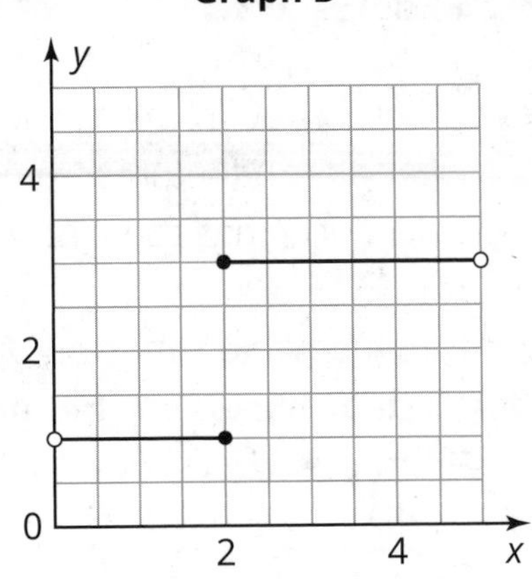

Graph C

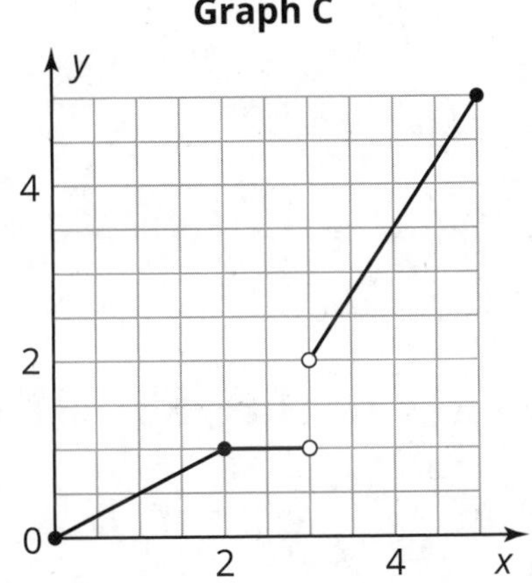

ason's Fitness Plan graph represents a specific discontinuous function, a *step function*. A **step function** is a piecewise function on a given interval whose pieces are discontinuous constant functions.

6. **How do you think step functions got their name?**

7. **Use technology to graph your piecewise function, *f*(*x*). Can you determine by viewing your graph using technology whether an endpoint is included or not included in the graph?**

NOTES

ACTIVITY

4.2

A Decreasing Step Function

Robert borrowed $400 from his older brother to take a weekend trip with h friends. A week after he returns from his trip, he will begin paying his brothe $80 per week until he has completely paid off his debt.

1. **Define a piecewise function, $f(x)$, for the total amount of Robert's debt based on the number of weeks he pays his brothe back. Then create a graph to represent the function.**

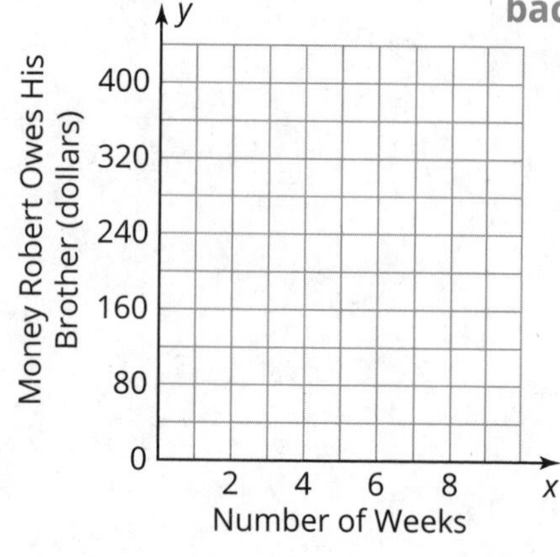

2. **How does each representation fit the definition of a step function?**

   a. **the context**

   b. **the function**

   c. **the graph**

3. **How did you determine where to place the open and closed circles?**

ACTIVITY
4.3
Special Linear Piecewise Functions

The *greatest integer function* is a special linear piecewise function. The **greatest integer function**, also known as a **floor function**, $G(x) = \lfloor x \rfloor$, is defined as the greatest integer less than or equal to x.

1. Evaluate each expression using the greatest integer function.

a. $\lfloor 2 \rfloor =$ ________ b. $\lfloor 0.17 \rfloor =$ ________

c. $\lfloor 2.34 \rfloor =$ ________ d. $\lfloor -1.2 \rfloor =$ ________

e. $\lfloor 2.99999 \rfloor =$ ________ f. $\lfloor -0.2 \rfloor =$ ________

2. Graph $G(x) = \lfloor x \rfloor$.

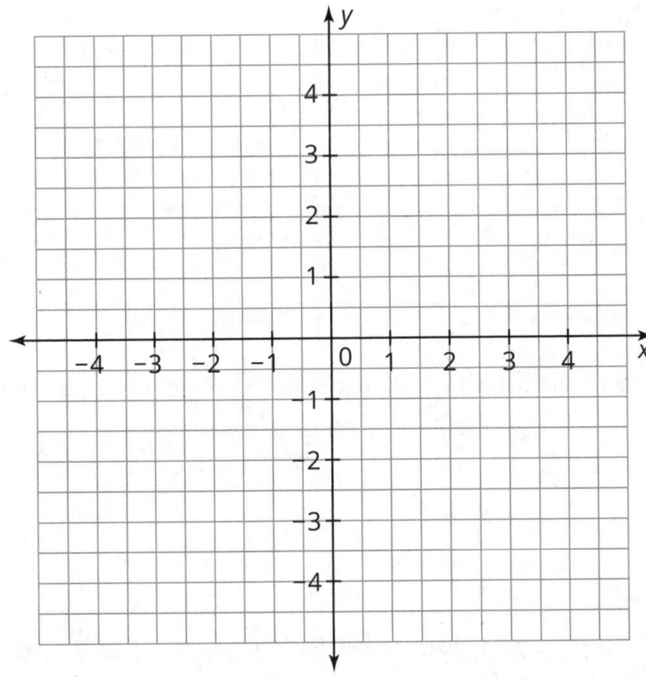

about:

Consider that the function $G(x)$ is equal to 0 when $0 \leq x < 1$. How can you graph this "step"? How can you graph the steps greater or less than this?

3. Why do you think the greatest integer function is also referred to as the floor function?

The *least integer function* is another special linear piecewise function. The **least integer function** $L(x) = \lceil x \rceil$, also known as the **ceiling function**, is defined as the least integer greater than or equal to x.

Do you notice the difference in the symbol for a least integer function?

4. **Evaluate each expression using the least integer function.**

a. $\lceil 2 \rceil =$ ________

b. $\lceil 0.17 \rceil =$ ________

c. $\lceil 2.34 \rceil =$ ________

d. $\lceil -1.2 \rceil =$ ________

e. $\lceil 2.99999 \rceil =$ ________

f. $\lceil -0.2 \rceil =$ ________

5. **Graph $L(x) = \lceil x \rceil$.**

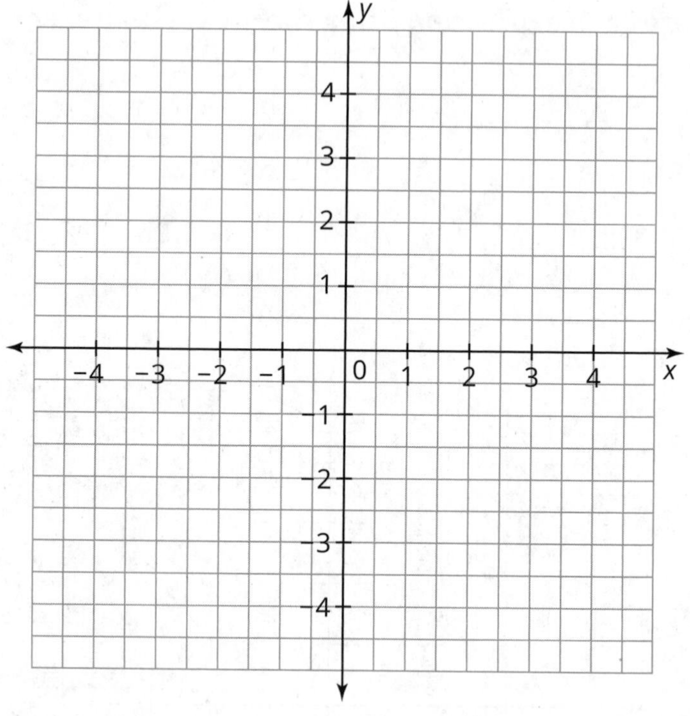

6. **Why do you think the least integer function is also referred to as the ceiling function?**

7. **Compare the graphs you created for the greatest integer function and the least integer function. What do you notice?**

8. **Use technology to graph $G(x) = \lfloor x \rfloor$ and $L(x) = \lceil x \rceil$. Compare the graphs and equations for the greatest integer function and the least integer function. What do you notice?**

9. **While technology provides a reasonable representation of the graph, why might it not be the best representation to use?**

0. **Determine whether each scenario identifies the greatest integer function, least integer function, or neither.**

   a. **Mark is parking his car in a garage that charges by the hour. When he parks there for 3.2 hours, he is charged for 4 hours. When he parks there for 3.9 hours, he is charged for 4 hours.**

   b. **Tamara gets reward points for every dollar she spends at the mall. When she spent $34.25, she received 34 reward points. When she spent $15.95, she received 15 reward points.**

   c. **Julie's teacher records only whole number values in her gradebook. When Julie earned 88.3 points, the teacher recorded 88 points. When Julie earned 92.5 points, the teacher recorded 93 points.**

   d. **The yogurt shop charges by the weight of the yogurt sundae you create. Everly is charged as if her 4.2-ounce sundae weighs 5 ounces, and Greyson is charged as if his 5.7-ounce sundae weighs 6 ounces.**

NOTES

TALK the TALK 

Wrapping It Up and Sending It Off

Consider these postal rates for first class mail.

- A letter weighing up to one ounce will cost $0.49 to mail.
- A letter weighing more than one ounce and up to two ounces will cost $0.70 to mail.
- A letter weighing more than two ounces and up to three ounces will cost $0.91 to mail.

1. Write a function, $f(x)$, to describe this situation.

2. Which graph best represents this situation? Explain your reasoning.

Graph A

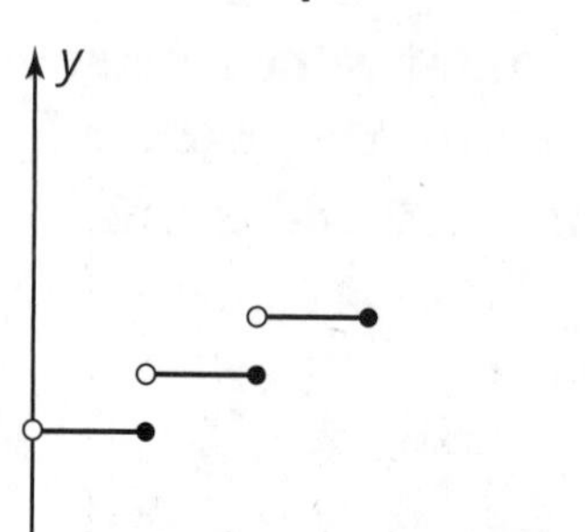

Graph B

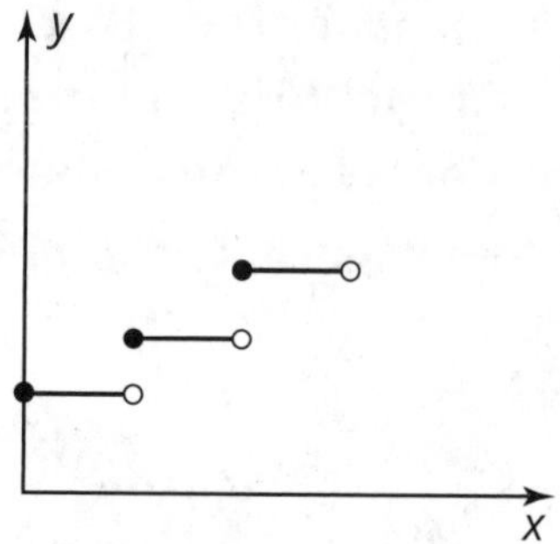

3. Complete each statement using *always*, *sometimes*, or *never*.

a. Step functions are __________ piecewise functions.

b. Piecewise functions are __________ step functions.

c. The graphs of step functions are __________ discontinuous.

d. The graphs of piecewise functions are __________ discontinuous.

Assignment

Write

Any part of a linear piecewise function is written in the form $ax + b$. Describe the possible a- and b-values that define a step function.

Remember

A discontinuous graph is a graph that is continuous for some values of the domain with at least one disjoint area between consecutive x-values. A step function is a piecewise function on a given interval whose pieces are discontinuous constant functions.

Practice

1. A department store offers store credit but has the listed rules.
   - For a bill less than \$15 the entire amount is due.
   - For a bill of at least \$15 but less than \$50, the minimum due is \$15.
   - For a bill of at least \$50 but less than \$100, the minimum due is \$20.
   - For a bill of \$100 or more, a minimum of 25% of the bill is due.

   a. Write a piecewise function, $f(x)$, for the minimum amount due for the amount of the bill, x.
   b. Graph the function. Be sure to label the axes.
   c. Is your piecewise function a step function? Why or why not?
   d. Describe the rate of change when $0 \le x < 15$. What does it mean in terms of this problem situation?
   e. A customer comes in the store to pay the minimum amount on his bill of \$100. The customer thinks he owes \$20, but the cashier tells him he owes \$25. Who is correct? Explain your reasoning.

2. A department store has an online site that customers can order from. The shipping rates are calculated as listed.
   - A package that weighs no more than 10 pounds costs \$5.
   - A package that weighs more than 10 pounds but no more than 20 pounds costs \$10.
   - A package that weighs more than 20 pounds but no more than 30 pounds costs \$15.
   - A package that weighs more than 30 pounds but no more than 40 pounds costs \$20.
   - A package that weighs more than 40 pounds but no more than 50 pounds costs \$25.

   a. Write a piecewise function, $f(x)$, for the shipping cost for the weight of the package, x.
   b. Graph the function. Be sure to label the axes.
   c. Is this piecewise function a step function? Why or why not?
   d. Rewrite the step function as a greatest integer function. How do the shipping costs change for a 10-pound package?

Stretch

After the first statistics test of the year, a professor asked her students to write down the number of hours they studied for the test. A student created the graph to show the relationship between the grade earned and the number of hours studied.

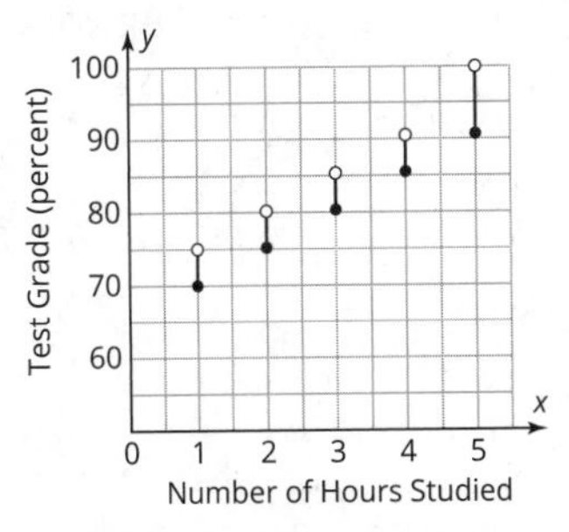

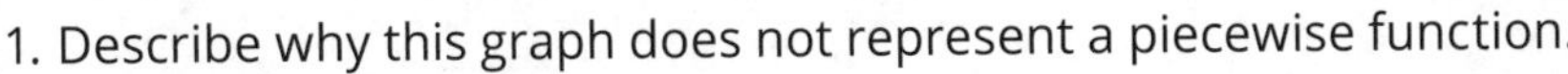

1. Describe why this graph does not represent a piecewise function.
2. Write the situation as a piecewise function.

Review

1. Arnav is saving money to buy a used car in six months, or 24 weeks. He already has $550 saved. For four weeks in a row, he is able to put $100 into the account. He goes through a period of three weeks during which he is unable to add to the account. The next seven weeks after that, he is able to put in $75 each week. For the next four weeks, he has to take out $50 a week to pay some bills. For the remaining weeks he is able to once again put $100 a week into the account.
   a. Write a piecewise function to model the problem situation and then create a graph.
   b. Determine how much money he will have in his account after 15 weeks. Identify the function you used and explain the reason.
2. A company sells paper popcorn cones to movie theaters. The cones are 9 inches high and have a diameter of 4.5 inches. How much popcorn does a cone hold? Use 3.14 for π and round your answer to the nearest tenth if necessary.
3. A spherical balloon that is filled with air has a diameter of 28 centimeters. What volume of air is inside the balloon? Use 3.14 for π and round your answer to the nearest tenth if necessary.
4. The value of a car, y, and its relationship to the age of the car, x, is represented by the graph. Determine the x- and y-intercepts of the graph, and explain their meanings in terms of this problem.

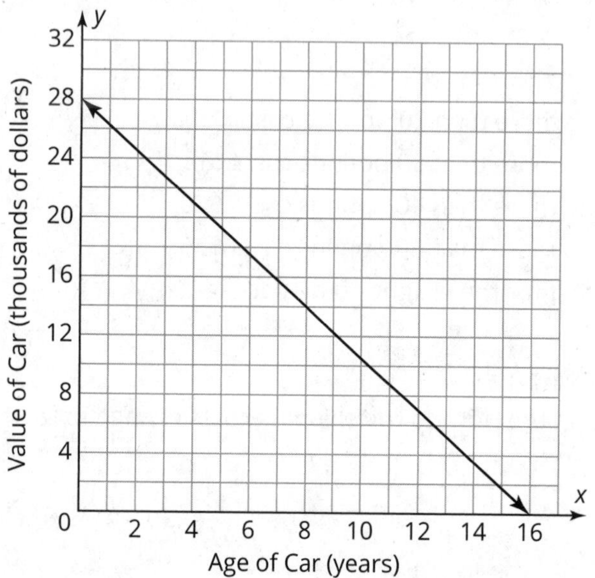

5. LaQuan has picked up a friend and they are on a road trip. The graph represents the relationship between the distance LaQuan is from his home and the number of hours he and his friend have traveled. Determine the slope and the y-intercept of the graph, and explain their meanings in terms of the problem.

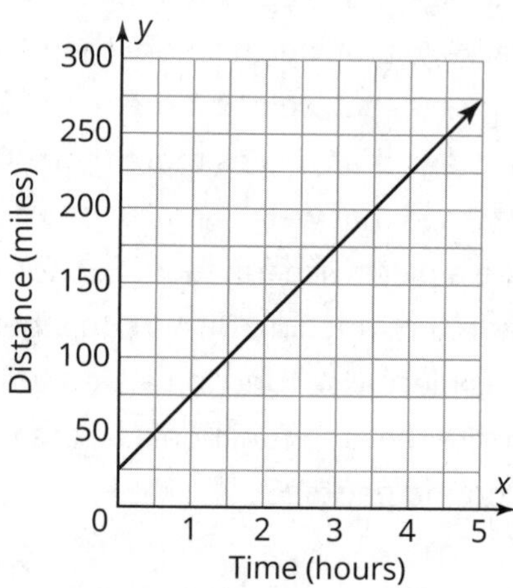

5

A Riddle Wrapped in a Mystery

Inverses of Linear Functions

Warm Up

Solve each equation.

1. $2x - 5 = 97$

2. $\frac{1}{3}x + 40 = 280$

3. $-4x - 10 = -26$

Learning Goals

- Determine the inverse of a given situation using words.
- Determine the inverse of a function numerically using a table, an equation, and a graph.
- Determine whether given functions are one-to-one functions.

Key Terms

- inverse of a function
- one-to-one function

You know that a function takes a set of inputs and maps them to a set of outputs. What happens when the outputs and inputs are reversed?

GETTING STARTED

Inside an Enigma

One of the simplest methods of creating a code is called a substitution cipher. For a substitution cipher, you can take each letter of the alphabet in numeric order and assign it to a different number using a mathematical rule.

1	2	3	4	5	6	7	8	9	10	11	12	13	14	15	16	17	18	19	20	21	22	23	24	25	26
A	B	C	D	E	F	G	H	I	J	K	L	M	N	O	P	Q	R	S	T	U	V	W	X	Y	Z

For example, if the cipher were written as $x + 4$, then L, which is currently assigned to 12, would be assigned to $12 + 4 = 16$, or P, in the code. The letter Y, which is currently assigned to 25, would be assigned to 3, or C, in the code. The word "inverse" would have the code "mrzivwi."

Cipher: $x + 4$

Word	Code
inverse	mrzivwi

1. **Write a substitution cipher rule. Then write a short note to a classmate in code. Give your rule and coded note to a classmate to decode.**

2. **Use mathematical notation to write the rule you used to decode your classmate's note.**

3. **Why is it important that the substitution cipher rule be a function?**

4. **Compare the inputs and outputs of the cipher rule you created and the rule used to decode your note. What do you notice?**

ACTIVITY

5.1

The Inverse of a Function

Miguel is planning a trip to Turkey. Before he leaves, he wants to exchange his money to the Turkish lira, the official currency of Turkey. The exchange rate at the time of his trip is 4 lira per 1 U.S. dollar.

1. Complete the table of values to show the currency conversion for U.S. dollars to Turkish lira.

U.S. Currency (dollars)	Turkish Currency (lira)
100	
250	
400	
650	
1000	

2. Write an equation to represent the number of lira in terms of the number of U.S. dollars.

Suppose at the end of his trip, Miguel needs to convert any remaining lira to dollars. This situation is the *inverse* of the original situation.

3. What are the independent and dependent quantities of the inverse of the problem situation? How do these quantities compare to the quantities in Question 1?

4. Complete the table of values to show the inverse of the problem situation.

5. Compare the tables in Questions 1 and 4. What do you notice?

6. Use the table to write an equation for the inverse of the problem situation. Does this equation represent a function? Explain your answer.

Recall that a function takes an input value, performs some operation(s) on this value, and creates an output value. The **inverse of a function** takes the output value, performs some operation(s) on this value, and arrives back at the original function's input value. In other words, an inverse of a function "undoes" the function.

Worked Example

Given a function, $f(x)$, you can determine the inverse algebraically by following these steps.

Step 1: Replace the function $f(x)$ with another variable, generally y.

Step 2: Switch the x and y variables in the equation.

Step 3: Solve for y.

7. **Use function notation to represent the number of lira $f(x)$ in terms of the number of U.S. dollars, x. Then complete the steps shown in the worked example to represent the number of U.S. dollars in terms of the number of lira. Compare the inverse to the equation you wrote in Question 6. What do you notice?**

ACTIVITY

5.2 Graphing Inverses of Functions

In the previous activity you wrote the inverse of a function using algebra. Let's consider how to show the inverse of a function using its graph.

Worked Example

Given a function, $f(x)$, you can determine the inverse of a function graphically by following these steps.

Step 1: Copy the coordinate plane and graph $f(x)$ and the line $y = x$ onto patty paper.

Step 2: Heavily trace the graph of $f(x)$ with a pencil.

Step 3: Reflect the patty paper across the line $y = x$, and rub the paper so that the image of the graph of its inverse appears.

How do the algebraic process and the graphical process to determine an inverse compare?

1. **Consider the graph of the function $f(x) = 4x$ from the previous activity. Complete the steps in the worked example to graph the inverse using patty paper.**

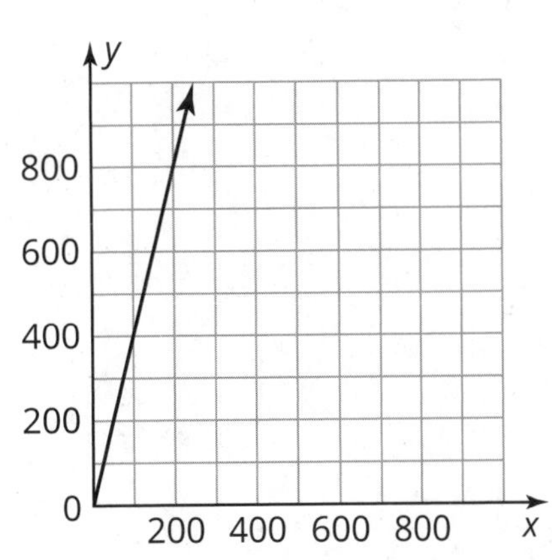

2. **Compare the image you created and the graph of the inverse.**

   a. **What do you notice about the image and the graph of the inverse?**

   b. **What does this tell you about the graph of a function and its inverse and about the line $y = x$?**

NOTES

3. For each function and a given point on the graph of the function determine the corresponding point on the graph of the inverse the function.

a. Given that (3, 2) is a point on the graph of $g(x)$, what is the corresponding point on the graph of the inverse of $g(x)$?

b. Given that (−1, 0) is a point on the graph of $h(x)$, what is the corresponding point on the graph of the inverse of $h(x)$?

c. Given that (a, b) is a point on the graph of $f(x)$, what is the corresponding point on the graph of the inverse of $f(x)$?

ACTIVITY

5.3 One-to-One Functions

n this activity, you will determine the inverse of a function using nultiple representations.

1. **For each given function, determine the inverse using each representation.**

   - **Complete a table of values for the function and its inverse.**
   - **Sketch the graph of the function using a solid line. Then sketch the inverse of the function on the same coordinate plane using a dashed line.**
   - **Write an equation for the inverse.**
   - **Determine whether the function is a one-to-one function. Explain your reasoning.**

A function is a **one-to-one function** if both the function and its inverse are functions.

   a. $f(x) = 3x - 6$

x	$f(x)$
−2	
−1	
0	
1	
2	

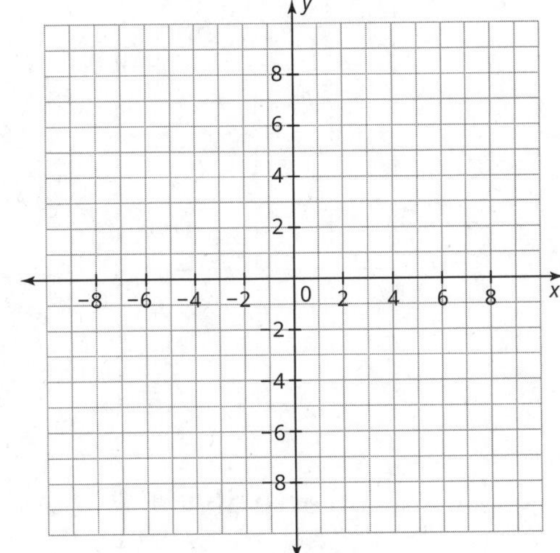

Inverse of $f(x)$	
x	y
	−2
	−1
	0
	1
	2

Use a straightedge to draw your lines.

b. $g(x) = -x + 4$

x	$g(x)$
−2	
−1	
0	
1	
2	

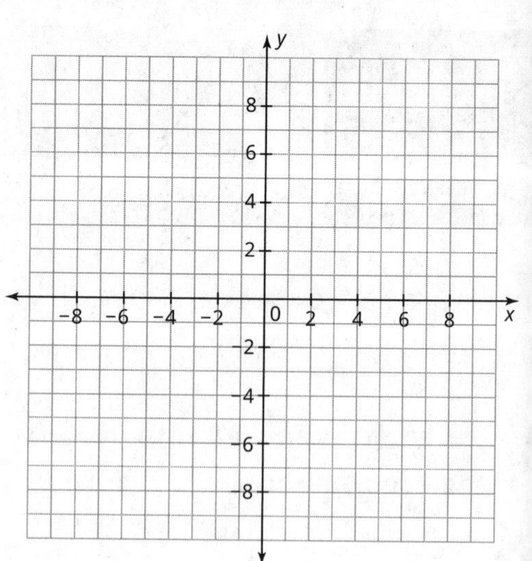

Inverse of $g(x)$	
x	y
	−2
	−1
	0
	1
	2

c. $h(x) = 2$

x	$h(x)$
−2	
−1	
0	
1	
2	

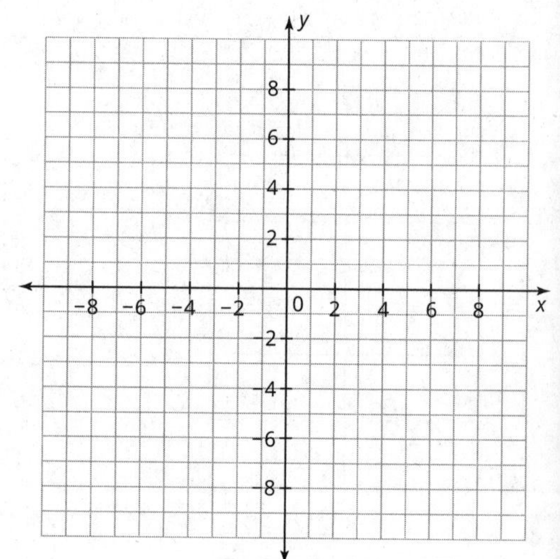

Inverse of $h(x)$	
x	y
	−2
	−1
	0
	1
	2

d. $r(x) = |x|$

x	$r(x)$
−2	
−1	
0	
1	
2	

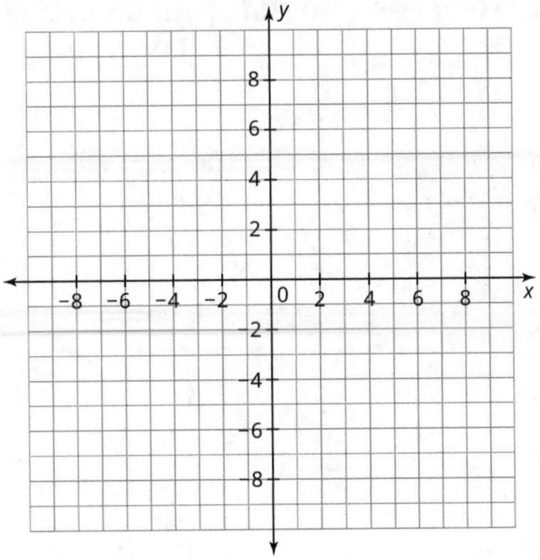

Inverse of $r(x)$	
x	y
	−2
	−1
	0
	1
	2

. **Adam and Stacey are working on a homework assignment in which they must identify all functions that are one-to-one functions. Adam says that all linear functions are one-to-one functions, so they don't even need to look at the linear functions. Stacey disagrees, and says that not all linear functions are one-to-one functions. Who is correct? Explain how you determined which student is correct.**

NOTES

3. **How can you determine whether an inverse exists given a linear function?**

4. **Can a linear function and its inverse be the same function? If so, provide an example. If not, explain why not.**

For a one-to-one function $f(x)$, the notation for its inverse is $f^{-1}(x)$. The notation for inverse, $f^{-1}(x)$, does not mean the same thing as x^{-1}. The expression x^{-1} can be rewritten as $\frac{1}{x}$; however, $f^{-1}(x)$ cannot be rewritten, because it is only used as notation. In other words, $f^{-1}(x) \neq \frac{1}{f(x)}$.

5. **Complete the graphic organizer on the next page. Write the definition for the inverse of a linear function. Then describe how to determine the inverse of a function algebraically, graphically, and numerically.**

Graphic Organizer

Definition

Algebraic Description

INVERSES OF LINEAR FUNCTIONS

Graphical Description

Numeric Description (Table of Values)

NOTES

TALK the TALK

Strike That. Invert It.

Consider the linear function $y = ax + b$, where $a \neq 0$.

1. **Use algebra to show that the inverse of this function is also a function.**

2. **Identify the slope and *y*-intercept of $f(x)$ and its inverse.**

3. **Given $y = 4x + 10$, identify the slope and *y*-intercept of $f(x)$ and its inverse.**

4. **Given $y = -3x + 6$, identify the slope and *y*-intercept of $f(x)$ and its inverse.**

5. **What happens to the slope and *y*-intercept of a linear function $y = ax + b$, where $a \neq 0$,when you take its inverse?**

Assignment

Write

Describe how to use a graph to prove two relationships are inverses of each other.

Remember

An inverse of a function "undoes" the function. The inverse of a function is determined by replacing $f(x)$ with y, switching the x and y variables, and solving for y. A one-to-one function is a function in which its inverse is also a function.

Practice

1. Clothing and shoe sizes typically vary from country to country. Kalinda is going to be spending a year in Italy and plans on shopping for dresses while she's there. While investigating the differences in sizing, she determines that to change the U.S. dress size to an Italian dress size, she must add 12 to the U.S. dress size and then double the sum.
   a. Complete the table of values to show the dress size conversion for U.S. dresses to Italian dresses.
   b. Write a function, $f(x)$, to represent the Italian dress size in terms of x, the U.S. dress size.
   c. Determine the inverse of this problem situation using words.
   d. Determine the inverse of the function algebraically. What does the inverse function represent in terms of the problem situation?
   e. Sketch the graph of the original function. Then, sketch the inverse on the same graph.

U.S. Dress Size	Italian Dress Size
4	
6	
10	
14	
18	

2. Determine the inverse of each function. Is the inverse also a function? Explain why or why not.
   a. $f(x) = 0.6x - 2$
   b. $g(x) = \frac{8}{3}x + 12$
3. Determine whether the functions $j(x) = 3 - 1.5x$ and $k(x) = -\frac{2}{3}x + 2$ are inverses. If so, explain how you know. If not, determine each function's inverse.
4. Sketch the inverse of the given function on the same graph as the function. Is the inverse also a function? Explain why or why not.

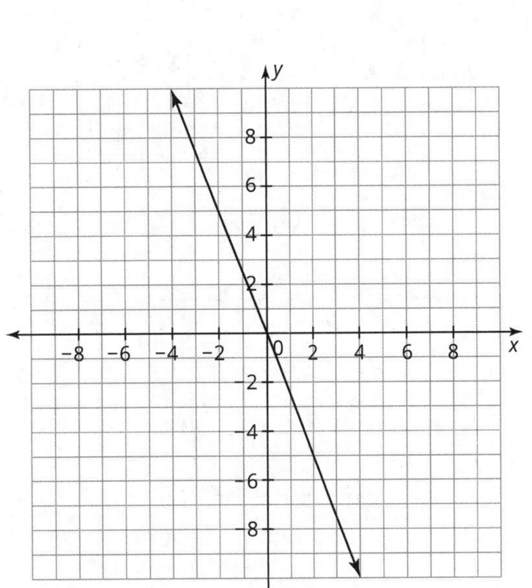

Stretch

1. For the function $f(x) = x + 1$, the inverse function is $f^{-1}(x) = x - 1$. Evaluate the function $f(x)$ by replacing x with $x - 1$. What do you notice? How does this relate to the process of using a graph to determine an inverse?

Review

1. A school P.T.A. is organizing a Fun Run to benefit the school. A local business has agreed to donate cases of lemonade, with the following conditions:
   - for less than 50 runners they will donate two cases,
   - for at least 50 but less than 100 runners they will donate five cases,
   - for at least 100 but less than 150 runners they will donate twelve cases, and
   - for at least 150 runners they will donate twenty cases.

   a. Write a piecewise function $f(x)$ for the number of cases the business will donate, x.

   b. Is this piecewise function a step function? Explain your reasoning.

   c. Graph the function. Be sure to label the axes.

   d. Describe the rate of change when $100 \leq x < 150$. What does it mean in terms of the problem situation?

   e. The P.T.A. has 79 runners signed up for the Fun Run. How many cases of lemonade will they get? Explain your reasoning.

2. Each graph represents a form of the function $g(x) = Af(x) + D$, given $f(x) = |x|$. Determine A and D, and then explain the transformations those values make on the basic linear absolute value function. Write the function in terms of the basic function.

   a.

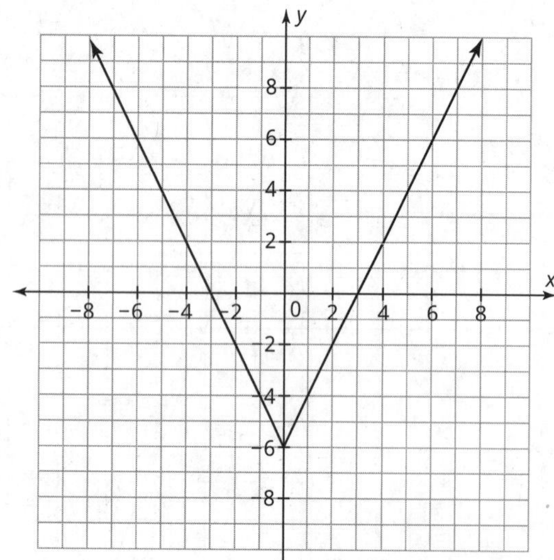

   b.

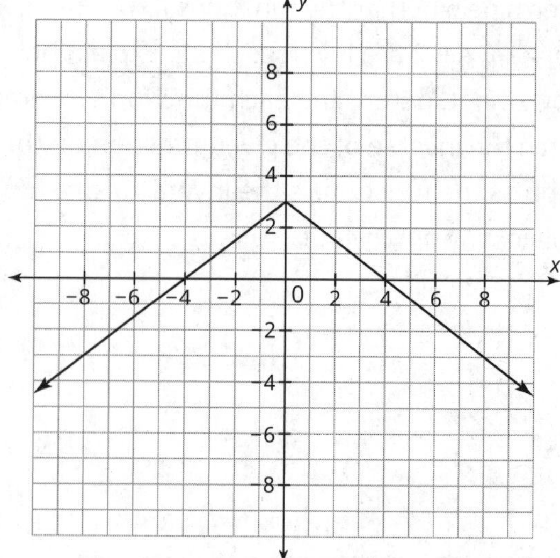

Functions Derived from Linear Relationships Summary

KEY TERMS

- absolute value
- reflection
- line of reflection
- argument of a function
- linear absolute value equation
- linear absolute value inequality
- equivalent compound inequality
- piecewise function
- linear piecewise function
- discontinuous graph
- step function
- greatest integer function (floor function)
- least integer function (ceiling function)
- inverse of a function
- one-to-one function

LESSON 1 Putting the V in Absolute Value

The **absolute value** of a number is its distance from zero on the number line. Absolute value is indicated with vertical bars: $|-4| = 4$.

The graph of the absolute value function $f(x) = |x|$ is in a V shape. It is the combination of the graphs of $f(x) = x$ and $f(x) = -x$.

For the basic function $f(x) = |x|$, the transformed function $g(x) = f(x) + D$ is a vertical translation of the function $f(x)$. For $D > 0$, the graph vertically shifts up. For $D < 0$, the graph vertically shifts down. The amount of shift is given by $|D|$.

For the basic function $f(x) = |x|$, the transformed function $g(x) = A \cdot f(x)$ is a vertical dilation of the function $f(x)$. For $|A| > 1$, the graph vertically stretches by a factor of A units. For $0 < |A| < 1$, the graph vertically compresses by a factor of A units. For $A < 0$, the graph reflects across a horizontal line.

A **reflection** of a graph is the mirror image of the graph about a line of reflection. A **line of reflecti** is the line that the graph is reflected across. A horizontal line of reflection affects the y-coordinates.

The **argument of a function** is the expression inside the parentheses. For $y = f(x - C)$ the expressic $x - C$ is the argument of the function. A change to the argument of a function is said to happen "inside the function." These values affect the input to a function, x. For the basic function $f(x) = |x|$, the transformed function $g(x) = f(x - C)$ is a horizontal translation of the function $f(x)$. For $C > 0$, the grap horizontally shifts right. For $C < 0$, the graph horizontally shifts left. The amount of shift is given by $|C$

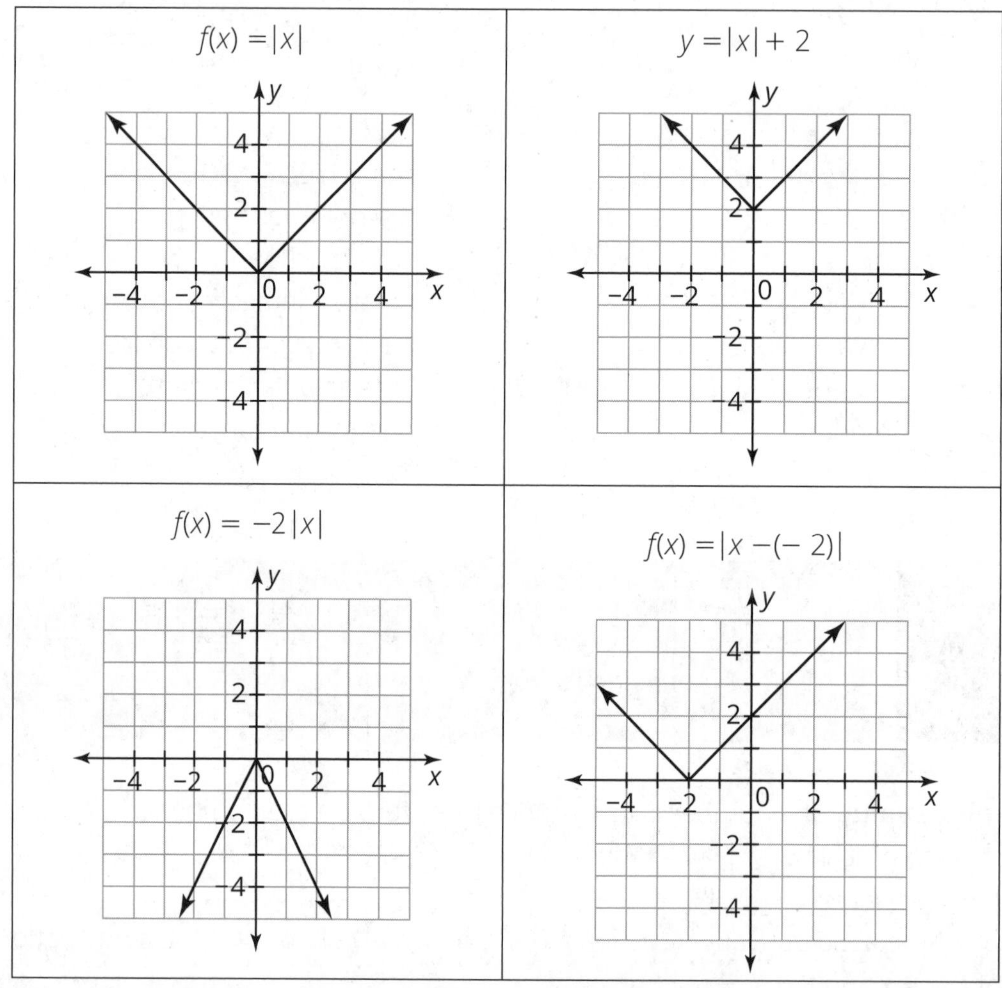

LESSON 2

Play Ball!

To solve a **linear absolute value equation**, write the positive and negative equations that the linear absolute value equation represents. Then solve each equation.

$$|5x - 4| = 21$$

$$+(5x - 4) = 21 \qquad -(5x - 4) = 21$$
$$5x - 4 = 21 \qquad 5x - 4 = -21$$
$$5x - 4 + 4 = 21 + 4 \qquad 5x - 4 + 4 = -21 + 4$$
$$5x = 25 \qquad 5x = -17$$
$$\frac{5x}{5} = \frac{25}{5} \qquad \frac{5x}{5} = \frac{(-17)}{5}$$
$$x = 5 \qquad x = -3\frac{2}{5}$$

If there is a range of solutions that satisfy a problem situation, you can write a **linear absolute value inequality**. To evaluate for a specific value, substitute the value for the variable.

For example, suppose a swimmer who wants to compete on the green team at the City Swim Club should be able to swim the 100-meter freestyle in 54.24 seconds plus or minus 1.43 seconds. Can a swimmer with a time of 53.15 seconds qualify for the green team?

$$|t - 54.24| \leq 1.43$$
$$|53.15 - 54.24| \leq 1.43$$
$$|-1.09| \leq 1.43$$
$$1.09 \leq 1.43$$

The swimmer qualifies because his time is less than 1.43 seconds from the base time.

Absolute value inequalities can take four different forms with the absolute value expression compared to a value, c. To solve an absolute value inequality, you must first write it as an **equivalent compound inequality**. "Less than" inequalities will be conjunctions and "greater than" inequalities will be disjunctions.

Absolute Value Inequality	Equivalent Compound Inequality
$\lvert ax + b\rvert < c$	$-c < ax + b < c$
$\lvert ax + b\rvert \leq c$	$-c \leq ax + b \leq c$
$\lvert ax + b\rvert > c$	$ax + b < -c$ or $ax + b > c$
$\lvert ax + b\rvert \geq c$	$ax + b \leq -c$ or $ax + b \geq c$

LESSON 3

I Graph in Pieces

A **piecewise function** is a function that can be represented by more than one function, each of which corresponds to a part of the domain. To write a piecewise function, write the equation and domain for each piece of the function. The graph of a piecewise function will contain more than or piece or section of graph. A **linear piecewise function** is a function that can be represented by linear functions only, each of which corresponds to a part of the domain.

For example, suppose Victoria is starting a new babysitting job that will last for 10 days. She plans to save all of the money she earns. She will earn \$7.50 per hour and will work 2 hours after school during the week and 4 hours a day on the weekends. She started work on a Monday and did so we that she got a \$0.50 per hour raise by the next Monday.

Time (days)	Amount of Money Saved (dollars)
0 (Sun)	0
1 (Mon)	15
2 (Tues)	30
3 (Wed)	45
4 (Thurs)	60
5 (Fri)	75
6 (Sat)	105
7 (Sun)	135
8 (Mon)	151
9 (Tues)	167
10 (Wed)	183

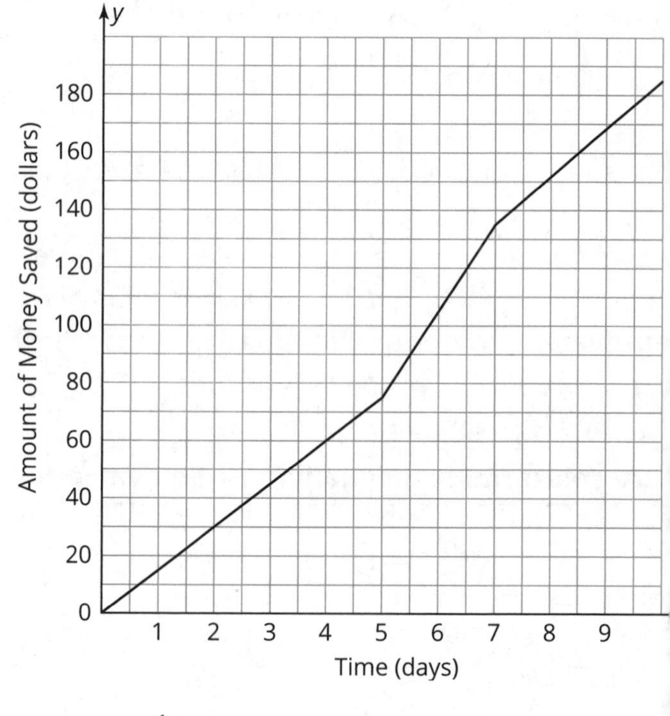

$$f(x) = \begin{cases} 15x, & 0 \leq x \leq 5 \\ 30x - 75, & 5 < x \leq 7 \\ 16x + 23, & 7 < x \leq 10 \end{cases}$$

LESSON 4

Step by Step

A **step function** is a piecewise function on a given interval whose pieces are disjoint constant functions.

The graph of a step function looks like a set of steps and is discontinuous. A **discontinuous graph** is a graph that is continuous for some values of the domain with at least one disjoint area between consecutive *x*-values. The endpoints are interpreted in the same way as the endpoints on a number line. A segment of a discontinuous piecewise function will have closed endpoints when the domain includes $\geq$ or $\leq$ and open endpoints when the domain includes $>$ or $<$. It may also be a ray with just one endpoint.

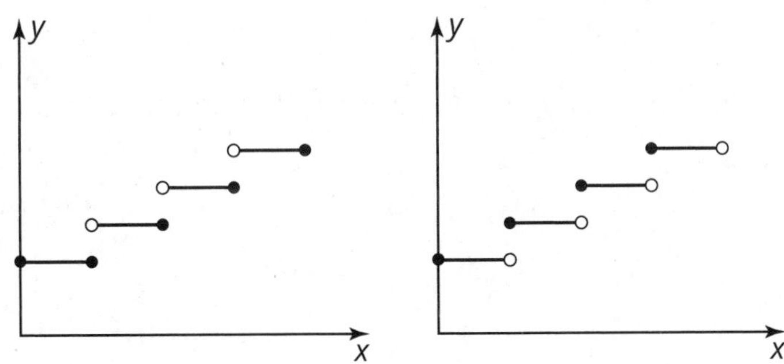

The greatest integer function, also known as the floor function, is a special kind of step function. The greatest integer function $G(x) = \lfloor x \rfloor$ is defined as the greatest integer less than or equal to *x*. The **least integer function** is another special kind of step function. The least integer function $L(x) = \lceil x \rceil$, also known as the **ceiling function**, is defined as the least integer greater than or equal to *x*.

$\lfloor 3.14 \rfloor = 3$ The greatest integer less than or equal to 3.14 is 3.

$\lceil 5.56 \rceil = 6$ The least integer greater than or equal to 5.56 is 6.

LESSON 5

A Riddle Wrapped in a Mystery

A function takes an input value, performs some operation(s) on this value, and creates an output value. The inverse of a function takes the output value, performs some operation(s) on this value, and arrives back at the original function's input value. In other words, an **inverse of a function** is a function that "undoes" another function.

For a function $f(x)$, you can determine the inverse of a function algebraically by following these steps.

Step 1: Replace $f(x)$ with y.
Step 2: Switch the x and y variables.
Step 3: Solve for y.
Step 4: If y is a function, replace y with $f^{-1}(x)$.

The graph of the inverse of a function is a reflection of the function across the line $y = x$.

For example, given that (4, 5) is a point on the graph of $g(x)$, the corresponding point on the graph of $g^{-1}(x)$ is (5, 4).

A function is a **one-to-one function** if both the function and its inverse are functions.

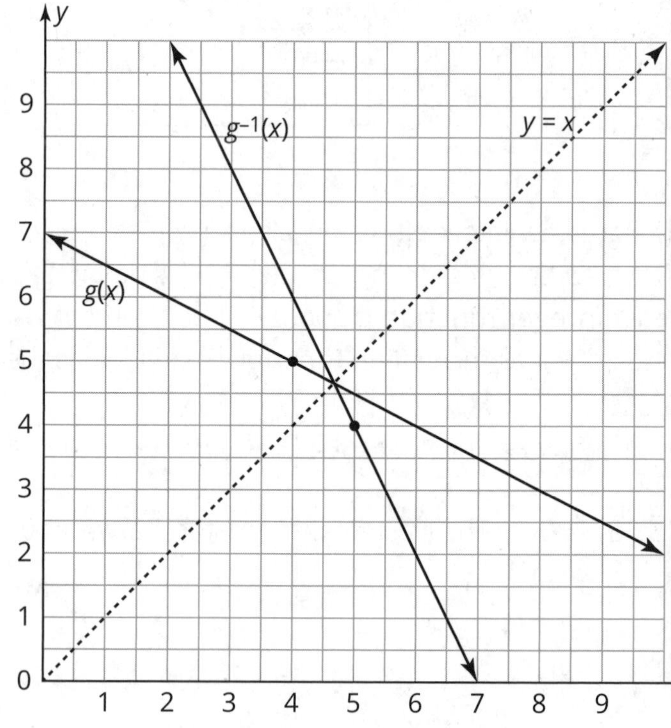

OPIC 2

xponentials

ponential curves become progressively flatter or progressively steeper. Slopes of mountains, sand dunes, or icebergs y resemble exponential curves.

Module 3: Exploring Functions

TOPIC 2: EXPONENTIALS

Students begin this topic by examining the structure of exponential functions. Next, students compare the value of a simple interest account and a compound interest account. They graph and write equations for these two scenarios and compare the average rate of change of each for a given interval. Students graph and analyze horizontal reflections and dilations of exponential functions. Considering the transformed graph of $f(Bx)$, they generalize the effect of the B-value transformation on the graph of the function and specifically on the coordinates (x, y). Throughout the rest of the topic, students solve real-world problems that can be modeled by exponential functions, including one that requires students to combine function types to best model the scenario.

Where have we been?

In middle school, students learned the rules of exponents and used those rules to rewrite expressions in equivalent forms. In a previous course, students extensively studied the properties of both linear and exponential functions. They have connected geometric sequences and exponential functions, and they understand that exponential functions increase or decrease by a common multiplier.

Where are we going?

The work in *Exponentials* serves as a bridge between the work students did with exponential functions in the previous course and the deep dive they will take into exponential and logarithmic functions in the next course. Learning the features of exponential functions and contrasting them with linear functions allows students to model situations involving constant growth or decay. As students gain proficiency in solving increasingly complex equations, they are able to model more interesting and complex real-life phenomena.

The *B*-Value

The B-value of a function in transformation form affects the horizontal shape of the graph. The B-value of an exponential function is written in the exponent:

$$f(x) = a \cdot (b)^{Bx}$$

The B-value compresses the graph of an exponential function horizontally. When it is negative, it can also reflect the graph of an exponential function across the y-axis.

I Feel the Earth. Move.

How do scientists measure the intensity of earthquakes? You may know that scientists who study earthquakes—seismologists—refer to a scale known as a Richter scale when reporting the strength of an earthquake. The Richter scale is a kind of exponential scale.

The scale generally goes from 1 to 9 (though it doesn't really have an upper limit), but an earthquake which has an intensity of 6 on the Richter scale is 10 times more powerful than an earthquake which measures 5.

One of the strongest earthquakes in history occurred in Chile on May 22, 1960. This earthquake measured an amazing 9.5 on the Richter scale—over 30,000 times stronger than a magnitude 5 earthquake!

Talking Points

It can be helpful to understand exponential functions for college admissions tests.

Here is an example of a sample question:

You deposit \$500 into a bank account that pays 3% interest compounded annually. What equation could you use to compute the amount in the account (in dollars), *A*, at the end of two years?

To solve this problem, you can identify the starting amount, \$500, the constant multiplier, which is 1 + the interest rate, or 1.03, and the time in years, 2.

The equation that models the situation is $A = 500 \cdot 1.03^2$.

Check to see if the answer is reasonable: $500 \cdot 1.03^2 = 530.45$.

Key Terms

simple interest

In a simple interest account, a percent of the starting balance is added to the account at each interval. The formula for simple interest is $I = Prt$, where P represents the starting amount, or principal, r represents the interest rate, t represents time, and I represents the interest earned.

compound interest

In a compound interest account, the balance is multiplied by the same amount at each interval.

extracting square roots

The process of removing perfect square numbers from under a radical symbol is called extracting square roots.

1

Got Chills... They're Multiplyin'

Exponential Functions and Rational Exponents

Warm Up

Determine each product or quotient. Write each answer with the given base and a single exponent.

1. $(2^3)(2^5)$
2. $\frac{2^4}{2^8}$
3. $\frac{5^5}{5^4}$
4. $4^0 \cdot 4^1$

Learning Goals

- Determine an explicit exponential expression and the steps used to calculate the value of an exponential expression from a context.
- Rewrite powers with rational exponents as radical expressions.
- Rewrite radical expressions as powers with rational exponents.
- Solve simple exponential equations using common bases.

You have studied exponential functions that have positive and negative integer exponents. How can you make sense of contexts in which exponents are rational numbers?

GETTING STARTED

Practice Your Scales

The crowd waits quietly—almost silently—in the dark hall while the orchestra begins its warmup. One of the oboists plays a single note, an A note. The rest of the orchestra then uses this note to tune their instruments.

The tuning note played by the oboe is called an A note. It is a sound wave that vibrates at a certain frequency. This frequency is given in a special unit called Hertz. The A note vibrates at 440 Hertz, so it is referred to as A440. There are other notes called A which have different frequencies, as shown on the keyboard.

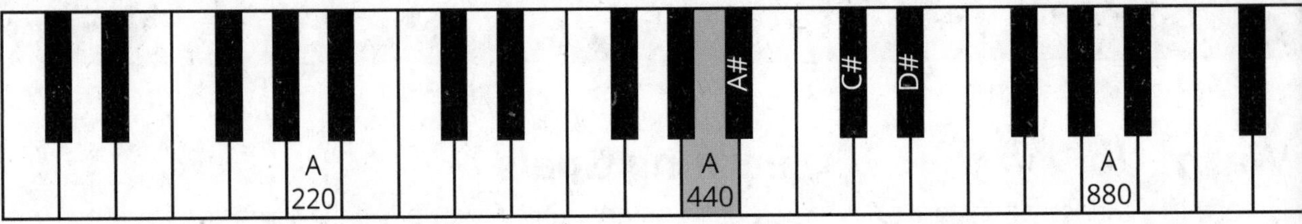

A# means the first note higher than A. It is read "A sharp."

1. Compare the frequencies of the different A-notes. Write each frequency ratio as a power of 2.

a. $\frac{880}{440}$

b. $\frac{440}{220}$

c. $\frac{440}{880}$

d. $\frac{220}{440}$

As you move up and down the keyboard, you multiply by a power of 2 to determine the frequencies of the notes. The note A880 is located 12 keys to the right of A440 on a keyboard. Its frequency is double the frequency of A440 and can be written as an exponential expression:

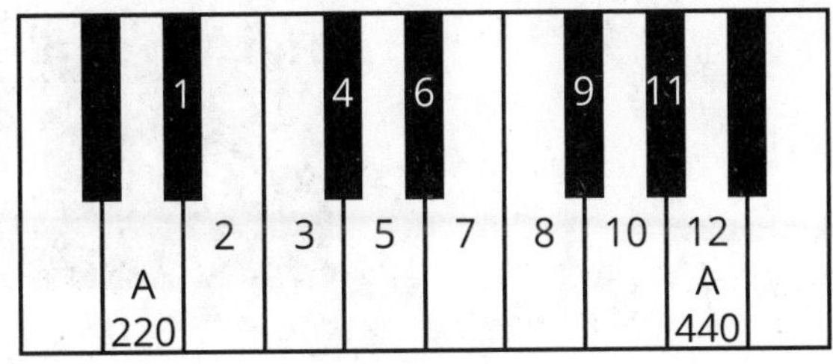

$440 \cdot 2^{\frac{12}{12}} = 440 \cdot 2^1 = 880$

The note A220 is located 12 keys to the left of A440. Its frequency is half the frequency of A440 and can be written as:

$$440 \cdot 2^{-\frac{12}{12}} = 440 \cdot 2^{-1}$$
$$= 440 \cdot \frac{1}{2}$$
$$= 220$$

Use the distance (in keys) between A440 and D# to write an expression for the frequency of D#. Then use the distance between A220 and D# to write an expression for the frequency of D#. Do you get the same result?

2. Write an exponential expression to represent each note.

a. The D# note above and to the right of A440

b. The C# note above and to the right of A440

c. The lowest note on the keyboard

3. Use a calculator to evaluate each exponential expression in Question 2.

ACTIVITY
1.1

Characteristics of Exponential Growth

Let's consider another scenario that can have integer or fractional interval.

In a laboratory experiment, a certain bacteria doubles each hour.

1. Suppose a bacteria population starts with just 1 bacterium.

a. Complete the table to show the population of bacteria, *f*(*x*), over time, *x*.

x	1	2	3	4
f(*x*)				

b. Determine the constant ratio and *y*-intercept. Then write the exponential function that represents the growth of the bacteria population over time. Show your work.

The population sequence is a geometric sequence, which has a constant ratio between terms. The constant ratio is a multiplier. To determine the next term of a geometric sequence, you multiply by this value.

c. How is the constant multiplier evident in the problem situation?

2. Graph the exponential function to show bacteria growth over time on the coordinate plane located at the end of the lesson.

ACTIVITY
1.2

The Square Root Constant Ratio of an Exponential Function

The table shown represents the function $f(x) = 2^x$, which models the laboratory experiment that a certain population of bacteria can double each hour.

An exponential function is continuous, meaning that there is a value $f(x)$ for every real number value x.

x	0	1	2	3
$f(x)$	2^0	2^1	2^2	2^3
	1	2	4	8

In the table, the interval between the input values is 1, and the constant multiplier is 2 at the point when the interval changes. What effect, if any, is there on the constant multiplier if the input interval is different?

1. Consider the ratio $\frac{f(2)}{f(0)}$.

a. Describe the interval of input values. Then determine the multiplier.

b. Write two additional ratios that have the same multiplier. Explain your reasoning.

c. Write a new pair of ratios that have the same multiplier but span a different input interval than the intervals you have already analyzed. Justify your answer.

Vicky, Nate, and Taylor are interested in the population of bacteria at each $\frac{1}{2}$-hour interval. They have values for the exponential function $f(x)$ when x is an integer. They need the values of the exponential function when x is a rational number between integers.

2. **The three students used the idea of the constant multiplier to estimate the value of $f\left(\frac{1}{2}\right)$ for the function $f(x) = 2^x$.**

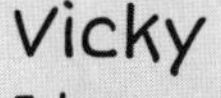

I know the constant multiplier for an interval of 1 is 2.
I want to split each interval of 1 into two equal parts, which means I need two equal multipliers.

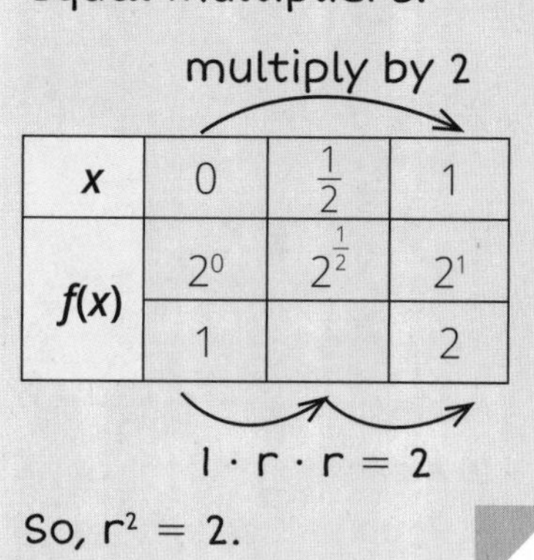

multiply by 2
x
0
$\frac{1}{2}$
1
f(x)
2^0
$2^{\frac{1}{2}}$
2^1
1
2
$1 \cdot r \cdot r = 2$

So, $r^2 = 2$.

Nate

If r is a constant multiplier for the function as it grows by consecutive integers, it can be split into two equal multipliers of $\sqrt{r}$, because r can be split into two equal factors of $\sqrt{r}$.

$(\sqrt{r})^2 = r$

Taylor

If $f(0) = 2^0 = 1$ and $f(1) = 2^1 = 2$, then $f(\frac{1}{2}) = 2^{\frac{1}{2}}$ must be equal to 1.5.

a. **Use Vicky's and Nate's thinking to determine $f\left(\frac{1}{2}\right)$. Write $f\left(\frac{1}{2}\right)$ as a power of 2 and in radical form. Then, enter the values in the table.**

x	0	$\frac{1}{2}$	1	2	3
$f(x)$	2^0		2^1	2^2	2^3
	1		2	4	8

b. **Use the graph you created in the previous activity to approximate $f\left(\frac{1}{2}\right)$ as a decimal.**

c. **Explain why Taylor's thinking is incorrect.**

he expression $\sqrt{2} = 2^{\frac{1}{2}}$. The square root symbol ($\sqrt{\ }$) is interpreted as the tional exponent $\frac{1}{2}$. All the properties with integer exponents you previously arned continue to apply even when the exponent is a rational number.

he tables shown represent two different equivalent representations of the onstant multiplier, $2^{\frac{1}{2}}$ or $\sqrt{2}$, for the function $f(x) = 2^x$.

The number 2 is a rational number because it can be represented as the ratio of two integers. The number $\sqrt{2}$ is an irrational number, because it cannot be represented as the ratio of two integers.

	Rational Exponent Representation	
$f(0)$	2^0	
		$2^0 \cdot 2^{\frac{1}{2}}$
$f\left(\frac{1}{2}\right)$	$2^{\frac{1}{2}}$	
		$2^{\frac{1}{2}} \cdot 2^{\frac{1}{2}}$
$f(1)$	2^1	
		$2^1 \cdot 2^{\frac{1}{2}}$
$f\left(\frac{3}{2}\right)$	$2^{\frac{3}{2}}$	

	Radical Form Representation	
$f(0)$	1	
		$1 \cdot \sqrt{2}$
$f\left(\frac{1}{2}\right)$	$\sqrt{2}$	
		$\sqrt{2} \cdot \sqrt{2}$
$f(1)$	2	
		$2 \cdot \sqrt{2}$
$f\left(\frac{3}{2}\right)$	$2\sqrt{2}$	

. Use the properties of exponents to justify that $2^1 \cdot 2^{\frac{1}{2}} = 2^{\frac{3}{2}}$. Then use the graph to estimate $2^{\frac{3}{2}}$ as a decimal.

rational exponent can be rewritten in radical form using the definition $a^{\frac{1}{n}} = \sqrt[n]{a}$. When the index is 2, it is usually implied rather than written.

In the expression $\sqrt[n]{a}$, the n is called the index.

et's consider the properties of exponents to rewrite expressions in quivalent forms.

Worked Example

Consider the expression $2^{\frac{3}{2}}$.

Using the Power to a Power Rule: $2^{\frac{3}{2}} = \left(2^{\frac{1}{2}}\right)^3$ or $(2^3)^{\frac{1}{2}}$.

You can use the definition of rational exponents to rewrite each expression in radical form.

$$\left(2^{\frac{1}{2}}\right)^3 = (\sqrt{2})^3 = \sqrt{2} \cdot \sqrt{2} \cdot \sqrt{2} = 2\sqrt{2}$$

$$(2^3)^{\frac{1}{2}} = \sqrt{2^3} = \sqrt{2 \cdot 2 \cdot 2} = \sqrt{2^2 \cdot 2} = 2\sqrt{2}$$

The process of removing perfect square numbers from under a radical symbol is called extracting square roots.

ou can see that $\sqrt{2} \cdot \sqrt{2} \cdot \sqrt{2} = \sqrt{2 \cdot 2 \cdot 2}$.

4. Use the worked example to explain the Product Property of Radicals.

The Product Property of Radicals states that $\sqrt{a} \cdot \sqrt{b} = \sqrt{a \cdot b}$ when a and b are greater than 0.

Now let's consider how to use the Product Rule of Powers to rewrite the expression with rational exponents in radical form.

Worked Example

Consider the expression $2^{\frac{3}{2}}$.

Using the Product Rule of Powers:

$$\begin{aligned} 2^{\frac{3}{2}} &= 2^{\frac{1}{2}+\frac{1}{2}+\frac{1}{2}} \\ &= \left(2^{\frac{1}{2}}\right)\left(2^{\frac{1}{2}}\right)\left(2^{\frac{1}{2}}\right) \\ &= \sqrt{2} \cdot \sqrt{2} \cdot \sqrt{2} \\ &= \sqrt{2 \cdot 2 \cdot 2} \end{aligned}$$

You can use the definition of rational exponents to rewrite each expression in radical form.

5. **Analyze the two worked examples. Use the Properties of Exponents to explain each.**

   a. $\sqrt{2} \cdot \sqrt{2} = 2$

   b. $\sqrt{2^2} = 2$

6. **Tony and Bobby each calculate the population of bacteria when $t = \frac{5}{2}$ hours.**
   Tony says that when $t = \frac{5}{2}$ hours, $f\left(\frac{5}{2}\right) = (\sqrt{2})^5$ bacteria.
   Bobby says that $f\left(\frac{5}{2}\right) = 4\sqrt{2}$ bacteria.
   Who's correct?
   Use definitions and rules to justify your reasoning. Then use the graph to estimate the value of $f\left(\frac{5}{2}\right)$ as a decimal on the graph.

You will learn and practice more with rational exponents later in this lesson.

ACTIVITY
1.3

The Cube Root Constant Ratio of an Exponential Function

In the previous activity, you looked at the exponential function $f(x) = 2^x$. When the input interval is 1, the constant ratio is 2^1, and when the input interval is $\frac{1}{2}$, the multiplier is $2^{\frac{1}{2}}$.

Now, let's think about the constant multiplier when the input interval is $\frac{1}{3}$.

What is the constant multiplier you can use to build this relationship over intervals of $\frac{1}{3}$?

×2

x	0	$\frac{1}{3}$	$\frac{2}{3}$	1	$\frac{4}{3}$
$f(x)$	2^0			2^1	
	1			2	

r r r

1. **Complete table of values for the exponential function $f(x) = 2^x$. Represent $f(x)$ as a rational exponent and in radical form. Show your work.**

In the expression $\sqrt[n]{a}$, only $n = 2$ is implied rather than written. All other index values must be written.

2. **Write the points represented in the table as ordered pairs. Use the graph you created in the previous activity to estimate each output value as a decimal.**

ACTIVITY

1.4

Rational Exponents

In the expression $\sqrt[n]{a}$, the n is called the index.

In this lesson, you have been writing powers with rational exponents. You have shown that you can rewrite a rational exponent in radical form, $a^{\frac{1}{n}} = \sqrt[n]{a}$.

1. Rewrite each expression as a power.

a. $\sqrt[3]{7}$

b. $\sqrt[5]{x}$

c. $\sqrt{y}$

2. Rewrite each expression in radical form.

a. $8^{\frac{1}{4}}$

b. $z^{\frac{1}{5}}$

c. $m^{\frac{1}{3}}$

3. Use the properties of exponents to rewrite $a^{\frac{m}{n}}$ in radical form.

Rewrite each expression in radical form.

a. $4^{\frac{3}{2}}$

b. $5^{\frac{3}{4}}$

c. $x^{\frac{4}{5}}$

d. $y^{\frac{2}{3}}$

Rewrite each expression as a power with a rational exponent.

a. $(\sqrt[4]{2})^3$

b. $(\sqrt{5})^4$

c. $(\sqrt[5]{x})^8$

d. $(\sqrt[5]{y})^{10}$

et's analyze the product of radicals.

Worked Example

You can rewrite the numeric expression $(\sqrt[3]{2})^2(\sqrt{2})$ in radical form using the rules of exponents.

$(2^{\frac{1}{3}})^2(2)^{\frac{1}{2}}$	Definition of rational exponents.
$(2^{\frac{2}{3}})(2^{\frac{1}{2}})$	Power to a Power Rule.
$2^{\frac{2}{3}+\frac{1}{2}}$	Product Rule of Powers.
$2^{\frac{7}{6}}$	Add fractions.
$\sqrt[6]{2^7}$	Definition of rational exponents.

6. Tonya rewrote the expression $\sqrt[6]{2^7}$ in a different way.

$$2^{\frac{7}{6}} = 2^{\frac{6}{6}} \cdot 2^{\frac{1}{6}} = 2\sqrt[6]{2}$$

Is she correct? Justify your reasoning.

Let's revisit the Product Property of Radicals and the process of extracting roots.

Suppose you have the product $\sqrt{15} \cdot \sqrt{5}$. You can use properties of exponents to rewrite this radical expression.

Worked Example

$$\begin{aligned}\sqrt{15} \cdot \sqrt{5} &= 15^{\frac{1}{2}} \cdot 5^{\frac{1}{2}} \\ &= (15 \cdot 5)^{\frac{1}{2}} \\ &= (3 \cdot 5 \cdot 5)^{\frac{1}{2}} \\ &= (3 \cdot 5^2)^{\frac{1}{2}} \\ &= 3^{\frac{1}{2}} \cdot 5 \\ &= 5\sqrt{3}\end{aligned}$$

$$\begin{aligned}\sqrt{15} \cdot \sqrt{5} &= \sqrt{15 \cdot 5} \\ &= \sqrt{3 \cdot 5 \cdot 5} \\ &= \sqrt{3 \cdot 5^2} \\ &= 5\sqrt{3}\end{aligned}$$

7. Rewrite each radical expression by extracting perfect squares.

a. $\sqrt{50}$

b. $\sqrt{24}$

c. $3\sqrt{20}$

d. $\sqrt{3} \cdot \sqrt{6}$

e. $\sqrt{3} \cdot \sqrt{12}$

f. $\sqrt{8} \cdot \sqrt{12}$

8. Explain how the properties of rational exponents extend from the properties of integer exponents.

Consider the calculations you made throughout this lesson and the definition of a rational number to answer each question.

a. **Is the product of a nonzero rational number and an irrational number always, sometimes, or never a rational number? Explain your reasoning.**

b. **Is the product of an irrational number and an irrational number always, sometimes, or never a rational number? Explain your reasoning.**

Worked Example

You can rewrite the numeric expression $\frac{\sqrt[3]{x}\sqrt{x}}{\sqrt[6]{x}}$ in radical form using rules of exponents.

$\frac{x^{\frac{1}{3}}x^{\frac{1}{2}}}{x^{\frac{1}{6}}}$	Rewrite using rational exponents.
$\frac{x^{\frac{1}{3}+\frac{1}{2}}}{x^{\frac{1}{6}}}$	Apply the Product Rule of Powers.
$\frac{x^{\frac{5}{6}}}{x^{\frac{1}{6}}}$	Add fractions.
$x^{\frac{4}{6}}$	Apply the Quotient Rule of Powers.
$x^{\frac{2}{3}}$	Rewrite fraction.
$\sqrt[3]{x^2}$	Rewrite in radical form.

10. Rewrite each expression using the Properties of Exponents.

a. $\left(3^{\frac{3}{2}}\right)^3$

b. $\frac{\left(2^{-\frac{1}{2}}\right)^3}{\left(2^{\frac{1}{3}}\right)^{-1}}$

c. $(2x^{\frac{1}{2}}y^{\frac{1}{3}})(3x^{\frac{1}{2}}y)$

d. $\left(\frac{24m^{\frac{3}{4}}n^{\frac{5}{2}}}{36m^{\frac{2}{7}}n^{\frac{2}{5}}}\right)^0$

TALK the TALK

The Power... You're Supplyin'

Now that you know how to represent fractional intervals using exponential expressions, let's revisit the keyboard from the beginning of the lesson.

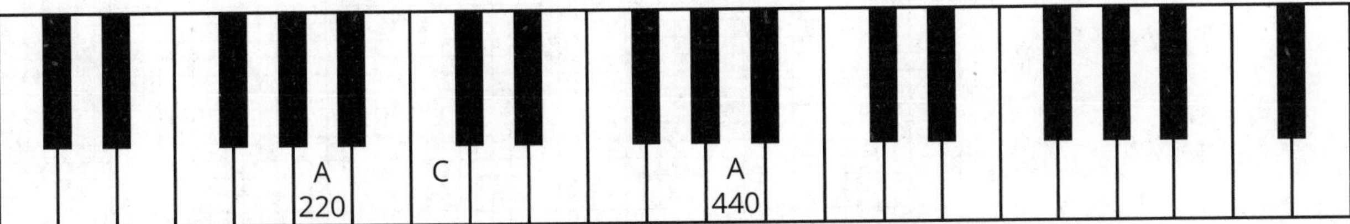

1. Consider the sequence of 12 notes from A220 to A440.

a. What is the constant ratio between each note's frequency and the next note's frequency? Write the ratio as a power and as a radical expression. Explain how you know.

b. Write a function of the form $a \cdot b^x$ to describe the frequency of a note given its distance (in keys) and direction (left or right) from A440.

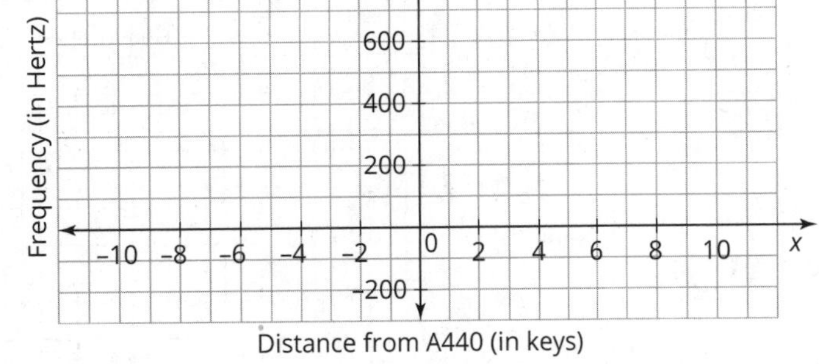

c. Sketch a graph of the function which describes the frequency of a note given its distance and direction from A440.

2. The *C* note shown on the keyboard is also called middle-*C*. Determine the frequency of middle-*C*, and write the steps you used to calculate it.

NOTES

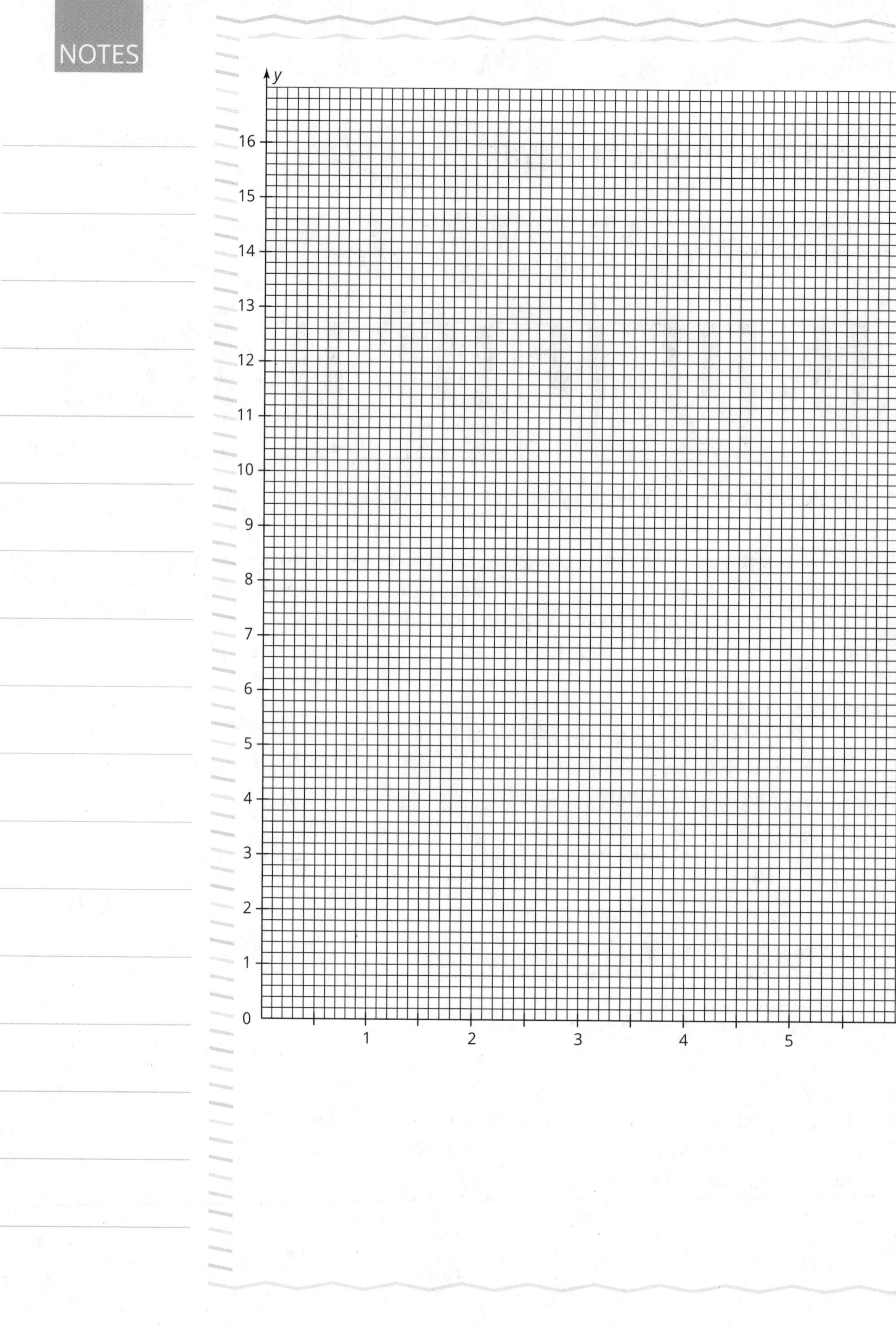

Assignment

Write

Describe how to extract a perfect root from $\sqrt{45}$.

Remember

If the difference in the input values is the same, an exponential function shows a constant multiplier between output values, no matter how large or how small the gap between input values.

If n is an integer greater than 1, then $\sqrt[n]{a} = a^{\frac{1}{n}}$.

Practice

Rewrite each radical using a rational exponent.

1. $\sqrt[4]{88}$
2. $\sqrt[10]{46}$
3. $\sqrt[6]{x}$
4. $\sqrt{z}$

Rewrite each power in radical form.

5. $9^{\frac{1}{3}}$
6. $5^{\frac{1}{2}}$
7. $20^{\frac{1}{5}}$
8. $41^{\frac{1}{8}}$
9. $8^{\frac{1}{4}}$
10. $100^{\frac{1}{4}}$
11. $32^{\frac{1}{2}}$
12. $70^{\frac{1}{7}}$
13. $n^{\frac{1}{6}}$
14. $m^{\frac{1}{9}}$

Rewrite each power in radical form. Simplify your answer, if possible.

15. $16^{\frac{3}{2}}$
16. $5^{\frac{7}{4}}$
17. $12^{\frac{2}{5}}$
18. $8^{\frac{4}{3}}$
19. $2^{\frac{5}{6}}$
20. $15^{\frac{6}{7}}$

Rewrite each expression using a rational exponent. Simplify your answer, if possible.

21. $(\sqrt[5]{10})^4$
22. $(\sqrt[4]{t})^4$
23. $(\sqrt{w})^6$
24. $(\sqrt[9]{h})^3$

Solve each exponential equation for x.

25. $4^x = 256$
26. $6^{3x} = 36$
27. $2^{5-x} = \frac{1}{16}$
28. $3^{-2x} = \frac{1}{81}$
29. $4^{x+3} = 4$
30. $\frac{1}{5^{x+4}} = 625$

Stretch

How do rational exponents help you to multiply or divide two radicals with different indices ($\sqrt[m]{a} \cdot \sqrt[n]{a}$ or $\frac{\sqrt[m]{a}}{\sqrt[n]{a}}$, when $m \neq n$)? Include two examples to support your answer.

Review

1. Solve each equation. Show your work.

   a. $|x - 4| = 7$

   b. $|3x + 5| = 11$

2. Determine the inverse of each function. Is the inverse also a function? Explain why or why not.

   a. $y = -4$

   b. $y = \left(\frac{1}{4}\right)x + \frac{3}{2}$

3. Solve each system of linear equations.

   a. $\begin{cases} y = -5x - 21 \\ -2x + 5y = -24 \end{cases}$

   b. $\begin{cases} 8x - 3y = 4 \\ 7x - 10y = -26 \end{cases}$

2

Turn That Frown Upside Down

Growth and Decay Functions

Warm Up

Determine the constant ratio for each sequence.

1. 5, 5.25, 5.5125, 5.788125 . . .
2. 100, 20, 4, $\frac{4}{5}$ . . .
3. 1, $\frac{2}{3}$, $\frac{4}{9}$, $\frac{8}{27}$, . . .

Learning Goals

- Classify exponential functions as increasing or decreasing.
- Compare formulas for simple interest and compound interest situations.
- Compare the average rate of change between common intervals of a linear and an exponential relationship.
- Write an exponential function that includes a percent increase or decrease with a *b*-value that is a decimal number.
- Solve exponential equations using graphs.

You know that exponential functions constantly increase or constantly decrease across the entire domain. How can you compare contexts modeled by exponential functions that increase or decrease?

GETTING STARTED

Wakey, Wakey, Eggs and Bakey!

You have studied linear and exponential functions. You know that a linear function increases or decreases by a constant difference, whereas an exponential function increases or decreases by a common ratio.

Remember:

An exponential function can be written as $f(x) = a \cdot b^x$, where b is greater than 0 and not equal to 1.

Consider each function shown.

$f(x) = -3x - 1$ $\quad$ $g(x) = 2^x + 5$ $\quad$ $h(x) = 0.5^x$

$q(x) = 2 \cdot 1.5^{(x + 1)}$ $\quad$ $r(x) = -3 \cdot 3^x$ $\quad$ $t(x) = -x + 2^3$

$a(x) = 10 \cdot 1^x$ $\quad$ $b(x) = 5(x - 1) + 4$ $\quad$ $c(x) = 2 \cdot (1 - 0.1)^x$

1. Sort the functions into linear and exponential functions. Justify your choices.

Linear Functions $\qquad$ **Exponential Functions**

yourself:

What does the structure of each equation tell you about its corresponding function?

2. Sort the functions into increasing and decreasing functions. Justify your choices.

Increasing Functions $\qquad$ **Decreasing Functions**

ACTIVITY 2.1

Calculating Interest with Linear and Exponential Functions

Let's consider which function type represents each situation.

Sanjay's family deposited \$20,000 in an interest bearing account for his college fund. Sanjay's account earns simple interest each year.

Chikonde's family deposited \$20,000 in an interest bearing account for her college fund that earns compound interest each year.

Time (years)	Simple Interest Balance (dollars)	Compound Interest Balance (dollars)
0	20,000	20,000
1	20,800	20,800
2	21,600	21,632
3	22,400	22,497.28
10	28,000	29,604.89

Recall that in a simple interest account, a percent of the starting balance is added to the account at each interval. The formula for simple interest is $I = Prt$, where P represents the starting amount, or principal, r represents the interest rate, t represents time, and I represents the interest earned. In a compound interest account, the balance is multiplied by the same amount at each interval.

1. Study the table of values.

a. Sketch a graph of each account balance in dollars as a function of the time in years.

Simple Interest Balance

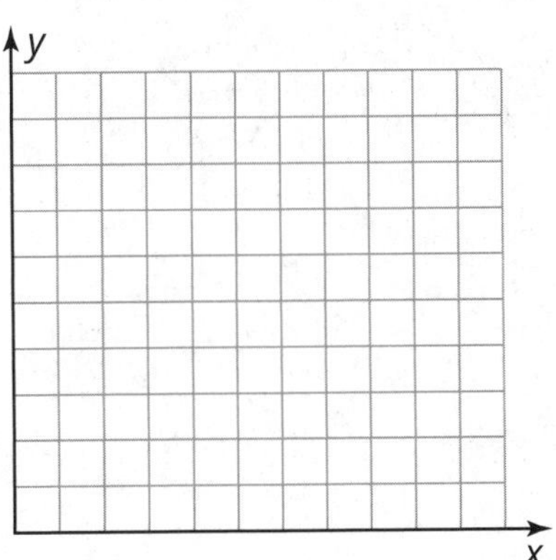

Compound Interest Balance

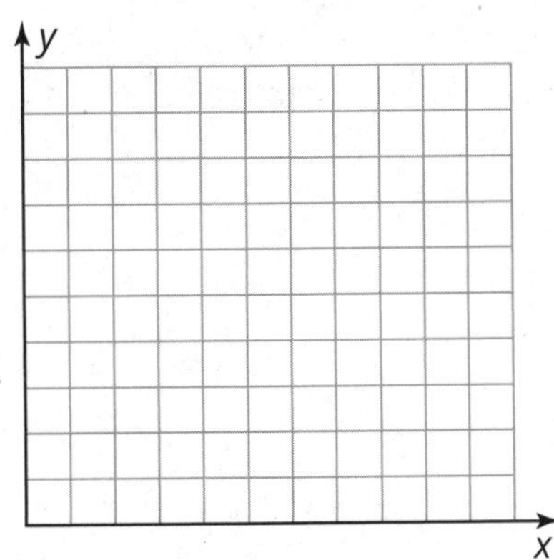

b. Write a function, $s(t)$, to represent the simple interest account and a function, $c(t)$, to represent the compound interest account.

2. **Use the functions $s(t)$ and $c(t)$ to determine each value.**

   a. $s(6)$

   b. $c(6)$

   c. $c(5)$

   d. $s(5)$

3. **Determine the average rate of change between each pair of values given for each relationship.**

Time Intervals (years)	Simple Interest Function (dollars)	Compound Interest Function (dollars)
Between $t = 0$ and $t = 1$		
Between $t = 1$ and $t = 2$		
Between $t = 2$ and $t = 6$		
Between $t = 6$ and $t = 10$		

4. **Compare the average rates of change for the simple and compound interest accounts. What does this tell you about linear and exponential functions?**

Use technology to determine when each account will reach the given dollar amount.

a. When does the simple interest account reach $100,000?

b. Approximately when does the compound interest account reach one million dollars?

. Takondwa says that given any increasing linear function and any exponential growth function, the output of the exponential function will eventually be greater than the output of the linear function. Is Takondwa correct? Use examples to justify your thinking.

ACTIVITY

2.2

Analyzing Exponential Growth and Decay Functions

In 2018, the population of Chicago, Illinois, was about 2.7 million, and the population of Columbus, Ohio, was about 880,000. Chicago's population had decreased from 2010 at a rate of 0.04% each year. At the same time, Columbus's population had grown at a rate of about 0.14% every year.

1. Which city's population can be represented as an increasing function, and which can be represented as a decreasing function?

Let's examine the properties of the graphs of the functions for Chicago and Columbus.

Chicago: $G(t) = 2{,}700{,}000(1 - 0.0004)^t$

Columbus: $B(t) = 880{,}000(1 + 0.0014)^t$

2. Sketch a graph of each function. Label key points.

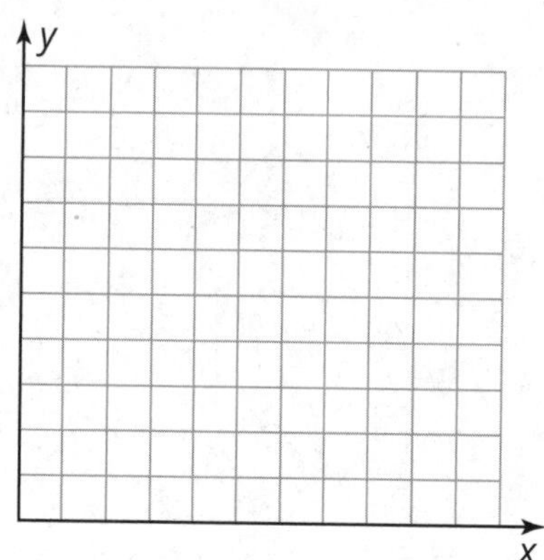

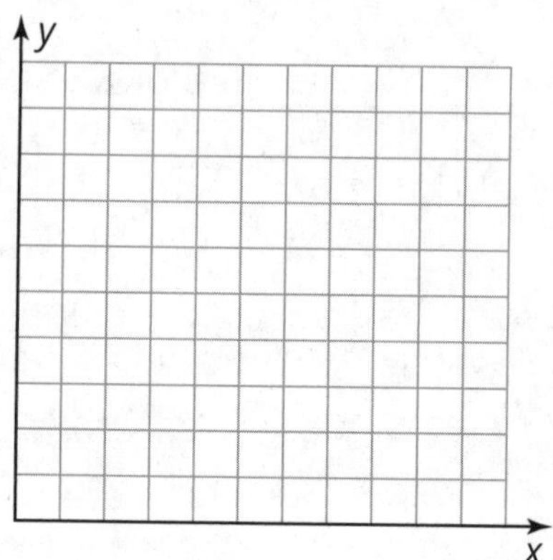

The functions $G(t)$ and $B(t)$ can each be written as an exponential function of the form $f(x) = a \cdot b^x$.

a. **What is the a-value for each function? What does each a-value mean in terms of this problem situation?**

b. **What is the b-value for each function? What does each b-value mean in terms of this problem situation?**

c. **Compare and explain the meanings of the expressions $(1 - 0.0004)^t$ and $(1 + 0.0014)^t$ in terms of this problem situation.**

Analyze the y-intercepts of each function. Describe how you can determine the y-intercept of each function using only the formula for population increase or decrease.

A decreasing exponential function is denoted by a decimal or fractional b-value between 0 and 1, not by a negative b-value.

Consider an exponential function of the form $f(x) = a \cdot b^x$ with $a > 0$. An exponential growth function has a b-value greater than 1 and is of the form $y = a \cdot (1 + r)^x$, where r is the rate of growth. The b-value is $1 + r$. An exponential decay function has a b-value greater than 0 and less than 1 and is of the form $y = a \cdot (1 - r)^x$, where r is the rate of decay. The b-value is $(1 - r)$.

ACTIVITY **2.3**

Comparing Increasing and Decreasing Exponential Functions

Consider the six different population scenarios.

1. Match each situation with the appropriate function. Explain your reasoning.

Functions

$f(x) = 17{,}000 \cdot (1 - 0.015)^x$

$f(x) = 17{,}000 \cdot (1 + 0.015)^x$

$f(x) = 17{,}000 \cdot 0.975^x$

$f(x) = 17{,}000 \cdot 1.01^x$

$f(x) = 17{,}000 \cdot 1.025^x$

$f(x) = 17{,}000 \cdot 1.1^x$

Aliso has a population of 17,000. Its population is increasing at a rate of 1.5%.

Charlestown has a population of 17,000. Its population is decreasing at a rate of 2.5%.

Youngstown has a population of 17,000. Its population is decreasing at a rate of 1.5%.

Point Park has a population of 17,000. Its population is increasing at a rate of 2.5%.

North Lake has a population of 17,000. Its population is increasing at a rate of 10%.

Springfield has a population of 17,000. Its population is increasing at a rate of 1%.

NOTES

TALK the TALK 

Things Are Looking Up!

In 2005, the population of a city was 42,500. By 2010, the population had grown to approximately 51,708 people.

1. **Identify any equations that are appropriate exponential models for the population of the city. Explain why. Then explain why the equations you did not choose are not appropriate models for the situation.**

$f(t) = 51{,}708(1.04)^t$

$j(t) = 51{,}708(0.96)^t$

$g(t) = 42{,}500(1.04)^{5t}$

$k(t) = 51{,}708(1.04)^{\frac{1}{5}t}$

$h(t) = 42{,}500(1.04)^t$

$m(t) = 42{,}500(0.96)^t$

Assignment

Write

Explain the difference between simple interest and compound interest.

Remember

An exponential growth function has a *b*-value greater than 1 and is of the form $y = a \cdot (1 + r)^x$, where *r* is the rate of growth. An exponential decay function has a *b*-value greater than 0 and less than 1 and is of the form $y = a \cdot (1 - r)^x$, where *r* is the rate of decay.

Practice

1. Taylor just received a $2500 bonus check from her employer. She is going to put it into an account that will earn interest. The Level 1 savings account at her bank earns 6% simple interest. The Platinum savings account earns 4.5% compound interest.
   a. Write a function for each account that can be used to determine the balance in the account based on the year, *t*. Describe each function.
   b. Use your answers to part (a) to create a table of values for each function.
   c. Use technology to graph the functions for the Level 1 and Platinum savings accounts. Then, sketch the graphs.
   d. Into which account would you recommend that Taylor deposit her money? Explain your reasoning.
   e. After reading the pamphlet about the different accounts a little more closely, Taylor realizes that there is a one-time fee of $300 for depositing her money in the Platinum account. Does this change the recommendation you made in part (d)? Why or why not?
   f. Compare the rates of change for the Level 1 and Platinum savings accounts. Explain what the rates of change tell you about the accounts.
   g. What do the rates of change for linear and exponential functions tell you about the graphs of the functions?
2. Brook works for the owners of a bookstore. Her starting salary was $24,500, and she gets a 3% raise each year.
   a. Write an equation in function notation to represent Brook's salary as a function of the number of years she has been working at the bookstore.
   b. What will Brook's salary be when she begins her fourth year working at the bookstore? Show your work.

Stretch

Consider a piece of paper that is 0.1 mm thick. How many times must it be folded so that it reaches the top of the Eiffel Tower? Assume the paper is as large as needed, and it is possible to fold it as many times as required.

Review

1. Roberto and Maeko open a pet store and start with 5 hamsters for sale. Hamster populations usually triple every cycle. One cycle is equal to 4 months. Write an equation in function notation to represent the change in the number of hamsters as a function of the cycle number, *c*. Explain how you determined your equation.
2. Write an exponential function to model this table of values.

x	$g(x)$
1	0.6
2	0.06
3	0.006
4	0.0006

3. Write a function, $g(x)$, and sketch a graph that is translated 3 units up from and 4 units to the right of $f(x) = \left(\frac{1}{2}\right)^x$.
4. Write a function, $h(x)$, and sketch a graph that is a reflection of $f(x) = -3^x$ across the line $y = 0$.
5. Solve each equation for x and justify each step.

   a. $-3x = -18$

   b. $\frac{(x + 4)}{2} = \frac{(x - 5)}{3}$

3

Just So... Basic

Horizontal Dilations of Exponential Functions

Warm Up

Determine each product or quotient. Write each answer with the given base and a single exponent or in radical form.

1. $2^{\frac{1}{2}} \cdot 2^3$

2. $\frac{4^{\frac{1}{4}}}{4}$

3. $(a^2)^{\frac{1}{3}} \cdot (a^3)^{\frac{1}{9}}$

4. $\frac{(x^{\frac{2}{5}})^2}{x}$

Learning Goals

- Use the properties of exponents to rewrite exponential functions.
- Analyze equations and graphs of exponential functions.
- Graph and analyze horizontal dilations of exponential functions.

You have studied transformations—including horizontal and vertical translations and reflections and vertical dilations—of linear, exponential, and absolute value functions. How can you make sense of horizontal dilations of exponential functions in different contexts?

GETTING STARTED

Music of the Night

Recall that the transformational form of a function $f(x)$ is given by:

$$g(x) = Af(B(x - C)) + D$$

1. **Write the basic exponential function, $f(x) = 2^x$, in transformational form. Use integer values to represent *A, B, C,* and *D*.**

A horizontal asymptote is a horizontal line that a function gets closer and closer to, but never intersects.

2. **What equation represents the location of the horizontal asymptote of a general exponential function? Explain your answer.**

In a previous lesson, you wrote an exponential function to describe the frequency of a note given its distance and direction from A440.

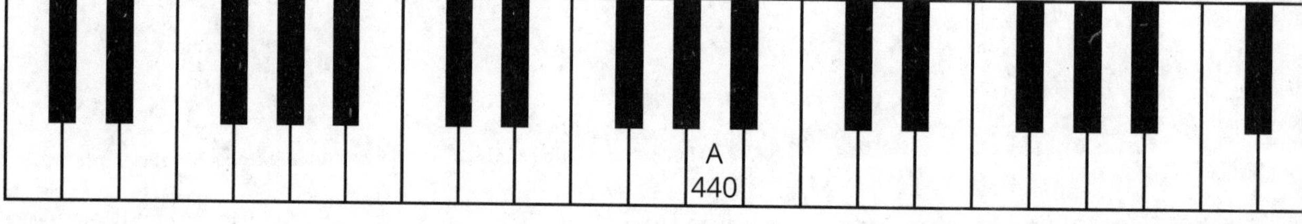

3. **Write the function. Then, identify the *B*-value in the function.**

What would playing the keyboard sound like if the *B*-value was 1?

ACTIVITY

3.1 Interpreting the *B*-value

In an exponential function, the *B*-value is the coefficient of the exponent. Let's use the power of exponents to investigate the *B*-value of exponential functions.

Simone has invested \$500 in a mutual fund which has shown an annual increase of about 10%.

1. Write a function, *f*(*t*), that represents Simone's investment in terms of *t*, time in years.

Suppose Simone is interested in determining the monthly rate of increase. What is the approximate equivalent monthly rate of increase for her mutual fund?

2. Consider the responses from two of Simone's friends. Describe the differences in their reasoning and why Rahsaan is correct.

Chitra

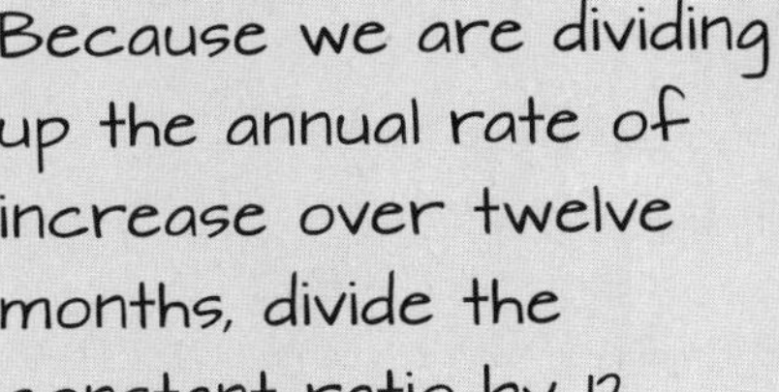

Because we are dividing
up the annual rate of
increase over twelve
months, divide the
constant ratio by 12.

$\frac{1.10}{12}$

Rahsaan

Because the annual rate of increase is represented as a multiplier, take the 12th root of the constant ratio.

$1.10^{\frac{1}{12}}$

Kirk wants to write a function that is equivalent to the annual rate of increase but reveals the monthly rate of increase.

3. Explain why Kirk's reasoning is not correct.

Kirk

Since Simone's monthly rate of increase is the twelfth root of the annual rate of increase, I can use the function

$f(x) = 500 \cdot \left(1.10^{\frac{1}{12}}\right)^{t}$.

To rewrite the function representing Simone's annual increase as an equivalent function that reflects the monthly rate of increase, you must change the *B*-value. The *B*-value of an exponential function can be written as the coefficient of *x*.

$$f(x) = a \cdot (b)^{Bx}$$

Worked Example

You can use what you know about common bases to rewrite the expression in an equivalent form.

$\left(1.10^{\frac{1}{12}}\right)^{Bx} = (1.10)^x$

$(1.10)^{\frac{Bx}{12}} = (1.10)^x$ Apply the Power to a Power Rule.

$\frac{Bx}{12} = x$ The bases are the same, so the exponents must be equivalent expressions.

$Bx = 12x$ Multiply both sides by 12.

$B = 12$

So, the function $f(x) = 500 \cdot \left(1.10^{\frac{1}{12}}\right)^{12x}$ is equivalent to the function $f(x) = 500 \cdot (1.10)^x$.

. **Suppose Simone wants to determine how much her mutual fund increases each quarter. Rewrite the original function in an equivalent form that reveals the approximate equivalent quarterly rate of increase.**

. **What is Simone's monthly increase, as a percent?**

ACTIVITY

3.2 Horizontal Dilations of Exponential Functions

You have studied the effects of the *A*-, *C*-, and *D*-values on the graphs of functions. Now let's consider how the *B*-value affects the graph of a function.

Consider the exponential functions, where $h(x) = 2^x$ is the basic function.

- $w(x) = 2^{\frac{1}{2}x}$
- $z(x) = 2^{2x}$

1. Write the functions $w(x)$ and $z(x)$ in terms of $h(x)$.

Label key points on graphs of functions, such as the *y*-intercept and the horizontal asymptote.

2. Use technology to sketch and label the graph of each function.

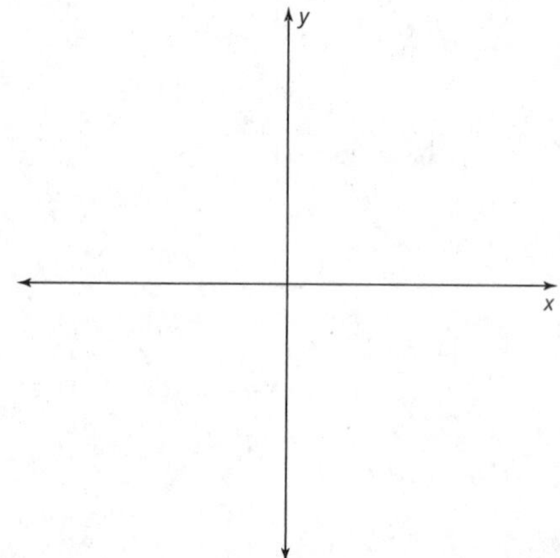

3. Compare the graphs of $w(x)$ and $z(x)$ to the graph of the basic function $h(x)$. What do you notice?

Write the x-value of each of the corresponding reference points on $w(x)$ and $z(x)$.

$h(x) = 2^x$	$w(x) = 2^{(\frac{1}{2}x)}$	$z(x) = 2^{(2x)}$
$\left(-2, \frac{1}{4}\right)$	$\left(\_\_\_\_, \frac{1}{4}\right)$	$\left(\_\_\_\_, \frac{1}{4}\right)$
$\left(-1, \frac{1}{2}\right)$	$\left(\_\_\_\_, \frac{1}{2}\right)$	$\left(\_\_\_\_, \frac{1}{2}\right)$
(0, 1)	(____, 1)	(____, 1)
(1, 2)	(____, 2)	(____, 2)
(2, 4)	(____, 4)	(____, 4)

Use the table to compare the ordered pairs of the graphs of $w(x)$ and $z(x)$ to the ordered pairs of the graph of the basic function $h(x)$. What do you notice?

Given that the point (x, y) is on the graph of the function $y = f(x)$, what ordered pair describes a point on the graph of $g(x) = f(Bx)$?

An exponential function can be rewritten to show an expression with no *B*-value transformations.

Worked Example

Given the function $h(x) = 2^x$, consider the function $t(x) = h(3x)$.

$t(x) = h(3x)$

$t(x) = 2^{3x}$

You can rewrite $t(x)$ with no *B*-value transformation.

$t(x) = 2^{3x}$

$= (2^3)^x$

$= 8^x$

7. **Explain the steps to rewrite a function with no *B*-value transformation. What effect does rewriting have on the *b*-value of the original function?**

8. **Given the function $f(x) = 2^x$:**

   a. **Rewrite $c(x) = f(2x)$ as an exponential function with no *B*-value transformation.**

   b. **Rewrite $b(x) = f(-2x)$ as an exponential function with no *B*-value transformation.**

NOTES

TALK the TALK

How Will It Change?

Consider each situation, which can be modeled by an exponential function. What effect would increasing or decreasing the *B*-value have in each situation?

1. **Carla's savings account opens with a balance of $500 and earns 4% interest every year.**

2. **A community art club started with a membership of 1000 people and has been decreasing at a rate of 5% every week.**

3. **Scientists monitoring cell growth observed that a starting population of 2 million cells doubled every minute.**

4. **The frequency of the sound produced by notes on a keyboard doubles every 12 notes you move to the right.**

Assignment

Write

Given a basic function and the equation for a reflection of a basic function, explain how to determine whether the line of reflection will be the *x*-axis or the *y*-axis.

Remember

Transformations performed on any function $f(x)$ can be described by the transformation function $g(x) = Af(B(x - C)) + D$ where the *D*-value translates the function $f(x)$ vertically, the *C*-value translates $f(x)$ horizontally, the *A*-value vertically stretches or compresses $f(x)$, and the *B*-value horizontally stretches or compresses $f(x)$.

Practice

1. Complete the table to determine the corresponding points on $c(x)$, given reference points on $f(x)$. Then, graph $c(x)$ on the same coordinate plane as $f(x)$ and state the domain, range, and asymptotes of $c(x)$.

a. $f(x) = 2^x$

$c(x) = 4f(x)$

Reference Points on $f(x)$	Corresponding Points on $c(x)$
$\left(-1, \frac{1}{2}\right)$	
(0, 1)	
(1, 2)	

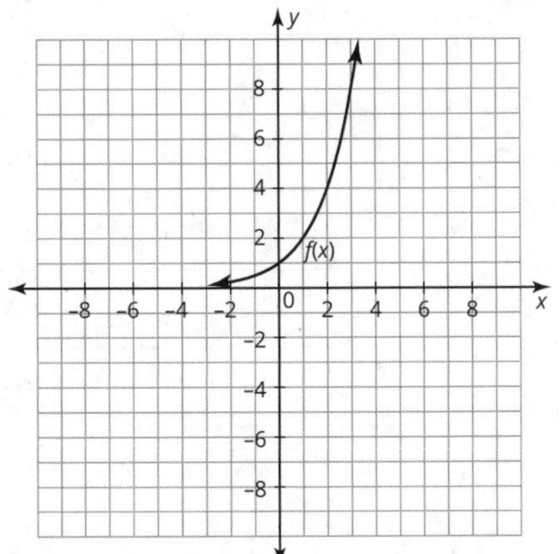

b. $f(x) = 4^x$

$c(x) = f(-x)$

Reference Points on $f(x)$	Corresponding Points on $c(x)$
$\left(-1, \frac{1}{4}\right)$	
(0, 1)	
(1, 4)	

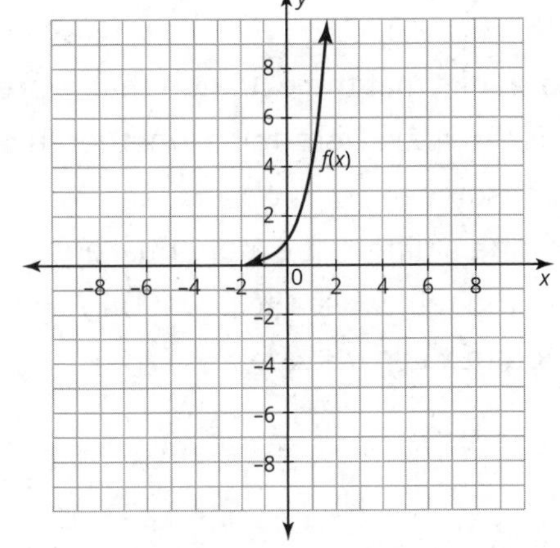

2. Describe the transformations performed on $m(x)$ that produced $t(x)$. Then, write an exponential equation for $t(x)$.

a. $m(x) = 3^x$

$t(x) = -m(3x)$

b. $m(x) = 5^x$

$t(x) = 3m(-2x)$

c. $m(x) = 5^x$

$t(x) = m(-x)$

d. $m(x) = 7^x$

$t(x) = m(-5x) + 3$

3. Ryan bought a brand new car for \$18,000. Its value depreciated at a rate of 1.2%.
   a. Write a function to represent the value of the car as a function of time.
   Use technology to estimate the number of years it will take for the value to reach each given amount.
   b. \$17,000
   c. \$15,000
   d. half of the starting value
   e. one-third the starting value
   f. \$0
   g. \$10,000

4. In 2012, the population of a city was 63,000. By 2017, the population was reduced to approximately 54,100. Identify any equations that are appropriate models for the population of the city, and explain why the others are not.
   a. $f(x) = 63{,}000(1.03)^t$
   b. $f(x) = 52{,}477(1.03)^t$
   c. $f(x) = 63{,}000(0.97)^t$
   d. $f(x) = 52{,}477(0.97)^t$
   e. $f(x) = 63{,}000(0.97)^{\frac{1}{5t}}$
   f. $f(x) = 52{,}477(0.97)^{5t}$

5. Oscar wants to own a bee colony so that he can extract honey from the hive. He starts a colony with 5,000 bees. The number of bees grows exponentially with a growth factor of 12% each month.
   a. Write a function, $f(x)$, for the bee population that can be used to determine the number of bees in the colony, based on the month, x.
   b. Use technology to graph the function, $f(x)$.
   c. Oscar feels that in order to get a decent amount of honey, there should be at least 15,000 bees in the colony. Estimate how many months it will take Oscar until he has 15,000 bees.

Stretch

Julissa and Megan developed a new art app for smart phones. The table shows the number of customers who downloaded the app by month.

Month	Number of Downloads
0	4
1	8
2	16
3	32
4	64
5	128

1. Julissa thinks that the equation that represents the data in the table is $y = 4(2)^x$. Determine whether Julissa is correct. Explain your reasoning.
2. Determine a different exponential equation that represents the data in the table. Use the equation $y = a \cdot b^{f(x)}$, where $f(x)$ is a function of x and $a = 2$.

Review

1. Rewrite each expression in rational exponent form.

a. $(\sqrt[3]{6})^4$

b. $(\sqrt[8]{8})^{12}$

c. $(\sqrt[7]{x})^3$

d. $(\sqrt[10]{y})^5$

2. Eleanor receives $1500 for her birthday. She is going to spend $500 and wants to put the rest into an account that will earn interest. She is considering two different accounts. Account A earns 6.5% annual simple interest. Account B earns 4.5% annual compound interest.

   a. Write a function for each account that can be used to determine the balance in the account based on the year, *t*.

   b. Graph the functions for Accounts A and B using technology. Then, graph the functions. Be sure to label your graph.

   c. If Eleanor plans on leaving the money in the account for 12 years, which account should she use to deposit her money? Explain your reasoning.

   d. If Eleanor plans on leaving the money in the account for 25 years, which account should she use to deposit her money? Explain your reasoning.

4

Saving Strategies

Modeling with and Combining Function Types

Warm Up

Identify the *A*-, *B*-, *C*-, and *D*-values of each exponential function.

1. $g(x) = 2 \cdot 3^{x+5} - 50$

2. $h(x) = 2^{\frac{x}{5}} + 1$

3. $j(x) = 2^x$

4. $k(x) = 60 \cdot 2^{-x} - 5$

Learning Goals

- Add an exponential function and a constant function.
- Write an exponential function to model a data set.
- Use exponential models to solve problems.
- Write an exponential function to model a table of values and a graph.

You have analyzed exponential functions and compared linear and exponential functions. How can you add linear and exponential functions to transform a function?

GETTING STARTED

A Constant Reminder

The graph shows the exponential function $f(x) = 2^x$ and the constant function $g(x) = 4$.

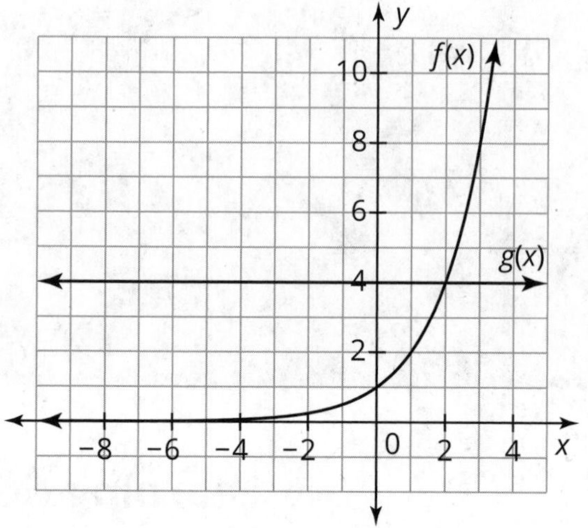

1. **Plot and connect points to show $h(x) = f(x) + g(x)$. Write the new function.**

2. **What do you notice? How did the exponential function $f(x)$ change?**

ACTIVITY

4.1 Adding Functions

Autumn has two different methods of saving money. Analyze her situation using functions.

1. Autumn received a graduation gift of $1000 from her wealthy aunt. She placed this money in a savings account with a 4% interest rate, compounded annually.

a. Write a function $f(x)$ to model this situation. Define the variables.

b. What will be the balance in Autumn's account after 5 years? 10 years? 15 years?

c. Estimate when Autumn will have $1600 in her account.

2. Autumn also saved $500 that she keeps in a safe at home. She never touches it nor adds to it.

a. Write a function $g(x)$ to model this situation. Define the variables.

b. How much money will Autumn have in the safe after 5 years? 10 years? 15 years?

c. When will Autumn have $1600 in the safe?

3. Autumn's total savings can be represented as $h(x) = f(x) + g(x)$. Write a function $h(x)$ to represent this sum and predict what the graph of $h(x)$ will look like.

4. **Graph $f(x)$, $g(x)$, and $h(x)$ on the coordinate plane. Label each function.**

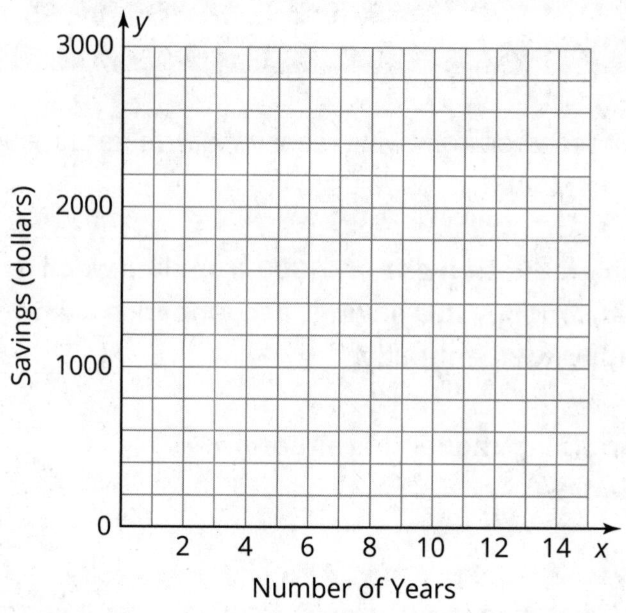

5. **Did the graph of $h(x)$ appear as you predicted? How does it relat to what you learned about transformations?**

6. **How does the graph of $h(x)$ relate to the graphs of $f(x)$ and $g(x)$?**

7. **The exponential function $h(x)$ can be written in the form $h(x) = A \cdot b^{B(x-C)} + D$. Identify three places where the value of D is evident in the graph of each of the three functions.**

ACTIVITY
4.2

Modeling with Multiple Functions

Naiah observed the temperature change as water in her coffee cup cooled. She heated water, poured it into the cup, and then recorded the temperature of the water every five minutes for 30 minutes. The temperature of the room where the coffee cup was placed was 70°F.

Let's use reasoning to approximate an exponential function that can model these data as temperature over time.

Time (min)	Temperature (°F)
0	200
5	151
10	119
15	100
20	88
25	81
30	77

1. **What will be the *y*-intercept of the function? Explain how you know.**

2. **Describe the rate at which the function is decreasing. Use average rates of change to justify your answer.**

Draw a sketch of the function with the critical values you know to help you think about it.

3. **The table shown gives values for the function $f(x) = 200 \cdot 2^{-x}$. What reasons can you give for why the graph of this function equation would not appropriately model the data?**

Time (min)	Temperature (°F)
0	200
5	6.25
10	0.195
15	0.006
20	0.00019
25	0.000006
30	$1.863 \cdot 10^{-7}$

4. **Consider the transformational form of $f(x)$:**

$$f(x) = A \cdot 2^{B(x - C)} + D$$

   a. **What are the values of A, B, C, and D for the function shown in the table, $f(x) = 200 \cdot 2^{-x}$? What is the b value?**

   b. **Which of these values could you change to make the function model the data more closely? Use technology to test your conjectures, and explain your reasoning.**

. The graph of the function that most closely models the data is shown. Test your functions on the graph. Write the exponential function that you think best models the data and explain your reasoning.

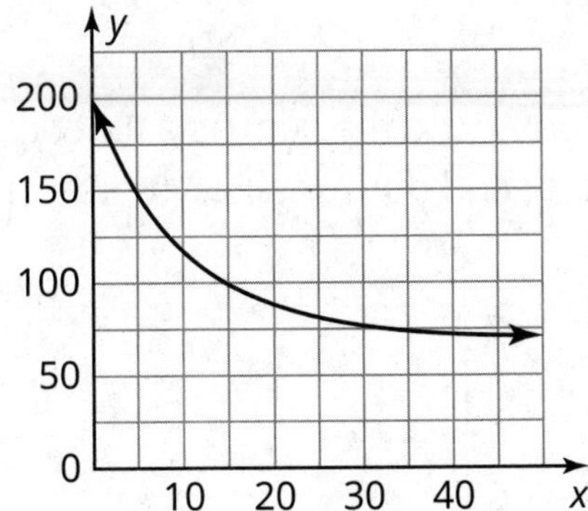

. Consider the basic decreasing exponential function $f(x) = 200 \cdot 2^{-x}$ provided as an inappropriate model for the data and the new function you created to more closely model the data.

a. Explain why it is necessary to add a constant function to the exponential function to model the data more precisely.

b. What do you think is the meaning of this constant function in terms of the situation?

NOTES

TALK the TALK 

Sketchy

Sketch each of the functions and their sum. Write the sum as a function in general form and identify the *y*-intercept and horizontal asymptote.

1. $f(x) = 2^x + 1$
$g(x) = -1$
$h(x) = f(x) + g(x)$

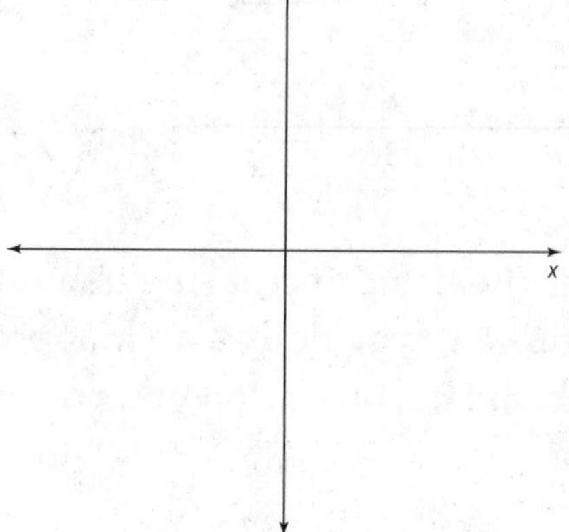

2. $f(x) = 2^{-x} + 4$
$g(x) = 3$
$h(x) = f(x) + g(x)$

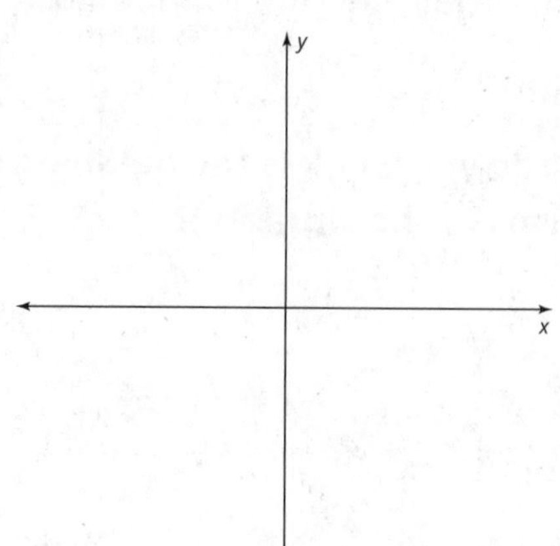

Assignment

Write

Describe the differences between a constant function and an exponential function.

Remember

When a constant function is added to an exponential function, the *D*-value of the exponential function is affected.

A constant function can be added to an exponential function to create a new asymptote for the exponential function.

Practice

Add the functions in each pair. Identify the *y*-intercept and horizontal asymptote of the sum function, $h(x)$.

1. $f(x) = -3^x$, $g(x) = 2$
2. $f(x) = 5^{-x}$, $g(x) = -1$
3. $f(x) = 2^{4x}$, $g(x) = 10$
4. $f(x) = -4^x$, $g(x) = 5$
5. $f(x) = 6^{-2x}$, $g(x) = -8$
6. $f(x) = 2^x + 1$, $g(x) = 0$

Stretch

1. The number of fixed landline phone subscribers in the U.S. has been declining. The bar graph shows the decrease in the number of subscribers from 2010 to 2015.

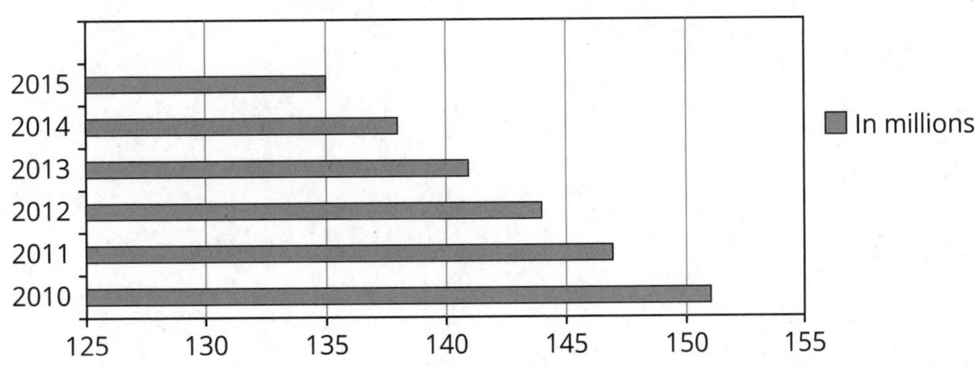

   a. To estimate the number of subscribers per year, create a scatter plot of the ordered pairs, with *x* representing the number of years since 2010 and *y* representing the number of subscribers in millions.
   b. Determine both an exponential and a linear regression function to model the situation.
   c. Which model would you use from part (b)? Explain your reasoning.

Review

1. Given $f(x) = 2^x$, graph $g(x) = -f(x - 1) + 2$.

2. Given $a(x) = \frac{1}{2}^{x}$, graph $b(x) = a(-x) - 1$.

3. An experiment begins with 400 bacteria. The bacteria population doubles each day. Write an equation in function notation to represent the number of bacteria as a function of the day number, x. Explain how you determined the equation.

4. Write the absolute value function for the graph shown.

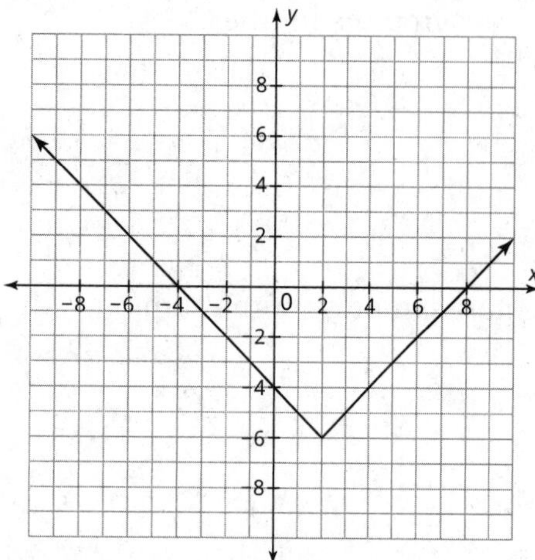

5. Write the piecewise function for the graph shown.

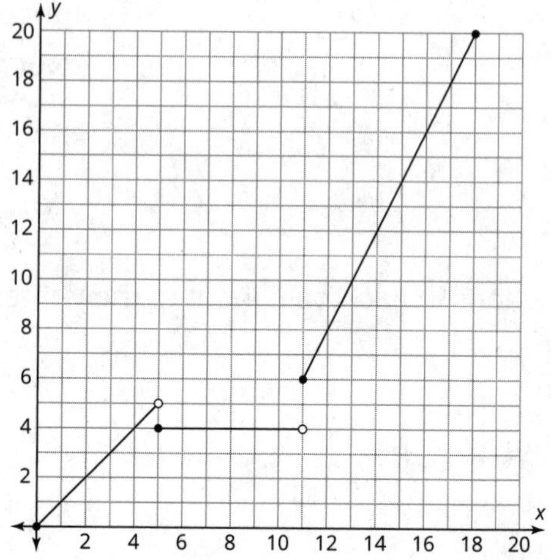

Exponentials Summary

LESSON 1

Got Chills . . . They're Multiplyin'

In a geometric sequence, there is a constant ratio between terms. The constant ratio is a multiplier. To determine the next term of a geometric sequence, you multiply by this value. An exponential function of the form $f(x) = a \cdot b^x$ that models a geometric sequence also has a constant multiplier, represented by the value b. An exponential function is continuous, meaning that there is a value $f(x)$ for every real number value x.

A rational exponent is an exponent that is a rational number. You can write each nth root using a rational exponent. If n is an integer greater than 1, then $\sqrt[n]{a} = a^{\frac{1}{n}}$.

For example, $\sqrt[4]{b} = b^{\frac{1}{4}}$ and $6^{\frac{1}{5}} = \sqrt[5]{6}$.

Write expressions with rational exponents in radical form using the known properties of integer exponents. Write the power as a product using a unit fraction. Use the Power of a Power Rule and the definition of a rational exponent to write the power as a radical.

For example, consider the expressions $8^{\frac{2}{3}}$ and $\left(2^{\frac{1}{3}}\right)^2(2)^{\frac{1}{2}}$.

$$8^{\frac{2}{3}} = 8^{\left(\frac{1}{3}\right)(2)}$$
$$= \left(\sqrt[3]{8}\right)^2$$

$$\left(2^{\frac{1}{3}}\right)^2(2)^{\frac{1}{2}} = \left(2^{\frac{2}{3}}\right)\left(2^{\frac{1}{2}}\right)$$
$$= 2^{\frac{2}{3} + \frac{1}{2}}$$
$$= 2^{\frac{7}{6}}$$
$$= \sqrt[6]{2^7} = \sqrt[6]{128}$$

LESSON 2

Turn That Frown Upside Down

In a simple interest account, a percent of the starting balance is added to the account at each interval. The formula for simple interest is $I = Prt$, where P represents the starting amount, or principal, r represents the interest rate, t represents time, and I represents the interest earned.

In a compound interest account, the balance is multiplied by the same amount at each interval. Because the entire balance is multiplied by the same percent for each interval, the formula is represented by an exponential equation: $I = P \cdot (1 + r)^t$.

The rate of change for a simple interest account is constant. The rate of change between the values for the compound interest account is increasing as t becomes larger. A constant rate of change means that the graph of the linear equation is a straight line. An increasing rate of change means that the graph of the exponential function is a smooth curve.

For example, consider two accounts that each have an initial balance of \$500. One account earns 3% simple interest each year while the other earns 3% compound interest each year.

Time (years)	Simple Interest Balance (dollars)	Compound Interest Balance (dollars)
0	500	500
1	515	515
2	530	530.45
10	650	671.96
100	2000	9609.32

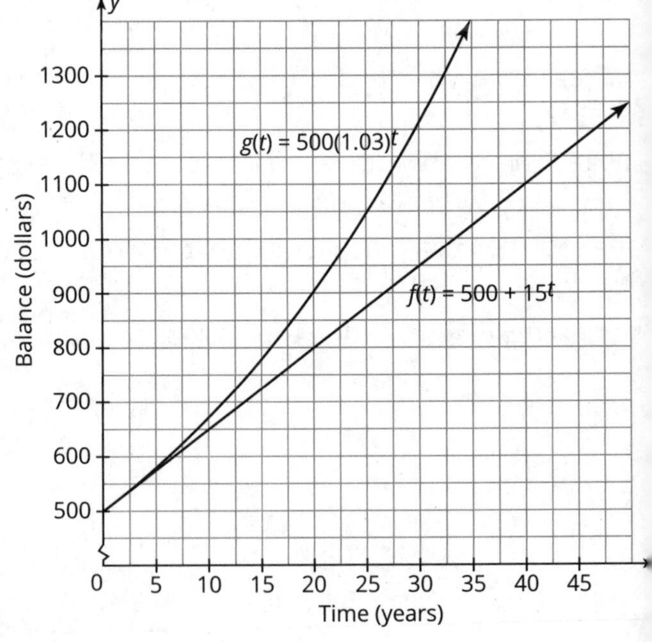

An exponential growth function has a b-value greater than 1 and is of the form $y = a(1 + r)^x$, where r is the rate of growth. An exponential decay function has a b-value greater than 0 and less than 1 and is of the form $y = a(1 - r)^x$, where r is the rate of decay.

For example, consider a population that starts at 50,000 and grows at a rate of 2% every year. The scenario can be modeled by the function $f(x) = 50{,}000 \cdot (1.02)^x$. The a-value of the exponential function is the initial population and since the population grows, the b-value is $(1 + 0.02)$, or 1.02.

LESSON 3 Just So . . . Basic

The transformational form of a function $f(x)$ is given by $g(x) = Af(B(x - C)) + D$. The B-value of an exponential function can be written as the coefficient of x: $f(x) = a \cdot (b)^{Bx}$.

You can use what you know about common bases to rewrite an exponential expression in an equivalent form.

For example, consider the situation in which Simone has invested \$500 in a compound interest account that earns 10% interest. Simone's monthly rate of increase is given by the expression $1.10^{\frac{1}{12}}$. To rewrite the function representing Simone's annual increase as an equivalent function that reflects the monthly rate of increase, determine the new B-value

$$\left(1.10^{\frac{1}{12}}\right)^{Bx} = (1.10)^x$$
$$(1.10)^{\frac{Bx}{12}} = (1.10)^x$$
$$\frac{Bx}{12} = x$$
$$Bx = 12x$$
$$B = 12$$

So, the function $f(x) = 500 \cdot \left(1.10^{\frac{1}{12}}\right)^{12x}$ is equivalent to the function $f(x) = 500 \cdot (1.10)^x$.

For the basic function, $f(x) = 2^x$, a change to the B-value results in a horizontal dilation of the function. For a point (x, y) on the graph of the function $y = f(x)$, the ordered pair $\left(\frac{1}{B}x, y\right)$ describes a point on the graph of $g(x) = f(Bx)$.

For example, consider the exponential functions, where $f(x) = 2^x$ is the basic function.

- $w(x) = 2^{\frac{1}{2}x}$
- $z(x) = 2^{2x}$

The point (2, 4) on the basic function $f(x)$ would correspond to the point (4, 4) on $w(x)$ and to the point (1, 4) on $z(x)$.

LESSON 4 Saving Strategies

You can add a constant function and an exponential function to model a situation.

For example, consider a situation in which Autumn places \$1000 in a savings account with a 4% interest rate, compounded annually. This can be represented by the function $f(x) = 1000 \cdot (1.04)^x$. She also has \$500 that she keeps in safe at home. This can be represented by the function $g(x) = 500$. Autumn's total savings can be represented as $h(x) = f(x) + g(x)$, or $h(x) = 1000 \cdot (1.04)^x + 500$. The graph of this function is the graph of $f(x)$ translated up by a value of 500, so the horizontal asymptote of the graph is $y = 500$.

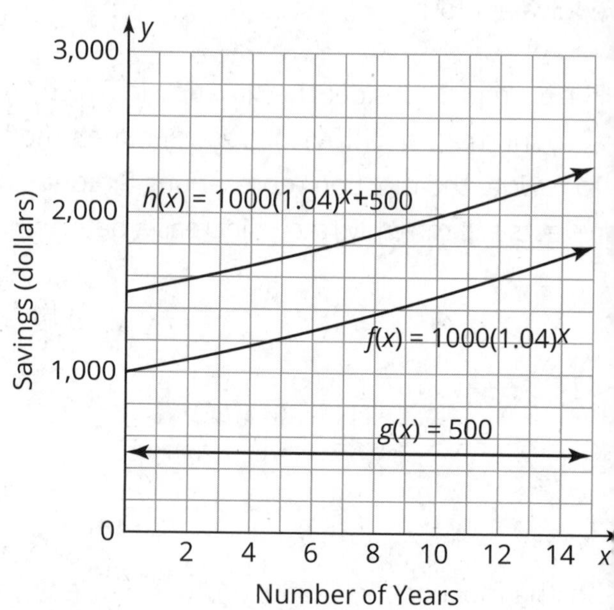

OPIC 3

ntroduction to Quadratic Functions

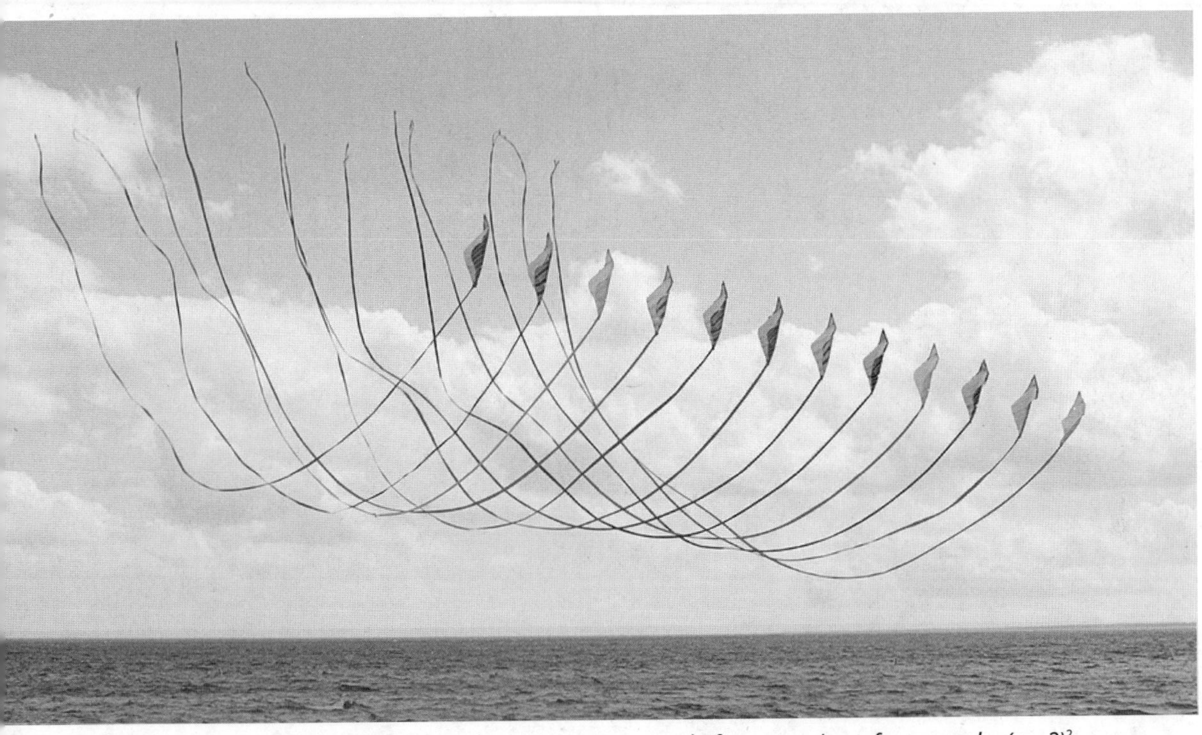

ou can translate a parabola horizontally by subtracting a constant before squaring – for example, $(x - 2)^2$.

Module 3: Exploring Functions

TOPIC 3: INTRODUCTION TO QUADRATIC FUNCTIONS

In this topic, students begin by exploring 4 scenarios which can be represented with quadratic functions. In the following lesson, students represent each situation with an equation, a graph, and a table of values and explore the characteristics of the functions represented by each situation and different forms of a quadratic function. Students then use what they have learned about function transformations and apply this knowledge to transforming quadratic functions. Finally, students summarize the key characteristics and attributes of the different forms of quadratic functions.

Where have we been?

Students build on their understanding of nonlinear functions as they explore the key characteristics of quadratic functions and compare them to linear functions.

Where are we going?

In future courses, students will explore higher-order polynomials. Understanding the structure of a degree 2 polynomial, both in terms of graphs and equations, prepares students to understand the structure of cubics, quartics, and beyond. In their extensive study of polynomials, students will come back to their knowledge of key characteristics of quadratics, particularly their understanding of zeros, roots, and intercepts.

Second Differences

Linear functions have a constant rate of change, so their first differences are constant: for each increase or decrease of 1 in the *x*-value, the *y*-value of a linear function goes up or down the same amount. But quadratic functions are different.

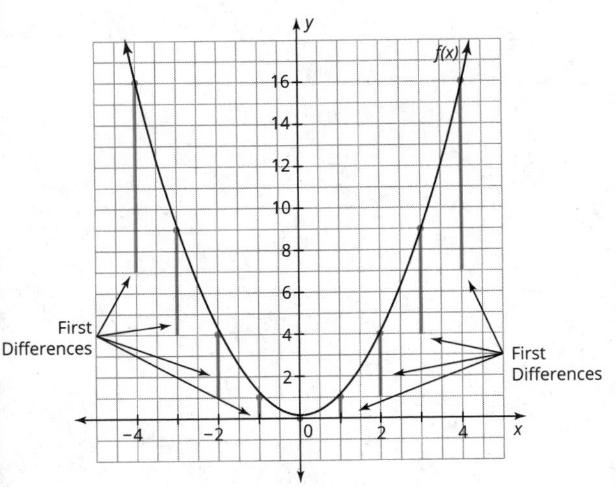

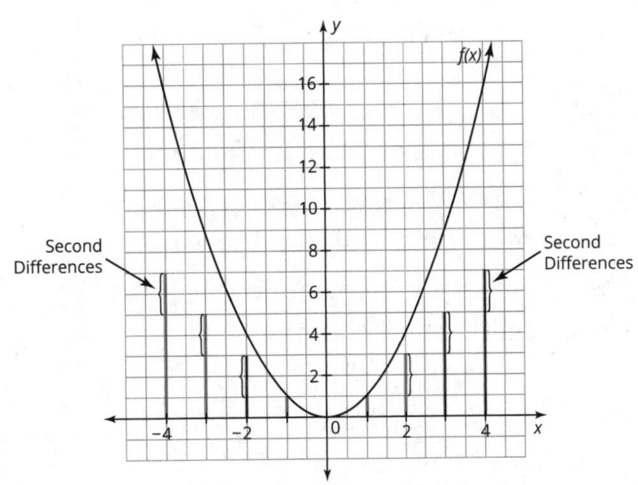

The first differences of a quadratic function are not constant. But the second differences—the differences between the first differences—are constant.

Punkin' Chunkin'

Every year the county of Sussex, Delaware, holds a competition called the Punkin' Chunkin' World Championships, which is a pumpkin-throwing competition. Participants build machines that hurl pumpkins great distances. The winner is the person whose machine hurls the pumpkin the farthest.

Talking Points

It can be helpful to understand quadratic functions for college admissions tests.

Here is an example of a sample question:

Given that $f(x) = ax^2 + bx + c$, which is the graph of f if $a < 0$ and $c > 0$?

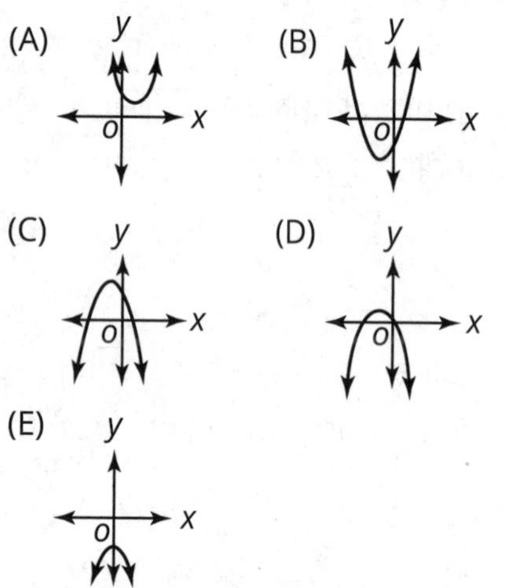

To solve this problem, you should know about transformations of quadratic functions. If $a < 0$, then you know that the parabola is an upside-down u shape. The variable c represents the y-intercept. Since $c > 0$, the y-intercept is above the x-axis.

So, Choice C is correct.

Key Terms

parabola

The shape that a quadratic function forms when graphed is called a parabola.

roots

The roots of an equation indicate where the graph of the equation crosses the x-axis.

vertex form

The vertex form of a quadratic function is $f(x) = a(x - h)^2 + k$, where $a \neq 0$.

general form

A quadratic function written in the form $f(x) = ax^2 + bx + c$, where $a \neq 0$, is in general form, or standard form.

factored form

A quadratic function written in the form $f(x) = a(x_1 - r)(x_2 - r)$, where $a \neq 0$, is in factored form.

1

Up and Down or Down and Up

Exploring Quadratic Functions

Warm Up

Consider $f(x) = x^2 + 3x + 4$. Evaluate the function for each given value.

1. $f(1)$

2. $f(-1)$

3. $f(2)$

4. $f(-2)$

Learning Goals

- Write quadratic functions to model contexts.
- Graph quadratic functions using technology.
- Interpret the key features of quadratic functions in terms of a context.
- Identify the domain and range of quadratic functions and their contexts.

Key Terms

- parabola
- vertical motion model
- root

You have used linear functions to model situations with constant change, and you have used exponential functions to model growth and decay situations. What type of real-world situations can be modeled by quadratic functions?

GETTING STARTED

Squaring It Up

Maddie is using pennies to create a pattern.

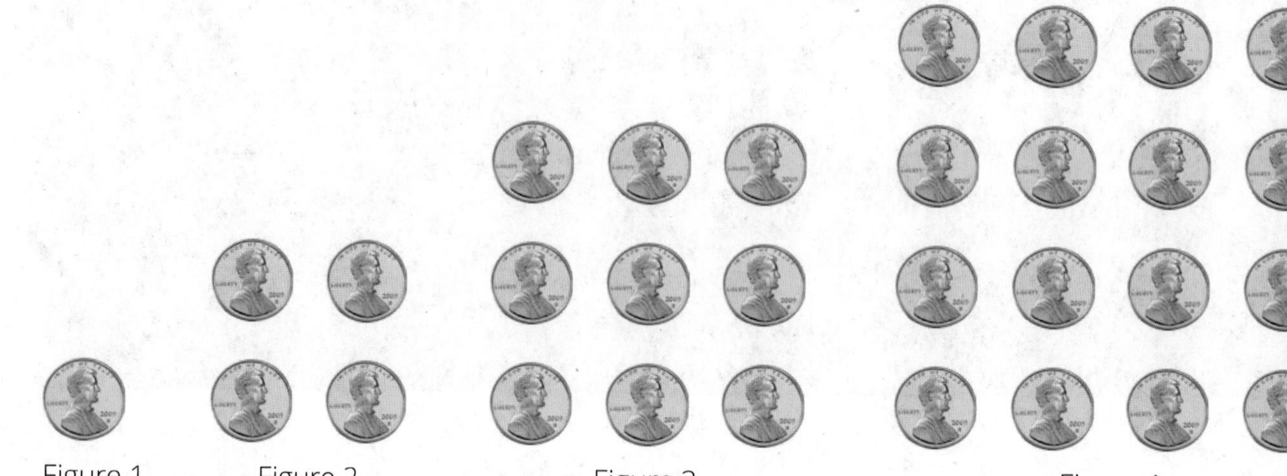

Figure 1 Figure 2 Figure 3 Figure 4

1. **Analyze the pattern and explain how to create Figure 5.**

2. **How many pennies would Maddie need to create Figure 5? Figure 6? Figure 7?**

3. **Which figure would Maddie create with exactly $4.00 in pennies**

4. **Write an equation to determine the number of pennies for any figure number. Define your variables.**

5. **Describe the function family to which this equation belongs.**

ACTIVITY 1.1

Using Area to Introduce Quadratic Functions

A dog trainer is fencing in an enclosure, represented by the shaded region in the diagram. The trainer will also have two square-shaped storage units on either side of the enclosure to store equipment and other materials. She can make the enclosure and storage units as wide as she wants, but she can't exceed 100 feet in total length.

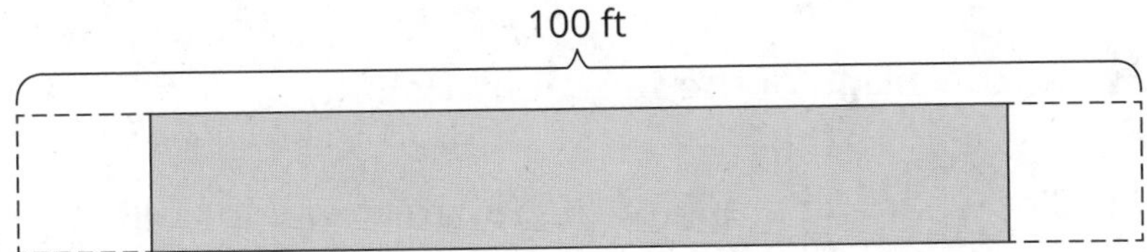

1. Let *s* represent a side length, in feet, of one of the storage units.

a. Label the length and width of the enclosure in terms of *s*.

b. Write the function *L*(*s*) to represent the length of the enclosure as a function of side length, *s*.

c. Sketch and label a graph of the function on the given coordinate plane. Identify any key points.

To identify key points on the graph, think about the function you are representing. Are there any intercepts? Are there any other points of interest?

2. Describe the domain and range of the context and of the function.

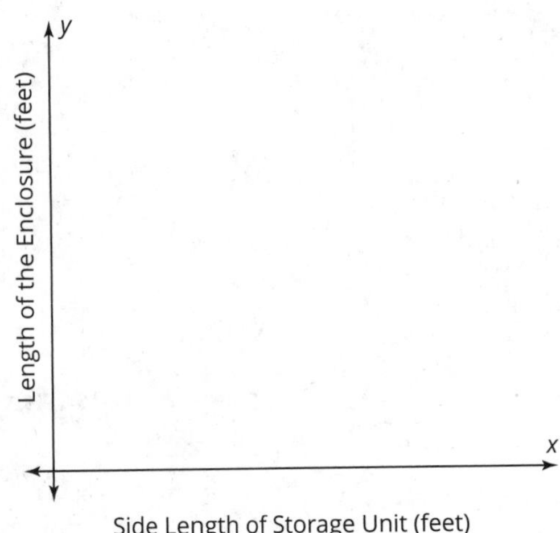

3. Identify each key characteristic of the graph. Then, interpret the meaning of each in terms of the context.

a. slope

b. *y*-intercept

c. increasing or decreasing

d. *x*-intercept

The progression of diagrams below shows how the area of the enclosure, $A(s)$, changes as the side length, s, of each square storage unit increases.

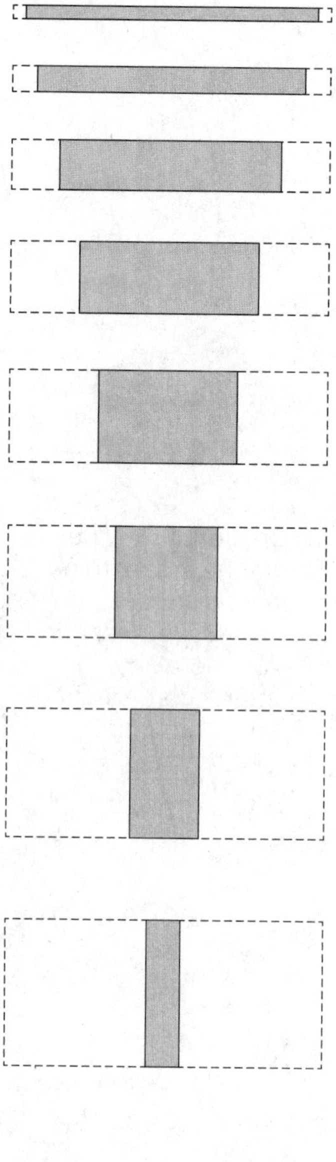

4. Write the function $A(s)$ to represent the area of the enclosure as a function of side length, s.

5. Describe how the area of the enclosure changes as the side length increases.

6. Consider the graph of the function, $A(s)$.

a. Predict what the graph of the function will look like.

b. Use technology to graph the function $A(s)$. Then sketch the graph and label the axes.

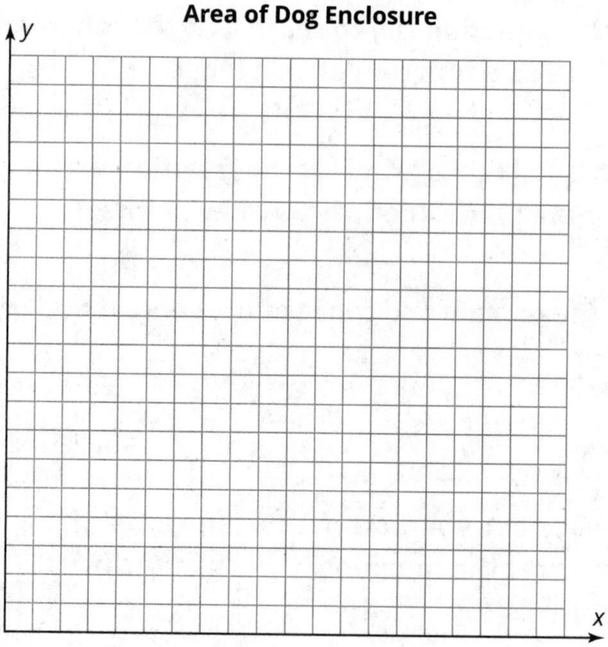

Area of Dog Enclosure

y

x

7. Describe what all the points on the graph represent.

e function $A(s)$ that you wrote to model area is a quadratic function. e shape that a quadratic function forms when graphed is called **parabola**.

Quadratic functions model area because area is measured in square units.

. Think about the possible areas of the enclosure.

a. Is there a maximum area that the enclosure can contain? Explain your reasoning in terms of the graph and in terms of the context.

b. Use technology to determine the maximum of $A(s)$. Describe what the x- and y-coordinates of the maximum represent in this context.

c. Determine the dimensions of the enclosure that will provide the maximum area. Show your work and explain your reasoning.

9. Identify the domain and range of the context and of the function.

0. Identify each key characteristic of the graph. Then, interpret the meaning of each in terms of the context.

a. y-intercept

b. increasing and decreasing intervals

c. symmetry

d. x-intercepts

ACTIVITY 1.2 Writing and Interpreting a Quadratic Function

Suppose that there is a monthly meeting at CIA headquarters for all employees. How many handshakes will it take for every employee at the meeting to shake the hand of every other employee at the meeting once?

1. **Use the figures shown to determine the number of handshakes that will occur between 2 employees, 3 employees, and 4 employees.**

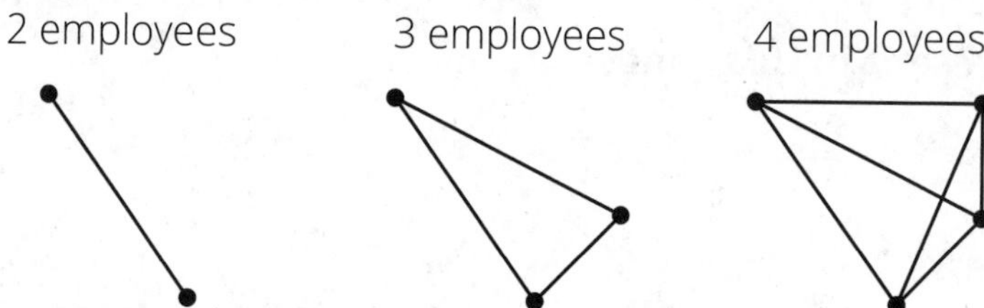

2. **Draw figures to represent the number of handshakes that occur between 5 employees, 6 employees, and 7 employees and determine the number of handshakes that will occur in each situation.**

Can you tell what shape the graph will be?

3. **Enter your results in the table.**

Number of Employees	2	3	4	5	6	7	n
Number of Handshakes							

4. **Write a function to represent the number of handshakes given any number of employees. Enter your function in the table.**

Use technology to graph the function you wrote in Question 4. Sketch the graph and label the axes.

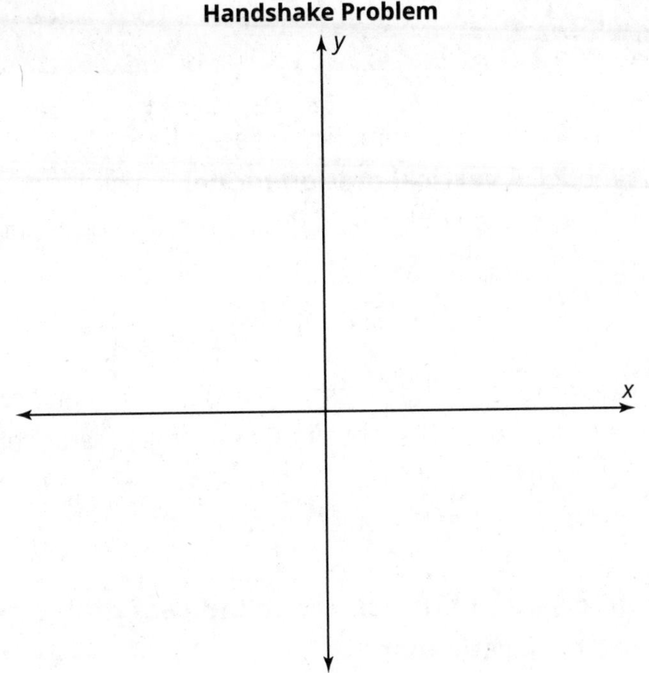

What do all the points on this graph represent?

How is the orientation of this parabola different from the parabola for the area of the dog enclosure? How is this difference reflected in their corresponding equations?

Determine the minimum of your function. Then, describe what the *x*- and *y*-coordinates of this minimum represent in this problem situation.

Identify the domain and range of the problem situation and of the function.

ACTIVITY

1.3

Using a Quadratic Function to Model Vertical Motion

You can model the motion of a pumpkin released from a catapult using a vertical motion model. A **vertical motion model** is a quadratic equation that models the height of an object at a given time. The equation is of the form shown.

$$y = -16t^2 + v_0t + h_0$$

In this equation, y represents the height of the object in feet, t represents the time in seconds that the object has been moving, v_0 represents the initial vertical velocity (speed) of the object in feet per second, and h_0 represents the initial height of the object in feet.

1. **What characteristics of this situation indicate that it can be modeled by a quadratic function?**

Suppose that a catapult hurls a pumpkin from a height of 68 feet at an initial vertical velocity of 128 feet per second.

2. **Write a function for the height of the pumpkin, $h(t)$, in terms of time, t.**

3. **Does the function you wrote have a minimum or maximum? How can you tell from the form of the function?**

Use technology to graph the function. Sketch your graph and label the axes.

Punkin' Chunkin'

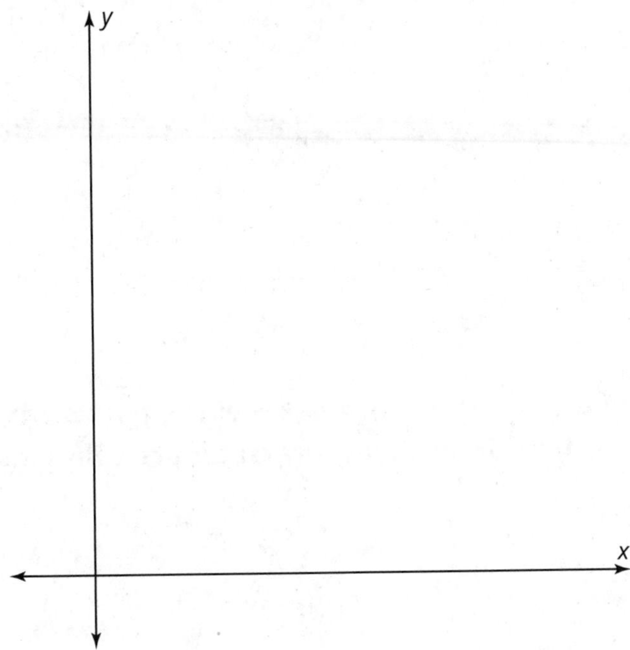

Ask yourself:

What do all the points on this graph represent?

. **Use technology to determine the maximum or minimum and label it on the graph. Explain what it means in terms of the problem situation.**

5. **Determine the *y*-intercept and label it on the graph. Explain what it means in terms of the problem situation.**

7. **Use a horizontal line to determine when the pumpkin reaches each height after being catapulted. Label the points on the graph.**

   a. **128 feet**

   b. **260 feet**

   c. **55 feet**

8. **Explain why the *x*- and *y*-coordinates of the points where the graph and each horizontal line intersects are solutions.**

9. **When does the catapulted pumpkin hit the ground? Label this point on the graph. Explain how you determined your answer.**

The zeros of a function are the *x*-values when the function equals 0.

The time when the pumpkin hits the ground is one of the *x*-intercepts, $(x, 0)$. When an equation is used to model a situation, the *x*-coordinate of the *x*-intercept is referred to as a root. The **root** of an equation indicates where the graph of the equation crosses the *x*-axis.

ACTIVITY 1.4

Expressing a Quadratic Function as the Product of Two Linear Functions

The Jacobson brothers own and operate their own ghost tour business. They take tour groups around town on a bus to visit the most notorious "haunted" spots throughout the city. They charge $50 per tour. Each summer, they book 100 tours at that price. The brothers are considering a decrease in the price per tour because they think it will help them book more tours. They estimate that they will gain 10 tours for every $1 decrease in the price per tour.

1. **According to the scenario, how much money do the Jacobson brothers currently generate each summer with their ghost tour business?**

Revenue is the amount of money regularly coming into a business. In the ghost tour business, the revenue is the number of tours multiplied by the price per tour. Your response to Question 1 can be referred to as revenue. Because the Jacobson brothers are considering different numbers of tours and prices per tour, the revenue can be modeled by a function.

2. **Write a function, $r(x)$, to represent the revenue for the ghost tour business.**

   a. **Let x represent the decrease in the price per tour. Write an expression to represent the number of tours booked if the decrease in price is x dollars per tour.**

   b. **Write an expression to represent the price per tour if the brothers decrease the price x dollars per tour.**

You can always check your function by testing it with values of x. What is the value of $r(x)$ when $x = 0$? Does it make sense?

c. **Use your expressions from parts (a) and (b) to represent the revenue, $r(x)$, as the number of tours times the price per tour.**

Revenue	=	**Number of Tours**	•	**Price per Tour**
$r(x)$	=	________	•	________

3. **Use technology to graph the function $r(x)$. Sketch your graph an label the axes.**

Don't forget to label key points!

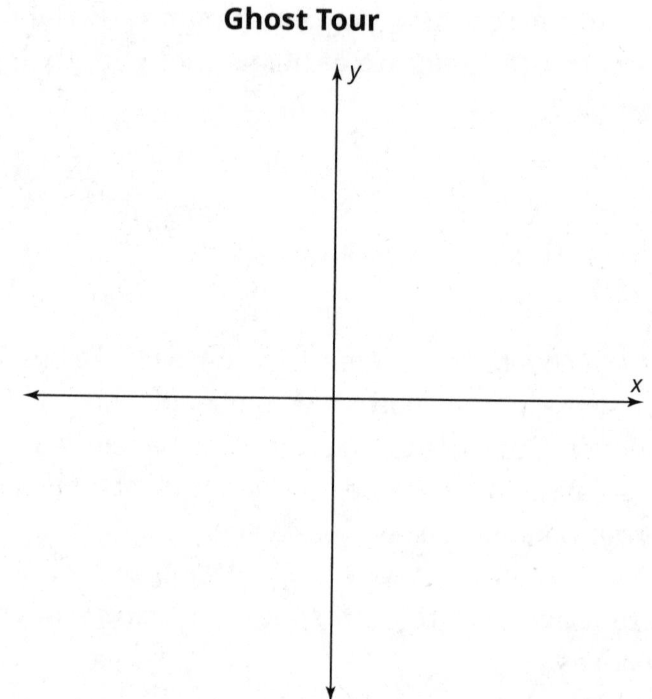

4. **Assume that the Jacobson brothers' estimate that for every $1 decrease in the price per tour, they will gain 10 tours is accurate.**

   a. **What is the maximum revenue that the Jacobson brothers could earn for the summer?**

b. Katie and Bryce are calculating the number of tours that would yield the maximum revenue.

Katie said that according to the graph, a tour should cost \$20. Since \$9000 ÷ \$20 = 450, the number of tours would be 450.

Bryce said that the cost of a tour should be \$30, and \$9000 divided by \$30 per tour is 300 tours.

Who is correct? Explain your reasoning.

c. Would you advise the Jacobson brothers to adjust their cost per tour to make the maximum revenue? Why or why not?

Identify each key characteristic of the graph. Then, interpret its meaning in terms of the context.

a. *x*-intercepts

b. *y*-intercept

c. increasing and decreasing intervals

NOTES

TALK the TALK

Making Connections

Analyze the graphs of the four quadratic functions in this lesson.

1. **Summarize what you know about the graphs of quadratic functions. Include a sketch or sketches and list any characteristics.**

2. **Compare your sketch or sketches and list with your classmates. Did you all sketch the same parabola? Why or why not?**

Assignment

Write

Fill in the blank.

1. The x-intercepts of a graph of a quadratic function are also called the ______________ of the quadratic function.
2. A quadratic equation that models the height of an object at a given time is a ______________.
3. The shape that a quadratic function forms when graphed is called a ______________.
4. The ______________ of an equation indicate where the graph of the equation crosses the x-axis.

Remember

The graph of a quadratic function is called a parabola. Parabolas are smooth curves that have an absolute maximum or minimum, both increasing and decreasing intervals, up to two x-intercepts, and symmetry.

Practice

1. The citizens of Herrington County have an existing dog park for dogs to play, but have decided to build another one so that one park will be for small dogs and the other will be for large dogs. The plan is to build a rectangular fenced in area that will be adjacent to the existing dog park, as shown in the sketch. The county has enough money in the budget to buy 1000 feet of fencing.

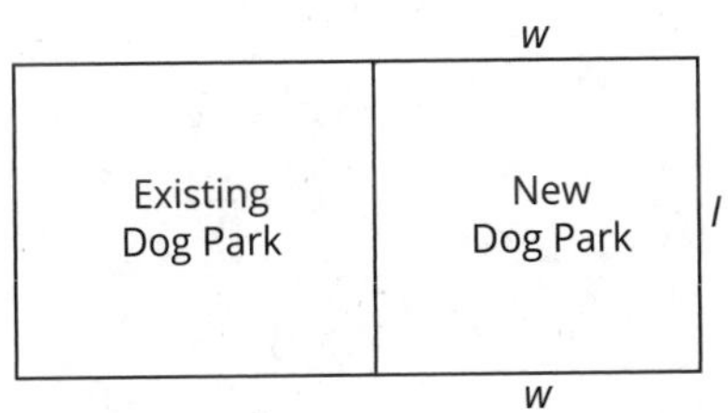

   a. Determine the length of the new dog park, l, in terms of the width, w.
   b. Write the function $A(w)$ to represent the area of the new dog park as a function of the width, w. Does this function have a minimum or a maximum? Explain your answer.
   c. Determine the x-intercepts of the function. Explain what each means in terms of the problem situation.
   d. What should the dimensions of the dog park be to maximize the area? What is the maximum area of the park?
   e. Sketch the graph of the function. Label the axes, the maximum or minimum, the x-intercepts, and the y-intercept.
   f. Use the graph to determine the dimensions of the park if the area was restricted to 105,000 square feet.

Stretch

1. Sketch a graph of a quadratic function that has a maximum value of (0, 2) and x-intercepts when $x = \pm 2$.
2. What is the quadratic function of your graph? Explain your reasoning.

Review

1. Rewrite each expression using a radical.
   a. $7^{\frac{3}{4}}$ b. $2^{\frac{1}{5}}$
2. Rewrite each expression using a rational exponent.
   a. $\left(\sqrt[6]{3}\right)^5$ b. $\left(\sqrt[3]{5}\right)^2$
3. If the basic function $f(x) = |x|$ is translated 3 units to the right and 4 units up, what is the transformed equation?
4. If the basic function $f(x) = 4^x$ is vertically stretched by a factor of 2 and translated 5 units down, what is the transformed equation?

2

Endless Forms Most Beautiful

Key Characteristics of Quadratic Functions

Warm Up

Determine the slope and y-intercept of each linear function.

1. $h(x) = 3x$

2. $g(x) = \frac{1}{2}(x - 5)$

3. $k(x) = x - 2$

4. $m(x) = \frac{8x}{4} + 1$

Learning Goals

- Identify the factored form and general form of an equation for a quadratic function.
- Determine the equation for the axis of symmetry of a quadratic function, given the equation in general form or factored form.
- Determine the absolute minimum or absolute maximum point on the graph of a quadratic function and identify this point as the vertex.
- Describe intervals of increase and decrease in relation to the axis of symmetry on the graph of a quadratic function.
- Use key characteristics of the graph of a quadratic function to write an equation in factored form.

Key Terms

- second differences
- concave up
- concave down
- general form of a quadratic function
- factored form
- vertex of a parabola
- axis of symmetry

You have identified key characteristics of linear and exponential functions. What are the key characteristics of quadratic functions?

Dogs, Handshakes, Pumpkins, Ghosts

Consider the four quadratic models you investigated in the previous lesso
There are multiple equivalent ways to write the equation to represent eac
situation and a unique parabola to represent the equivalent equations. Yc
can also represent the function using a table of values.

Area of Dog Enclosure

$A(s) = -2s^2 + 100s$

$= -2(s)(s - 50)$

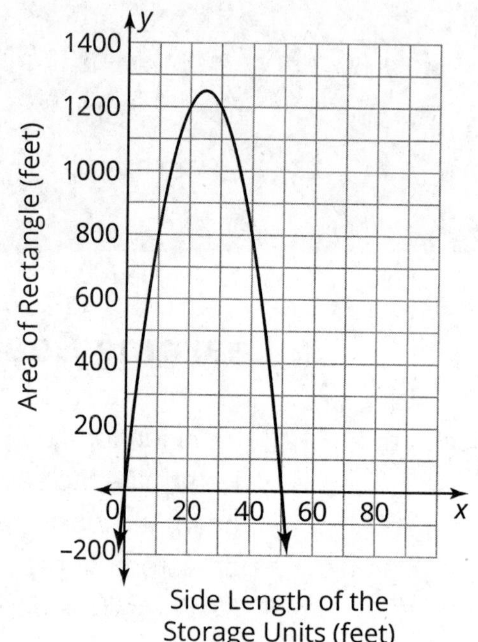

s	$A(s)$
0	0
1	98
2	192
3	282
4	368

Handshake Problem

$f(n) = \frac{1}{2}n^2 - \frac{1}{2}n$

$= \frac{1}{2}(n)(n - 1)$

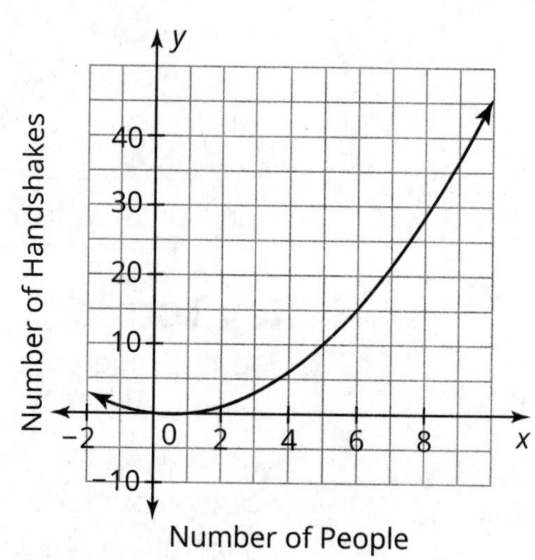

n	$f(n)$
0	0
1	0
2	1
3	3
4	6

nkin' Chunkin'

$) = -16t^2 + 128t + 68$

$= -16(t - \frac{17}{2})(t + \frac{1}{2})$

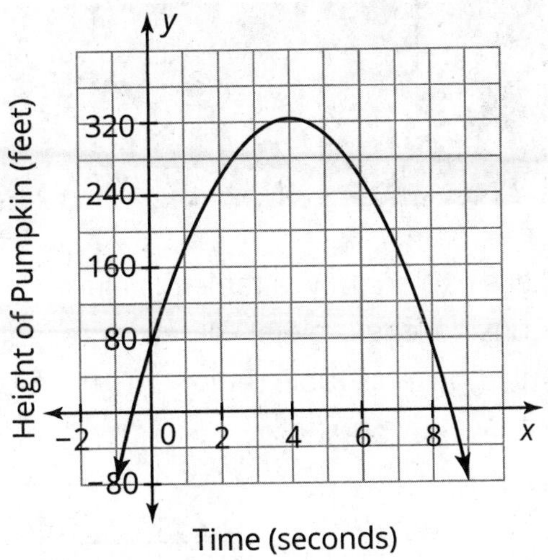

t	$h(t)$
0	68
1	180
2	260
3	308
4	324

ıost Tour

$) = -10(x + 10)(x - 50)$

$= -10x^2 + 400x + 5000$

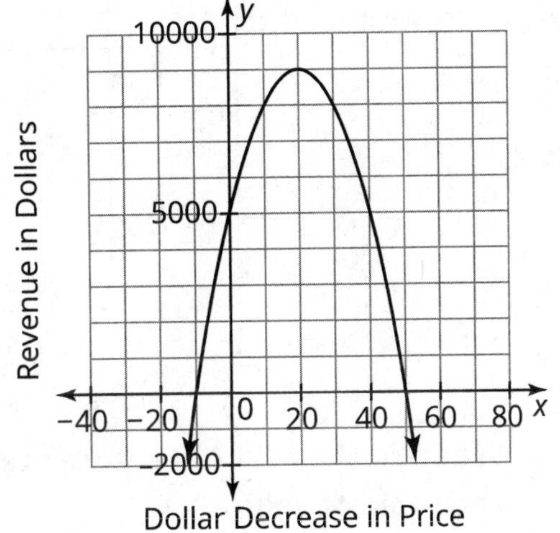

x	$r(x)$
0	5000
1	5390
2	5760
3	6110
4	6440

Consider each representation.

a. How can you tell from the structure of the equation that it is quadratic?

b. What does the structure of the equation tell you about the shape and characteristics of the graph?

c. How can you tell from the shape of the graph that it is quadratic?

d. How can you tell from the table that the relationship is quadratic?

ACTIVITY

2.1 Second Differences

You can tell whether a table represents a linear function by analyzing first differences. First differences imply the calculation of $y_2 - y_1$.

Let's explore how a table of values can show that a function is quadratic. Consider the table of values represented by the basic quadratic function. This table represents the first differences between seven consecutive points.

x	$f(x)$	First Differences
−3	9	
		4 − 9 = −5
−2	4	
		1 − 4 = −3
−1	1	
		0 − 1 = −1
0	0	
		1 − 0 = 1
1	1	
		4 − 1 = 3
2	4	
		9 − 4 = 5
3	9	

1. **What do the first differences tell you about the relationship of the table of values?**

Let's consider the *second differences*. The **second differences** are the differences between consecutive values of the first differences.

2. **Calculate the second differences for $f(x)$. What do you notice?**

u know that with linear functions, the first differences are constant. For adratic functions, the second differences are constant.

t's consider the graph of the basic quadratic function, $f(x) = x^2$ and the stances represented by the first and second differences. Graph 1 shows e distances between consecutive values of $f(x)$. The colored line segments e different lengths because the first differences are not the same.

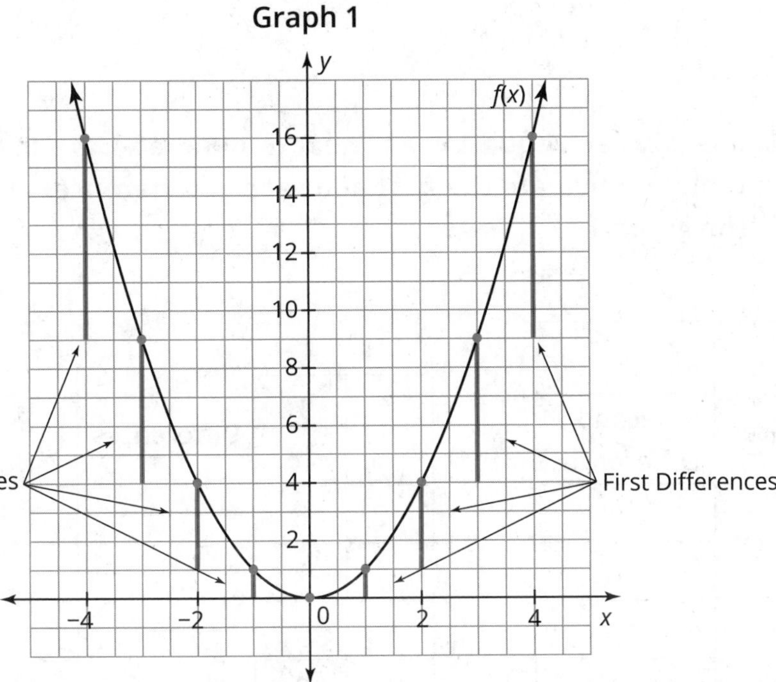

aph 2 shows the lengths of the first differences positioned along the axis. By comparing these lengths, you can see the second differences.

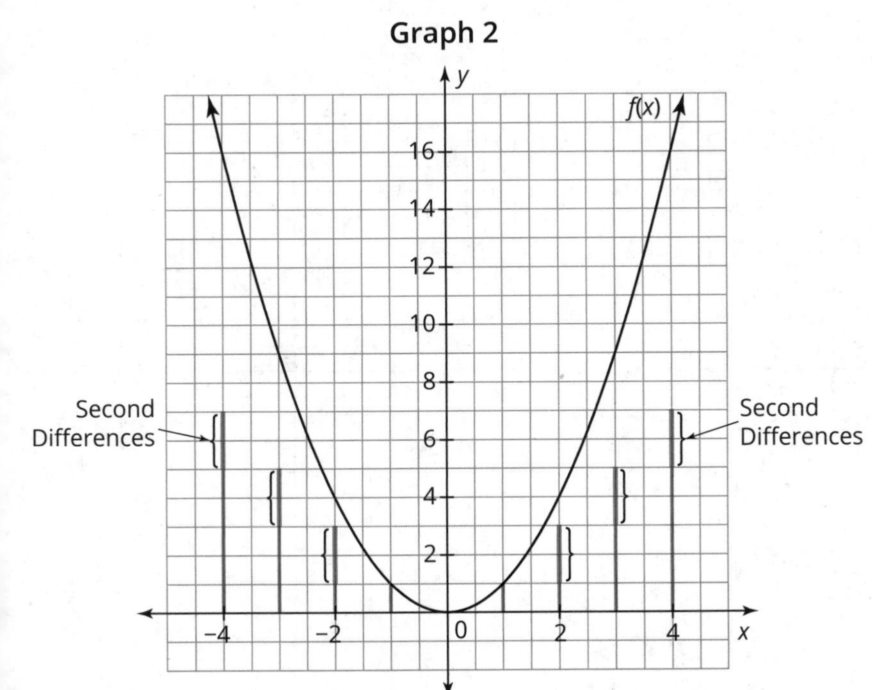

Quadratic equations are polynomials with a degree of 2. Their second differences are constant. Linear functions are polynomials with a degree of 1, and their first differences are constant.

3. **How does the representation in Graph 1 support the first differences calculated from the table of values?**

4. **How does the representation in Graph 2 support the second differences you calculated in the table?**

5. **Identify each equation as linear or quadratic. Complete the table to calculate the first and second differences. Then sketc the graph.**

a. $y = 2x$ ______________________

x	y	First Differences	Second Differences
−3	−6		
−2	−4		
−1	−2		
0	0		
1	2		
2	4		
3	6		

b. $y = 2x^2$ ______________________

x	y	First Differences	Second Differences
−3	18		
−2	8		
−1	2		
0	0		
1	2		
2	8		
3	18		

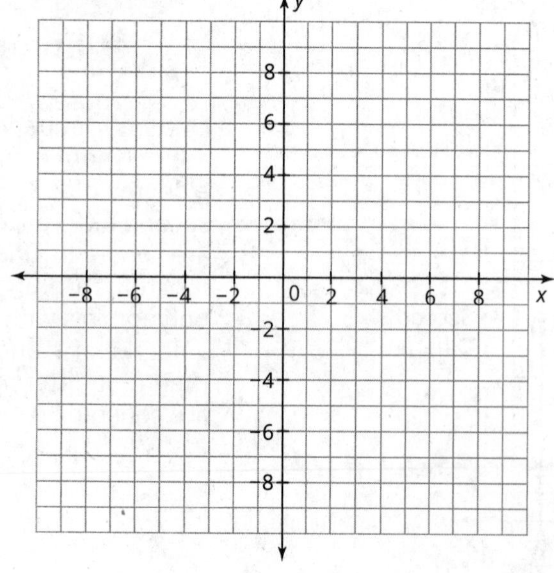

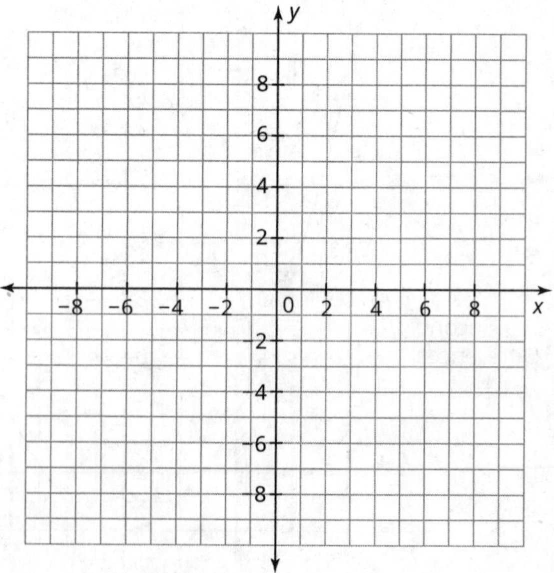

c. $y = -x + 4$ ____________________

x	y	First Differences	Second Differences
−3	7		
−2	6		
−1	5		
0	4		
1	3		
2	2		
3	1		

d. $y = -x^2 + 4$ ____________________

x	y	First Differences	Second Differences
−3	−5		
−2	0		
−1	3		
0	4		
1	3		
2	0		
3	−5		

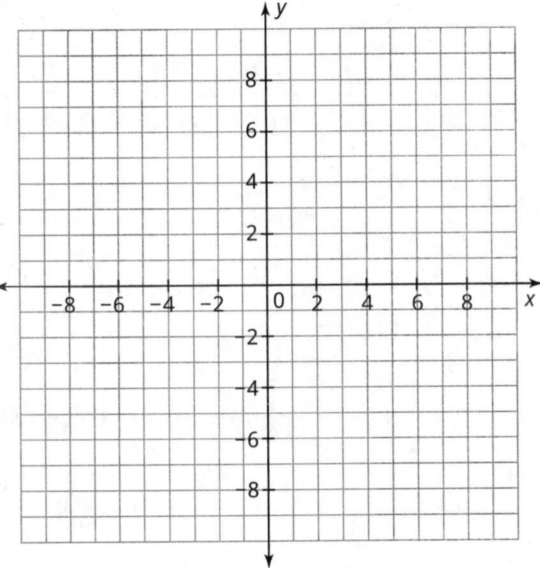

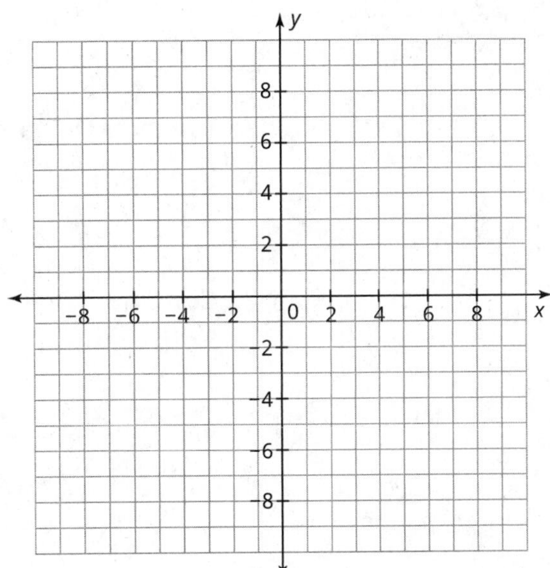

Compare the signs of the first and second differences for each function and its graph.

A graph that opens upward is identified as being **concave up**. A graph that opens downward is identified as begin **concave down**.

a. **How do the signs of the first differences for a linear function relate to the graph either increasing or decreasing?**

b. **How do the signs of the second differences for quadratic functions relate to whether the parabola is opening upward or downward?**

ACTIVITY 2.2 Analyzing the Leading Coefficient

The leading coefficient of an equation is the numeric coefficient of the term with the greatest power.

You know that different forms of an equation can reveal different characteristics about functions. Quadratic functions can be written in different forms.

A quadratic function written in the form $f(x) = ax^2 + bx + c$, where $a \neq 0$, is in **general form**, or standard form. In this form, a and b are numerical coefficients and c is a constant.

A quadratic function written in **factored form** is in the form $f(x) = a(x - r_1)(x - r_2)$, where $a \neq 0$.

1. Identify the general form and factored form of each equation in the Getting Started.

2. Consider the leading coefficient of each function equation in both general form and factored form.

a. What does the leading coefficient tell you about the graph of each function?

The graph of a quadratic function has either an absolute maximum or absolute minimum.

b. How is the leading coefficient related to the absolute minimum or absolute maximum of each function?

c. How can you determine the *y*-intercept of the graph using general form?

NOTES

Determine from the equation whether each quadratic function has an absolute maximum or absolute minimum. Explain how you know.

a. $f(n) = 2n^2 + 3n - 1$

b. $g(x) = -2x^2 - 3x + 1$

c. $r(x) = -\frac{1}{2}x^2 - 3x + 1$

d. $b(x) = -0.009(x + 50)(x - 250)$

e. $f(t) = \frac{1}{3}(x - 1)(x - 1)$

f. $j(x) = 2x(1 - x)$

ACTIVITY 2.3 Axis of Symmetry

The vertex is identified as either the absolute minimum or absolute maximum.

The **vertex of a parabola** is the lowest or highest point on the graph of the quadratic function. The **axis of symmetry** or the line of symmetry of a parabola is the vertical line that passes through the vertex and divides the parabola into two mirror images. Because the axis of symmetry always divides the parabola into two mirror images, you can say that a parabola has reflectional symmetry.

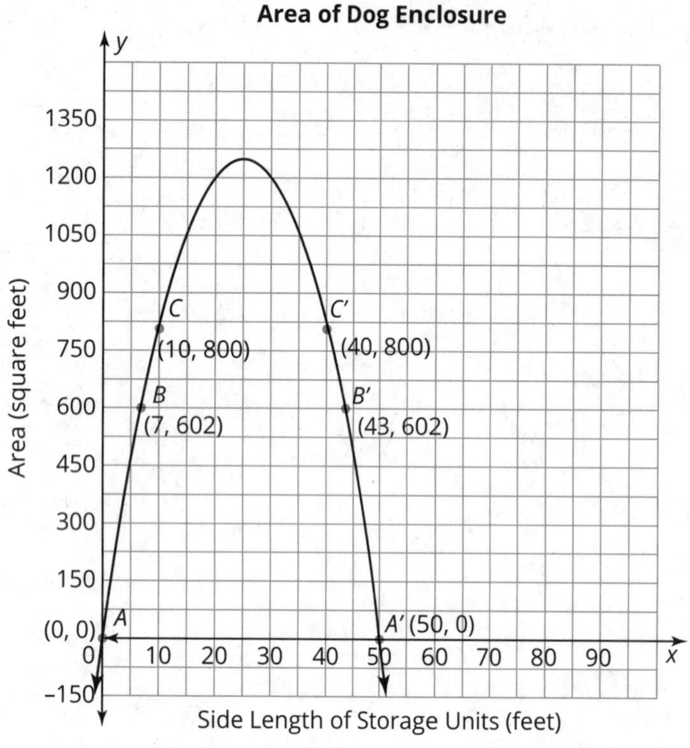

1. **Use patty paper to trace the graph representing the area of the dog enclosure. Then fold the graph to show the symmetry of the parabola and trace the axis of symmetry.**

   a. **Place the patty paper over the original graph. What is the equation of the axis of symmetry?**

   b. **Draw and label the axis of symmetry on the graph from your patty paper.**

2. **Analyze the symmetric points labeled on the graph.**

   a. **What do you notice about the *y*-coordinates of the points?**

b. **What do you notice about each point's horizontal distance from the axis of symmetry?**

c. **How does the *x*-coordinate of each symmetric point compare to the *x*-coordinate of the vertex?**

r a function in factored form, $f(x) = a(x - r_1)(x - r_2)$, the equation for the is of symmetry is given by $x = \frac{r_1 + r_2}{2}$. For a quadratic function in general rm, $f(x) = ax^2 + bx + c$, the equation for the axis of symmetry is $x = \frac{-b}{2a}$.

Identify the axis of symmetry of the graph of each situation from the Getting Started using the factored form of each equation.

Describe the meaning of the axis of symmetry in each situation, if possible.

Describe how you can use the axis of symmetry to determine the ordered pair location of the absolute maximum or absolute minimum of a quadratic function, given the equation for the function in factored form.

s you analyze a parabola from left to right, it will have either an interval increase followed by an interval of decrease, or an interval of decrease llowed by an interval of increase.

How does the absolute maximum or absolute minimum help you determine each interval?

Consider the graph of the quadratic function representing the Punkin' Chunkin' problem situation.

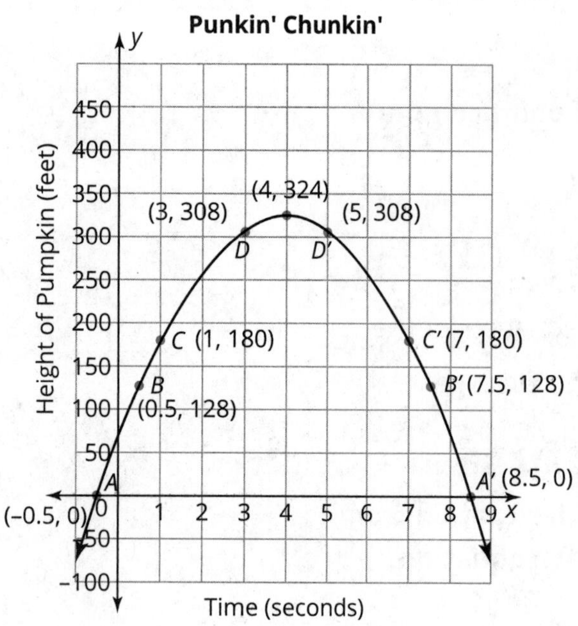

7. Determine the average rate of change between each pair. Then summarize what you notice.

a. points *A* and *B*

b. points *A'* and *B'*

c. points *B* and *C*

d. points *B'* and *C'*

e. What do you notice about the average rates of change between pairs of symmetric points?

The formula for the average rate of change is $\frac{f(b) - f(a)}{b - a}$.

For each function shown, identify the domain, range, *x*-intercepts, *y*-intercept, axis of symmetry, vertex, and interval of increase and decrease.

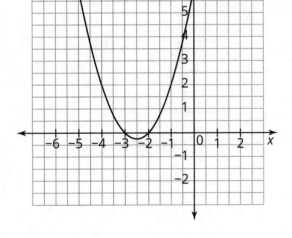

a. The graph shown represents the function $f(x) = -2x^2 + 4x$.

Domain: **Range:**

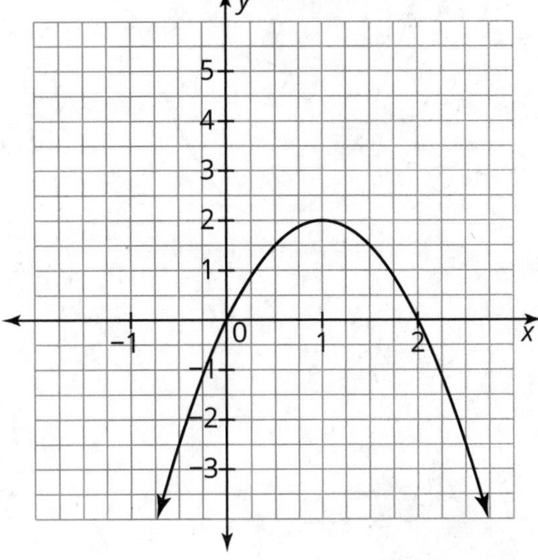

***x*-intercepts:** ***y*-intercept:**

Axis of symmetry: **Vertex:**

Interval of increase: **Interval of decrease:**

b. The graph shown represents the function $f(x) = x^2 + 5x + 6$.

Domain: **Range:**

***x*-intercepts:** ***y*-intercept:**

Axis of symmetry: **Vertex:**

Interval of increase: **Interval of decrease:**

c. **The graph shown represents the function $f(x) = x^2 - x - 2$.**

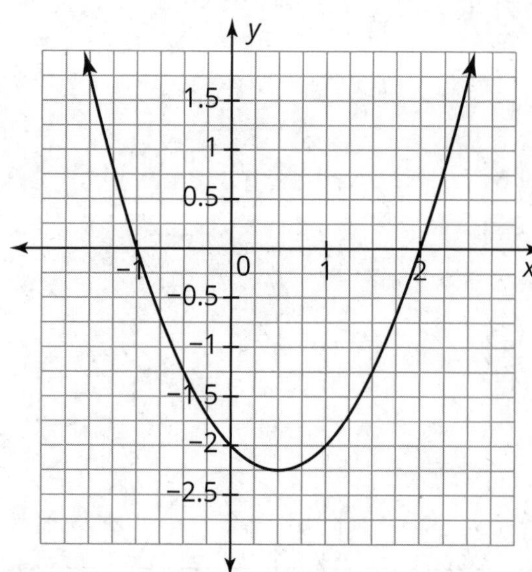

Domain:

Range:

x-intercepts:

y-intercept:

Axis of symmetry:

Vertex:

Interval of increase:

Interval of decrease

d. **The graph shown represents the function $f(x) = x^2 - 3x + 2$.**

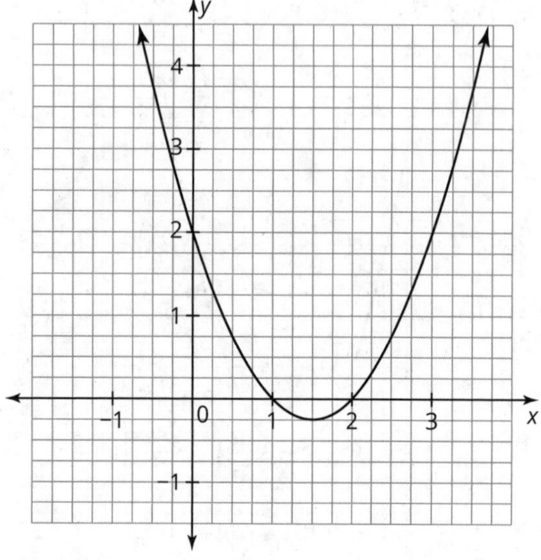

Domain:

Range:

x-intercepts:

y-intercept:

Axis of symmetry:

Vertex:

Interval of increase:

Interval of decrease

ACTIVITY

2.4 Exploring Factored Form

ou have analyzed quadratic functions and their equations. Let's look at the ctored form of a quadratic function in more detail.

If given a function $g(x)$ with a zero at $x = 4$, then $g(4) = 0$. This can also be interpreted as an x-intercept at $(4, 0)$.

A group of students each write a quadratic function in factored form to represent a parabola that opens downward and has zeros at $x = 4$ and $x = -1$.

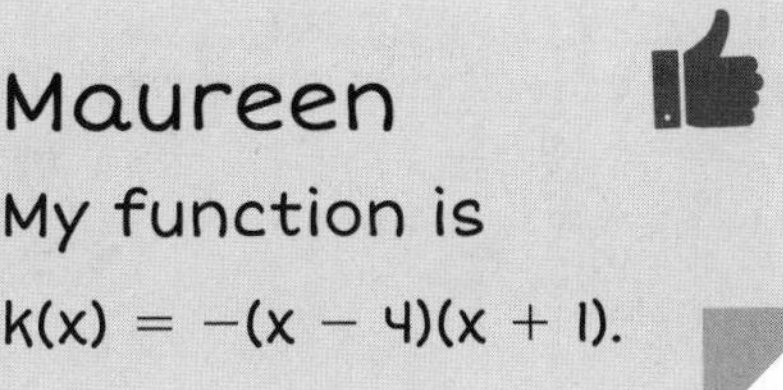
Maureen
My function is
k(x) = −(x − 4)(x + 1).

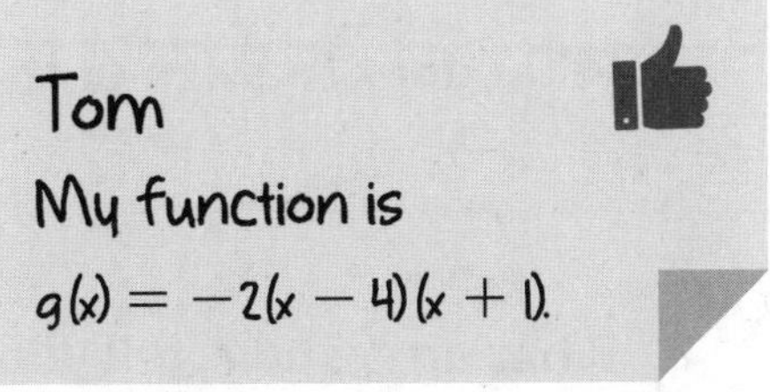
Tom
My function is
g(x) = −2(x − 4)(x + 1).

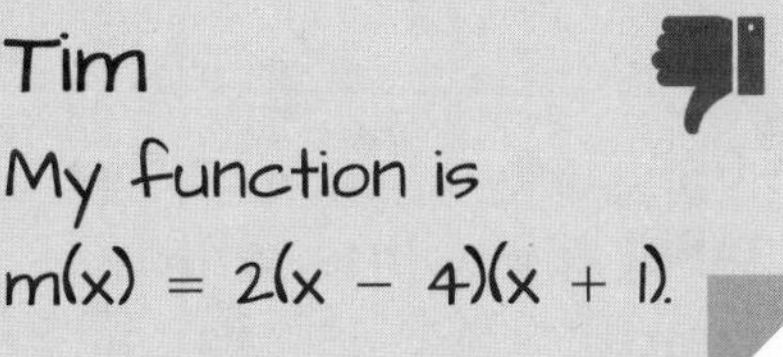
Tim
My function is
m(x) = 2(x − 4)(x + 1).

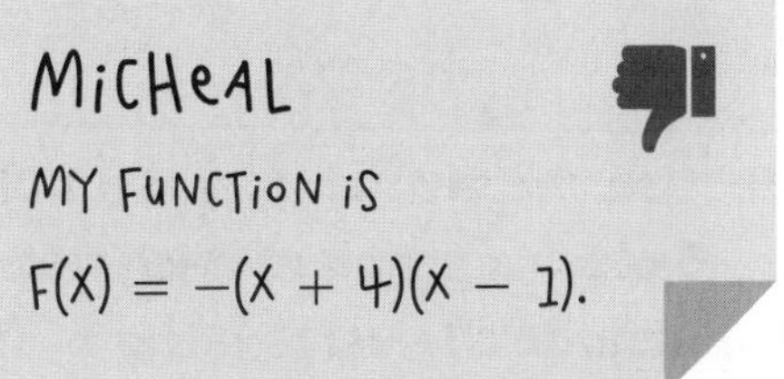
MiCHeAL
MY FUNCTiON iS
F(X) = −(X + 4)(X − 1).

a. Sketch a graph of each student's function and label key points. What are the similarities among all the graphs? What are the differences among the graphs?

b. What would you tell Tim and Micheal to correct their functions?

c. **How is it possible to have more than one correct function?**

d. **How many possible functions can represent the given characteristics? Explain your reasoning.**

2. **Consider a quadratic function written in factored form, $f(x) = a(x - r_1)(x - r_2)$.**

   a. **What does the sign of the a-value tell you about the graph?**

   b. **What do r_1 and r_2 tell you about the graph?**

3. **Use the given information to write a function in factored form. Sketch a graph of each function and label key points, which include the vertex, the x- and y-intercepts.**

   a. **The parabola opens upward, and the zeros are at $x = 2$ and $x = 4$.**

   b. **The parabola opens downward, and the zeros at $x = -3$ and $x = 1$.**

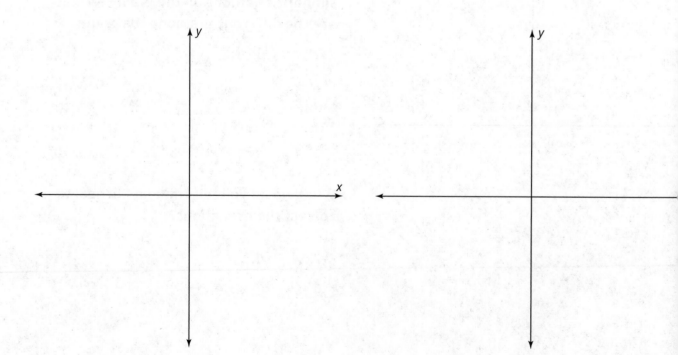

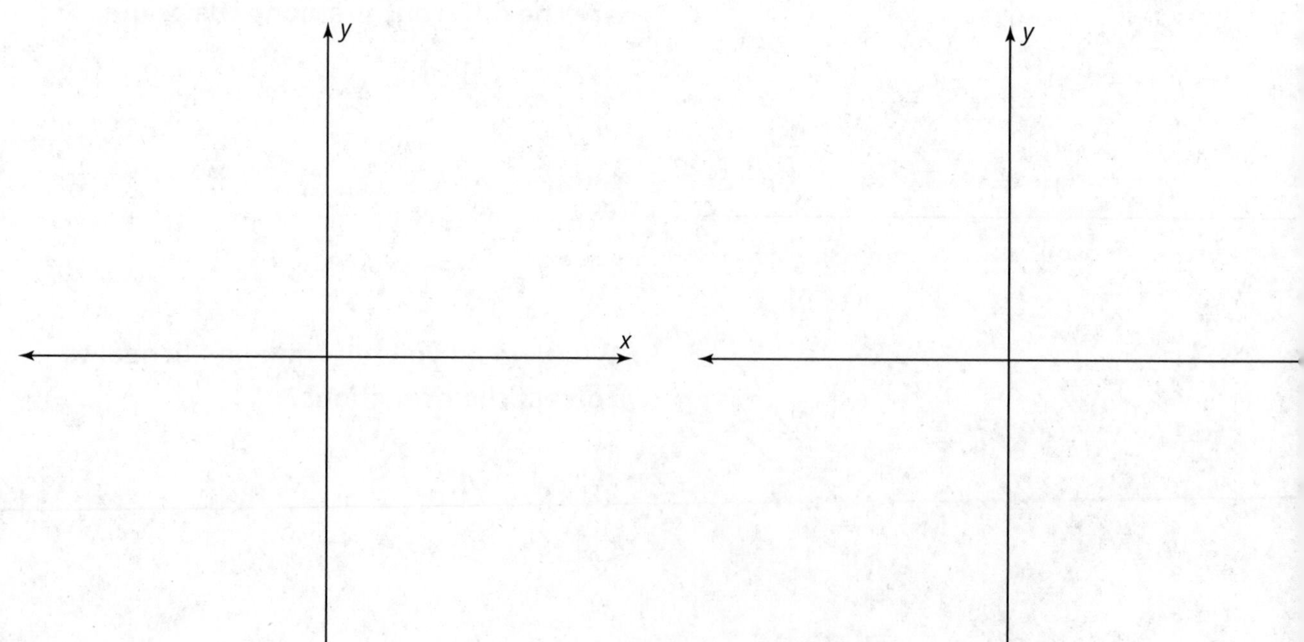

c. The parabola opens downward, and the zeros are at $x = 0$ and $x = 5$.

d. The parabola opens upward, and the zeros are at $x = -2.5$ and $x = 4.3$.

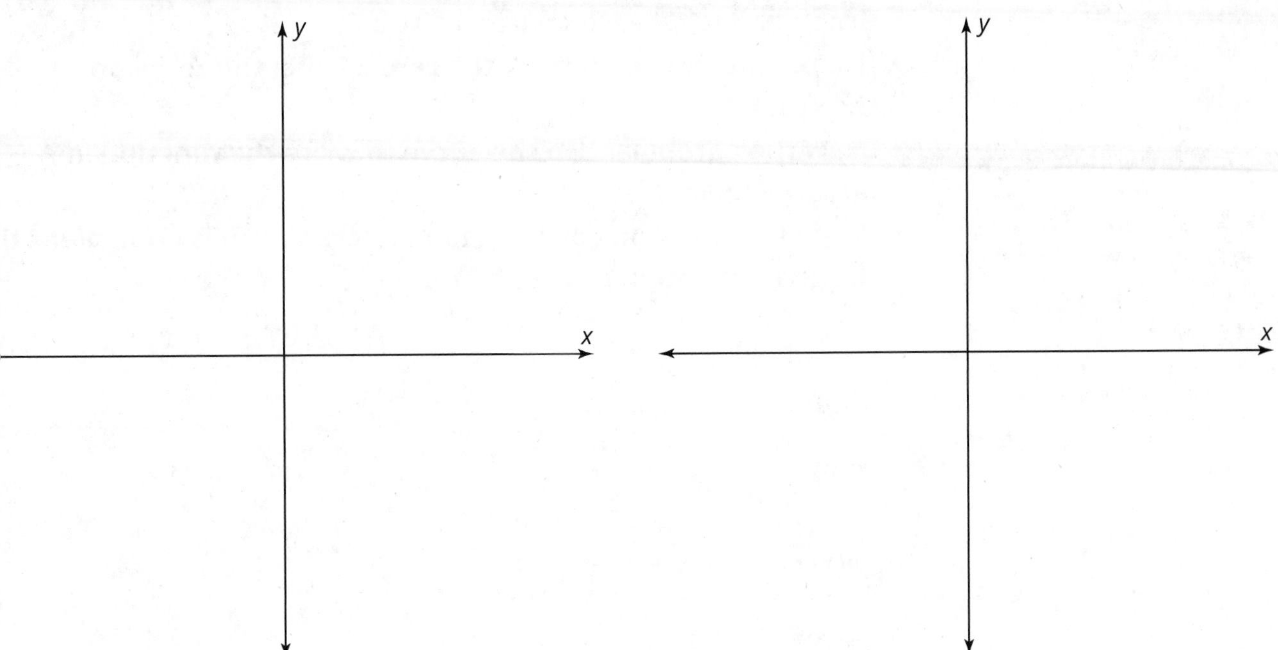

Compare your quadratic functions with your classmates' functions. How does the a-value affect the shape of the graph?

A function written in general form $f(x) = ax^2 + bx + c$ has an axis of symmetry at $x = \frac{-b}{2a}$.

5. **For each quadratic function,**

   - **Use the general form to determine the axis of symmetry, the absolute maximum or absolute minimum, and the *y*-intercept. Graph and label each characteristic.**
   - **Use technology to identify the zeros. Label the zeros on the graph.**
   - **Draw the parabola. Use the curve to write the function in factored form.**
   - **Verify the function you wrote in factored form is equivalent to the given function in general form.**

   a. $h(x) = x^2 - 8x + 12$

   zeros: ____________________

   factored form: ____________________

y

x

b. $r(x) = -2x^2 + 6x + 20$

zeros: ______________________

factored form: ______________________

c. $w(x) = -x^2 - 4x$

zeros: ______________________

factored form: ______________________

NOTES

d. $c(x) = 3x^2 - 3$

zeros: ____________

factored form: ____________

NOTES

TALK the TALK 

Quadratic Sleuthing

Use the given information to answer each question. Do not use technology. Show your work.

1. **Determine the axis of symmetry of each parabola.**

   a. **The x-intercepts of the parabola are (1, 0) and (5, 0).**

   b. **The x-intercepts of the parabola are (−3.5, 0) and (4.1, 0).**

   c. **Two symmetric points on the parabola are (−7, 2) and (0, 2).**

2. **Describe how to determine the axis of symmetry given the x-intercepts of a parabola.**

3. **Determine the location of the vertex of each parabola.**

   a. **The function $f(x) = x^2 + 4x + 3$ has the axis of symmetry $x = -2$.**

   b. **The equation of the parabola is $y = x^2 - 4$, and the x-intercepts are (−2, 0) and (2, 0).**

Sketch a graph by hand if you need a model.

NOTES

c. The function $f(x) = x^2 + 6x - 5$ has two symmetric points $(-1, -10)$ and $(-5, -10)$.

4. Describe how to determine the vertex of a parabola given the equation and the axis of symmetry.

5. Determine another point on each parabola.

a. The axis of symmetry is $x = 2$, and a point on the parabola is $(0, 5)$.

b. The vertex is $(0.5, 9)$, and an x-intercept is $(-2.5, 0)$.

c. The vertex is $(-2, -8)$, and a point on the parabola is $(-1, -7)$.

6. Describe how to determine another point on a parabola if you are given one point and the axis of symmetry.

Assignment

Write

1. Describe the characteristics of a quadratic function that you can determine from its equation in general form.

2. Describe the characteristics of a quadratic function that you can determine from its equation in factored form.

Remember

The sign of the leading coefficient of a quadratic function in standard form or factored form describes whether the function has an absolute maximum or absolute minimum.

A parabola is a smooth curve with reflectional symmetry. The axis of symmetry contains the vertex of the graph of the function, which is located at the absolute minimum or absolute maximum of the function.

Practice

1. Analyze each quadratic function.

   $g(x) = 12x - 4x^2 + 16$ $\qquad$ $h(x) = -\frac{1}{4}(x - 3)(x + 2)$

   a. Identify the quadratic function as general form or factored form.
   b. Does the quadratic function have an absolute maximum or absolute minimum?
   c. Does the graph open upward or downward?
   d. Determine any intercepts from the given form of the function.

2. Analyze each quadratic function.

   $f(x) = -\frac{2}{3}x^2 - 3x + 15$ $\qquad$ $g(x) = \frac{3}{4}x^2 + 12x - 27$

   a. Identify the axis of symmetry.
   b. Use the axis of symmetry to determine the ordered pair of the absolute maximum or absolute minimum value.
   c. Describe the intervals of increase and decrease.
   d. Sketch the graph based on the information you just calculated.
   e. Use technology to identify the zeros.
   f. Place two pairs of symmetric points on your graph. What is the average rate of change between these pairs of symmetric points?
   g. Write the function in factored form.

3. Given a parabola that opens downward and has zeros at $x = -2$ and $x = 3$.
   a. Represent it as a quadratic equation in factored form.
   b. Sketch a graph of the quadratic function.
   c. What is the axis of symmetry and y-intercept of the quadratic function?

Stretch

1. Sketch the graph $f(x) = -3x^2 - 4$. How could you change the quadratic function to make the graph open upward? Show the change on the graph.
2. How could you change the quadratic function $f(x) = -3x^2 - 4$ to shift the graph up or down? Show on the graph.
3. How could you change the quadratic function $f(x) = -3x^2 - 4$ to shift the graph right or left? Show the change on the graph.

Review

1. A camp wants to create a larger space for their albino rabbit, Clover. They want to reuse the materials from Clover's current enclosure in the construction of the new enclosure. The perimeter of Clover's current space is 6 feet. The perimeter of his new enclosure will be 3 times larger than his former enclosure.
   a. What is the area of the new enclosure $A(w)$ in terms of width, w?
   b. What is the maximum area of the new enclosure? What are the dimensions?
2. Is $7x^{2t} \cdot 5x^{2t}$ equivalent to $35x^{2t}$? Justify your answer.
3. Is $(16^{3z})^{6y}$ equivalent to 16^{18yz}? Justify your answer.
4. Alejandra has $900 to open a bank account. She wants to put her money in the bank where she will earn the most money over time. Alejandra has a choice between the Platinum Bank that offers an account with 3% compound interest and the Diamond Bank that offers an account with 4% simple interest.
   a. What is the function used to calculate the balance in each account based on the year, t? Describe each function.
   b. In which bank should Alejandra deposit her money? Explain your reasoning.

3

More Than Meets the Eye

Transformations of Quadratic Functions

Warm Up

Write the equation for the axis of symmetry given each quadratic function.

1. $f(x) = -3x^2 - 4x + 5$

2. $f(x) = \frac{1}{4}(x - 1)(x + 2)$

3. $f(x) = -x^2 + 3$

Learning Goals

- Translate, reflect, and dilate quadratic functions horizontally and vertically.
- Write equations of quadratic functions given multiple transformations.
- Graph quadratic functions given multiple transformations.
- Identify multiple transformations of quadratic functions given equations.
- Understand the form in which a quadratic function is written can reveal different key characteristics.
- Write quadratic equations in vertex and factored form.

Key Term

- vertex form

You know how to transform linear, absolute value, and exponential functions. How can you apply what you know about the transformation form of a function, $g(x) = A \cdot f(B(x - C)) + D$, to quadratic functions?

GETTING STARTED

Quadratics and Absolutes

The coordinate plane shows the graph of the absolute value function $f(x) = |x - 4|$ and a quadratic function, $q(x)$.

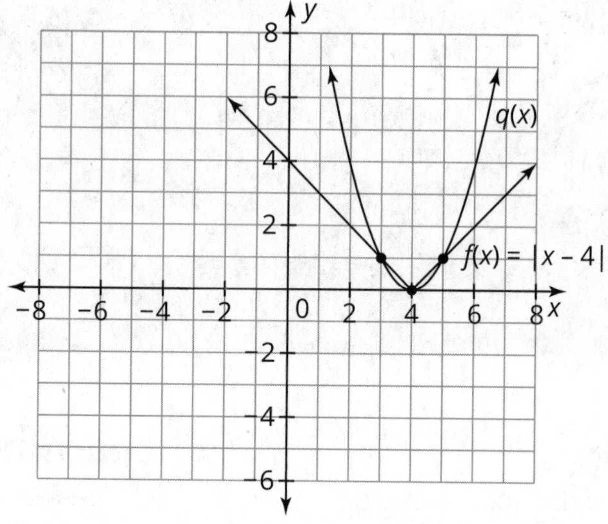

1. **How was the basic absolute value function $f(x) = |x|$ transformed to produce the graph shown?**

2. **Write an equation which can represent the quadratic function, $q(x)$. Test your equation with the graph to see if it is correct.**

3. **How does knowing that $1^2 = |1|$ and $(-1)^2 = |-1|$ explain the intersection points of the graph of the absolute value function and the graph of the quadratic function?**

ACTIVITY 3.1

Translations and Reflections of Quadratic Functions

Given $g(x) = f(x - C) + D$, consider how to transform the basic function, $f(x) = x^2$, to graph the transformed function.

1. Consider the four quadratic functions shown, where $f(x) = x^2$ is the basic function.

- $c(x) = x^2 + 3$
- $d(x) = x^2 - 3$
- $j(x) = (x + 3)^2$
- $k(x) = (x - 3)^2$

How do you think translating quadratics may be similar to translating other functions?

a. Write the functions $c(x)$, $d(x)$, $j(x)$, and $k(x)$ in terms of the basic function. For each, determine whether an operation is performed on the function or on the argument of the function. Describe the operation.

b. Given the form $ax^2 + bx + c$, the functions $c(x)$ and $d(x)$ each have a b-value equal to 0. What does this tell you about the axis of symmetry of each graph? Explain your answer.

c. Sketch a graph of each function. Label each graph and include key points.

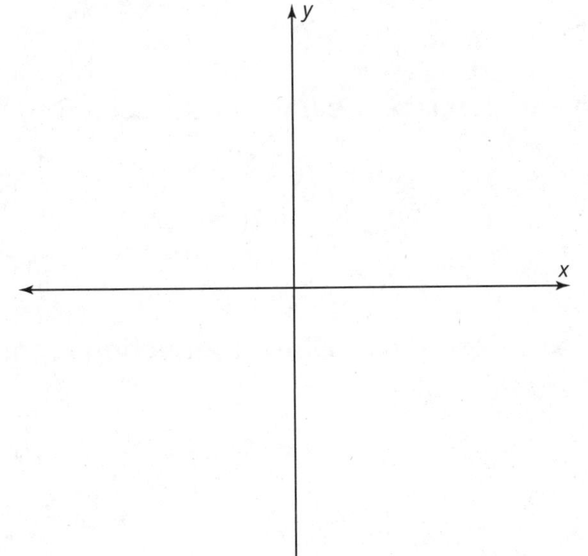

d. Use coordinate notation to represent the vertical or horizontal translation of each function, c, d, j, and k. Each point (x, y) on the graph of $f(x)$:

- **becomes the point ______________ on the graph of $c(x)$.**
- **becomes the point ______________ on the graph of $d(x)$.**
- **becomes the point ______________ on the graph of $j(x)$.**
- **becomes the point ______________ on the graph of $k(x)$.**

You know that for any basic function, the C- and D-values describe translations of the function. The C-value defines an operation that is performed on the argument, and it describes a horizontal translation that affects the input values. The D-value defines an operation performed on the function, and it describes a vertical translation that affects the output values.

Now, let's consider reflections of graphs. You know that when a negative is on the outside of a function, the graph is reflected across a horizontal line of reflection. When a negative is on the inside of a function, the graph is reflected across a vertical line of reflection. Given $f(x) = x^2$, consider $g(x) = -f(x)$ and $h(x) = f(-x)$.

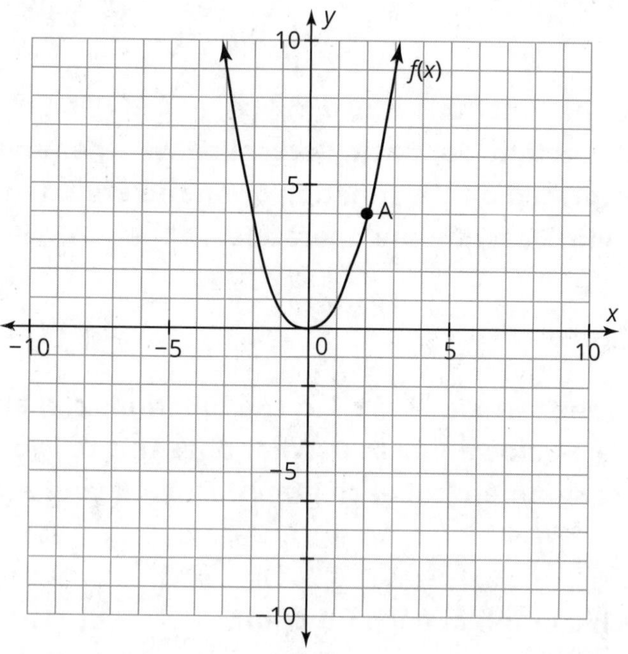

2. Consider the placement of the negative sign in each function, $g(x)$ and $h(x)$.

a. Sketch the graph and describe the line of reflection for $g(x)$. Label A' on your graph.

b. Sketch the graph and describe the line of reflection for $h(x)$. Label A'' on your graph.

c. **Use coordinate notation to represent the reflection of each function. Each point (x, y) on the graph of $f(x)$:**

- **becomes the point ____________________ on the graph of $g(x)$.**

- **becomes the point ____________________ on the graph of $h(x)$.**

d. **Given the basic quadratic function, $f(x) = x^2$, why does the graph of $f(-x)$ map onto itself?**

Consider the graph of each given function. Sketch the result of the transformed function. Label A' on your graph. Then describe the transformation you performed.

a. **Given the graph of $v(x)$, sketch $m(x) = v(-x)$.**

b. **Given the graph of $w(x)$, sketch $z(x) = -w(x)$.**

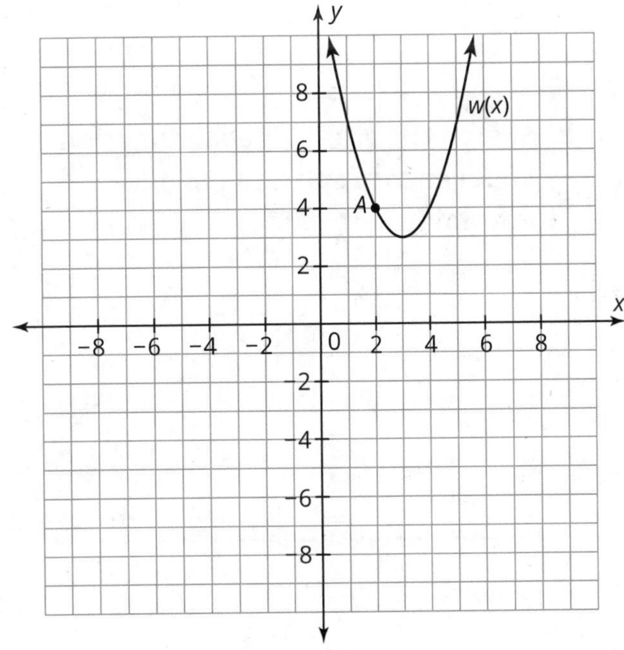

Vertical and Horizontal Dilations of Quadratic Functions

You can vertically and horizontally dilate quadratic functions just like oth
functions you have studied.

1. **Consider the three quadratic functions shown, where $f(x) = x^2$ is the basic function.**

   - $f(x) = x^2$
   - $n(x) = \frac{1}{2}x^2$
   - $p(x) = 2x^2$

   a. **Write the functions $n(x)$ and $p(x)$ in terms of the basic function $f(x)$. For each, determine whether an operation is performed on the function $f(x)$ or on the argument of the function $f(x)$. Describe the operation.**

   b. **Sketch the graph of each function. Label each graph and include key points.**

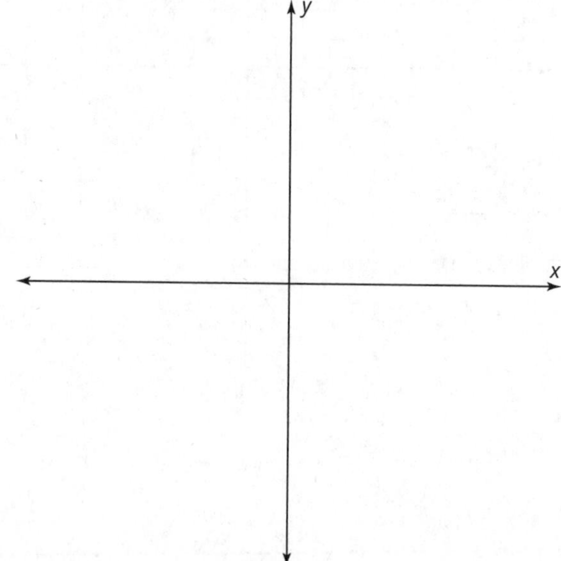

   c. **Use coordinate notation to represent the dilation of each function. Each point $(x, y$ on the graph of $f(x)$:**

   - **becomes the point _______________ on the graph of $n(x)$.**
   - **becomes the point _______________ on the graph of $p(x)$.**

Consider the three quadratic functions, where $f(x) = x^2$ is the basic function.

- $f(x) = x^2$
- $t(x) = (3x)^2$
- $q(x) = \left(\frac{1}{3}x\right)^2$

a. Write the functions $t(x)$ and $q(x)$ in terms of the basic function $f(x)$. For each, determine whether an operation is performed on the function $f(x)$ or on the argument of the function $f(x)$. Describe the operation.

b. Sketch the graph of each function. Label each graph and include key points.

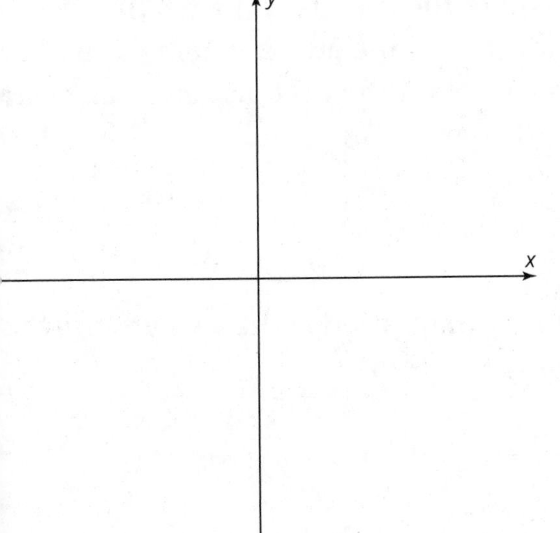

c. Use coordinate notation to represent the dilation of each function. Each point (x, y) on the graph of $f(x)$:

- becomes the point ________ on the graph of $t(x)$.
- becomes the point ________ on the graph of $q(x)$.

emember, a horizontal dilation is a type of transformation that stretches r compresses the entire graph. Horizontal stretching is the stretching of a raph away from the y-axis. Horizontal compression is the squeezing of a raph towards the y-axis.

3. Now, let's compare the graph of $f(x) = x^2$ with $r(x) = f\left(\frac{1}{2}x\right)$.

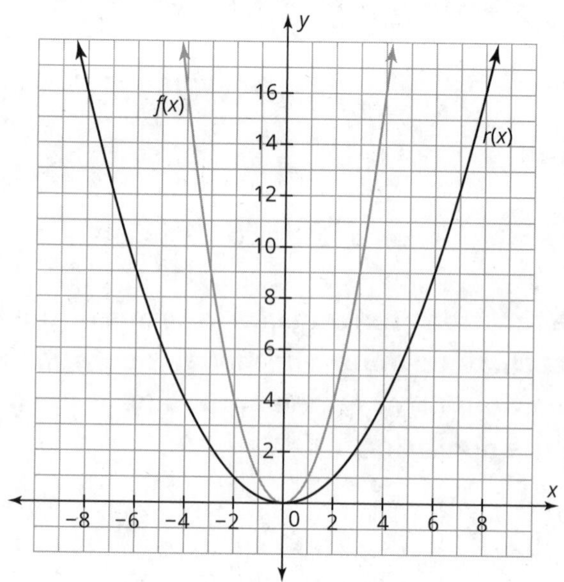

x	$f(x) = x^2$	$r(x) = p(\frac{1}{2}x)$
0	0	0
1	1	0.25
2	4	1
3	9	2.25
4	16	4
5	25	6.25
6	36	9

a. Analyze the table of values that correspond to the graph.

Circle instances where the *y*-values for each function are the same. Then, list all the points where *f*(*x*) and *r*(*x*) have the same *y*-value. The first instance has been circled for you.

b. How do the *x*-values compare when the *y*-values are the same?

c. Complete the statement.

The function *r*(*x*) is a __________ of *f*(*x*) by a factor of __________

d. How does the factor of stretching or compression compare to the *B*-value in *r*(*x*)?

mpared with the graph of $f(x)$, the graph of $f(Bx)$ is:

- horizontally compressed by a factor of $\frac{1}{|B|}$ if $|B| > 1$.
- horizontally stretched by a factor of $\frac{1}{|B|}$ if $0 < |B| < 1$.

Worked Example

You can use reference points to graph the function $q(x) = f(\frac{1}{3}x)$ when $f(x) = x^2$.

From $q(x)$ you know that $C = 0$, $D = 0$, and $B = \frac{1}{3}$. The vertex for $q(x)$ is (0, 0).

Notice $0 < |B| < 1$, so the graph will horizontally stretch by a factor of $\frac{1}{\frac{1}{3}}$ or 3.

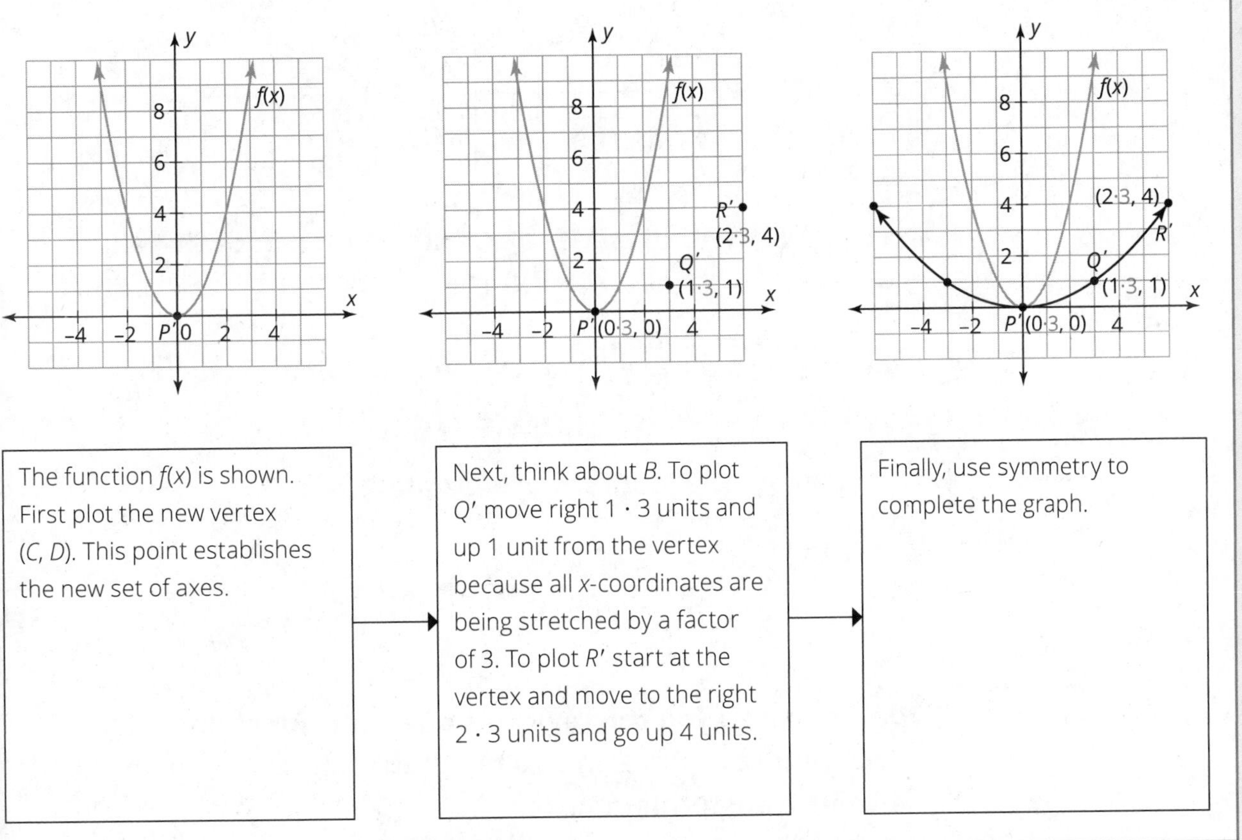

y
f(x)
8
6
4
2
–4
–2
P′ 0
2
4
x
f(x)
R′
(2·3, 4)
Q′
(1·3, 1)
P′(0·3, 0)
(2·3, 4)
R′
Q′
(1·3, 1)
P′(0·3, 0)
The function f(x) is shown. First plot the new vertex (C, D). This point establishes the new set of axes.
Next, think about B. To plot Q′ move right 1 · 3 units and up 1 unit from the vertex because all x-coordinates are being stretched by a factor of 3. To plot R′ start at the vertex and move to the right 2 · 3 units and go up 4 units.
Finally, use symmetry to complete the graph.

. If you were asked to graph $p(x) = f(3x)$, describe how the graph would change. If (x, y) is any point on $f(x)$, describe any point on $p(x)$.

5. **Consider the graph showing the quadratic functions $k(x)$ and $m(x)$. Antoine and Xi Ling are writing the function $m(x)$ in terms of $k(x)$.**

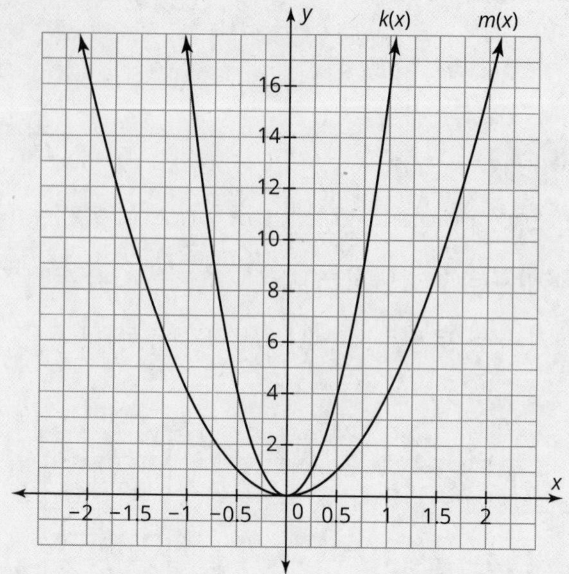

Antoine says that $m(x)$ is a transformation of the A-value.

$$m(x) = \frac{1}{4}k(x)$$

Xi Ling says that $m(x)$ is a transformation of the B-value.

$$m(x) = k(\frac{1}{2}x)$$

Who's correct? Justify your reasoning.

6. **Describe how you can rewrite a quadratic function with a B-value transformation as a quadratic function with an A-value transformation.**

7. **Rewrite the function from the worked example, $q(x) = f(\frac{1}{3}x)$, without a B-value.**

nsider the formula to calculate the area of a circle, $A = \pi r^2$. You can present the area formula as the function $A(r) = \pi r^2$ and represent it on a ordinate plane.

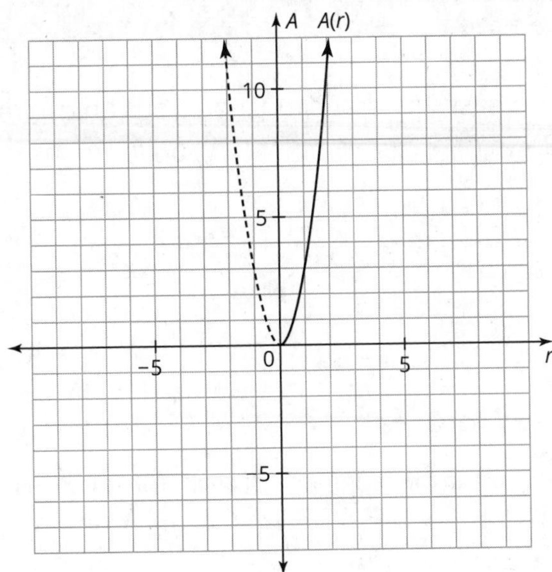

Why is part of the graph represented with a dashed smooth curve?

How is the area affected if you double the radius? Explain the change in area in terms of a transformation of the graph.

What is the pattern of the *A*-value when transforming the basic quadratic function?

ACTIVITY 3.3 Using Reference Points to Graph Quadratic Functions

Given $y = f(x)$ is the basic quadratic function, you can use reference points to graph $y = Af(B(x - C)) + D$. Any point (x, y) on $f(x)$ maps to the point $(\frac{1}{B}x + C, Ay + D)$.

Worked Example

Given $f(x) = x^2$, graph the function $g(x) = 2f(x - 3) + 4$.

You can use reference points for $f(x)$ and your knowledge about transformations to graph the function $g(x)$.

From $g(x)$, you know that $A = 2$, $C = 3$, and $D = 4$.

The vertex for $g(x)$ will be at (3, 4). Notice $A > 0$, so the graph of the function will vertically stretch by a factor of 2.

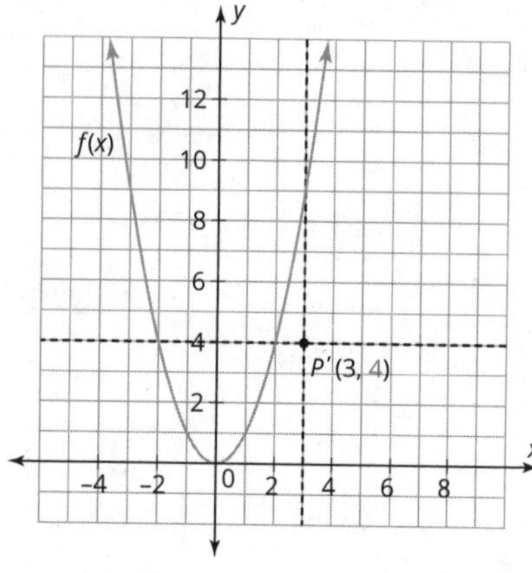

First, plot the new vertex, (*C*, *D*). This point establishes the new set of axes.

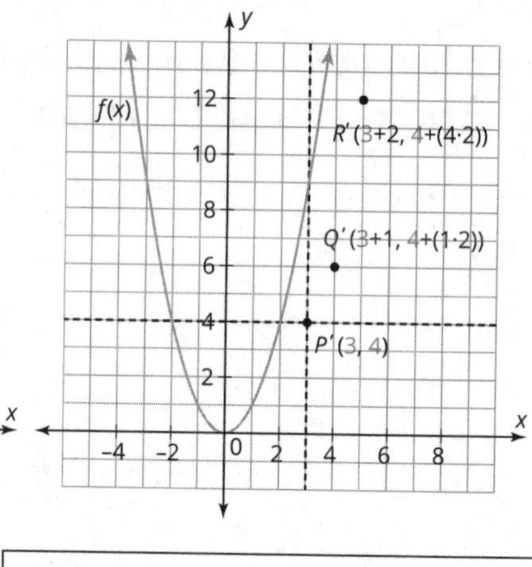

Next, think about the reference points for the basic quadratic function and that $A = 2$. To plot point Q' move right 1 unit and up, not 1, but 1×2 units from the vertex P' because all *y*-coordinates are being multiplied by a factor of 2. To plot point R' move right 2 units from P' and up, not 4, but 4×2 units.

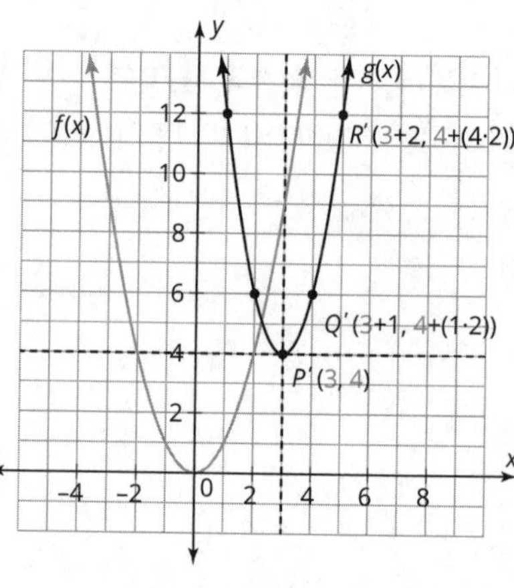

Finally, use symmetry to complete the graph.

Christian, Julia, and Emily each sketched a graph of the equation $y = -x^2 - 3$ using different strategies. Provide the step-by-step reasoning used by each student.

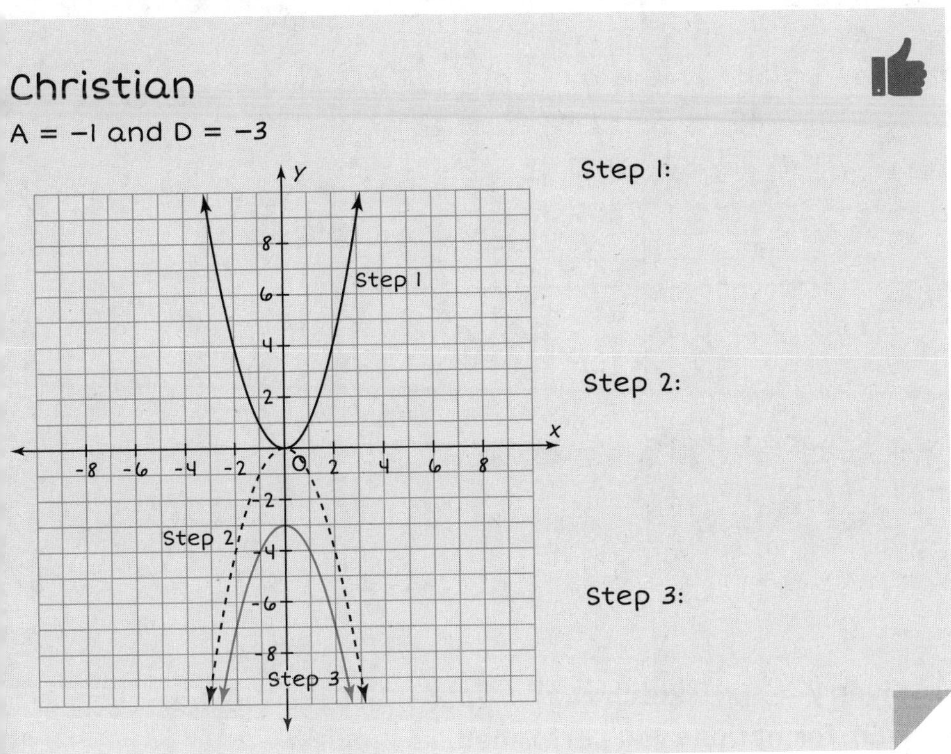

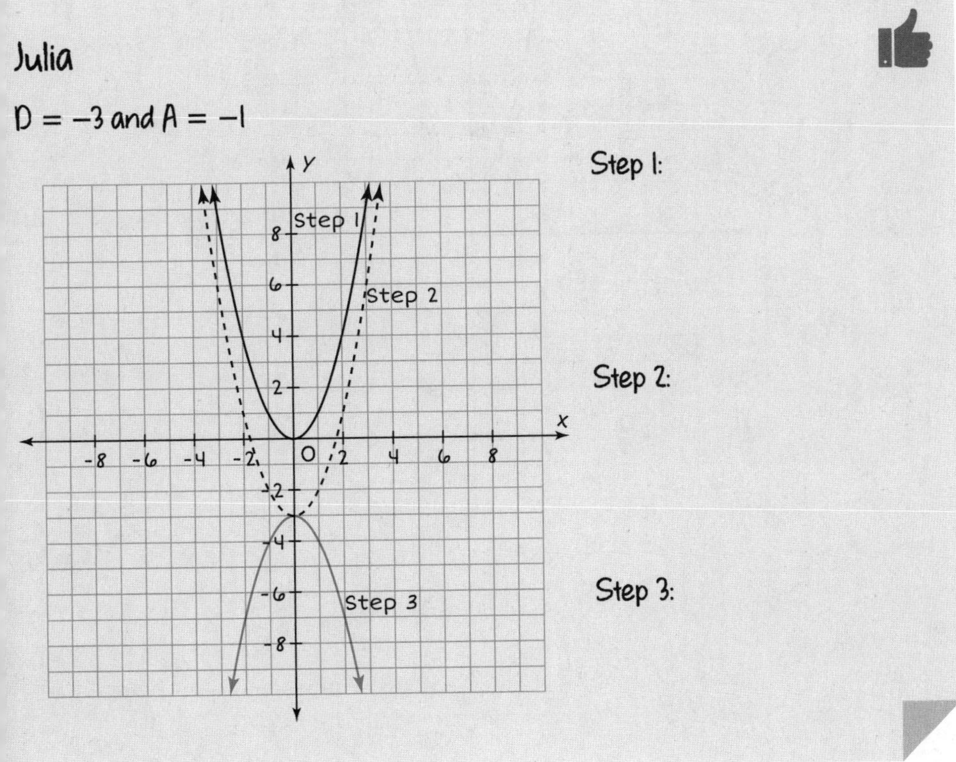

Emily

I rewrote the equation as $y = -(x^2 + 3)$.

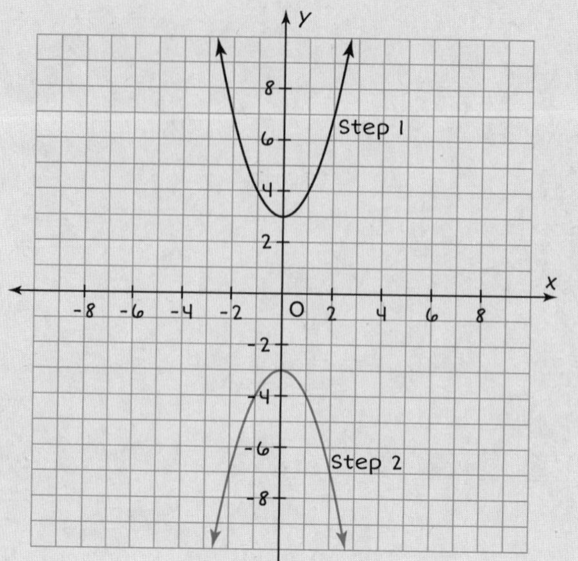

Step 1:

Step 2:

2. Given $y = p(x)$, sketch $m(x) = -p(x + 3)$. Describe the transformations you performed.

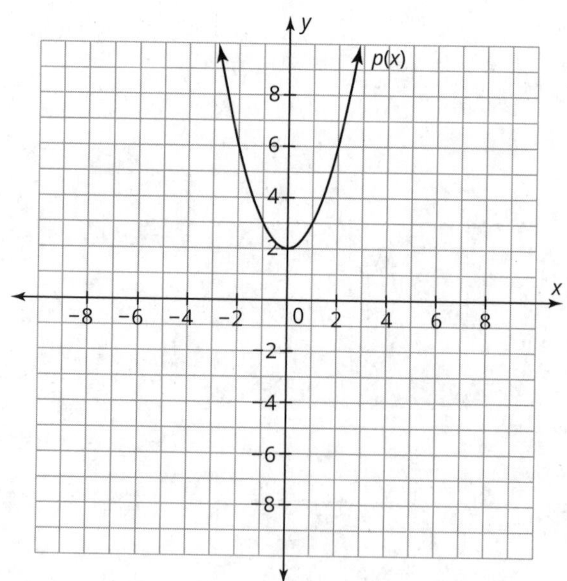

Given $f(x) = x^2$, graph each function. Then write each corresponding quadratic equation.

a. $f'(x) = \frac{1}{2}f(x - 2) + 3$

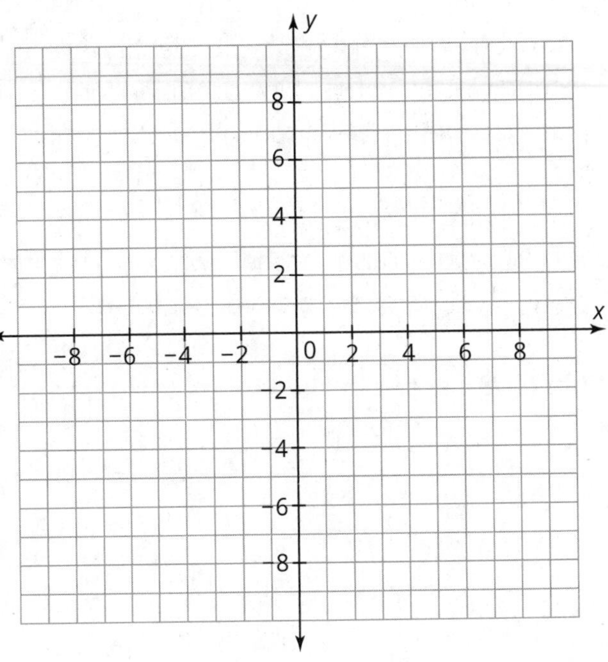

b. $f'(x) = -3f(x + 1) + 1$

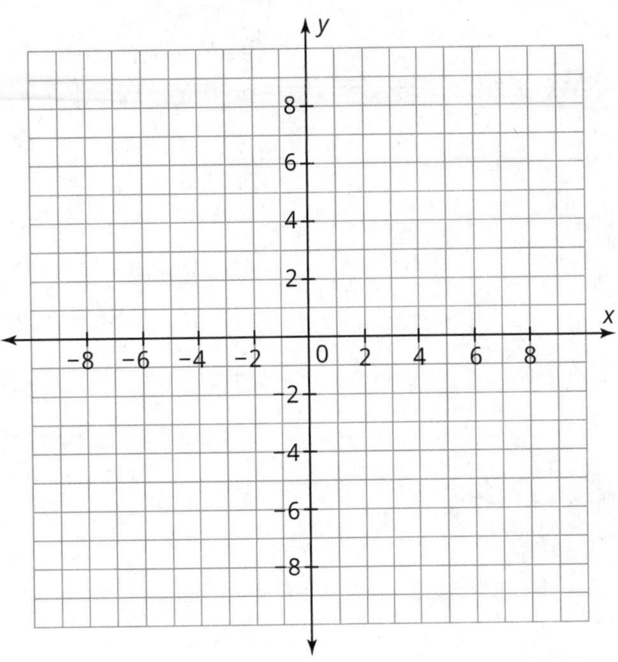

. Write $n(x)$ in terms of $d(x)$. Then write the quadratic equation for $n(x)$.

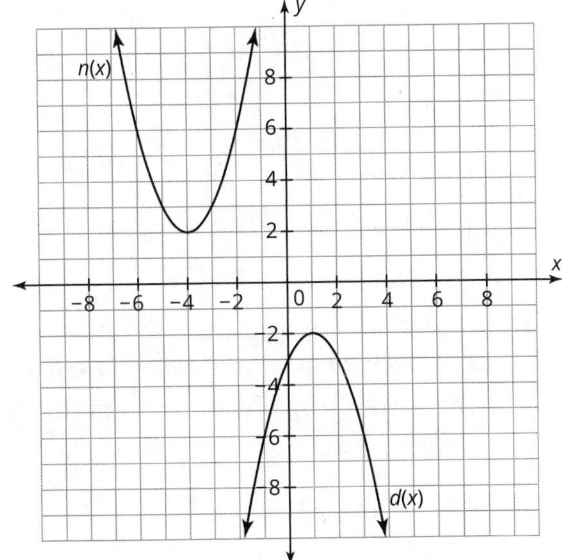

ACTIVITY

3.4 Vertex Form of a Quadratic Function

In vertex form, the coefficient of x is always 1. Therefore, the B-value in the transformation form in this case is also 1 and is left out of the expression.

Do you see how this form of the function tells you about the vertex?

Given a basic function $y = f(x)$, you have learned how to identify the effects and graph a function written in the transformation form $g(x) = Af(x - C) + D$. For quadratic functions written in transformation form, $A \neq 0$.

For quadratic functions specifically, you will also see them written in the form $f(x) = a(x - h)^2 + k$, where $a \neq 0$. This is referred to as **vertex form**.

1. **What does the variable h represent in the vertex form of a quadratic function?**

2. **What does the variable k represent in the vertex form of a quadratic function?**

3. **What key characteristics can you determine directly from the quadratic function when it is written in vertex form?**

Simone, Teresa, Jesse, Aricka, and Leon are working together to write a quadratic function to represent a parabola that opens upward and has a vertex at (−6, −4).

Simone 

My function is

$s(x) = 3(x + 6)^2 - 4.$

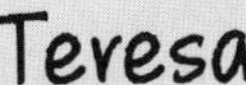
Teresa 

My function is

$t(x) = \frac{1}{4}(x + 6)^2 - 4.$

Jesse 

My function is

$j(x) = -3(x + 6)^2 - 4.$

ARICKA

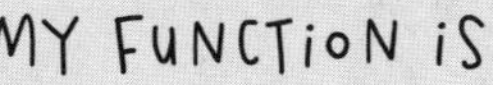
MY FUNCTION IS

$D(X) = (X + 6)^2 - 4.$

Leon 

My function is

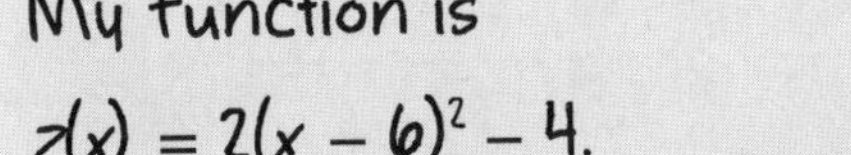
$z(x) = 2(x - 6)^2 - 4.$

a. What are the similarities among all the graphs of the functions? What are the differences among the graphs?

b. How is it possible to have more than one correct function?

c. What would you tell Jesse and Leon to correct their functions?

d. How many possible functions can you write for the parabola described in this problem? Explain your reasoning.

5. **Use technology to graph each function. Use the graph to rewrit the function in vertex form and in factored form.**

a. $h(x) = x^2 - 8x + 12$

vertex: ______________________

vertex form: ______________________

zero(s): ______________________

factored form: ______________________

b. $r(x) = -2x^2 + 6x + 20$

vertex: ______________________

vertex form: ______________________

zero(s): ______________________

factored form: ______________________

c. $w(x) = -x^2 - 4x$

vertex: ______________________

vertex form: ______________________

zero(s): ______________________

factored form: ______________________

d. $c(x) = 3x^2 - 3$

vertex: ______________________

vertex form: ______________________

zero(s): ______________________

factored form: ______________________

Identify the form(s) of each quadratic function as either general form, factored form, or vertex form. Then state all you know about each quadratic function's key characteristics, based only on the given equation of the function.

NOTES

a. $g(x) = -(x - 1)^2 + 9$

b. $g(x) = x^2 + 4x$

c. $g(x) = -\frac{1}{2}(x - 3)(x + 2)$

d. $g(x) = x^2 - 5$

ACTIVITY

3.5 Writing Equations in Vertex and Factored Forms

You can write a quadratic function in vertex form if you know the coordinates of the vertex and another point on the graph.

Worked Example

Write an equation for a quadratic function with vertex (1, −2) that passes through the point (0, 1).

Step 1: Substitute the coordinates of the vertex into vertex form of a quadratic function.

$y = a(x - h)^2 + k$

$y = a(x - 1)^2 - 2$

Step 2: Substitute the coordinates of the other point on the graph for x and y.

$1 = a(0 - 1)^2 - 2$

Step 3: Solve for the value of a.

$1 = a(-1)^2 - 2$

$1 = a(1) - 2$

$1 = a - 2$

$3 = a$

Step 4: Rewrite the equation in vertex form, substituting the vertex and the value of a.

$f(x) = 3(x - 1)^2 - 2$

1. **How would you determine an equation of a quadratic function in factored form given the zeros and another point on the graph**

Dawson and Dave each wrote an equation for the function represented by the graph shown.

Dawson

$y = a(x + 1)^2 - 3$

$0 = a(1 + 1)^2 - 3$

$0 = 4a - 3$

$3 = 4a$

$a = \frac{3}{4}$

$y = \frac{3}{4}(x + 1)^2 - 3$

Dave

$y = a(x + 3)(x - 1)$

$-3 = a(-1 + 3)(-1 - 1)$

$-3 = a(2)(-2)$

$-3 = -4a$

$a = \frac{3}{4}$

$y = \frac{3}{4}(x + 3)(x - 1)$

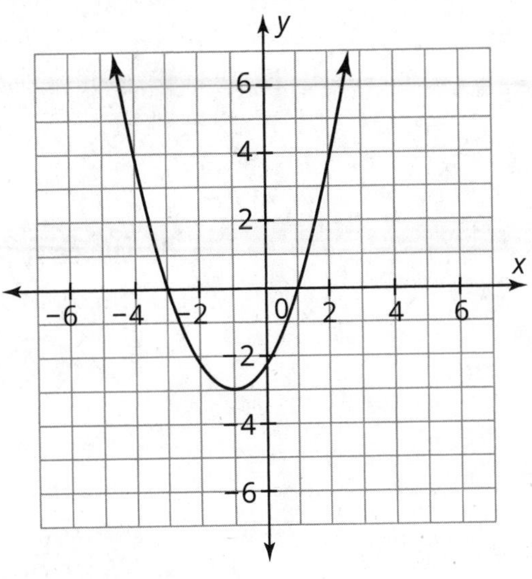

a. **Explain Dawson's reasoning.**

b. **Explain Dave's reasoning.**

c. **Use technology to show that Dawson's equation and Dave's equation are equivalent.**

3. Write an equation for a quadratic function in vertex form with vertex (3, 1) that passes through the point (1, 9).

4. Write an equation for a quadratic function in factored form wit zeros at $x = -4$ and $x = 0$ that passes through the point (−3, 6).

5. Write an equation for a quadratic function in vertex form with vertex (−1, 6) that passes through the point (−3, 4).

6. Write an equation for a quadratic function $g(x)$ in vertex form given the graph of $g(x)$.

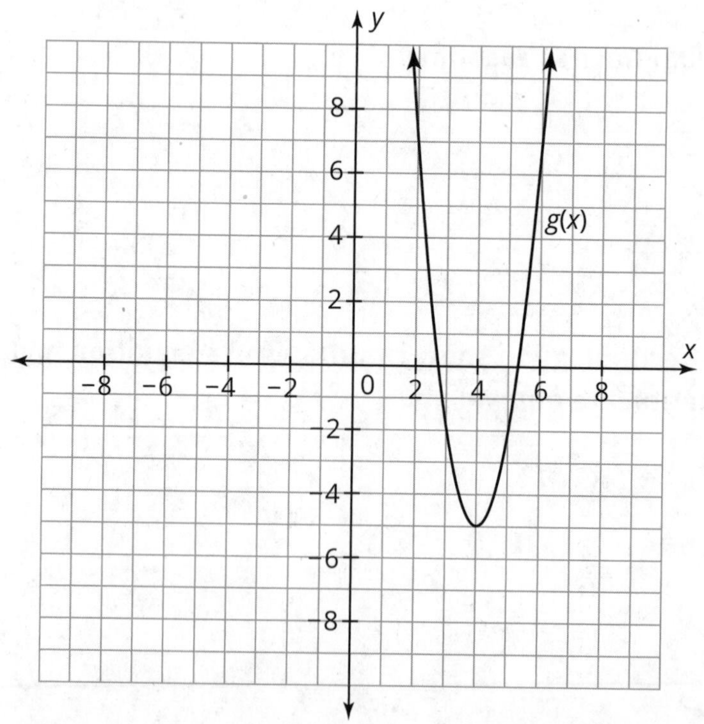

NOTES

TALK the TALK 

Show What You Know

1. Based on the equation of each function, describe how the graph of each function compares to the graph of $f(x) = x^2$.

a. $z(x) = -(x - 1)^2 - 10$

b. $r(x) = \frac{1}{2}(x + 6)^2 + 7$

c. $m(x) = (4x)^2 + 5$

2. Describe each transformation in relation to the basic function $f(x) = x^2$.

a. $h(x) = f(x) + D$ when $D > 0$

b. $h(x) = f(x) + D$ when $D < 0$

NOTES

c. $h(x) = f(x - C)$ when $C > 0$

d. $h(x) = f(x - C)$ when $C < 0$

e. $h(x) = Af(x)$ when $|A| > 1$

f. $h(x) = Af(x)$ when $0 < |A| < 1$

g. $h(x) = Af(x)$ when $A = -1$

Assignment

Write

Describe the connections between the vertex form of a quadratic function, $f(x) = a(x - h)^2 + k$, and the transformation form, $g(x) = A \cdot f(x - C) + D$, of the basic quadratic function, $y = f(x)$.

Remember

Transformations performed on any function $f(x)$ can be described by the transformation function $g(x) = Af(B(x + C)) + D$ where the C-value translates the function $f(x)$ horizontally, the D-value translates $f(x)$ vertically, the A-value vertically stretches or compresses $f(x)$, and the B-value horizontally stretches or compresses $f(x)$. When the A-value is negative the function $f(x)$ is reflected across a horizontal line of reflection and when the B-value is negative the function $f(x)$ is reflected across a vertical line of reflection.

Practice

1. Given $f(x) = x^2$, graph each function and write the corresponding quadratic equation.
   a. $g(x) = 3f(x - 1)$
   b. $g(x) = f(3x) - 1$
   c. $g(x) = \frac{1}{2}f(x) + 5$
   d. $g(x) = 2f(x - 3) + 1$
2. The graph shows the basic function $f(x) = x^2$, and also shows the function $h(x)$.
   a. Describe the types of transformations performed on $f(x)$ to result in $h(x)$.
   b. If the dilation factor is 16, write the function $h(x)$.

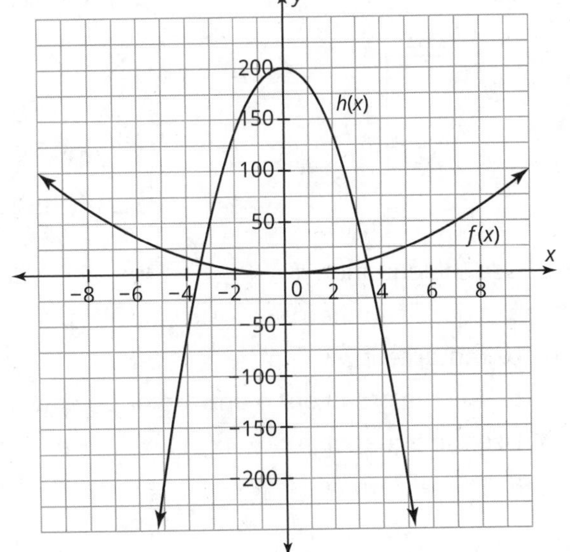

3. Use the given characteristics to write a function $R(x)$ in vertex form. Then, sketch the graph of $R(x)$ and the basic function $f(x) = x^2$.
   - The function has an absolute maximum.
   - The function is translated 70 units up and 100 units to the right.
   - The function is vertically dilated by a factor of $\frac{1}{5}$.

Stretch

Given $f(x) = x^2$. Sketch each function. Label point A' for each transformation.

1. $m(-x + 3)$
2. $n(-(x + 3))$
3. $r(-(x - 3))$
4. $t(-x - 3)$

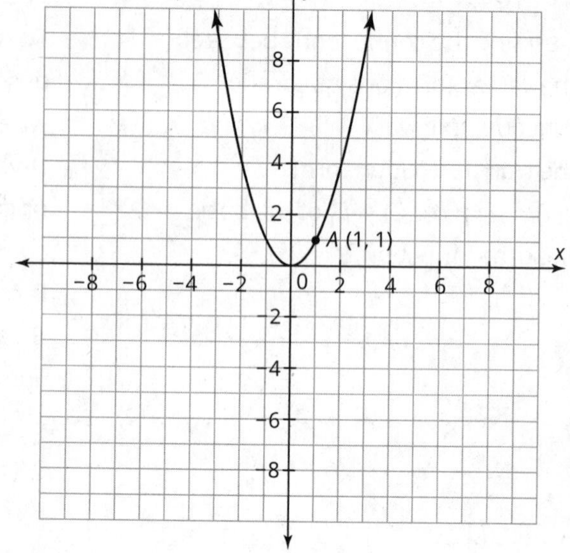

Review

1. Solve for the unknown side lengths of each figure.

   a. 8 cm, 60°, 30°, g, h

   b. 45°, 7 cm, 45°, x

2. Use the equation $f(x) = \frac{1}{3}(x - 5)(x - 3)$ to determine each characteristic.
   a. axis of symmetry
   b. x-intercepts
   c. Will the graph open upward or downward?
3. Use the equation $f(x) = 4x^2 + 3x - 10$ to determine each characteristic.
   a. axis of symmetry
   b. y-intercept

4

You Lose Some, You Lose Some

Comparing Functions Using Key Characteristics and Average Rate of Change

Warm Up

Write the ordered pair for the y-intercept of each quadratic function.

1. $f(x) = 4(x - 2)(x - 3)$

2. $f(x) = -6x^2 + 9x - 5$

3. $f(x) = 5(x - 1)^2 + 14$

Learning Goals

- Understand the form in which a quadratic function is written can reveal different key characteristics.
- Show different rearrangements of quadratic functions in general form, factored form, and vertex form and analyze their properties.
- Compare properties of quadratic functions represented in different ways.
- Compare functions increasing linearly, quadratically, and exponentially by analyzing the average rate of change of the function.
- Use multiple representations of quadratic functions to identify key characteristics, such as the maximum, minimum, intercepts, and the axis of symmetry.

You have seen quadratic functions modeled using tables, equations, and graphs. How can you use the different representations of quadratic functions to analyze their key characteristics?

GETTING STARTED

Function Form File Cabinet

1. **Complete each graphic organizer located at the end of the lessc using the general form of the function given. For each form of the equation, check the box of any characteristic that can be identified in that form of the equation. Then, sketch a graph of the equation and identify key points.**

ACTIVITY 4.1

Comparing Functions Increasing Linearly, Quadratically, and Exponentially

Think about the two functions you studied in the previous activity.

$$f(x) = x^2 + 2x - 3$$

$$g(x) = 2x^2 - 4x - 30$$

1. **Compare the two functions. Show your work and explain your reasoning.**

   a. **Which function has the lowest minimum point?**

   b. **Which function has a greater value at $x = 8$?**

   c. **Which function has a greater value at $x = 9$?**

Complete the table to compare the average rate of change of the two functions on the given intervals. Show your work.

The average rate of change of any function over an interval is the slope of a linear function passing through the beginning and end points of the interval.

Interval	Average Rate of Change $f(x) = x^2 + 2x - 3$	Average Rate of Change $g(x) = 2x^2 - 4x - 30$
[0, 1]		
[0, 2]		
[0, 3]		
[4, 5]		

The two functions you compared increase or decrease quadratically, but they do not have the same average rates of change on the given intervals. Explain why.

t's compare a quadratic function with other function types you have udied. You can say that a quadratic function increases or decreases adratically, so a linear function increases or decreases linearly, and an ponential function increases or decreases exponentially.

Consider the linear, exponential, and quadratic functions shown.

$h(x) = 2x$

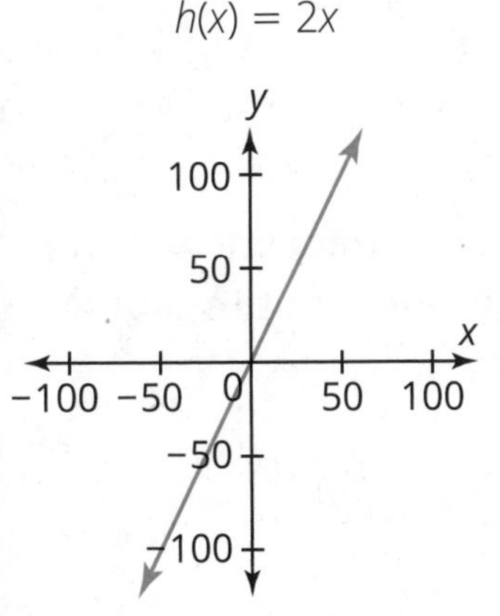

$j(x) = 2^x$

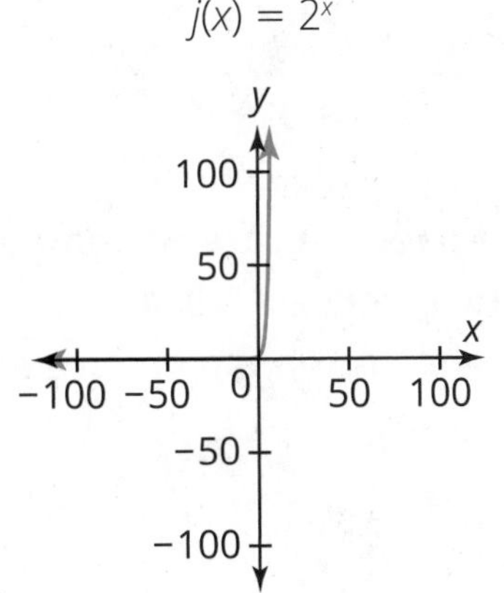

$k(x) = x^2$

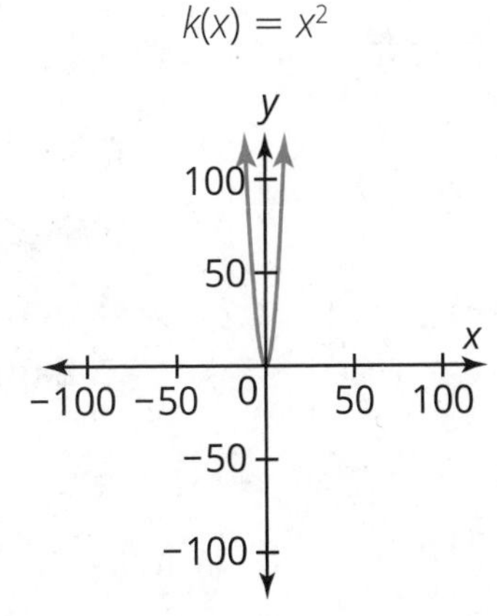

a. **At what point do the three graphs intersect? Explain how you know.**

b. **Which function do you think has the greatest average rate of change from negative infinity to positive infinity? Explain your reasoning.**

The table shown organizes the average rates of change of the three functions across different intervals of their domains. Some of the rates have been provided.

	[−10, 10]	[10, 100]	[100, 1000]
$h(x) = 2x$			
$j(x) = 2^x$		6.34×10^{27}	1.07×10^{298}
$k(x) = x^2$	0		

5. **Consider the quadratic function.**

   a. **Why is the average rate of change for the quadratic function 0 across the interval [−10, 10]? Use a calculation to explain your reasoning.**

   b. **Enter the average rate of change for the quadratic function across the intervals [10, 100] and [100, 1000] in the table. Explain why your answers are correct.**

6. Enter the average rate of change for the linear function across each of the three intervals in the table. Justify your answers.

7. Enter the average rate of change for the exponential function across the interval [−10, 10] in the table. Show your work.

8. Do the average rates of change for the exponential function in the table seem reasonable? Explain why or why not.

9. Compare the change in the average rates of change for the functions shown in the table across the different intervals. What do you notice?

10. Parker says that any function increasing exponentially will eventually have a greater value than any function increasing linearly or quadratically.

Is Parker correct? Explain why or why not.

ACTIVITY **4.2**

Comparing Equations, Tables, and Graphs

Maya saved up some money and decided to take a risk and invest in some stocks. She invested her money in Doogle, a popular computer company. Unfortunately she lost it all in just 25 months. The change in her money during this time can be represented by the function $v(x) = 75 + 72x - 3x^2$, where v is the value of her investment and x is the time in months.

1. **Three quadratic functions are shown. Which of these models represents Maya's investment money over time? Explain your choice and why you eliminated the other model(s).**

Model 1

$v(x) = -3(x + 1)(x - 25)$

Model 2

x	y
0	0
3	197
15	450
25	0

Model 3

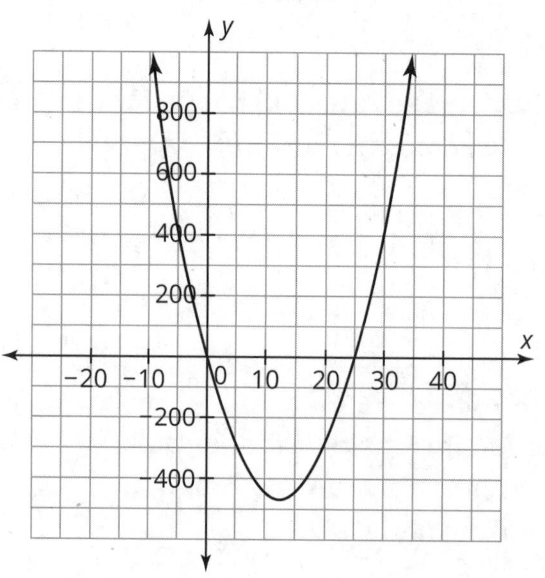

2. **How much money did Maya initially invest? Explain how you determined your answer.**

The function that models Maya's investment over time has a maximum value.

a. What was the greatest value of Maya's investment account over the time of her investment? Show your work.

b. How much time did it take for Maya's account to reach its maximum value?

c. On average, how much did Maya's account gain in value each month from the time she opened the account to the time it reached its maximum value?

ACTIVITY

4.3

Representations of Transformations of Quadratic Functions

Consider the quadratic function $h(t) = -5(t - 3)^2 + 60$.

1. Sketch a graph of the function and label the vertex and the *y*-intercept. Explain your work.

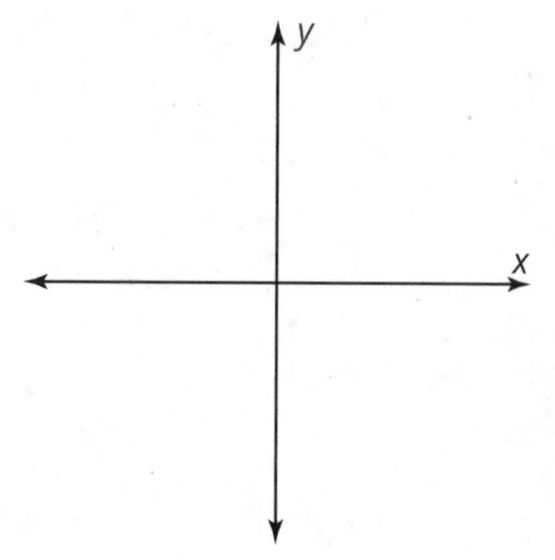

2. Identify the table that represents the function. Explain why you eliminated the other tables.

A

t	$h(t)$
−1	55
0	60
1	55
2	40

B

t	$h(t)$
0	45
1	20
4	5
5	20

C

t	$h(t)$
$-\sqrt{12} + 3$	0
0	15
3	60
$\sqrt{12} + 3$	0

D

t	$h(t)$
$-\sqrt{12} + 3$	−60
0	−45
3	0
$\sqrt{12} + 3$	−60

3. Describe how the function $h(x)$ has been transformed from the basic function $f(x) = x^2$.

ACTIVITY

4.4

Comparing Quadratics in Different Forms

n this activity, you will compare quadratic functions represented in different forms.

1. Josiah compared the table of values for $f(x)$ and the graph of $g(x)$ to determine which quadratic function has the greater maximum.

x	$f(x)$
−1	0
0	4.5
1	8
2	10.5
3	12

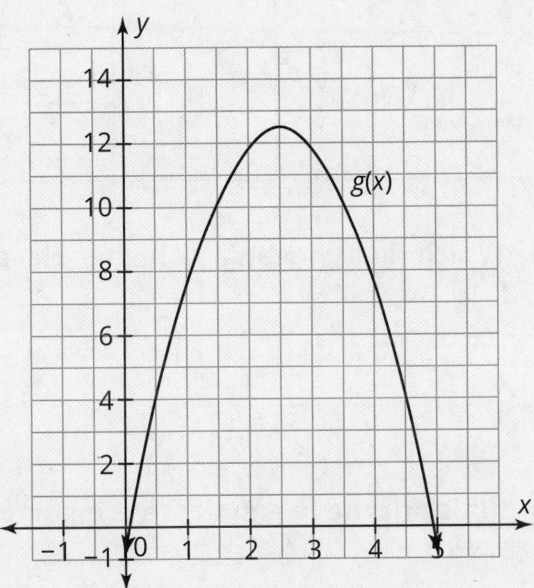

Josiah says that the function $g(x)$ has a greater maximum, because it has an output value greater than 12 at its maximum while the table for $f(x)$ shows a greatest output of 12. Is Josiah's reasoning correct? Explain your answer.

2. Approximate the absolute maximum for each function. Show your work.

Ben and Corinne are trying out their new drones, but they're not very goo
at flying them yet. The drones keep very precise records of their elevation

3. Compare these two drone flights, launched at the same time.

The height in feet of Corinne's drone flight over time in seconds can be approximated by the function $c(x) = -3x^2 + 7x + 1$.	The table of values shows the height in feet of Ben's drone at different times.

x	$b(x)$
0	4
0.25	4.25
0.5	4
1	2
1.281	0

a. Which flight began at a higher elevation? How do you know?

b. Which drone began descending first? Show your work.

c. Which of the drones had a greater average increase in height over time up to its maximum height? Explain your reasoning

NOTES

TALK the TALK 

More Ups and Downs

1. **Analyze each pair of representations. Then, answer each question and justify your reasoning.**

   a. **Which function has a greater average rate of change for the interval (2, 4)?**

A

$f(x) = (x + 1)^2 + 20$

B

x	y
0	4
2	0
4	4

   b. **Which function has a greater absolute minimum?**

A

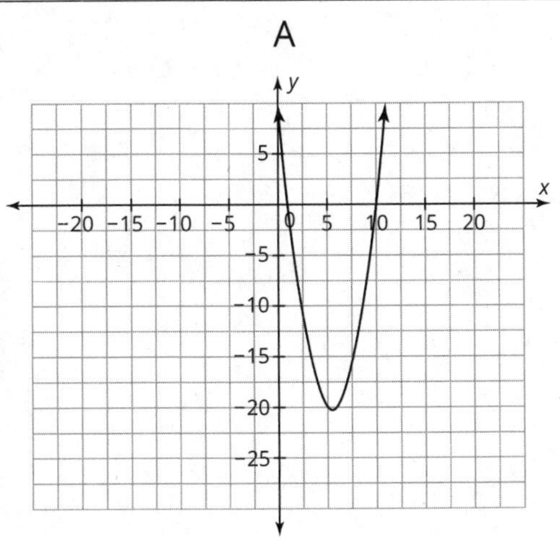

B

x	y
0	4
1	0
4	0

NOTES

c. Which function's axis of symmetry has a greater *x*-value?

<table>
<tr><th>A</th><th>B</th></tr>
<tr><td>$f(x) = 2x^2 + 4$</td><td>

x	*y*
−3	30
0	0
5	30

</td></tr>
</table>

Graphic Organizer

General Form

Equation: $f(x) = x^2 + 2x - 3$

Select which key features of the graph can be identified from the general form of the equation.

- □ parabola opens up/down
- □ location of vertex
- □ zeros
- □ y-intercept

Factored Form

Equation: ____________________

Select which key features of the graph can be identified from the factored form of the equation.

- □ parabola opens up/down
- □ location of vertex
- □ zeros
- □ y-intercept

KEY CHARACTERISTICS OF A QUADRATIC FUNCTION

Equation: ____________________

Select which key features of the graph can be identified from the vertex form of the equation.

- □ parabola opens up/down
- □ location of vertex
- □ zeros
- □ y-intercept

Vertex Form

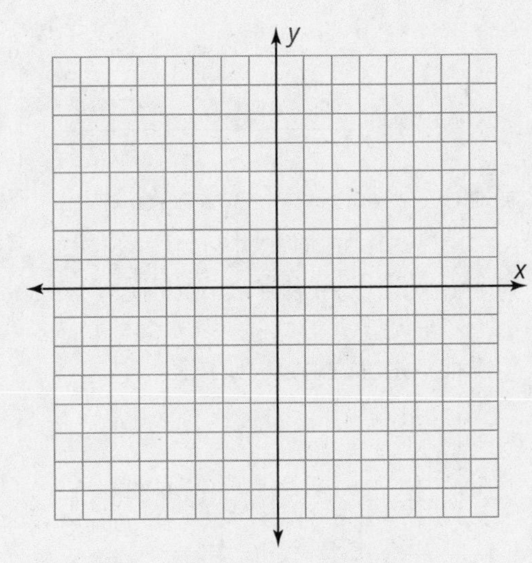

Graph of the Quadratic Function

Graphic Organizer

General Form

Equation: $g(x) = 2x^2 - 4x - 30$

Select which key features of the graph can be identified from the general form of the equation.

- ☐ parabola opens up/down
- ☐ location of vertex
- ☐ zeros
- ☐ y-intercept

Factored Form

Equation: ____________________

Select which key features of the graph can be identified from the factored form of the equation.

- ☐ parabola opens up/down
- ☐ location of vertex
- ☐ zeros
- ☐ y-intercept

KEY CHARACTERISTICS OF A QUADRATIC FUNCTION

Vertex Form

Equation: ____________________

Select which key features of the graph can be identified from the vertex form of the equation.

- ☐ parabola opens up/down
- ☐ location of vertex
- ☐ zeros
- ☐ y-intercept

Graph of the Quadratic Function

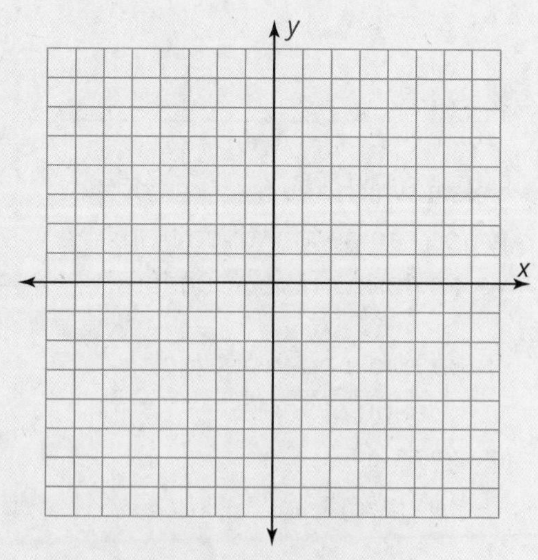

Assignment

Write

Describe the difference between quadratic equations in general form, factored form, and vertex form.

Remember

You can use what you know about the structure of quadratic functions represented as tables, equations, graphs and scenarios to compare the characteristics of two quadratic functions represented in different forms.

Practice

1. Analyze each pair of representations. Then, answer each question and justify your reasoning.

   a. Which function has a greater y-intercept?

   A

   $f(x) = \frac{1}{3}x^2 - 4x + 12$

   B

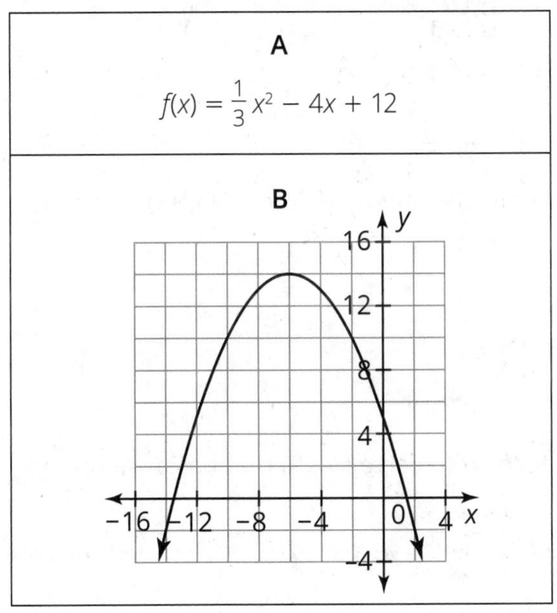

   b. Which function has a greater average rate of change for the interval (1, 2)?

   A

   $f(x) = \frac{1}{2}x^2 + 9$

   B

x	y
0	9
1	7
2	1

   c. Which function has an absolute maximum with a greater y-value?

   A

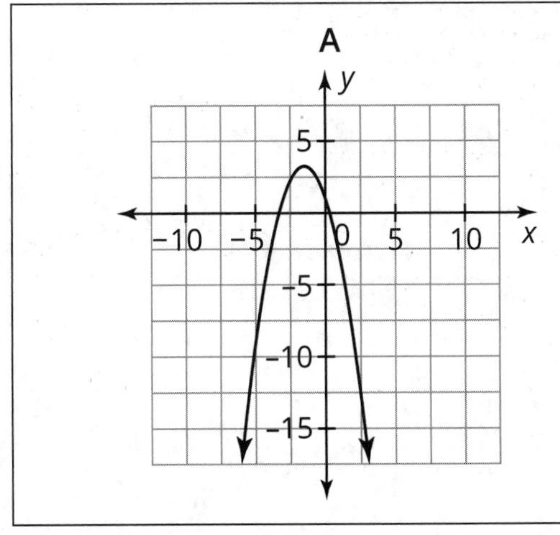

   B

x	y
−1	0
0	0
0.5	−0.75

Stretch

Analyze each pair of representations.

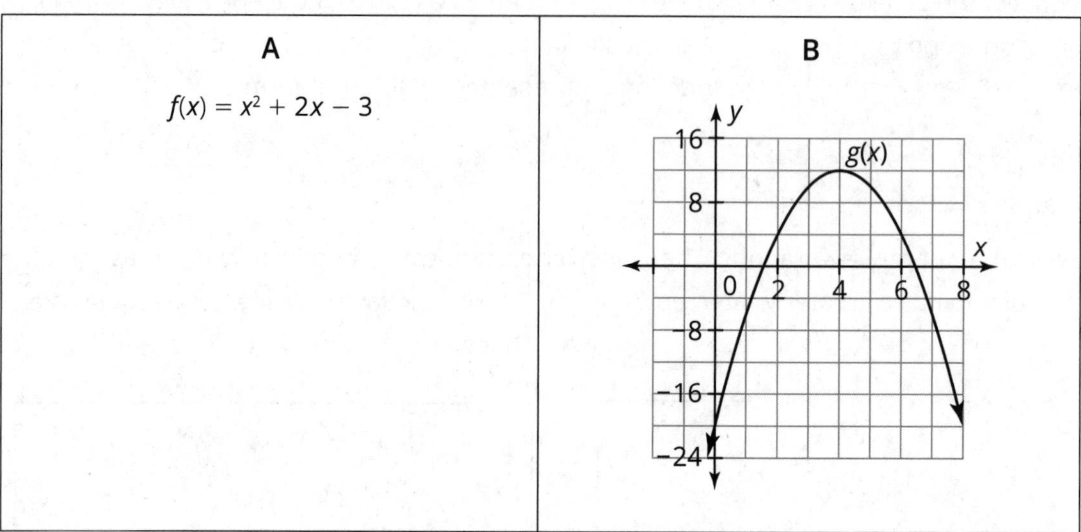

Write a function $m(x)$ that has an average rate of change for the interval (1, 2) that falls between the average rate of change for the same interval for $f(x)$ and $g(x)$.

Review

1. Write an equation for a quadratic function in vertex form with vertex (4, 9) that has a y-intercept of (0, 12.2).
2. Write an equation for a quadratic function in factored form with zeros (−7, 0) and (10, 0) that passes through the point (−4, −10).
3. For each exponential expression, determine an equivalent expression with a B-value of 1 and a C-value of 0.
   a. $g(x) = 2^{5x}$
   b. 2^{x-5}

Introduction to Quadratic Functions Summary

KEY TERMS

- parabola
- vertical motion model
- roots
- second differences
- general form of a quadratic function
- factored form
- vertex
- axis of symmetry
- vertex form

LESSON 1 Up and Down or Down and Up

The shape that a quadratic function forms when graphed is called a parabola. A **parabola** is a smooth curve in a U-shape that has symmetry. The parabola can open upward, decreasing to a minimum point before increasing, or can open downward, increasing to a maximum point before decreasing. The domain of a quadratic function is all real numbers. The range of a quadratic function is all real numbers greater than or equal to the minimum *y*-value or less than or equal to the maximum *y*-value. The graph of a quadratic function has one *y*-intercept and, at most, 2 *x*-intercepts.

Quadratic functions model area because area is measured in square units.

For example, suppose you have 20 feet of fencing with which to enclose a rectangular area. The graph represents a quadratic function for the area of the rectangle given possible lengths of the rectangle. The maximum of the parabola is at the point (5, 25). It has x-intercepts at (0, 0) and (10, 0), and a y-intercept at (0, 0).

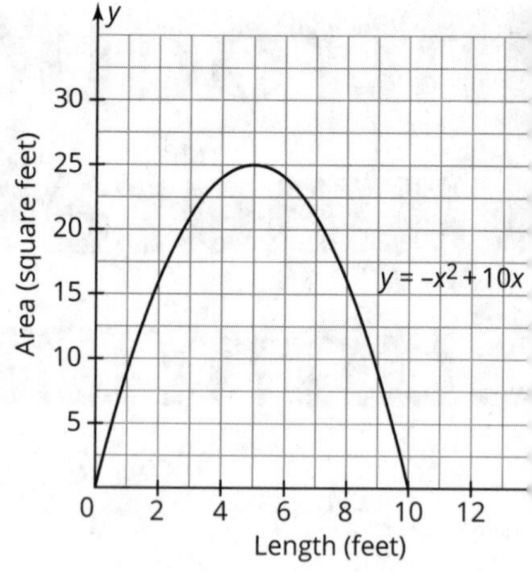

A **vertical motion model** is a quadratic equation that models the height of an object at a given time. The equation is of the form $y = -16t^2 + v_0t + h_0$, where y represents the height of the object in feet, t represents the time in seconds that the object has been moving, v_0 represents the initial vertical velocity of the object in feet per second, and h_0 represents the initial height of the object in feet.

For example, suppose a firework is launched into the air from the ground with a vertical velocity of 128 feet per second. The function that describes the height of the firework in terms of time is $g(t) = -16t^2 + 128t$.

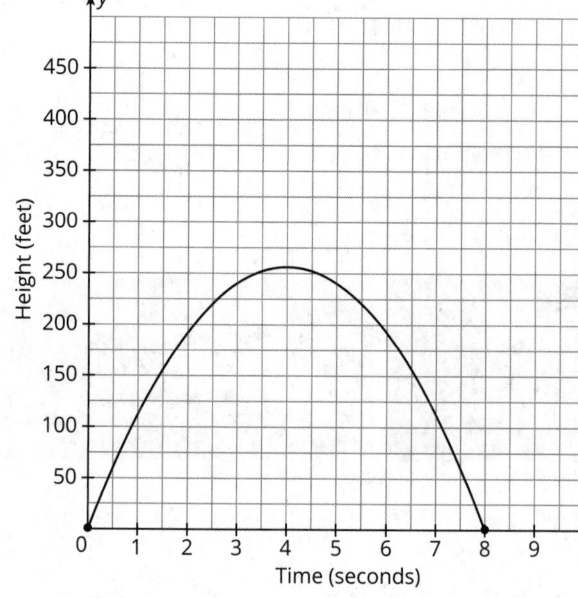

The x-intercepts of a graph of a quadratic function are also called the zeros of the quadratic function. The x-intercepts, or zeros, of $g(t) = -16t^2 + 128t$ are (0, 0) and (8, 0).

When an equation is used to model a situation, the x-intercepts are referred to as **roots**. The roots of an equation indicate where the graph of the equation crosses the x-axis.

LESSON 2

Endless Forms Most Beautiful

First differences are the differences between successive output values when successive input values have a difference of 1. **Second differences** are the differences between consecutive values of first differences. Linear functions have constant first differences and second differences of 0. Quadratic functions have changing first differences and constant second differences.

Linear function: $f(x) = -x + 2$

x	$f(x)$	First Differences	Second Differences
0	2		
		−1	
1	1		0
		−1	
2	0		0
		−1	
3	−1		0
		−1	
4	−2		

Quadratic function: $f(x) = 2x^2 - 3x$

x	$f(x)$	First Differences	Second Differences
0	0		
		−1	
1	−1		4
		3	
2	2		4
		7	
3	9		4
		11	
4	20		

A quadratic function written in standard form, which is also called the **general form of a quadratic function**, is in the form, $f(x) = ax^2 + bx + c$, where $a \neq 0$. In this form, a and b represent numerical coefficients and c represents a constant. A quadratic function written in factored form is in the form $f(x) = a(x - r_1)(x - r_2)$, where $a \neq 0$ and r_1 and r_2 represent the roots.

When the leading coefficient a is negative, the graph of the quadratic function opens downward and has a maximum. When a is positive, the graph of the quadratic function opens upward and has a minimum. When a quadratic function is written in general form, the constant c is the y-intercept.

The **vertex** of a parabola is the lowest or highest point on the graph of the quadratic function. The **axis of symmetry** of a parabola is the vertical line that passes through the vertex and divides the parabola into two mirror images.

For a quadratic function in factored form, the equation for the axis of symmetry is given by $x = \frac{r_1 + r_2}{2}$. For a quadratic function in general form, the equation for the axis of symmetry is $x = \frac{-b}{2a}$.

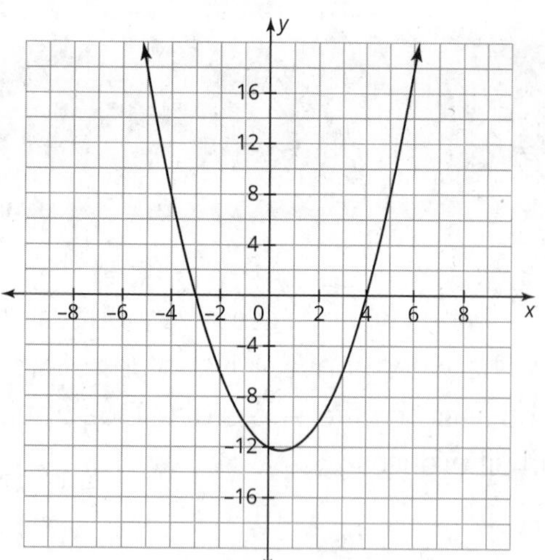

The graph shown represents the function $f(x) = x^2 - x - 1$
The axis of symmetry is $x = -\frac{(-1)}{2(1)} = \frac{1}{2}$. The vertex is $\left(\frac{1}{2}, -12\frac{1}{4}\right)$. The x-intercepts, or zeros, of the function are $x = -3$ and $x = 4$, so the function can be written in factore form as $f(x) = (x + 3)(x - 4)$. The y-intercept is $(0, -12)$. The domain of the function is all real numbers and the range is all real numbers greater than or equal to $-12\frac{1}{4}$. The graph has an interval of decrease from $-\infty$ to $\frac{1}{2}$ and an interval of increase from $\frac{1}{2}$ to ∞.

You can use the fact that the graph of a quadratic function is symmetric along the axis of symmetr to determine a second point on the parabola given a point on the parabola, and to determine the axis of symmetry given two symmetric points on the parabola.

For example, the vertex of a parabola is (3, 5). A point on the parabola is (0, 3). Another point on the parabola is (6, 3).

$\frac{0 + a}{2} =$

$0 + a =$

$a =$

Suppose two symmetric points on a parabola are (−7, 20) and (4, 20). The axis of symmetry is $x = -\frac{3}{2}$ because $\frac{-7 + 4}{2} = -\frac{3}{2}$.

LESSON 3 More Than Meets the Eye

You can use function transformation form, $g(x) = A \cdot f(B(x - C)) + D$, to transform quadratic functions.

Vertical translations are performed on a basic quadratic function $g(x) = x^2$ by adding a constant to or subtracting a constant from the function. Adding to the function translates it up, and subtracting translates it down. Horizontal translations are performed on the basic quadratic function $g(x) = x^2$ by adding a constant to or subtracting a constant from the argument, x, of the function. Adding to the argument translates the function to the left, and subtracting from the argument translates the function to the right.

Vertical translations

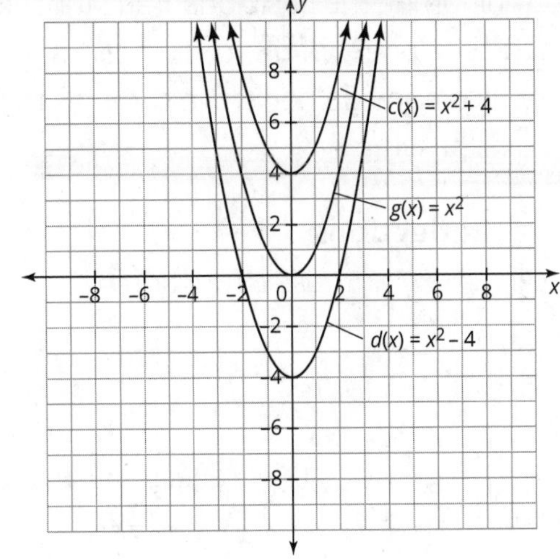

$g(x) = x^2$	basic function
$c(x) = g(x) + 4$	$g(x)$ translated 4 units up, so $(x, y) \longrightarrow (x, y + 4)$.
$d(x) = g(x) - 4$	$g(x)$ translated 4 units down, so $(x, y) \longrightarrow (x, y - 4)$.

Horizontal translations

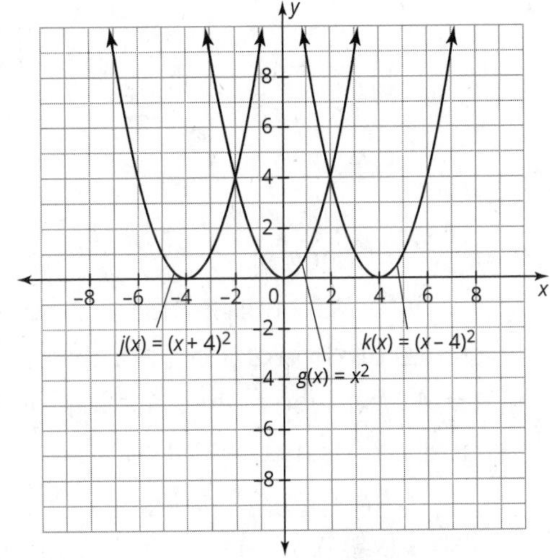

$g(x) = x^2$	basic function
$j(x) = g(x + 4)$	$g(x)$ translated 4 units left, so $(x, y) \longrightarrow (x - 4, y)$.
$k(x) = g(x - 4)$	$g(x)$ translated 4 units right, so $(x, y) \longrightarrow (x + 4, y)$.

Multiplying the basic quadratic function by −1 results in a reflection across the line $y = 0$. Multiplying the argument of the basic quadratic function by −1 results in a reflection across the line $x = 0$, which ends up being the same as the original function because quadratic functions have a vertical axis of symmetry.

Reflections

$g(x) = x^2$ basic function

$m(x) = -g(x)$ $g(x)$ is reflected across $y = 0$, so $(x, y) \longrightarrow (x, -y)$.

$n(x) = g(-x)$ $g(x)$ is reflected across $x = 0$, so $(x, y) \longrightarrow (-x, y)$.

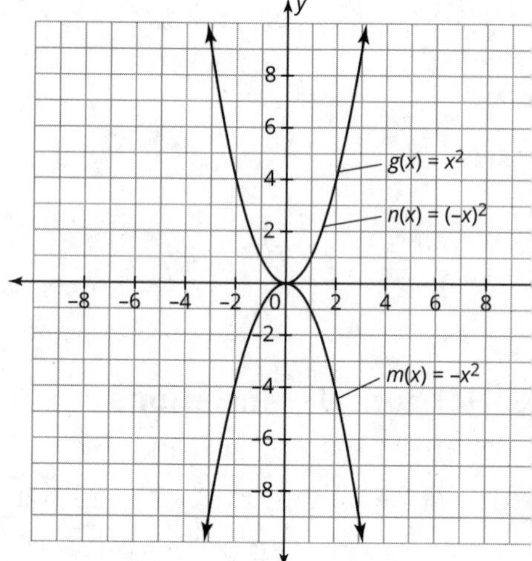

A vertical dilation of a function is a transformation in which the y-coordinate of every point on the graph of the function is multiplied by a common factor called the dilation factor. A vertical dilation stretches or shrinks the graph of a function vertically. For the transformed basic quadratic function, $g(x) = A \cdot f(x)$, when $|A| > 1$, the graph of $f(x)$ is stretched vertically. When $0 < |A| < 1$, $f(x)$ shrinks vertically. You can use the coordinate notation shown to indicate a vertical dilation.

$(x, y) \longrightarrow (x, Ay)$, where A is the dilation factor.

A horizontal dilation of a function is a transformation in which the x-coordinate of every point on the graph of the function is multiplied by a dilation factor. For the transformed basic quadratic function $g(x) = f(Bx)$, when $|B| > 1$, the graph of the function is compressed horizontally. When $0 < |B| < 1$, the function is stretched horizontally. You can use the coordinate notation shown to indicate a horizontal dilation.

$(x, y) \longrightarrow \left(\frac{1}{|B|}x, y\right)$, where $\frac{1}{|B|}$ is the dilation factor.

Vertical dilations

$g(x) = x^2$ basic function

$v(x) = 2g(x)$ $g(x)$ stretched by a dilation factor of 2, so $(x, y) \longrightarrow (x, 2y)$.

$w(x) = \frac{1}{2}g(x)$ $g(x)$ shrunk by a dilation factor of $\frac{1}{2}$, so $(x, y) \longrightarrow (x, \frac{1}{2}y)$.

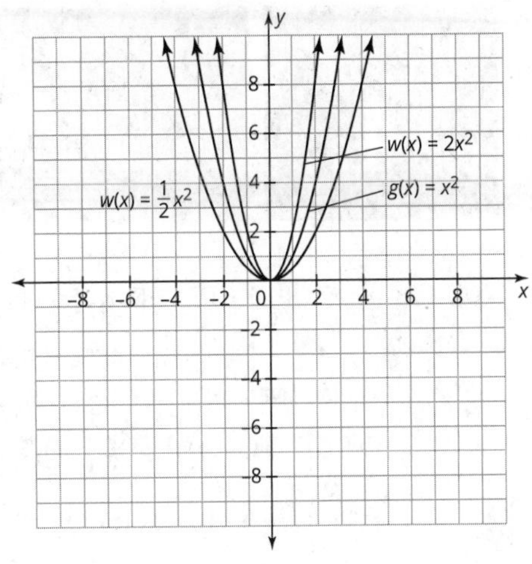

Horizontal dilations

$g(x) = x^2$ basic function

$v(x) = g(2x)$ $g(x)$ compressed by a dilation factor of $\frac{1}{2}$, so $(x, y) \longrightarrow \left(\frac{1}{2}x, y\right)$.

$w(x) = g\left(\frac{1}{2}x\right)$ $g(x)$ stretched by a dilation factor of 2, so $(x, y) \longrightarrow (2x, y)$.

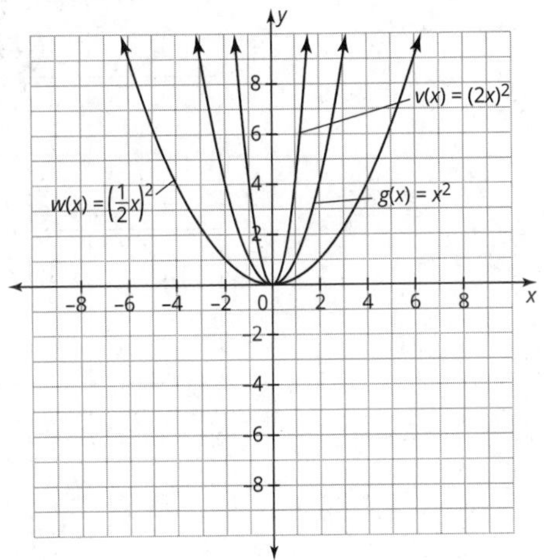

Given $y = f(x)$ is the basic function, you can use reference points to graph $y = A \cdot f(B(x - C)) + D$ without the use of technology. Any point (x, y) on $f(x)$ maps to the point $(\frac{1}{B}x + C, Ay + D)$.

Given $f(x) = x^2$, the function $g(x) = 2f(x - 3) + 4$ has been graphed.

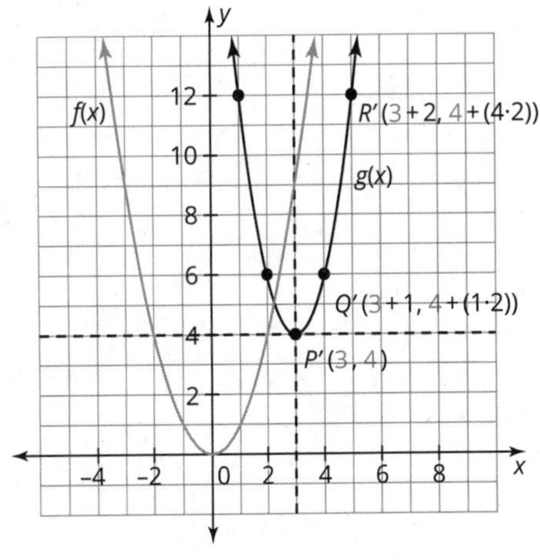

A quadratic function written in **vertex form** is in the form $f(x) = a(x - h)^2 + k$, where $a \neq 0$. The variable h represents the x-coordinate of the vertex. The variable k represents the y-coordinate of the vertex.

LESSON 4

You Lose Some, You Lose Some

You can use different representations of quadratic functions to analyze their key characteristics.

For example, the functions $f(x)$ shown with a table and $g(x)$ shown with a graph can be compared to determine which quadratic function has the greater maximum.

x	$f(x)$
0	0
0.5	1
0.75	1.125
1	1
1.5	0

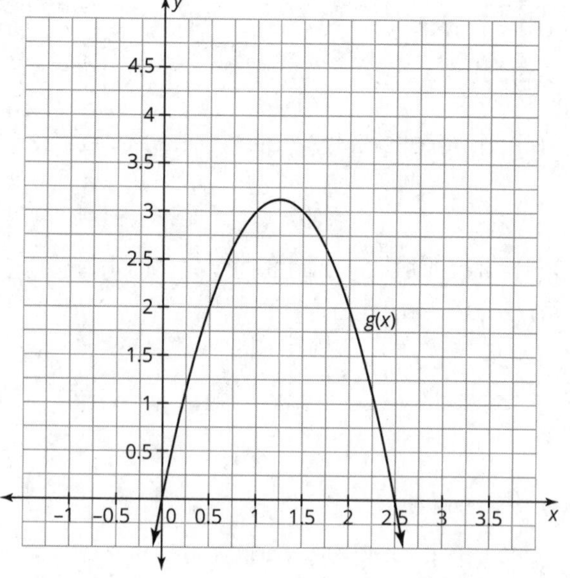

From the table, you can determine the maximum of $f(x)$ is (0.75, 1.125). From the graph, you can determine that the maximum of $g(x)$ is greater than $y = 3$. Therefore, $g(x)$ has a greater maximum than $f(x)$.

ODULE 4

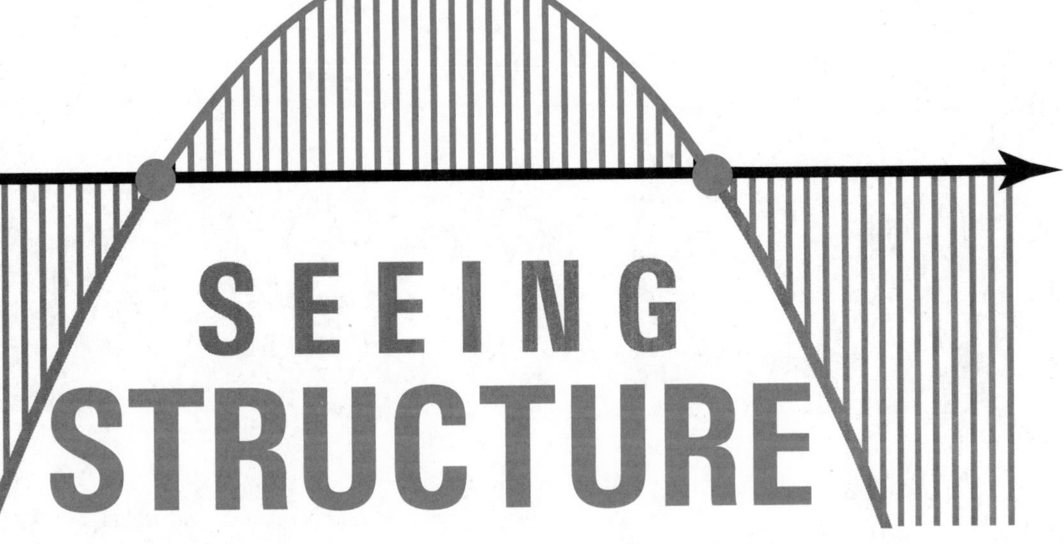

he lessons in this module build on your knowledge of equations, graphs, and solutions. You will xamine the structure of quadratic equations and their corresponding graphs to learn strategies solve quadratic equations. You will apply this knowledge to model quadratic inequalities, egressions, and systems. You will learn that a new number set is required for the square root f negative numbers and how to use these numbers to solve problems. You will examine circles nd parabolas on the coordinate plane and derive the equation for each.

OPIC 1

Solving Quadratic Equations

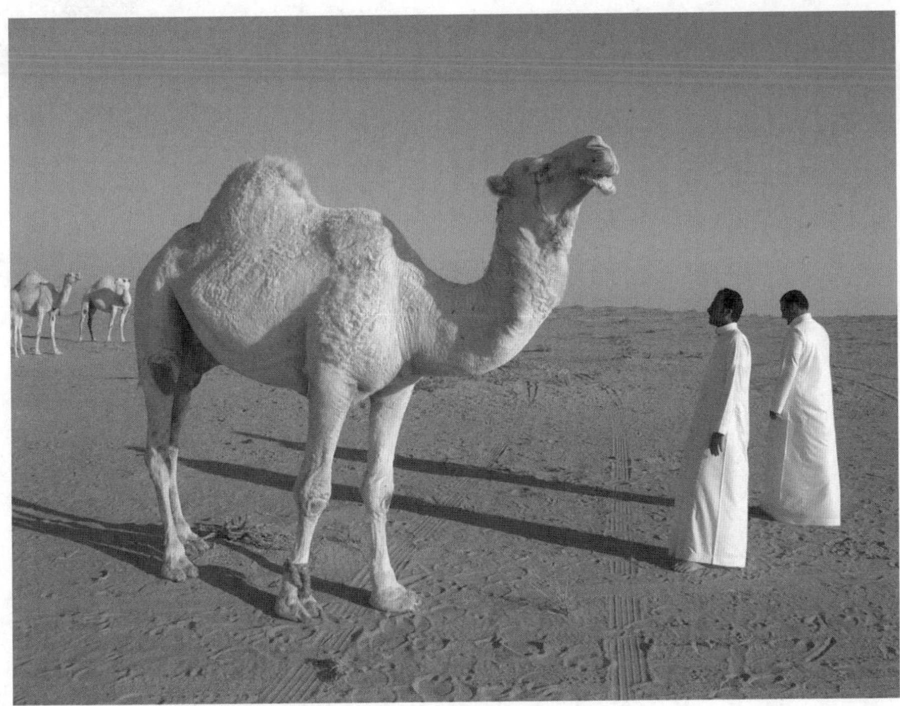

A parabola is U-shaped, though it may open up or down.

Module 4: Seeing Structure

TOPIC 1: SOLVING QUADRATIC EQUATIONS

Students use what they know about square roots and graphs of quadratic equations to solve equations of the form $x^2 = n$ and $ax^2 - c = n$. They see in the graphs that the solutions are both equidistant from the axis of symmetry. Students then learn to factor or complete the square to solve quadratic equations and real-world problems. Finally, they derive the Quadratic Formula. Students see the structure of solutions to quadratic equations in the Quadratic Formula: the axis of symmetry plus or minus the distance to the parabola.

Where have we been?

Students know the characteristics that define a quadratic function. They have explored zeros of functions and have interpreted their meaning in contextual situations. Students know that the factored form of a quadratic equation gives the zeros of the function. They can sketch quadratic equations using key characteristics from an equation written in general form, factored form, or vertex form. Importantly, students have extensive experience with locating solutions to equations using a graphical representation.

Where are we going?

The techniques for solving quadratics will be applicable as students solve higher-order polynomials in future courses. Understanding the structure and symmetry of a quadratic equation allows students to solve quadratics with complex roots as well as higher-order polynomials.

Completing the Square

The quadratic expression $x^2 + 10x$ can be represented in a square shape as $x^2 + 5x + 5x$. To complete the square, add $5 \cdot 5$, or 25. The expression $x^2 + 10 + 25$ can then be written in factored form as $(x + 5)(x + 5)$, or $(x + 5)^2$.

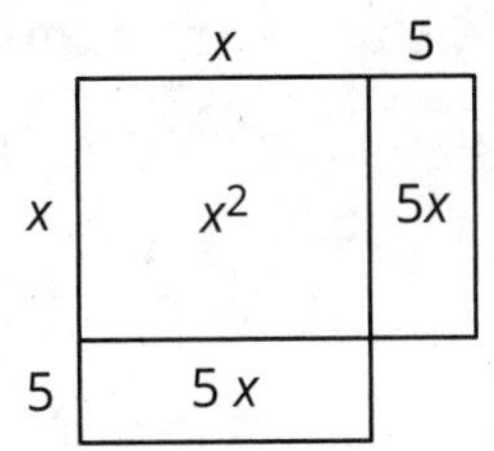

x 5
x | x^2 | 5x
5 | 5x | 25

The Roots of Zero

The word *zero* has had a long and interesting history. The word comes from the Hindu word *sunya*, which meant "void" or "emptiness." In Arabic, this word became *sifr*, which is also where the word *cipher* comes from. In Latin, it was changed to *cephirum*, and finally, in Italian it became *zevero* or *zefiro*, which was shortened to *zero*.

The ancient Greeks, who were responsible for creating much of modern formal mathematics, did not even believe zero was a number!

Talking Points

It can be helpful to understand quadratic functions for college admissions tests.

Here is an example of a sample question:

Solve: $x^2 + 6x + 9 = 0$

To solve this problem, you can first factor the quadratic expression on the left-hand side of the equation:

$$(x + 3)(x + 3)$$

The Zero Product Property tells us that when factors have a product of 0, one or more of the factors is equal to 0. So, set each factor equal to 0 and solve:

$$x + 3 = 0$$
$$x = -3$$

Key Terms

degree of a polynomial

The degree of a term in a polynomial is the exponent of the term. The greatest exponent in a polynomial determines the degree of the polynomial.

double root

The quadratic function $y = x^2$ has two solutions at $y = 0$. Therefore, it has two zeros: $x = +\sqrt{0}$ and $x = -\sqrt{0}$. These two zeros of the function, or roots of the equation, are the same number, 0, so $y = x^2$ is said to have a double root.

completing the square

Completing the square is a process for writing a quadratic expression in vertex form which then allows you to solve for the zeros.

Quadratic Formula

The Quadratic Formula is $x = \frac{-b \pm \sqrt{b - 4ac}}{2a}$.

1

This Time, With Polynomials

Adding, Subtracting, and Multiplying Polynomials

Warm Up

Rewrite each expression by combining like terms.

1. $-3x + 4y - 9x - 5y$

2. $2xy^2 + 5x^2y - 7xy + xy^2$

3. $6 - m^2 + 5m^2$

4. $-8 - (-4k) + 7 + 1 - 4k$

Learning Goals

- Name polynomials by number of terms or degree.
- Understand that operations can be performed on functions as well as numbers.
- Add, subtract, and multiply polynomials.
- Explain why polynomials are closed under addition, subtraction and multiplication.
- Recognize and use special products when multiplying binomials.

Key Terms

- polynomial
- monomial
- binomial
- trinomial
- degree of a polynomial
- closed, closure
- difference of two squares
- perfect square trinomial

You know that a linear expression is one type of polynomial expression. What are other polynomial expressions, and how do you add, subtract, and multiply them?

GETTING STARTED

Sorting It Out

You are familiar with many types of mathematical expressions. Cut out the 12 expressions located at the end of this lesson. Analyze and sort them into groups based upon common characteristics.

1. **Summarize the groups you formed by listing the expressions that you grouped together and your description for each group. Use mathematical terms in your descriptions.**

2. **Compare your groups of expressions to your classmates' groups. Describe any similarities and differences.**

3. **Jimmy and Andrew agree that $4x - 6x^2$ and $25 - 18m^2$ belong in the same group. They each are adding the expressions shown to the group. Who is correct? Explain your reasoning.**

Jimmy	Andrew
$5 - 7h$	$y^2 - 4y + 10$
$78j^3 - 3j$	$-3 + 7n + n^2$
$-13s + 6$	

4. **What characteristics do all twelve expressions share?**

ACTIVITY

1.1

Categorizing Polynomials

Previously, you worked with linear expressions in the form $ax + b$ and quadratic expressions in the form $ax^2 + bx + c$. Each is also part of a larger group of expressions known as *polynomials*.

A **polynomial** is a mathematical expression involving the sum of powers in one or more variables multiplied by coefficients. A polynomial in one variable is the sum of terms of the form ax^k, where a is any real number and k is a non-negative integer. In general, a polynomial is of the form $a_1x^k + a_2x^{k-1} + \ldots + a_nx^0$. Within a polynomial, each product is a term, and the number being multiplied by a power is a coefficient.

Worked Example

The polynomial $m^3 + 8m^2 - 10m + 5$ has four terms. Each term is written in the form ax^k.

- The first term is m^3.
- The power is m^3, and its coefficient is 1.
- In this term, the variable is m and the exponent is 3.

1. Write each term from the worked example and identify the coefficient, power, and exponent. The first term has already been completed for you.

	1st	2nd	3rd	4th
Term	m^3			
Coefficient	1			
Variable	m			
Power	m^3			
Exponent	3			

2. **Identify the terms and coefficients in each polynomial.**

   a. $-2x^2 + 100x$

   b. $4m^3 - 2m^2 - 5$

   c. $y^5 - y + 3$

Polynomials are named according to the number of terms they have. Polynomials with only one term are **monomials**. Polynomials with exactly two terms are **binomials**. Polynomials with exactly three terms are **trinomials**.

The degree of a term in a polynomial is the exponent of the term. The greatest exponent in a polynomial determines the **degree of the polynomial**. In the polynomial $4x + 3$, the greatest exponent is 1, so the degree of the polynomial is 1.

3. **Khalil says that $3x^{-2} + 4x - 1$ is a trinomial with a degree of 1 because 1 is the greatest exponent. Jazmin disagrees and says that this is not a polynomial at all because the power on the first term is not a whole number. Who is correct? Explain your reasoning.**

4. **Determine whether each expression is a polynomial. Explain your reasoning.**

$5^x + 4^{x-1} + 3^{x-2}$

$x^2 + \sqrt{x}$

$x^4y + x^3y^2 + x^2y$

A polynomial is written in general form when the terms are in descending order, starting with the term with the largest degree and ending with the term with the smallest degree.

Revisit the cards you sorted in the Getting Started.

a. Identify any polynomial not written in general form and rewrite it in general form on the card.

b. Identify the degree of each polynomial and write the degree on the card.

c. Glue each card in the appropriate column based on the number of terms in each polynomial. Write your own polynomial to complete any empty boxes.

Monomial	Binomial	Trinomial

ACTIVITY 1.2 Interpreting the Graphs of Polynomial Functions

The graphs of functions $V(x)$ and $A(x)$ are shown. The function $V(x)$ models people's reaction times to visual stimuli in milliseconds, based upon the ag of a person in years. The function $A(x)$ models people's reaction times to audio stimuli in milliseconds based on the age of a person in years.

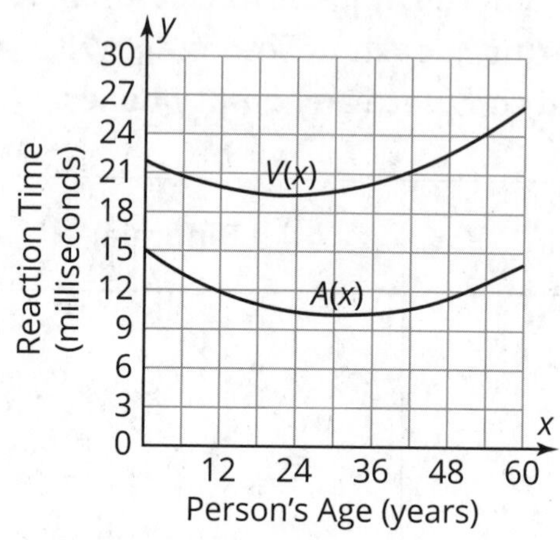

1. Interpret the graphs of the functions.

a. Describe the functions $V(x)$ and $A(x)$.

b. Write a summary to describe people's reaction times to visua stimuli and audio stimuli.

c. Do you think a person would react faster to a car horn or a flashing light? Explain your reasoning.

Estimate the age that a person has the quickest reaction time to each stimuli. Explain how you determined each answer.

a. visual stimuli

b. audio stimuli

any times, auto insurance companies use test results similar to the ones own to create insurance policies for different drivers.

How do you think the information provided in the graphic representation may be used by an auto insurance company?

Consider a new function $h(x)$, where $h(x) = V(x) - A(x)$. What does $h(x)$ mean in terms of the problem situation?

Write a report about drivers' reaction times to visual and audio stimuli. Discuss actions that may improve drivers' reaction times and distractions that may worsen drivers' reaction times. Discuss the importance of flashing lights and sirens on emergency vehicles.

How can you incorporate information about auto insurance rates and a driver's age in your report?

ACTIVITY

1.3 Adding and Subtracting Polynomial Functions

You are playing a new virtual reality game called "Species." You are an environmental scientist who is responsible for tracking two species of endangered parrots, the orange-bellied parrot and the yellow-headed parrot Suppose the orange-bellied parrots' population can be modeled by the function $B(x)$, where x represents the number of years since the current yea Suppose that the population of the yellow-headed parrot can be modeled by the function $H(x)$.

$$B(x) = -18x + 120$$

$$H(x) = 4x^2 - 5x + 25$$

The two polynomial functions are shown on the coordinate plane.

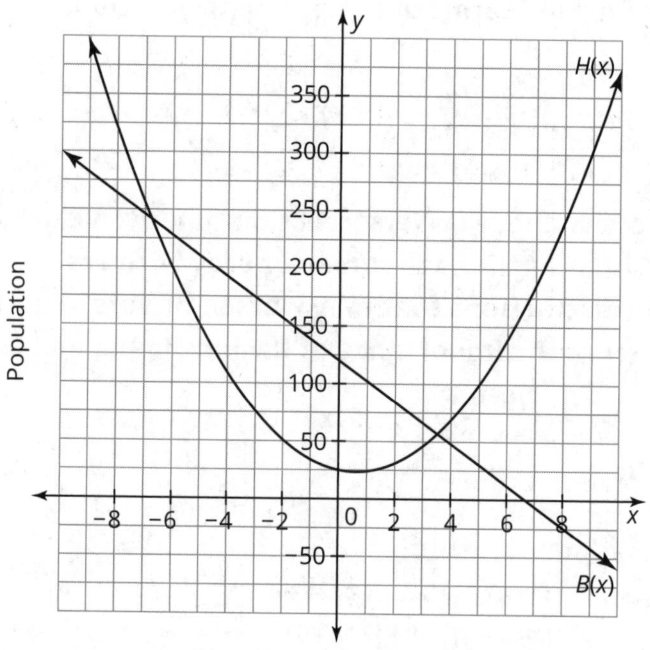

One place to start the sketch of $T(x)$ would be to consider the y-intercept for each function. What would the new y-intercept be for $T(x)$?

Your new task in this game is to determine the total number of these endangered parrots each year over a six-year span. You can calculate the total population of parrots using the two graphed functions.

1. Use the graphs of $B(x)$ and $H(x)$ to determine the function, $T(x)$, t represent the total population of parrots.

a. Write $T(x)$ in terms of $B(x)$ and $H(x)$.

b. **Predict the shape of the graph of $T(x)$.**

x	$B(x)$	$H(x)$	$T(x)$

c. **Sketch a graph of $T(x)$ on the coordinate plane shown. First choose any 5 x-values and add their corresponding y-values to create a new point on the graph of $T(x)$. Then connect the points with a smooth curve. Record the values in the table.**

d. **Did the graph of $T(x)$ match your prediction in part (b)? Identify the function family to which $T(x)$ belongs.**

ou can write a function, $T(x)$, in terms of x to calculate the total number of arrots at any time.

Worked Example

$T(x) = B(x) + H(x)$	Write $T(x)$ in terms of two known functions.
$T(x) = (-18x + 120) + (4x^2 - 5x + 25)$	Substitute the functions in terms of x.
$T(x) = 4x^2 + (-18x + (-5x)) + (120 + 25)$	Use the Commutative Property to reorder and the Associative Property to group like terms.
$T(x) = 4x^2 - 23x + 145$	Combine like terms.

. **Choose any two x-values in your table. Use the new polynomial function, $T(x)$, to confirm that your solution in the table for those times is correct. Show your work.**

The table feature on a graphing calculator is an efficient tool to determine y-values.

. **Use technology to confirm that your graph and the remaining solutions in the table are correct. Explain any discrepancies and how you corrected them.**

4. **Zoe says that using $T(x)$ will not work for any time after 6 year from now because by that point the orange-bellied parrot will be extinct. Is Zoe's statement correct? Why or why not?**

Throughout the game "Species," you must always keep track of the difference between the population of each type of species. If the differenc gets to be too great, you lose the game. The graphs of $B(x) = -18x + 120$ and $H(x) = 4x^2 - 5x + 25$ are shown.

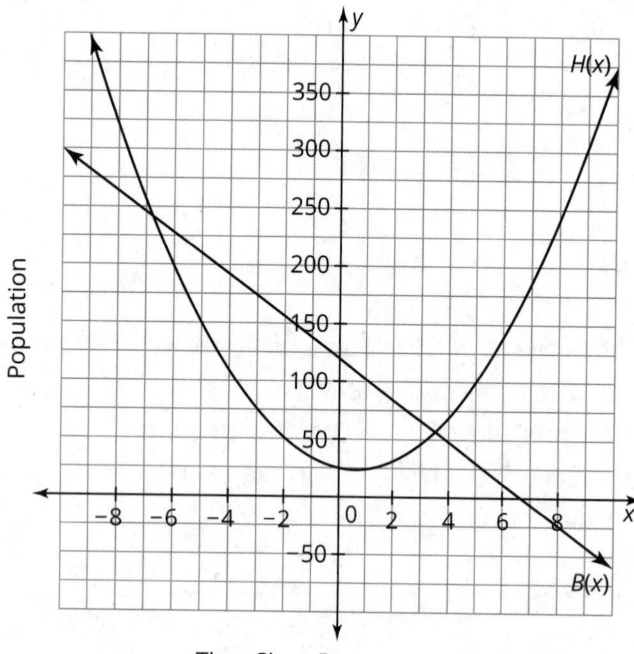

5. **Use the graphs of $B(x)$ and $H(x)$ to determine the function, $D(x)$, to represent the difference between th populations of each type of species.**

   a. **Write $D(x)$ in terms of $B(x)$ and $H(x$**

   b. **Predict the shape of the graph of $D(x)$.**

   c. **Sketch a graph of $D(x)$ on the coordinate plane shown. First choose any 5 x-values and subtrac their corresponding y-values to create a new point on the graph of $D(x)$. Then connect the points with a smooth curve. Record the values in the table.**

   d. **Did the graph of $D(x)$ match your prediction in part (b)? Identify the function family to which $D(x)$ belongs.**

x	$B(x)$	$H(x)$	$D(x)$

Write a function, $D(x)$, in terms of x to calculate the difference between the population of the orange-bellied parrots and the yellow-headed parrots. Write $D(x)$ as a polynomial in general form.

Refer to the Worked Example for adding polynomials as a guide.

Choose any two x-values in your table. Use your new polynomial function to confirm that your solution in the table for those times is correct. Show your work.

Use technology to confirm that your graph and the remaining solutions in the table are correct. Explain any discrepancies and how you corrected them.

9. Eric uses his function $D(x) = -4x^2 - 13x + 95$ to determine that th difference between the number of orange-bellied parrots and th number of yellow-headed parrots 7 years from now will be -192. Is Eric correct or incorrect? If he is correct, explain to him what h answer means in terms of the problem situation. If he is incorrec explain where he made his error and how to correct it.

10. The next round of the Species game included the red-winged parrot, whose population can be modeled by the function $W(x) = -9x + 80$ and the rainbow lorikeet parrot, whose populatio can be modeled by the function $L(x) = 2x^2 - 4x + 10$. In both cases, represents the number of years since the current year.

    a. Write a function, $S(x)$, in terms of x to calculate the total number of red-winged parrots and rainbow lorikeet parrots at any time.

    b. Write a function, $M(x)$, in terms of x to calculate the difference in the number of red-winged parrots and rainbow lorikeet parrots at any time.

    c. Calculate $S(4)$ and $M(4)$. Interpret the meaning of your results.

    d. In four years, how many red-winged parrots will there be? How many rainbow lorikeet parrots will there be?

ACTIVITY 1.4

Combining Functions and Addressing Closure

n this activity, you will practice adding and subtracting polynomials.

1. Analyze each student's work. Determine the error and make the necessary corrections.

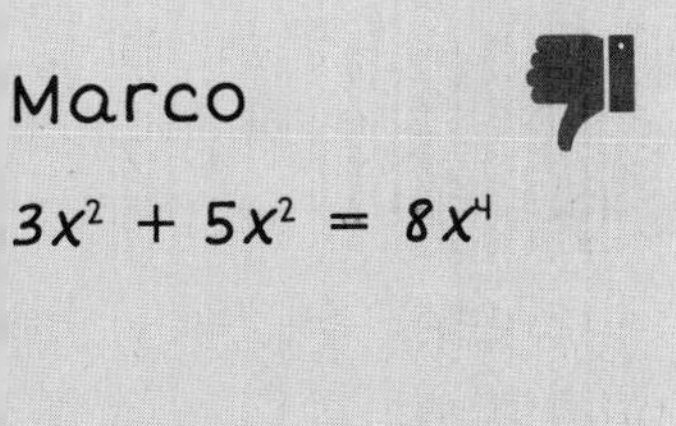

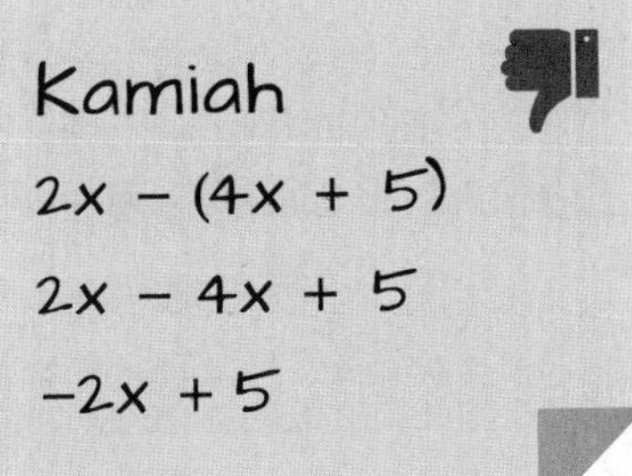

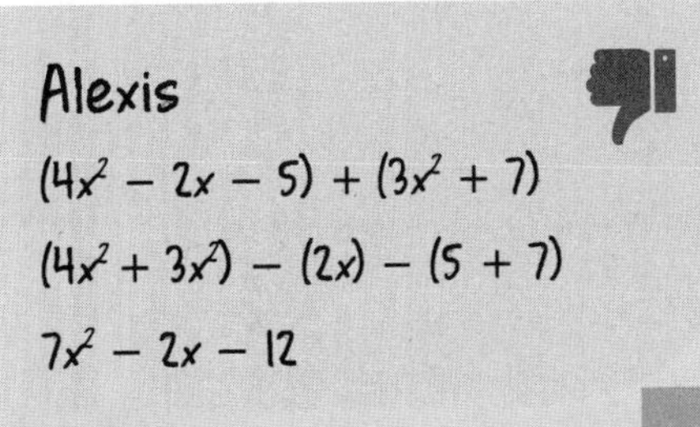

Consider each polynomial function.

$A(x) = x^3 + 5x^2 - 9$ $\quad B(x) = -3x^2 - x + 1$ $\quad C(x) = 2x^2 + 7x$ $\quad D(x) = -2x^2 - 8x$

2. Determine each function. Write your answers in general form.

a. $J(x) = A(x) + C(x)$

b. $K(x) = D(x) - B(x)$

c. $L(x) = C(x) + D(x)$

d. $M(x) = B(x) - A(x)$

e. $N(x) = A(x) - C(x) - D(x)$

NOTES

3. **Are the functions *J*(*x*), *K*(*x*), *L*(*x*), *M*(*x*) and *N*(*x*) polynomial functions? Explain why or why not.**

When an operation is performed on any of the numbers in a set and the result is a number that is also in the same set, the set is said to be **closed** or have **closure**, under that operation.

For example, the set of integers is closed under addition and subtraction. That means whenever two integers are added or subtracted, the result is also an integer.

The definition of closure can also be applied to polynomials.

4. **Based on the definition of closure, determine whether polynomials are closed under addition and subtraction. Justify your answer.**

ACTIVITY 1.5 Multiplying Polynomial Functions

nsider the dog enclosure scenario from the previous topic.

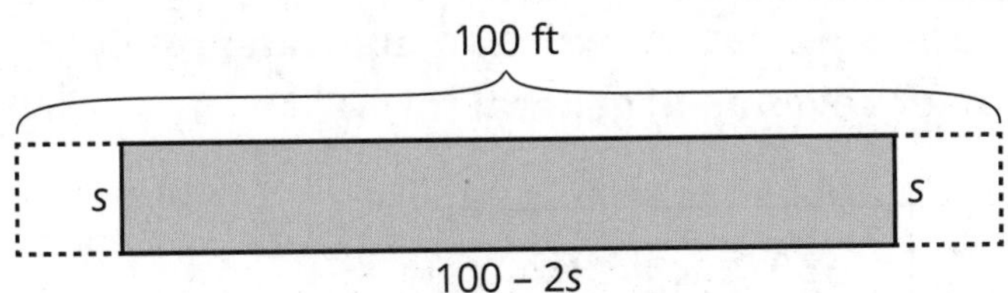

e area of the enclosure is expressed as $A(s) = s(100 - 2s)$, or the product a monomial and a binomial.

Consider how Jason and Julie wrote an equivalent polynomial function in general form by calculating the product.

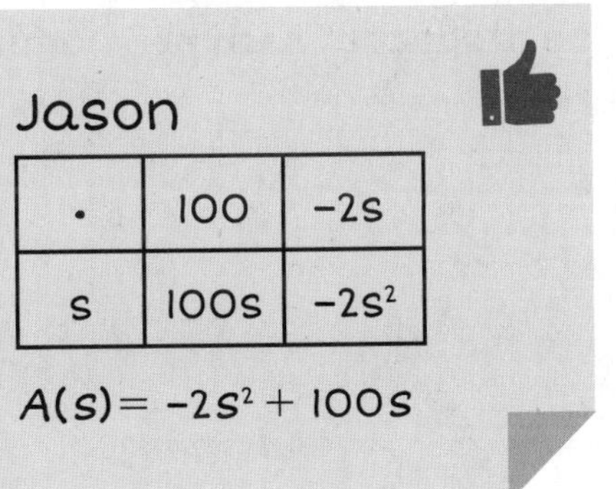

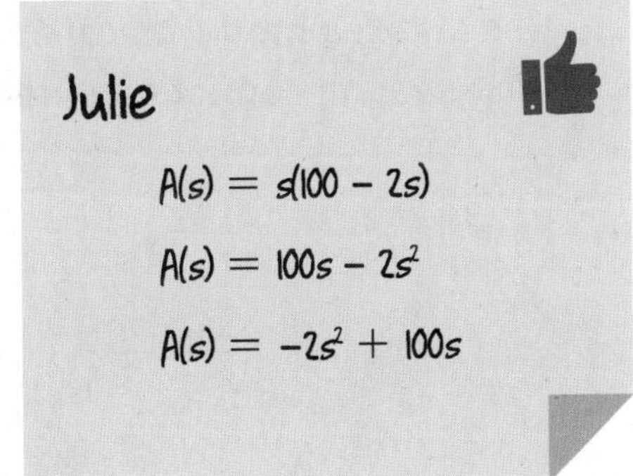

Develop a habit of writing answers in general form. It makes them easier to compare with others' answers.

a. Describe the strategy Jason used to calculate the product.

b. How is Jason's strategy similar to Julie's strategy?

Consider the ghost tour scenario from the previous topic. The revenue f the business is expressed as the product of a binomial times a binomial

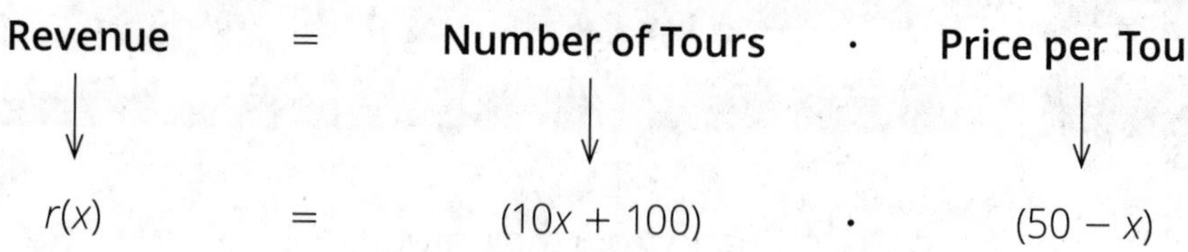

Revenue = Number of Tours · Price per Tour
$r(x) = (10x + 100) \cdot (50 - x)$

2. Finish Jason's process to write an equivalent polynomial function for revenue in general form.

The process of using a multiplication table to multiply polynomials is referred to as an area model.

·	50	$-x$
$10x$	$500x$	$-10x^2$
100		

3. Use an area model to calculate the product of each polynomia Write each product in general form.

Does it matter where you place the polynomials in the multiplication table?

a. $(3x + 2)(x - 4)$

b. $(x - 5)(x + 5)$

c. $(2x + 3)^2$

d. $(4x^2 + x - 1)(3x - 7)$

In Question 1, Julie uses the Distributive Property to multiply a monomial and a binomial. She wants to use the Distributive Property to multiply any polynomials.

How can you use technology to check your answers?

Worked Example

Consider the polynomials $x + 5$ and $x - 2$. You can use the Distributive Property to multiply these polynomials.

Distribute x to each term of $(x - 2)$, and then distribute 5 to each term of $(x - 2)$.

$$(x + 5)(x - 2) = (x)(x - 2) + (5)(x - 2)$$

$$= x^2 - 2x + 5x - 10$$

$$= x^2 + 3x - 10$$

4. Use the Distributive Property to determine each product. Write the polynomial in general form.

a. $(5x - 1)(2x + 1)$

b. $(x - 7)(x + 7)$

c. $(x + 2)(x - 9)$

d. $(2x^2 + 1)(3x^2 + x - 1)$

5. Explain the mistake in Cheyanne's thinking. Then determine the correct product.

Cheyanne

$$(x + 4)^2 = x^2 + 16.$$

I can just square each term to determine the product.

6. Based on the definition of closure, are polynomials closed under the operation of multiplication? Justify your answer.

ACTIVITY
1.6 Special Products When Multiplying Binomials

In this activity you will investigate the product of two linear factors when one is the sum of two terms and the other is the difference of the same two terms, and when the two linear factors are the same.

1. Determine each product.

a. $(x - 4)(x + 4) =$ ____________

$(x + 4)(x + 4) =$ ____________

$(x - 4)(x - 4) =$ ____________

b. $(x - 3)(x + 3) =$ ____________

$(x + 3)(x + 3) =$ ____________

$(x - 3)(x - 3) =$ ____________

c. $(3x - 1)(3x + 1) =$ ____________

$(3x + 1)(3x + 1) =$ ____________

$(3x - 1)(3x - 1) =$ ____________

d. $(2x - 1)(2x + 1) =$ ____________

$(2x + 1)(2x + 1) =$ ____________

$(2x - 1)(2x - 1) =$ ____________

2. What patterns do you notice between the factors and the products?

3. Multiply each pair of binomials.

$(ax - b)(ax + b) =$ ____________

$(ax + b)(ax + b) =$ ____________

$(ax - b)(ax - b) =$ ____________

Questions 1 and 3, you should have observed a few special products. e first type of special product is called the *difference of two squares*. The **ference of two squares** is an expression in the form $a^2 - b^2$ that has :tors $(a - b)(a + b)$.

Label the expressions in Questions 1 and 3 that are examples of the difference of two squares.

e second type of special product is called a *perfect square trinomial*. **erfect square trinomial** is an expression in the form $a^2 + 2ab + b^2$ the form $a^2 - 2ab + b^2$. A perfect square trinomial can be written as the uare of a binomial.

$$a^2 + 2ab + b^2 = (a + b)^2$$
$$a^2 - 2ab + b^2 = (a - b)^2$$

Label the expressions in Questions 1 and 3 that are examples of perfect square trinomials.

Use special products to determine each product.

a. $(x - 8)(x - 8)$

b. $(x + 8)(x - 8)$

c. $(x + 8)^2$

d. $(3x + 2)^2$

e. $(3x - 2)(3x - 2)$

f. $(3x - 2)(3x + 2)$

NOTES

TALK the TALK 

Putting It Into Practice

Match each expression with the equivalent polynomial.

Expressions	Polynomials
1. $(x^2 - 3) + (x^2 + 2)$	A. -1
2. $(x^2 - 3) - (x^2 + 2)$	B. $-2x^2 - 1$
3. $(x^2 - 3) - (x^2 - 2)$	C. $-2x^2 - 5$
4. $(x^2 - 3) + (x^2 - 2)$	D. $2x^2 - 1$
5. $-(x^2 + 3) - (x^2 - 2)$	E. $2x^2 - 5$
6. $-(x^2 + 3) - (x^2 + 2)$	F. -5
7. $(x - 3)(x + 2)$	G. $x^2 + 5x + 6$
8. $(x + 3)(x - 2)$	H. $x^2 - 5x + 6$
9. $(x + 3)(x + 2)$	I. $x^2 - x - 6$
10. $(x - 3)(x - 2)$	J. $x^2 + x - 6$

Expression Cards

$4x - 6x^2$	$125p$	$\frac{4}{5}r^3 + \frac{2}{5}r - 1$
$-\frac{2}{3}$	$y^2 - 4y + 10$	$5 - 7h$
$-3 + 7n + n^2$	-6	$-13s + 6$
$12.5t^3$	$78j^3 - 3j$	$25 - 18m^2$

Assignment

Write

Match each definition with its corresponding term.

1. polynomial
2. term
3. coefficient
4. monomial
5. binomial
6. trinomial
7. degree of a term
8. degree of a polynomial

a. a polynomial with only 1 term
b. the degree of the term with the greatest exponent
c. a mathematical expression involving the sum of powers in one or more variables multiplied by coefficients
d. a polynomial with exactly 3 terms
e. any number being multiplied by a power within a polynomial expression
f. each product in a polynomial expression
g. a polynomial with exactly 2 terms
h. the exponent of a term in a polynomial

Remember

- The difference of two squares is an expression in the form $a^2 - b^2$ that has factors $(a + b)(a - b)$.
- A perfect square trinomial is an expression in the form $a^2 + 2ab + b^2$ or in the form $a^2 - 2ab + b^2$ that has the factors $(a + b)^2$ and $(a - b)^2$, respectively.

Practice

1. Ramona and James each build a rocket launcher. They launch a model rocket using Ramona's launcher and on its way back down it lands on the roof of a building that is 320 feet tall. The height of the rocket can be represented by the equation $H_1(x) = -16x^2 + 200x$, where x represents the time in seconds and $H_1(x)$ represents the height. Ramona and James take the stairs to the roof of the building and re-launch the rocket using James's rocket launcher. The rocket lands back on the ground. The height of the rocket after this launch can be represented by the equation $H_2(x) = -16x^2 + 192x + 320$.
   a. Compare and contrast the polynomial functions.
   b. Use technology to sketch a graph of the functions.
   c. Does it make sense in terms of the problem situation to graph the functions outside of Quadrant I? Explain your reasoning.
   d. Explain why the graphs of these functions do not intersect.
   e. Ramona believes that she can add the two functions to determine the total height of the rocket at any given time. Write a function $S(x)$ that represents the sum of $H_1(x)$ and $H_2(x)$. Show your work.

f. Is Ramona correct? Explain your reasoning.

g. Subtract $H_1(x)$ from $H_2(x)$ and write a new function, $D(x)$, that represents the difference. Then, explain what this function means in terms of the problem situation.

2. Determine whether each expression is a polynomial. If so, identify the terms, coefficients, and degree of the polynomial. If not, explain your reasoning.

a. $-2b^4 + 4b - 1$

b. $6 - g^{-2}$

c. $8h^4$

d. $9w - w^3 + 5w^2$

e. $x^{\frac{1}{2}} + 2$

f. $\frac{4}{5}y + \frac{2}{3}y^2$

3. Given $A(x) = x^3 - 5x + 4$, $B(x) = 2x^2 + 5x - 6$, and $C(x) = -x^2 + 3$, determine each function. Write your answer in general form.

a. $D(x) = B(x) + C(x)$

b. $E(x) = A(x) + B(x)$

c. $F(x) = A(x) - C(x)$

d. $G(x) = C(x) - B(x)$

e. $H(x) = A(x) + B(x) - C(x)$

f. $J(x) = B(x) - A(x) + C(x)$

4. Determine each product.

a. $(x - 7)(x - 7)$

b. $(x + 10)(x - 10)$

c. $(x + 6)^2$

d. $(2x + 5)^2$

e. $(2x - 5)(2x - 5)$

f. $(2x - 5)(2x + 5)$

Stretch

Consider the binomials $(x + 3)$, $(2x + 1)$, and $(x - 4)$.

1. Without multiplying, make a conjecture about the degree of the product of these binomials. Explain how you determined your answer.
2. Without multiplying, make a conjecture about the number of terms in the product of these binomials. Explain your reasoning.
3. Two students determine the product of the 3 binomials using two different methods. Student 1 uses a multiplication table, and Student 2 uses the distributive Property. Their work is shown below. Determine which student multiplied correctly and identify the mistake the other student made. Explain how you determined your answer.

Student 1

·	x	3	$2x$	1
x	x^2	$3x$	$2x^2$	x
-4	$-4x$	-12	$-8x$	-4

The product is $3x^2 - 8x - 16$.

Student 2

$$(x + 3)(2x + 1)(x - 4) = (2x^2 + 7x + 3)(x - 4)$$
$$= 2x^3 - x^2 - 25x - 12$$

The product is $2x^3 - x^2 - 25x - 12$.

Review

1. Alfonzo is building a deck on his house. He was originally going to make it a square with a side length of x feet. Alfonzo decides to make it a rectangular deck, with 1 foot added to one pair of opposite sides and 2 feet added to the other pair of opposite sides.
   a. Determine the expressions for the length and width of the new deck in terms of x, the length of the sides of the original deck.
   b. Write the function for the area of the new deck, $A(x)$, in terms of x, the length of the sides of the original deck. Does this function have a minimum or maximum? Explain your answer.
2. Analyze each pair of representations. Then, answer each question and justify your reasoning.
   a. Which function's axis of symmetry has a greater x-value?

Function A

$f(x) = x^2 - 4x + 9$

Function B

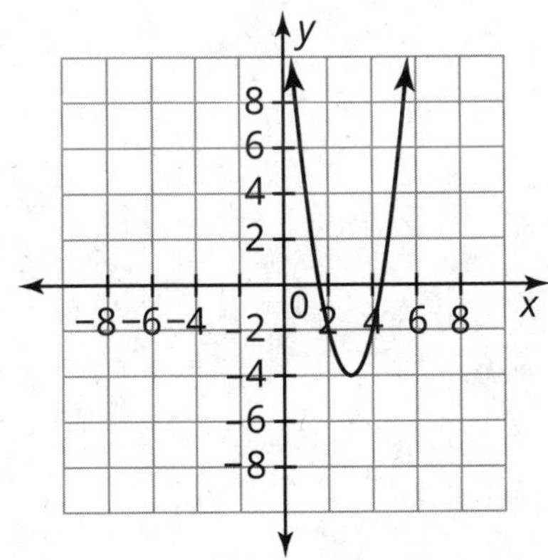

   b. Which function has a greater absolute minimum?

Function A

$f(x) = 3(x - 2)^2 - 6$

Function B

x	y
1	8
3	0
5	0

3. Write the equation of the function, $g(x)$, whose graph transforms the graph $f(x) = x^2$ by reflecting it across the x-axis, vertically stretching it by a factor of 2, and translating it up 5 units.
4. Graph the function, $g(x)$, whose graph transforms the graph $f(x) = x^2$ by vertically compressing it by a factor of $\frac{1}{3}$ and translating it down 7 units.

2

Solutions, More or Less

Representing Solutions to Quadratic Equations

Warm Up

1. Complete the grid by continuing to make squares with side lengths of 4 through 8. Connect the side lengths together, and then write an equation using exponents to represent each perfect square.

$1^2 = 1$, $2^2 = 4$, $3^2 = 9$

	1	2	3	4	5	6	7	8
1								
2								
3								
4								
5								
6								
7								
8								

Learning Goals

- Identify the zeros of a quadratic function, the roots of a quadratic equation, and the *x*-intercepts of a parabola using the equation of a quadratic function.
- Identify the double root of a quadratic equation as the two solutions of a quadratic equation at the minimum or maximum of the function.
- Write solutions of quadratic equations at specific output values using the axis of symmetry and the positive and negative square roots of the output value.
- Identify quadratic equations written as the difference of two perfect squares and rewrite these equations in factored form with a leading coefficient of 1.

Key Terms

- principal square root
- roots
- double root
- Zero Product Property

You have studied the graphs and equations for quadratic functions. How can you determine solutions of quadratic equations given different output values?

Plus or Minus

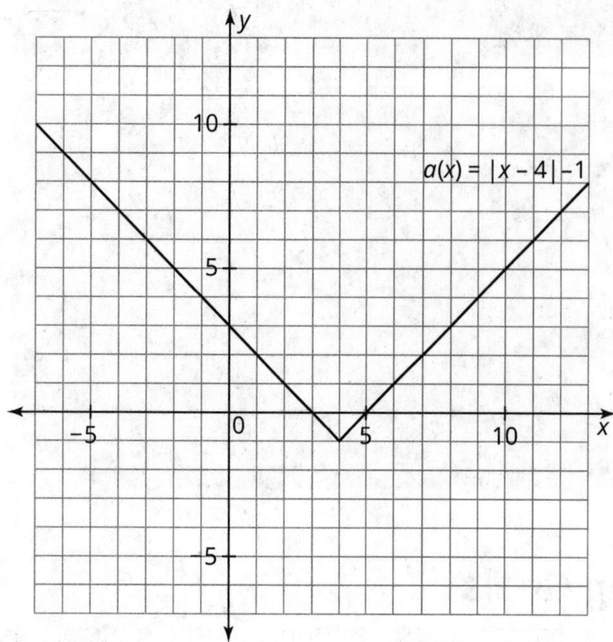

Consider the absolute value function graphed.

1. **Describe how the function is transformed from the basic function $f(x) = |x|$.**

2. **For each $y > -1$, how many solutions does the equation $y = |x - 4| - 1$ have? Use the graph to explain your answer.**

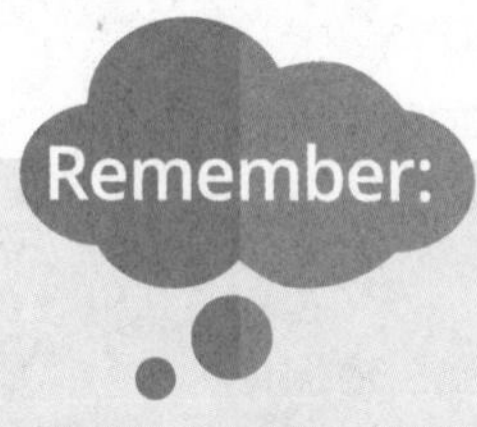

Solutions for a function at $y = 0$ are called the zeros of the function.
The symbol ± means "plus or minus."

3. **Determine the solutions to $|x - 4| - 1 = 0$ and identify the solutions on the graph.**

4. **Use the graph and the function equation to explain why Escher's equation is correct.**

> **Escher**
> This absolute value function is symmetric about the line $x = 4$. So, for every y-value greater than −1, the solutions to the absolute value function are $x = 4 \pm (y + 1)$.

ACTIVITY

2.1 Solutions of a Quadratic Function

Recall that a quadratic function is a function of degree 2, because the greatest power for any of its terms is 2. This means that it has 2 zeros, or 2 solutions at $y = 0$.

The two solutions of a basic quadratic function can be represented as square roots of numbers. Every positive number has two square roots, a positive square root (which is also called the **principal square root**) and a negative square root. To solve the equation $x^2 = 9$, you can take the square root of both sides of the equation.

$$\sqrt{x^2} = \pm\sqrt{9}$$
$$x = \pm 3$$

Solving $x^2 = 9$ on a graph means that you are looking for the points of intersection between $y = x^2$ and $y = 9$.

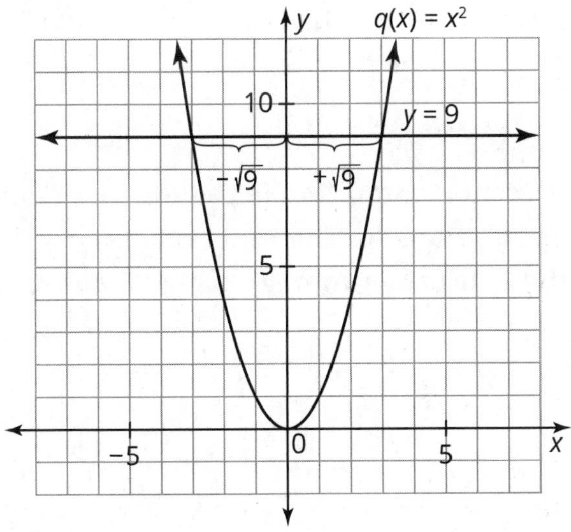

The square root property is $\sqrt{a^2} = \pm a$.

1. **Consider the graph of the function $q(x) = x^2$ shown.**

   a. **What is the equation for the axis of symmetry? Explain how you can use the function equation to determine your answer.**

   b. **Explain how the graph shows the two solutions for the function at $y = 9$ and their relationship to the axis of symmetry. Use the graph and the function equation to explain your answer.**

c. **Describe how you can determine the two solutions for the function at $y = 2$. Indicate the solutions on the graph.**

d. **Describe how you can determine the two solutions for the function at each y-value for $y \geq 0$.**

The x-coordinates of the x-intercepts of a graph of a quadratic function are called the zeros of the quadratic function. The zeros are called the **roots** of the quadratic equation.

The quadratic function $q(x) = x^2$ has two solutions at $y = 0$. Therefore, it ha 2 zeros: $x = +\sqrt{0}$ and $x = -\sqrt{0}$. These two zeros of the function, or roots of the equation, are the same number, 0, so $y = x^2$ is said to have a **doubl root,** or **1 unique root**.

The root of an equation indicates where the graph of the equation crosses the x-axis. A double root occurs when the graph just touches the x-axis bu does not cross it.

2. **Look back at Escher's equation in the Getting Started. How can you write the solutions for the function $q(x) = x^2$ in the same way, using the axis of symmetry? Explain your reasoning.**

e graphs of three quadratic functions, $f(x)$, $h(x)$, and $g(x)$, are shown.

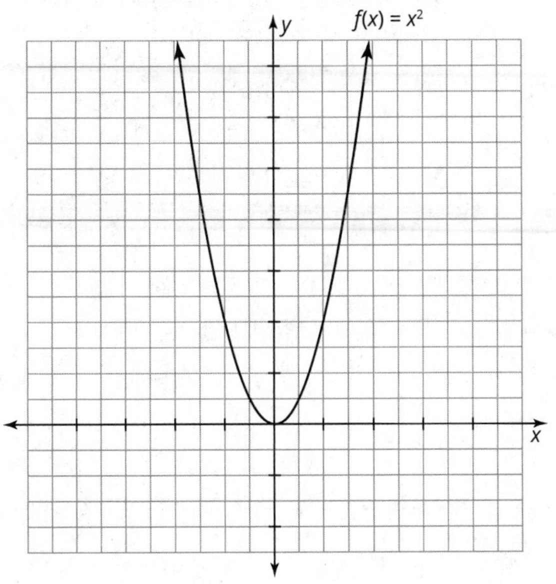

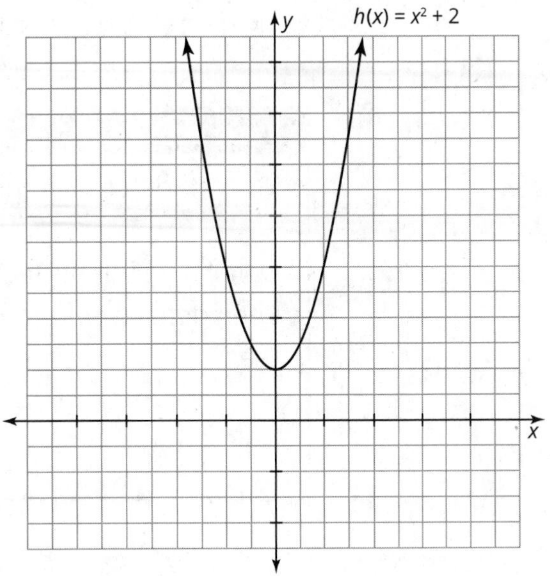

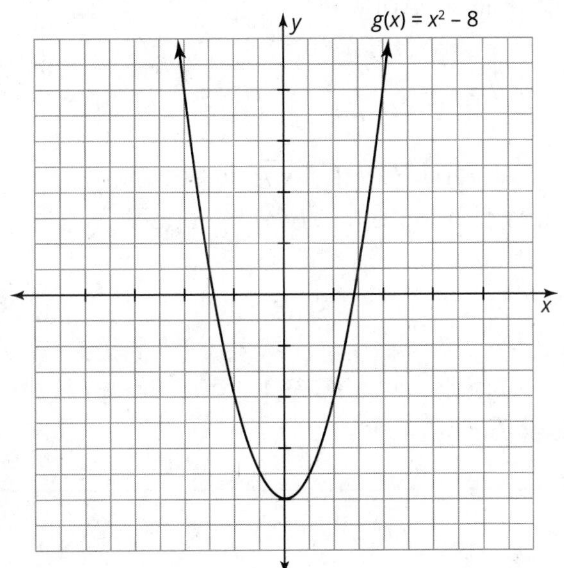

Use the graphs to identify the solutions to each equation. Then determine the solutions algebraically and write the solutions in terms of their respective distances from the axis of symmetry.

a. $14 = x^2 + 2$

b. $x^2 = 10$

c. $-5 = x^2 - 8$

d. $19 = x^2 + 4$

e. $x^2 - 8 = 1$

f. $6 = x^2$

Consider the graphs of $f(x)$, $h(x)$, and $g(x)$, which function has a double root? Explain your answer.

When you are solving quadratic equations you may encounter solutions that are not perfect squares. You can either determine the approximate value of the radical or rewrite it in an equivalent radical form.

Worked Example

You can determine the approximate value of $\sqrt{75}$.

Determine the perfect square that is closest to but less than 75. Then determine the perfect square that is closest to but greater than 75.

$$64 \leq 75 \leq 81$$

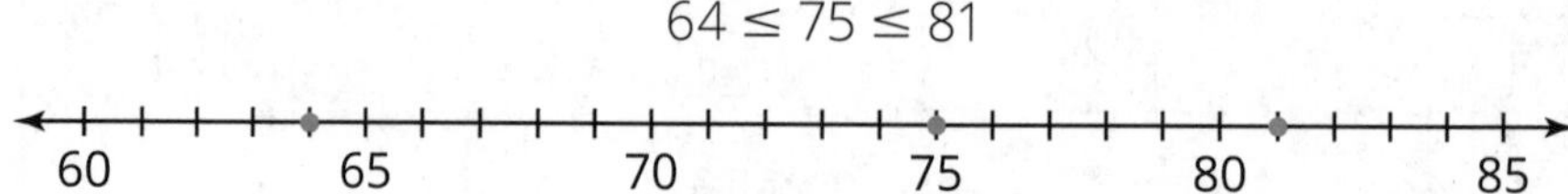

Determine the square roots of the perfect squares.

$\sqrt{64} = 8$ $\qquad$ $\sqrt{75} = ?$ $\qquad$ $\sqrt{81} = 9$

Now that you know that $\sqrt{75}$ is between 8 and 9, you can test the squares of numbers between 8 and 9.

$8.6^2 = 73.96$ $\qquad$ $8.7^2 = 75.69$

Since 75 is closer to 75.69 than 73.96, 8.7 is the approximate square root of $\sqrt{75}$.

Can you name all the perfect squares from 1^2 through 15^2?

Worked Example

You can use prime factors to rewrite $\sqrt{75}$ in an equivalent radical form.
First, rewrite the product of 75 to include any perfect square factors, and then extract the square roots of those perfect squares.

$$\begin{aligned}\sqrt{75} &= \sqrt{3 \cdot 5 \cdot 5}\\ &= \sqrt{3 \cdot 5^2}\\ &= \sqrt{3} \cdot \sqrt{5^2}\\ &= 5\sqrt{3}\end{aligned}$$

How could listing the prime factors of a radical expression help to extract square roots of perfect squares?

Estimate the value of each radical expression. Then, rewrite each radical by extracting all perfect squares, if possible.

a. $\sqrt{20}$

b. $\sqrt{26}$

c. $\sqrt{18}$

d. $\sqrt{116}$

Rewrite your answers from Question 3 by extracting perfect squares, if possible. Verify your rewritten answers using the graphs in Question 3.

ACTIVITY 2.2 Solutions from Standard Form to Factored Form

Think about:

Do you recognize the form of this quadratic?

Recall that a quadratic function written in factored form is in the form $f(x) = a(x - r_1)(x - r_2)$, where $a \neq 0$. In factored form, r_1 and r_2 represent the x-intercepts of the graph of the function.

1. **Determine the zeros of the function $z(x) = x^2 - 16$. Then, write the function in factored form.**

The function $z(x)$ in factored form is a quadratic function made up of two linear factors. Let's analyze the linear factors as separate linear functions, $g(x)$ and $h(x)$. Therefore $z(x) = g(x) \cdot h(x)$.

2. **Complete the table by writing the algebraic expressions to represent $g(x)$ and $h(x)$, and then determine the output values for the two linear factors and the quadratic product. Finally, sketch a graph of $z(x)$.**

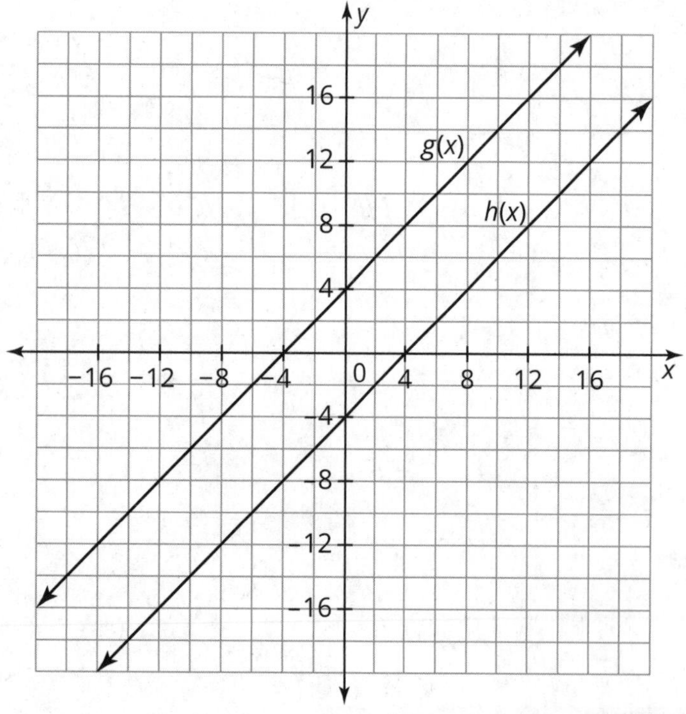

x	$g(x)$	$h(x)$	$z(x)$
			$x^2 - 16$
−4			
−2			
0			
2			
4			

e **Zero Product Property** states that if the product of two or more tors is equal to zero, then at least one factor must be equal to zero.

Worked Example

You can use the Zero Product Property to identify the zeros of a function when the function is written in factored form.

$0 = x^2 - 16$

$0 = (x + 4)(x - 4)$ Rewrite the quadratic as linear factors.

$x - 4 = 0$ and $x + 4 = 0$ Apply the Zero Product Property.

$x = 4$ $x = -4$ Solve each equation for x.

Explain how the zeros of the linear function factors are related to the zeros of the quadratic function product.

e function $z(x) = x^2 - 16$ has an a-value of 1 and a b-value of 0. u can use a similar strategy to determine the zeros of a function when e leading coefficient is not 1, but the b-value is still 0.

Worked Example

You can determine the zeros of the function $f(x) = 9x^2 - 1$ by setting $f(x) = 0$ and using the Properties of Equality to solve for x.

$$9x^2 - 1 = 0$$

$$9x^2 = 1$$

$$x^2 = \frac{1}{9}$$

$$x = \pm\frac{1}{3}$$

You can then use the leading coefficient of 9 and the zeros at $\frac{1}{3}$ and $-\frac{1}{3}$ to rewrite the quadratic function in factored form.

$$f(x) = 9\left(x - \frac{1}{3}\right)\left(x + \frac{1}{3}\right)$$

Consider the worked example.

a. Explain why $\sqrt{\frac{1}{9}} = \pm\frac{1}{3}$.

b. **Use graphing technology to verify that $9x^2 - 1 = 9\left(x - \frac{1}{3}\right)\left(x + \frac{1}{3}\right)$. How can you tell from the graph that the two equations are equivalent?**

Three students tried to rewrite the quadratic function $f(x) = 9\left(x - \frac{1}{3}\right)\left(x + \frac{1}{3}\right)$ as two linear factors using what they know about the difference of two squares.

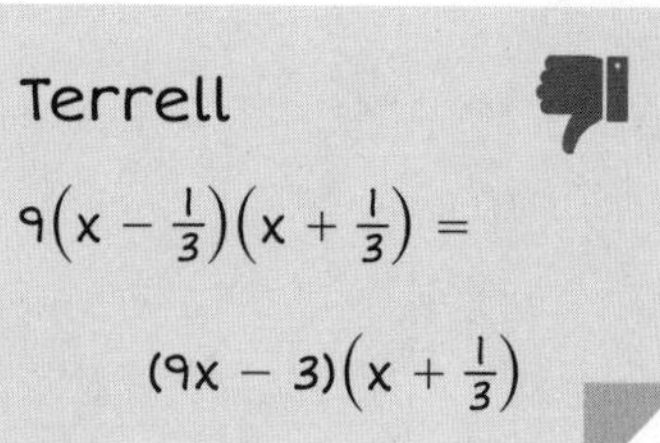

Jackson

$9\left(x - \frac{1}{3}\right)\left(x + \frac{1}{3}\right) =$

$(4.5x - 1.5)(4.5x + 1.5)$

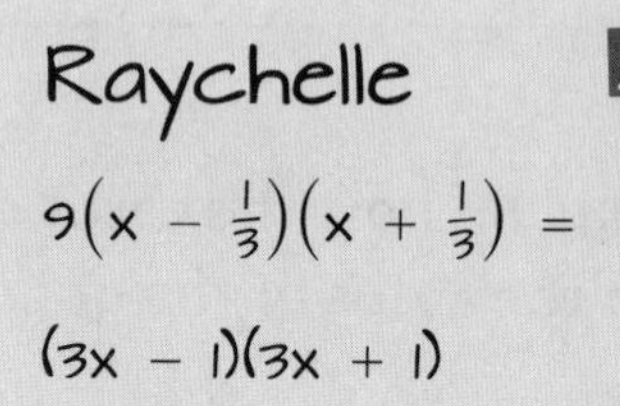

Are these expressions still in factored form?

5. **Explain why Terrell and Jackson are incorrect and why Raychelle is correct.**

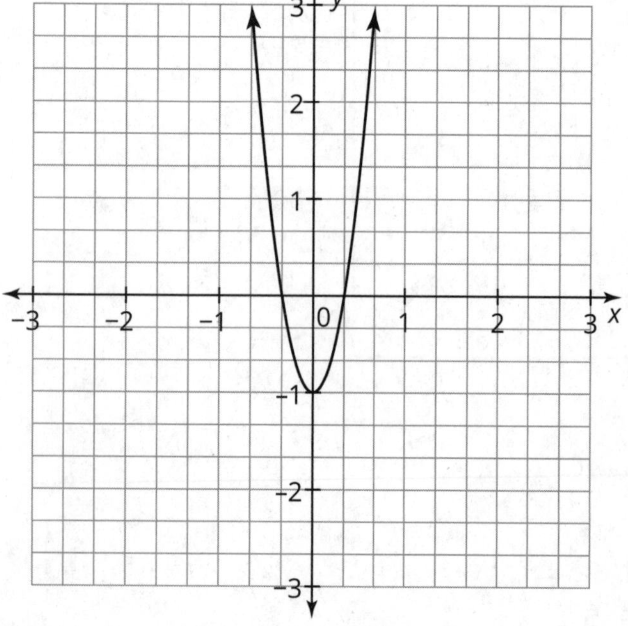

6. **The graph of $f(x) = 9x^2 - 1$ is shown.**

a. **Use Raychelle's function, $f(x) = (3x - 1)(3x + 1)$, to sketch a graph of the linear factors. Then use graphing technology verify that $9x^2 - 1 = (3x - 1)(3x + 1)$.**

b. **How do the zeros of the function relate to its two linear factors?**

For each function:

- **Sketch a graph. Label the axis of symmetry and the vertex.**
- **Use the Properties of Equality to identify the zeros, and then write the zeros in terms of their respective distances from the line of symmetry.**
- **Use what you know about the difference of two squares to rewrite each quadratic as the product of two linear factors. Then use the Zero Product Property to verify the values of x, when $f(x) = 0$.**
- **Use graphing technology to verify that the product of the two linear factors is equivalent to the given function.**

a. $f(x) = 4x^2 - 9$

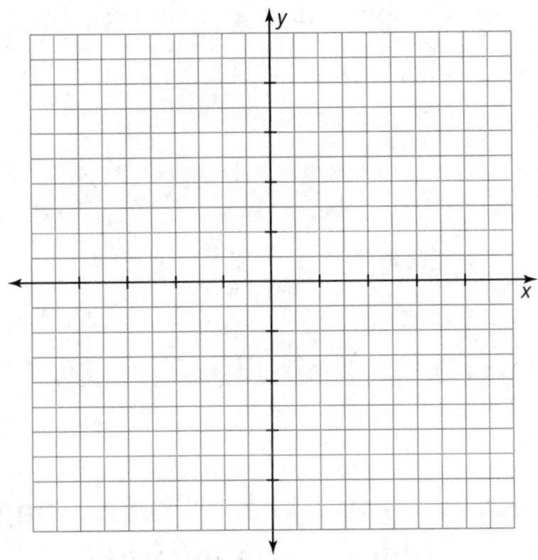

b. $f(x) = x^2 - 2$

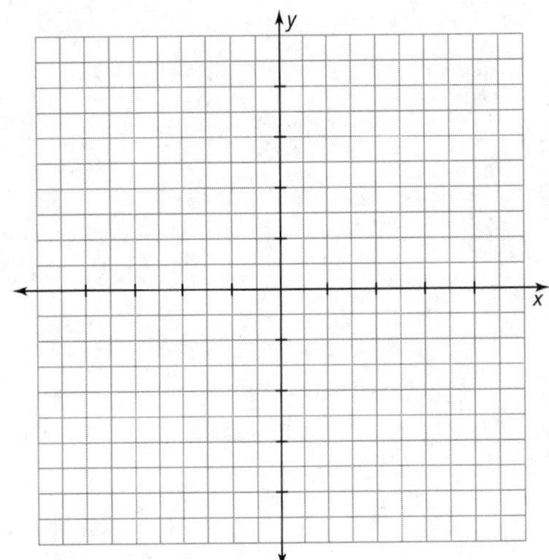

c. $f(x) = 25x^2 - 1$

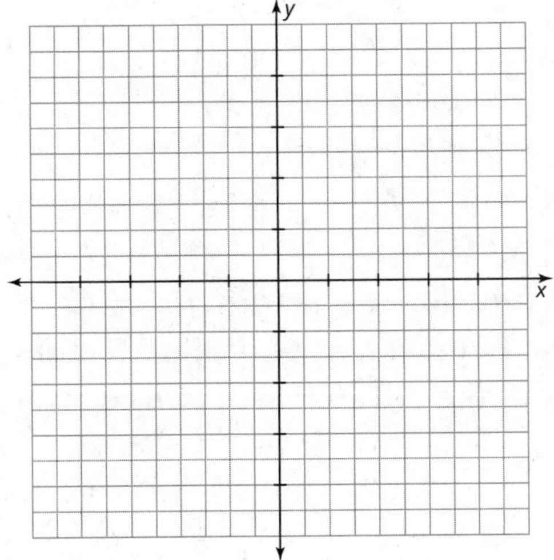

NOTES

TALK the TALK

The Difference of Squares

In this lesson you determined the zeros of quadratics written in the form $f(x) = ax^2 - c$.

1. Solve each equation.

a. $x^2 - 25 = 0$

b. $4x^2 - 1 = 0$

c. $9x^2 - 2 = 0$

d. $x^2 - 80 = 0$

2. Rewrite each quadratic function as two linear factors using what you know about the difference of two squares.

a. $f(x) = x^2 - 49$

b. $f(x) = \frac{4}{9}x^2 - 1$

c. $f(x) = 16x^2 - 10$

d. $f(x) = x^2 + 9$

3. Explain how to write any function of the form $f(x) = ax^2 - c$, where a and c are any real numbers, as two linear factors using what you know about the difference of two squares.

Assignment

Write

Complete each definition.

1. The Zero Product Property states that if the product of two or more factors is equal to ____________, then at least one factor must be equal to ____________.
2. Every positive number has both a ____________ square root and a ____________ square root.
3. The function $f(x) = x^2$ has a ____________ at (0, 0).

Remember

Any quadratic function of the form $f(x) = ax^2 - d$ can be rewritten as two linear factors in the form $(\sqrt{ax} - \sqrt{d})(\sqrt{ax} + \sqrt{d})$.

Practice

1. Determine the solutions for each equation. Identify the solutions on one of the graphs. Then, write the solutions in terms of their respective differences from the axis of symmetry.

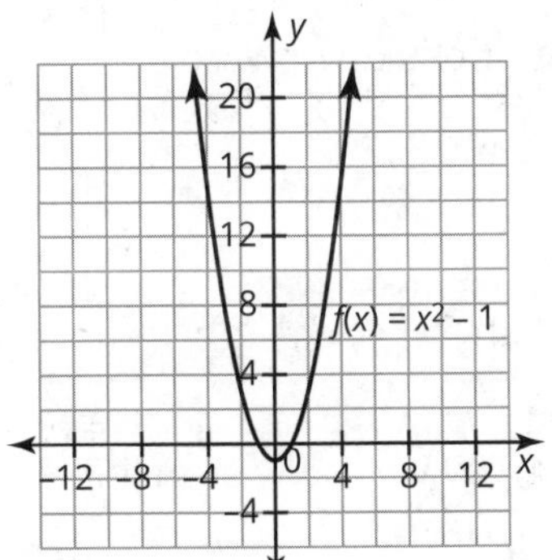

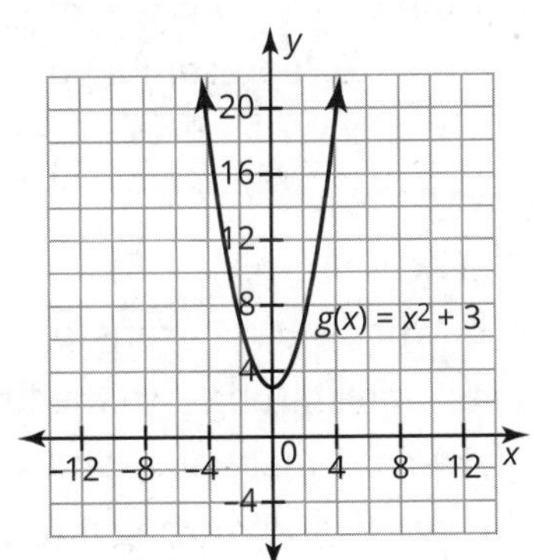

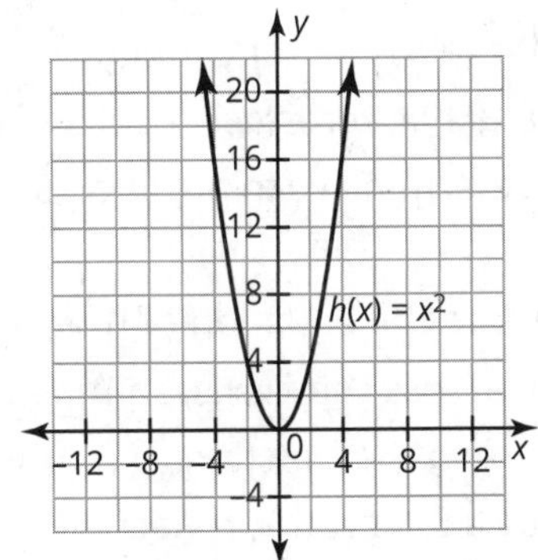

a. $8 = x^2 + 3$ b. $7 = x^2$ c. $2 = x^2 - 1$

d. $x^2 = 11$ e. $x^2 + 9 = 13$ f. $14 = x^2 - 1$

2. Estimate the value of each radical expression. Then, rewrite each radical by extracting all perfect squares, if possible.

a. $\sqrt{21}$ b. $\sqrt{80}$ c. $\sqrt{63}$

d. $\sqrt{32}$ e. $\sqrt{98}$ f. $\sqrt{192}$

3. Rewrite each quadratic function as two linear factors using what you know about the difference of two squares.

a. $f(x) = 9x^2 - 16$ b. $f(x) = x^2 - 8$

c. $f(x) = 36x^2 - 1$ d. $f(x) = 25x^2 - 12$

Stretch

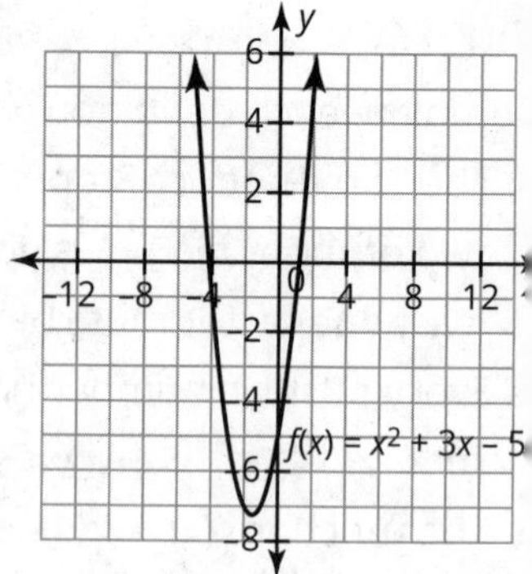

1. Consider the graph of the function $f(x) = x^2 + 3x - 5$.
   a. Determine the solutions for the equation $x^2 + 3x - 5 = 5$. Identify the solutions on the graph.
   b. Rewrite the equation from part (a) so that the right side of the equation is 0. What do the solutions from part (a) represent in this new equation?
   c. Use your solutions from part (a) to write a product of two binomials, $(x - a)(x - b)$, where a and b are the solutions from part (a). How does this relate to the left side of the equation in part (b)?

Review

1. Identify the axis of symmetry of the graph of $f(x) = -5(x - 3)(x + 12)$.
2. Write a quadratic function in factored form to represent a parabola that opens downward and has zeros at $(-6, 0)$ and $(-2, 0)$.
3. Determine each product. Show your work.
   a. $(2x - 3)(4x + 7)$
   b. $(3x + 5)\left(-\frac{1}{2}x + 16\right)$.
4. Write the equation of the function, $g(x)$, whose graph transforms the graph $f(x) = x^2 + 1$ by reflecting it across the x-axis, shifting it up 6 units, and shifting it to the left 4 units.
5. Graph the function, $g(x)$, whose graph transforms the graph $f(x) = (x - 4)^2$ by vertically stretching it by a factor of 2, reflecting it across the x-axis, and moving it to the left 3 units.

3

Transforming Solutions

Solutions to Quadratic Equations in Vertex Form

Warm Up

Describe the transformations to the graph of the basic function $f(x) = x^2$ given each equation.

1. $y = (x - 4)^2$

2. $y = \frac{1}{2}(x + 1)^2$

3. $y = -(10 + x)^2 - 3$

4. $y = (8 + x)^2 + 1$

Learning Goals

- Identify solutions to and roots of quadratic equations given in the form $f(x) = (x - c)^2$.
- Identify solutions to and roots of quadratic equations given in the form $f(x) = a(x - c)^2$.
- Identify solutions to and roots of quadratic equations given in the form $f(x) = a(x - c)^2 + d$.
- Identify zeros of quadratic functions written in vertex form.

You have explored transformations of quadratic functions and vertex form. How can you use vertex form and transformations to determine solutions to quadratic equations?

GETTING STARTED

Slide, Slide, Slippity Slide

The coordinate plane shows the graph of the function $f(x) = (x - 1)^2$.

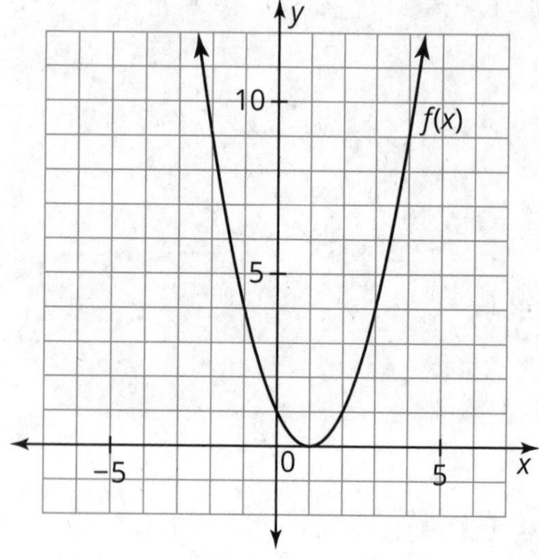

1. **Describe the transformation applied to the basic function $f(x) = x^2$ that produces the graph of this function.**

Lindsay and Casey determined the zeros of the function $f(x) = (x - 1)^2$ algebraically in different ways

Lindsay

$$0 = (x - 1)^2$$

$$0 = (x - 1)(x - 1)$$

The Zero Product Property says that one or both of the factors is equal to 0.

So, $x = 1$.

The equation has a double root at $x = 1$.

Casey

$$(x - 1)^2 = 0$$

$$\sqrt{(x - 1)^2} = \sqrt{0}$$

$$\pm(x - 1) = 0$$

$+(x - 1) = 0$	$-(x - 1) = 0$
$x = 1$	$-x + 1 = 0$
	$-x = -1$
	$x = 1$

The only unique solution for $y = 0$ is $x = 1$.

2. **How can you use Lindsay's or Casey's work to write solutions to the function in terms of their respective distances from the axis of symmetry?**

ACTIVITY 3.1

Solutions for Horizontal Translations

You have used graphs to solve equations. In this activity, you will use the graph of a quadratic equation to determine its solutions.

Solving $(x - 1)^2 = 9$ on a graph means locating where $y = (x - 1)^2$ intersects with $y = 9$.

Worked Example

Consider the equation $(x - 1)^2 = 9$.

You can use the Properties of Equality to determine the solutions to an equation in this form.

First take the square root of both sides of the equation and then isolate x.

$$(x - 1)^2 = 9$$

$$\sqrt{(x - 1)^2} = \sqrt{9}$$

$$x - 1 = \pm 3$$

$$x = 1 \pm 3$$

1. Consider the graph of $y = (x - 1)^2$ in the Getting Started.

a. Graph the equation $y = 9$ on the same graph.

b. Show the solutions on the graph. Interpret the solutions 1 ± 3 in terms of the axis of symmetry and the points on the parabola $y = (x - 1)^2$.

c. What are the solutions to the equation $(x - 1)^2 = 9$?

2. **For each equation, show the solutions on the graph and interpr the solutions in terms of the axis of symmetry and the points o the parabola. Then write the solutions.**

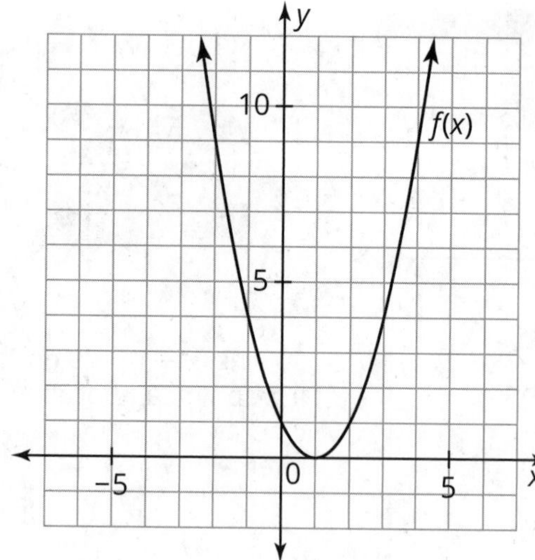

a. $(x - 1)^2 = 4$

b. $(x - 1)^2 = 5$

3. **Determine the exact and approximate solutions for each of the given equations.**

a. $(r + 8)^2 = 83$

b. $(17 - d)^2 = 55$

ACTIVITY
3.2 Solutions for Vertical Dilations

You have seen how to solve an equation for a quadratic function in the form $f(x) = (x - c)^2$, which represents a horizontal translation of the function. In this activity, you will consider quadratic equations with an additional vertical dilation. First, let's start with just a horizontal translation.

1. Consider the function $f(x) = (x - 5)^2$.

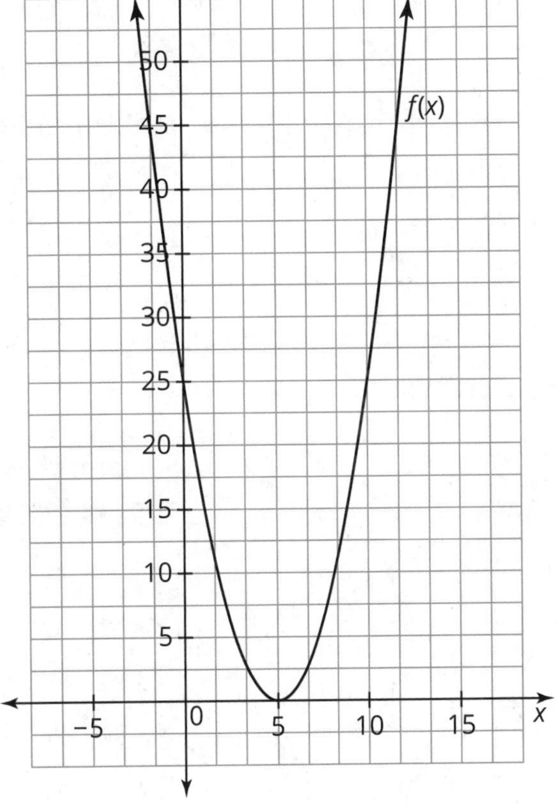

a. Determine the solutions to $0 = (x - 5)^2$. Solve algebraically and label the solution on the graph.

b. Interpret your solutions in terms of the axis of symmetry and the parabola $y = (x - 5)^2$.

c. Describe the zeros of this function.

Now let's add a dilation factor.

2. Consider the function $g(x) = 2(x - 5)^2$.

a. Write $g(x)$ in terms of $f(x)$ and describe the transformation.

b. Sketch a graph on the same coordinate plane as $f(x)$.

c. How have the zeros changed from $f(x)$ to $g(x)$?

3. Parker formulated a conjecture about how the solutions of the transformed quadratic equation change from the original equation.

The solutions of the original function are $x = 5 \pm \sqrt{y}$, so the solutions to the transformed equation will be $x = 5 \pm 2\sqrt{y}$.

Is Parker correct? If so, explain why. If not, describe the correc solutions for the transformed quadratic equation.

4. Make a conjecture. How does changing the sign of the *a*-value affect the solutions to the quadratic equations in this form?

5. Solve each quadratic equation. Give both exact and approximate solutions.

a. $(x - 4)^2 = 2$

b. $2(x - 1)^2 = 18$

c. $-2(x - 1)^2 = -18$

d. $4(x + 5)^2 = 21$

e. $-\frac{1}{2}(x + 8)^2 = -32$

f. $\frac{2}{3}(12 - x)^2 = 1$

ACTIVITY
3.3

Solutions for Vertical Translations

'ou have determined solutions to quadratic equations, given an equation n the form $f(x) = a(x - c)^2$. How can you solve a quadratic equation that ılso includes a vertical translation in the form $f(x) = a(x - c)^2 + d$?

A quadratic function in vertex form is written $f(x) = a(x - k)^2 + h$.

'he graph of $g(x) = 2(x - 5)^2$ is shown. You know that the solution to the equation $0 = 2(x - 5)^2$ is $x = 5$.

1. Consider the function $h(x) = 2(x - 5)^2 - 1$.

a. Write $h(x)$ in terms of $g(x)$ and describe the transformation.

b. Sketch a graph of $h(x)$ on the same coordinate plane as $g(x)$.

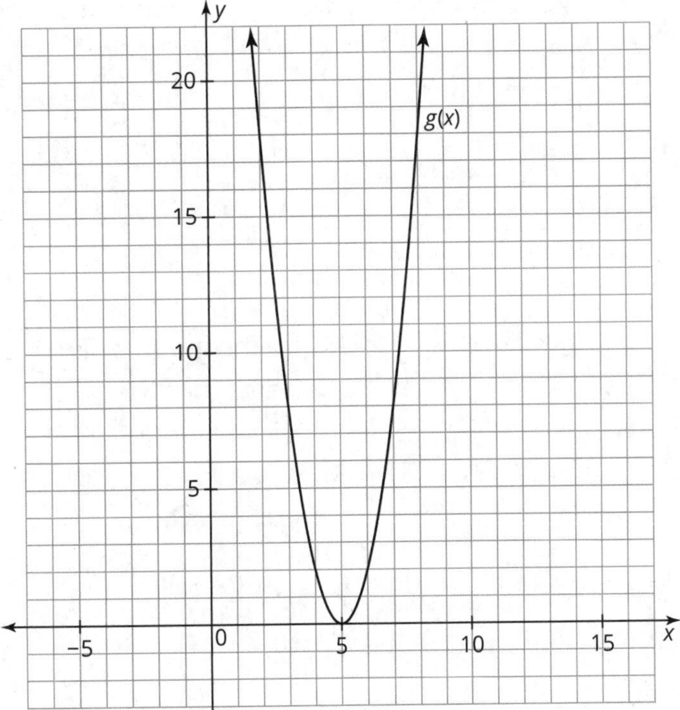

2. Consider the equation $0 = 2(x - 5)^2 - 1$.

a. Determine the solution algebraically and label the solution on the graph.

b. Interpret the solutions in terms of the axis of symmetry and the parabola $y = 2(x - 5)^2 - 1$.

c. Describe the zeros of this function.

Now, let's investigate the effect of an equation in the form $f(x) = a(x - c)^2 + d$ where $a > 0$ and $d > 0$. Consider the function $j(x) = 2(x - 5)^2 + 1$ graphed as shown.

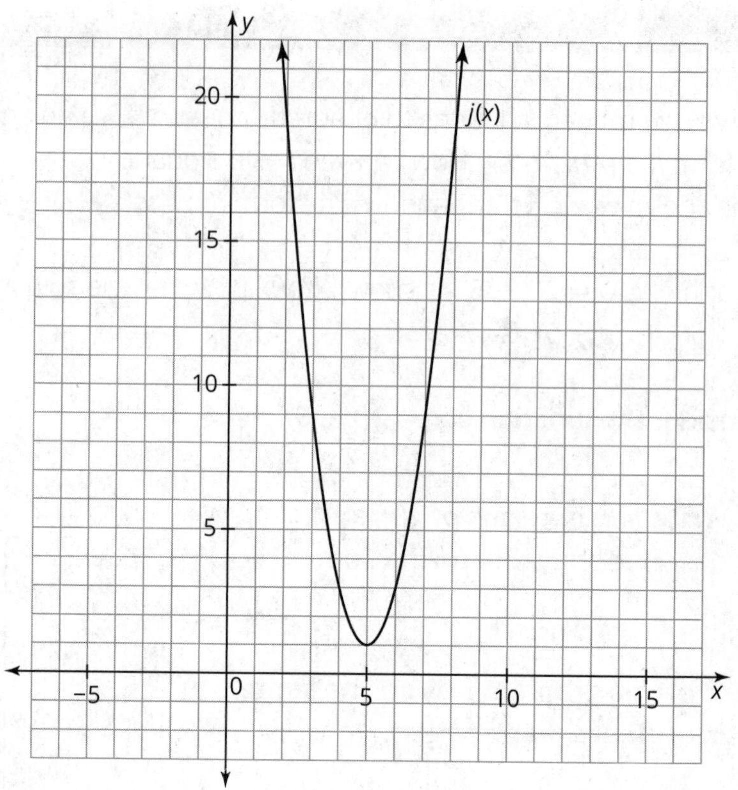

Notice the graph of $j(x)$ does not cross the x-axis, which means there are no real zeros for this function.

3. Solve $0 = 2(x - 5)^2 + 1$ algebraically to show that x is not a real number.

While there are no real zeros in this function, there is another type of zero you will learn about later in this topic.

Sketch a graph of each quadratic function. Determine the types of zeros of each function. Solve algebraically and interpret on the graph in terms of the axis of symmetry and the points on the parabola.

A quadratic function can have 1 unique real zero, 2 real zeros, or no real zeros.

a. $f(x) = -3(x - 2)^2 + 4$

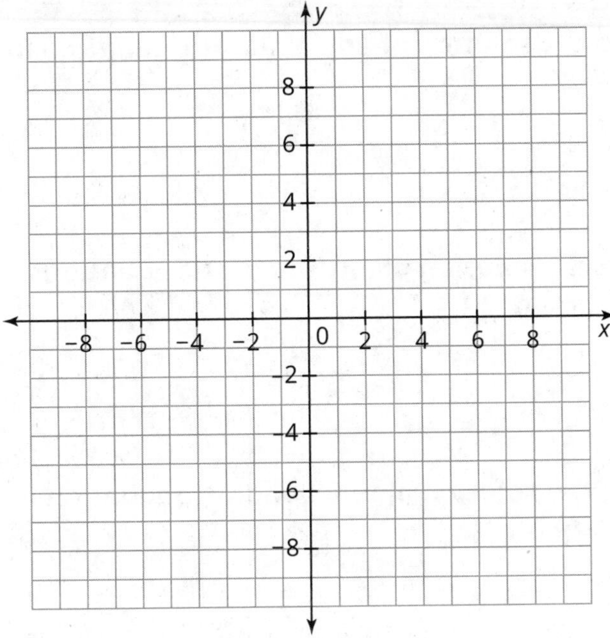

b. $f(x) = \frac{1}{4}(x + 5)^2 + 2$

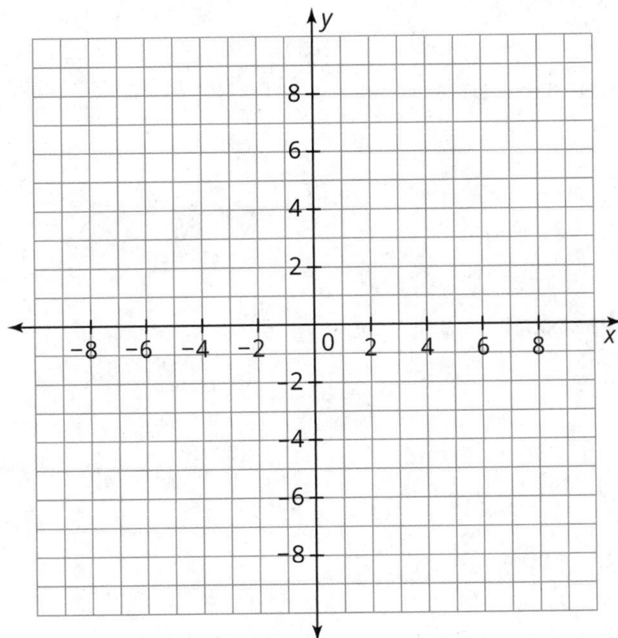

NOTES

TALK the TALK 

Spell It Out

1. Describe the solution of any quadratic equation in the form $(x - c)^2 = 0$.

2. Describe the solution of any quadratic equation in the form $(x - c)^2 + d = 0$.

3. Describe the solution of any quadratic equation in the form $a(x - c)^2 + d = 0$.

4. Write an equation and sketch a graph that shows each number of zeros.

   a. 1 unique real zero

   b. 2 real zeros

   c. no real zeros

Assignment

Write

Describe the number of possible real zeros for any quadratic function.

Remember

The solutions to a quadratic equation can be represented as the axis of symmetry plus or minus its distance to the parabola.

Practice

1. Sketch a graph of each quadratic function. Determine the zeros of each function and write each in terms of the axis of symmetry and its distance to the parabola.
   a. $f(x) = (x - 3)^2$
   b. $f(x) = (x + 5)^2$
   c. $f(x) = \left(x - \frac{1}{2}\right)^2$
   d. $f(x) = (x - 6)^2$
   e. $f(x) = \left(x + \frac{15}{7}\right)^2$
   f. $f(x) = (x + 7)^2$

2. Sketch a graph of each quadratic function. Determine the zeros of each function and write in terms of the axis of symmetry and its distance to the parabola.
   a. $f(x) = 2(x - 1)^2 - 1$
   b. $f(x) = \frac{1}{2}(x + 2)^2 - 5$
   c. $f(x) = 4\left(x + \frac{1}{3}\right)^2 - 1$
   d. $f(x) = -3(x - 6)^2$
   e. $f(x) = \frac{3}{4}(x + 5)^2 - \frac{2}{3}$
   f. $f(x) = (x - 4)^2 - 2$

Stretch

A quadratic function has zeros at $x = -2 \pm \sqrt{15}$. Write the function in general form. Show your work.

Review

1. Use the given characteristics to write a function $R(x)$ in vertex form. Then, sketch the graph of $R(x)$ and the basic function $f(x) = x^2$ on a coordinate plane.
   a. The function has an absolute maximum, is vertically dilated by a factor of $\frac{1}{3}$, and is translated 8 units down and 4 units to the left.
   b. The function has an absolute minimum, is vertically dilated by a factor of 4, and is translated 2 units up and 6 units to the right.
2. Estimate the value of the radical expression $\sqrt{54}$. Then, rewrite the radical by extracting all perfect squares, if possible.
3. Rewrite the quadratic function, $f(x) = 16x^2 - 3$, as the product of linear factors.
4. Identify the form of each quadratic equation. Then identify what characteristic of the function can be determined by the structure of the equation.
   a. $y = (x - 7)(x + 5)$
   b. $y = -3(x + 1)^2 - 4$

4

The Missing Link

Factoring and Completing the Square

Warm Up

Use the Distribute Property to determine each product.

1. $(x + 1)(x + 2)$

2. $(x + 4)(x - 5)$

3. $(2x - 3)(x - 4)$

4. $(x + 2)^2$

Learning Goals

- Factor out the greatest common factor (GCF) of polynomials.
- Rewrite quadratic equations of the form $x^2 + bx$ in vertex form by completing the square.
- Factor quadratic trinomials to determine the roots of quadratic equations and to rewrite quadratic functions in forms that reveal different key characteristics.
- Demonstrate the reasoning behind the method of completing the square and use the method to determine the roots of quadratic equations of the form $ax^2 + bx + c$.

Key Term

- completing the square

You have solved many different quadratic equations written as binomials. How can you solve trinomial quadratic equations?

LOL the GCF Again

In previous lessons, you multiplied two linear expressions to determine a quadratic expression. You have also rewritten quadratics in factored form

You may remember that one way to factor an expression is to factor out t greatest common factor.

Worked Example

Consider the polynomial $3x + 15$. You can factor out the greatest common factor of the two terms, 3.

$$3x + 15 = 3x + 3(5)$$

$$= 3(x + 5)$$

$$3x + 15 = 3(x + 5)$$

1. **Factor out the greatest common factor for each polynomial, if possible.**

   a. $4x + 12$

   b. $x^2 - 5x$

   c. $3x^2 - 9x - 3$

   d. $-x - 7$

   e. $2x - 11$

   f. $5x^2 - 10x + 5$

ACTIVITY

4.1

Factoring Trinomials

'ou have used special products—the difference of two squares and perfect square trinomials—to rewrite trinomials in factored form. In this activity, you will rewrite trinomials that are not special products in factored form.

1. **Consider the equation $y = x^2 + 10x + 16$.**

   a. **Use the graph to identify the roots of the equation.**

   b. **Rewrite the original equation in factored form.**

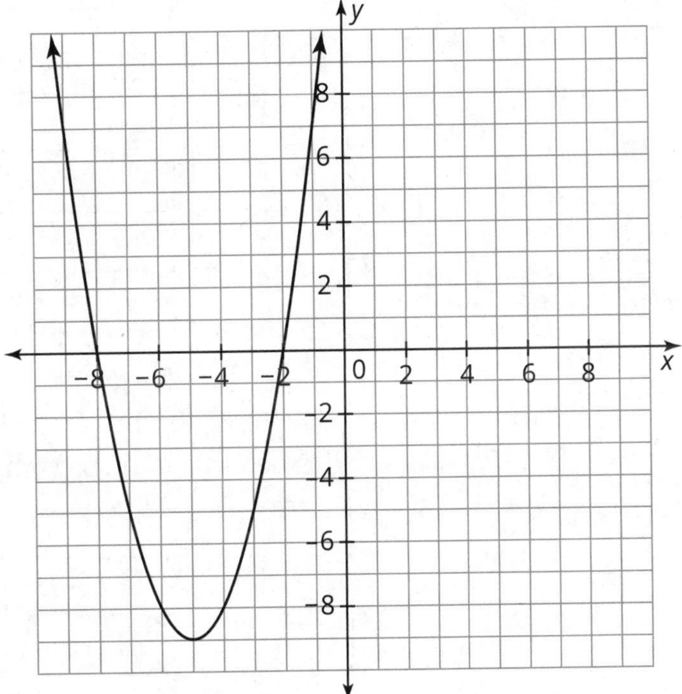

Let's consider a strategy to factor a trinomial without graphing.

You can use a multiplication table to factor trinomials.

Worked Example

Factor the trinomial $x^2 + 10x + 16$.

Start by writing the leading term (x^2) and the constant term (16) in the table.

·		
	x^2	
		16

Determine the two factors of the leading term and write them in the table.

·	x	
x	x^2	
		16

Determine the factor pairs of the constant term. The factors of 16 are (1)(16), (2)(8), and (4)(4). Experiment with factors of the constant term to determine the pair whose sum is the coefficient of the middle term, 10.

·	x	8
x	x^2	$8x$
2	$2x$	16

The sum of $2x$ and $8x$ is $10x$.
So, $x^2 + 10x + 16 = (x + 2)(x + 8)$.

2. Explain why the other factor pairs for $c = 16$ do not work.

Use the worked example to factor each trinomial.

a. $x^2 + 17x + 16$

$\cdot$		
	x^2	
		16

b. $x^2 + 6x - 16$

$\cdot$		
	x^2	
		-16

c. $x^2 - 6x - 16$

$\cdot$		
	x^2	
		-16

Factor each trinomial.

a. $x^2 + 5x - 24$

b. $x^2 - 3x - 28$

Consider the two examples shown.

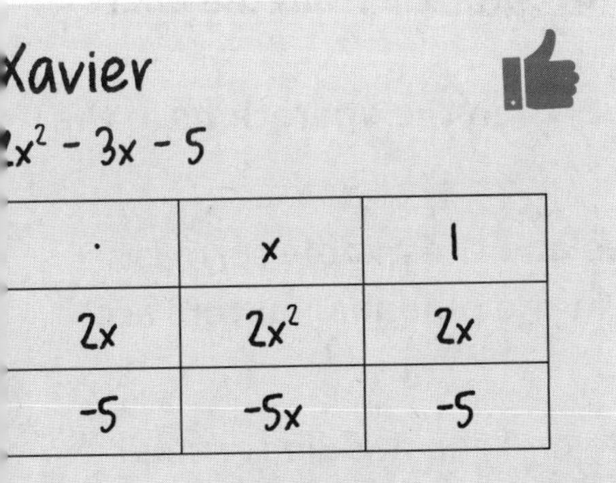

Xavier

$2x^2 - 3x - 5$

$\cdot$	x	1
$2x$	$2x^2$	$2x$
-5	$-5x$	-5

$2x^2 - 3x - 5 = (2x - 5)(x + 1)$

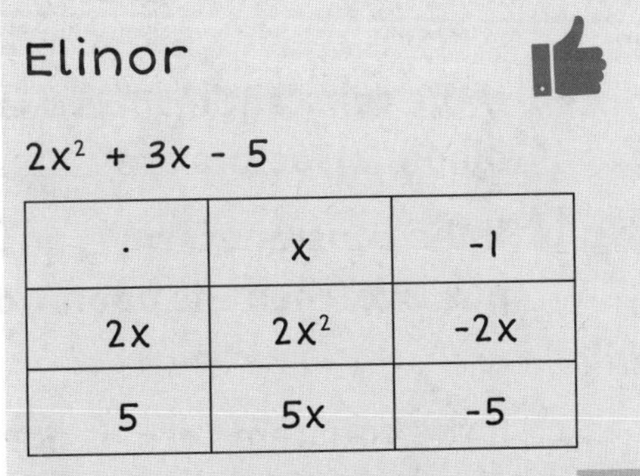

Elinor

$2x^2 + 3x - 5$

$\cdot$	x	-1
$2x$	$2x^2$	$-2x$
5	$5x$	-5

$2x^2 + 3x - 5 = (2x + 5)(x - 1)$

a. Compare the two given trinomials. What is the same and what is different about the values of a, b, and c?

The general form of a quadratic equation is a trinomial in the form $y = ax^2 + bx + c$.

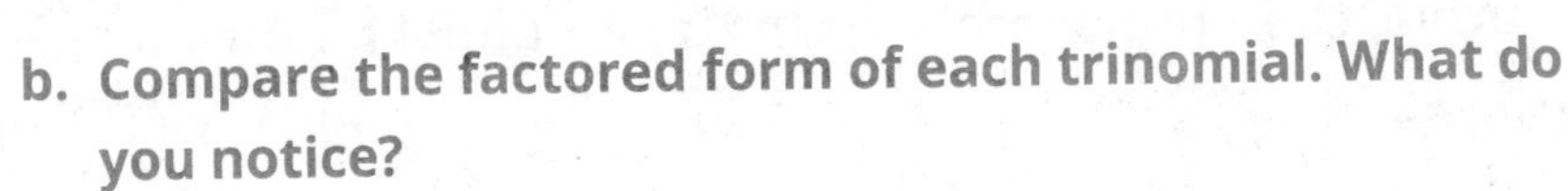

b. Compare the factored form of each trinomial. What do you notice?

6. **Choose from the list to write the correct factored form for each trinomial.**

a. $x^2 + 5x + 4 =$ ____________
$x^2 - 5x + 4 =$ ____________
$x^2 + 3x - 4 =$ ____________
$x^2 - 3x - 4 =$ ____________

- $(x + 1)(x - 4)$
- $(x + 1)(x + 4)$
- $(x - 1)(x + 4)$
- $(x - 1)(x - 4)$

b. $2x^2 + 7x + 3 =$ ____________
$2x^2 - 7x + 3 =$ ____________
$2x^2 + 5x - 3 =$ ____________
$2x^2 - 5x - 3 =$ ____________

- $(2x - 1)(x - 3)$
- $(2x - 1)(x + 3)$
- $(2x + 1)(x + 3)$
- $(2x + 1)(x - 3)$

c. $x^2 + 7x + 10 =$ ____________
$x^2 - 7x + 10 =$ ____________
$x^2 + 3x - 10 =$ ____________
$x^2 - 3x - 10 =$ ____________

- $(x - 2)(x + 5)$
- $(x + 2)(x + 5)$
- $(x - 2)(x - 5)$
- $(x + 2)(x - 5)$

7. **Analyze the signs of each quadratic expression written in general form and the operations in the binomial factors in Question 6. Then complete each sentence with a phrase from the box.**

the same
different
both positive
both negative
one positive and one negative

a. **If the constant term is positive, then the operations in the binomial factors are** ____________.

b. **If the constant term is positive and the middle term is positive, then the operations in the binomial factors are** ____________.

c. **If the constant term is positive and the middle term is negative, then the operations in the binomial factors are** ____________.

d. **If the constant term is negative, then the operations in the binomial factors are** ____________.

e. **If the constant term is negative and the middle term is positive, then the operations in the binomial factors are** ____________.

f. **If the constant term is negative and the middle term is negative, then the operations in the binomial factors are** ____________.

Factor each quadratic expression.

a. $x^2 + 8x + 15 =$ ______

$x^2 - 8x + 15 =$ ______

$x^2 + 2x - 15 =$ ______

$x^2 - 2x - 15 =$ ______

b. $x^2 + 10x + 24 =$ ______

$x^2 - 10x + 24 =$ ______

$x^2 + 2x - 24 =$ ______

$x^2 - 2x - 24 =$ ______

. Grace, Elaine, and Maggie were asked to factor the trinomial $15 + 2x - x^2$.

Grace	Elaine	Maggie
$15 + 2x - x^2$	$15 + 2x - x^2$	$15 + 2x - x^2$
$(5 - x)(3 + x)$	$(5 - x)(3 + x)$	$-x^2 + 2x + 15$
	$(x - 5)(x + 3)$	$-(x^2 - 2x - 15)$
		$-(x - 5)(x + 3)$

Who's correct? Explain how that student(s) determined the factors. For the student(s) who is not correct, state why and make the correction.

Marilynn and Jake were working together to factor the trinomial $4x^2 + 22x + 24$. They first noticed that there was a greatest common factor and rewrote the trinomial as

$$2(2x^2 + 11x + 12).$$

Next, they considered the factor pairs for $2x^2$ and the factor pairs for 12.

$2x^2$: $(2x)(x)$
12: $(1)(12)$
$(2)(6)$
$(3)(4)$

Marilynn listed out all the possible combinations.

$2(2x + 1)(x + 12)$
$2(2x + 12)(x + 1)$

$2(2x + 2)(x + 6)$
$2(2x + 6)(x + 2)$

$2(2x + 3)(x + 4)$
$2(2x + 4)(x + 3)$

Jake immediately eliminated four out of the six possible combinations because the terms of one of the linear expressions contained common factors.

$2(2x + 1)(x + 12)$
~~$2(2x + 12)(x + 1)$~~

~~$2(2x + 2)(x + 6)$~~
~~$2(2x + 6)(x + 2)$~~

$2(2x + 3)(x + 4)$
~~$2(2x + 4)(x + 3)$~~

10. Explain Jake's reasoning. Then circle the correct factored form of $4x^2 + 22x + 24$.

ACTIVITY 4.2

Solving Quadratic Equations by Factoring

'ou have used Properties of Equality to solve equations in the orms shown.

$$y = x^2 + d$$
$$y = (x - c)^2$$
$$y = a(x - c)^2$$
$$y = a(x - c)^2 + d$$

.et's consider strategies to solve quadratics in the form $y = ax^2 + bx + c$ ısing the factoring strategies you just learned.

Worked Example

You can calculate the roots for the quadratic equation $x^2 - 4x = -3$.

$$x^2 - 4x = -3$$
$$x^2 - 4x + 3 = -3 + 3$$
$$x^2 - 4x + 3 = 0$$
$$(x - 3)(x - 1) = 0$$

$(x - 3) = 0$	and	$(x - 1) = 0$
$x - 3 + 3 = 0 + 3$	and	$x - 1 + 1 = 0 + 1$
$x = 3$	and	$x = 1$

The Zero Product Property states that if the product of two or more factors is equal to zero, then at least one factor must be equal to zero.

1. **Consider the worked example. Why is 3 added to both sides in the first step?**

What is the connection between the Worked Example and determining the roots from factored form, $y = a(x - r_1)(x - r_2)$?

2. **Determine each student's error and then solve each equation correctly.**

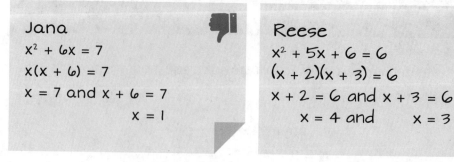

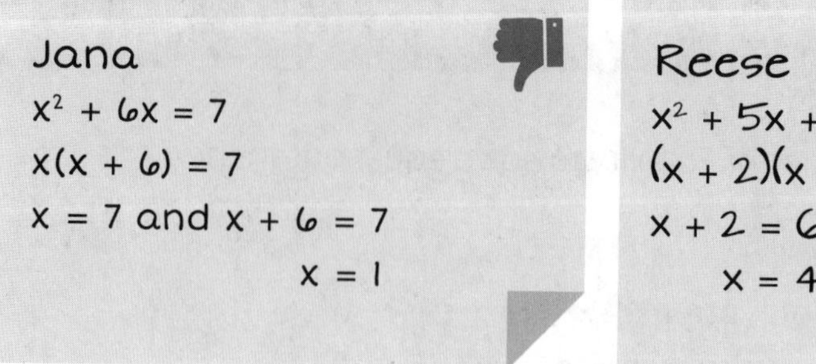

3. **Use factoring to solve each quadratic equation, if possible.**

a. $x^2 - 8x + 12 = 0$

b. $x^2 - 5x - 24 = 0$

c. $x^2 + 10x - 75 = 0$

d. $x^2 - 11x = 0$

e. $x^2 + 8x = -7$

f. $x^2 - 5x = 13x - 81$

g. $\frac{2}{3}x^2 - \frac{5}{6}x = 0$

h. $f(x) = x^2 + 10x + 12$

What efficiency strategies did you use to solve linear equations with fractional coefficients?

Describe the different strategies and reasoning that Deon and Kayla used to solve $4x^2 - 25 = 0$.

Deon 

$4x^2 - 25 = 0$

$4x^2 = 25$

$x^2 = \frac{25}{4}$

$x = \pm\sqrt{\frac{25}{4}}$

$x = \pm\frac{5}{2}$

Kayla

$4x^2 - 25 = 0$

$(2x - 5)(2x + 5) = 0$

$2x - 5 = 0$ and $2x + 5 = 0$

$2x = 5$ $\quad$ $2x = -5$

$x = \frac{5}{2}$ and $x = -\frac{5}{2}$

ACTIVITY

4.3 Completing the Square

If you cannot factor a quadratic function, does that mean it does not have zeros?

1. Consider the quadratic equation $y = x^2 + 10x + 12$. Use technology to graph the equation and then sketch it on the coordinate plane. Does this function have zeros? Explain your reasoning.

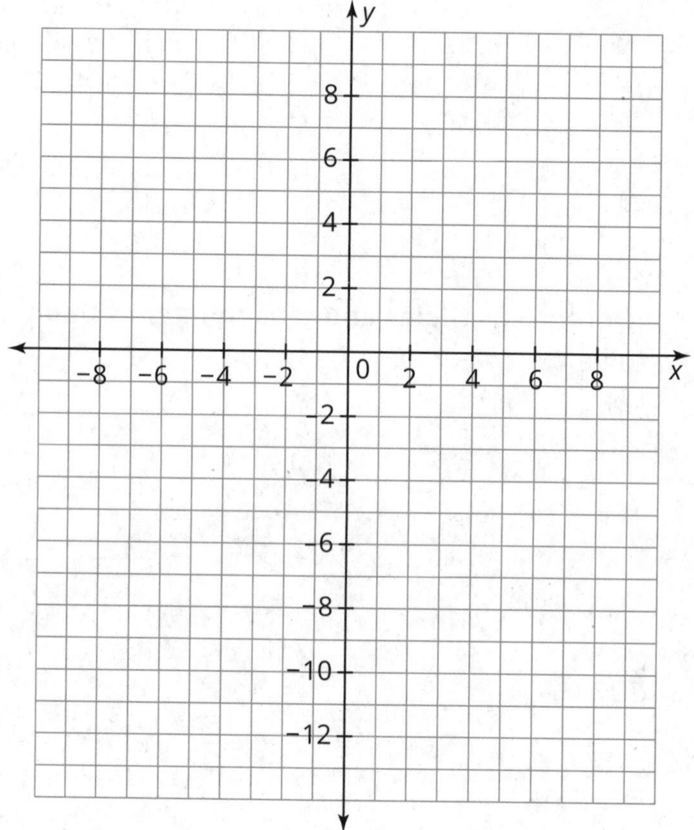

e quadratic function you graphed has zeros but cannot be factored, you must consider another method for calculating its zeros. You can e your understanding of the relationship among the coefficients of a rfect square trinomial to construct a procedure to solve any adratic equation.

eviously, you factored trinomials of the form $a^2 + 2ab + b^2$ as the rfect square $(a + b)^2$. This knowledge can help you develop a procedure solve any quadratic equation.

The expression $x^2 + 10x$ can be represented geometrically as shown. Write the area of each rectangle within the diagram.

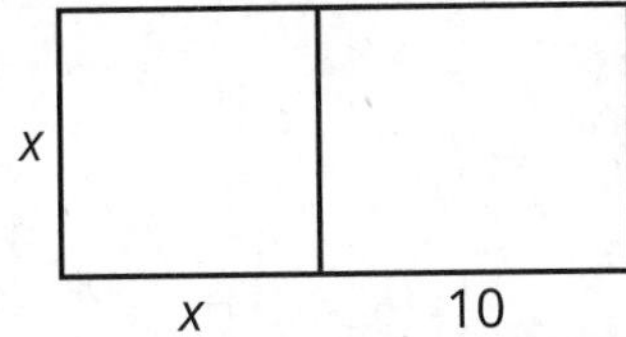

This figure can now be modified into the shape of a square by splitting the second rectangle in half and rearranging the pieces.

a. **Complete the side length labels for the split rectangle and write the area of each piece within the diagram.**

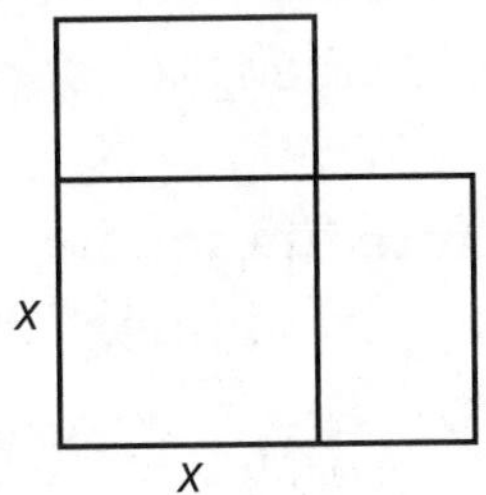

Why do you divide the second rectangle in half?

b. **Do the two figures represent the same expression? Explain your reasoning.**

c. **Complete the figure to form a square. Label the area of th piece you added.**

d. **Add the term representing the additional area to the original expression. What is the new expression?**

e. **Factor the new expression.**

The process you just worked through is a method known as *completing the square.* **Completing the square** is a process for writing a quadratic expression in vertex form which then allows you to solve for the zeros.

4. **Draw a model to complete the square for each expression. Then factor the resulting trinomial.**

a. $x^2 + 8x$

b. $x^2 + 5x$

Analyze your work in Question 4.

NOTES

a. Explain how to complete the square on an expression of the form $x^2 + bx$ where b is an integer.

b. Describe how the coefficient of the middle term, b, is related to the constant term, c, in each trinomial you wrote in Question 4.

Use the descriptions you provided in Question 5 to determine the unknown second or third term to make each expression a perfect square trinomial. Then write the expression as a binomial squared.

a. $x^2 - 8x +$ ______ = ______

b. $x^2 + 5x +$ ______ = ______

c. $x^2 -$ ______ $+ 100 =$ ______

d. $x^2 +$ ______ $+ 144 =$ ______

ACTIVITY

4.4

Completing the Square to Determine Roots

So far, you have considered quadratic equations that can be rewritten by completing the square or factoring a trinomial.

You can use the completing the square method to determine the roots of a quadratic equation that cannot be factored.

Worked Example

Determine the roots of the equation $x^2 + 10x + 12 = 0$.

Isolate $x^2 - 4x$. You can complete the square and rewrite this as a perfect square trinomial.	$x^2 + 10x + 12 - 12 = 0 - 12$ $x^2 + 10x = -12$
Determine the constant term that would complete the square. Add this term to both sides of the equation.	$x^2 + 10x + \_\_\_ = -12 + \_\_\_$ $x^2 + 10x + 25 = -12 + 25$ $x^2 + 10x + 25 = 13$
Factor the left side of the equation.	$(x + 5)^2 = 13$
Determine the square root of each side of the equation.	$\sqrt{(x + 5)^2} = \pm\sqrt{13}$ $x + 5 = \pm\sqrt{13}$
Set the factor of the perfect square trinomial equal to each square root of the constant. Solve for x.	$x + 5 = \sqrt{13}$ and $x + 5 = -\sqrt{13}$ $x = -5 + \sqrt{13}$ and $x = -5 - \sqrt{13}$ $x \approx -1.39$ and $x \approx -8.61$

The roots are approximately 3.41 and 0.59.

Ask yourself:

How was equality of the equation maintained through the completing the square process?

Consider the equation $y = x^2 + 8x + 10$.

a. Use this method to determine the roots of the equation. Show your work.

b. Use your work to label the zeros on the graph of the function $f(x) = x^2 + 8x + 10$.

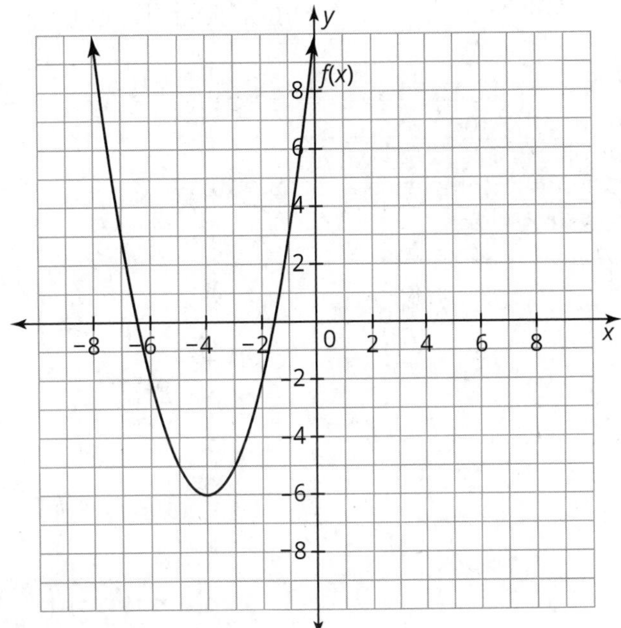

Determine the roots of each equation by completing the square.

a. $x^2 - 6x + 4 = 0$

b. $x^2 - 12x + 6 = 0$

ACTIVITY

4.5 Rewriting a Quadratic in Vertex Form

You can identify the axis of symmetry and the vertex of any quadratic function written in general form by completing the square.

Notice that the a-value was factored out before completing the square!

Worked Example

Consider the equation $y = ax^2 + bx + c$.

Step 1: $y - c = ax^2 + bx$

Step 2: $y - c = a\left(x^2 + \frac{b}{a}x\right)$

Step 3: $y - c + a\left(\frac{b}{2a}\right)^2 = a\left(x^2 + \frac{b}{a}x + \left(\frac{b}{2a}\right)^2\right)$

Step 4: $y - c + \frac{b^2}{4a} = a\left(x + \frac{b}{2a}\right)^2$

Step 5: $y = a\left(x + \frac{b}{2a}\right)^2 + \left(c - \frac{b^2}{4a}\right)$

1. **Explain why $a\left(\frac{b}{2a}\right)^2$ was added to the left side of the equation in Step 3.**

2. **Given a quadratic function in the form $y = ax^2 + bx + c$:**

   a. **Identify the axis of symmetry.**

   b. **Identify the location of the vertex.**

Rewrite each quadratic equation in vertex form. Then identify the zeros and sketch a graph of each function. Write the zeros in terms of the axis of symmetry and the parabola.

a. $y = x^2 + 8x - 9$

b. $y = 3x^2 + 2x - 1$

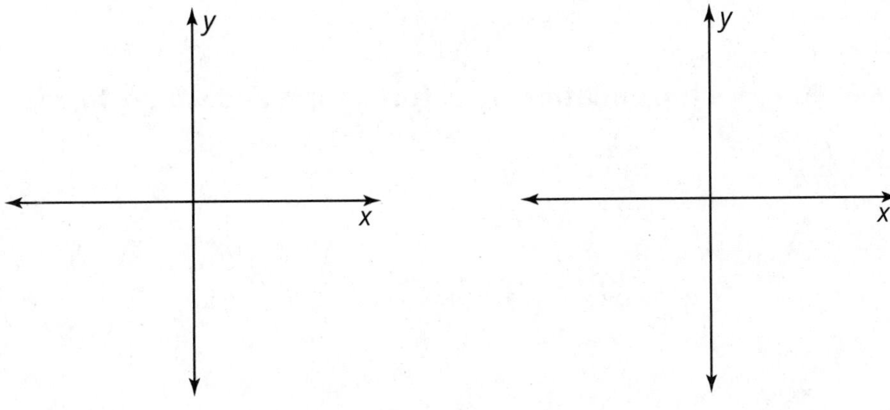

A ball is thrown straight up from 4 feet above the ground with a velocity of 32 feet per second. The height of the ball over time can be modeled with the function $h(t) = -16t^2 + 32t + 4$. What is the maximum height of the ball?

Jessie is fencing in a rectangular plot outside of her back door so that she can let her dogs out to play. She has 60 feet of fencing and only needs to place it on three sides of the rectangular plot because the fourth side will be bound by her house. What dimensions should Jesse use for the plot so that the maximum area is enclosed? What is the maximum area? Draw a diagram to support your work.

NOTES

TALK the TALK 

Play It Again

1. Consider the quadratic equation $y = x^2 - 4x - 5$.

a. Rewrite the equation in factored form and vertex form.

b. Graph the function. Identify the vertex, x- and y-intercepts, and the axis of symmetry. Then explain how these are evident in each form of the equation.

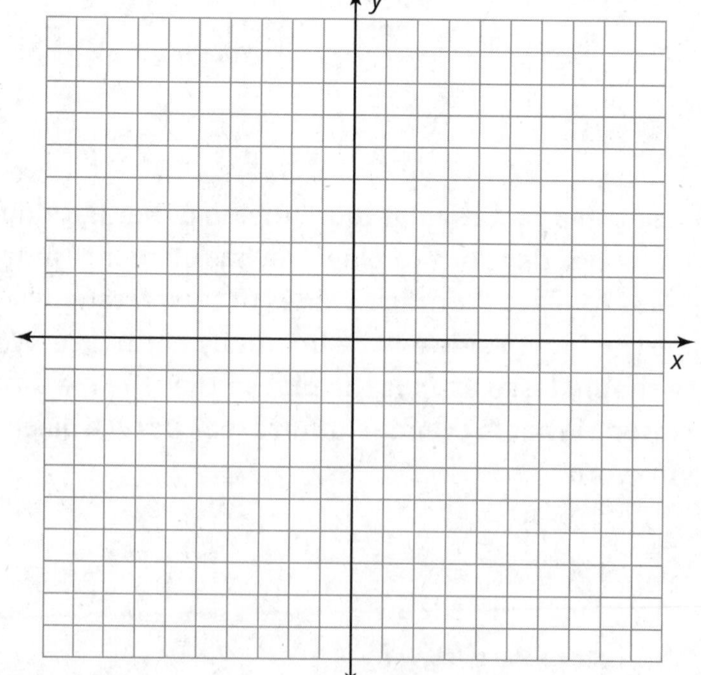

Assignment

Write

Describe the process to solve a quadratic equation by factoring.

Remember

- Completing the square is a process for writing a quadratic expression in vertex form which then allows you to solve for the zeros.
- Given a quadratic equation in the form $y = ax^2 + bx + c$, the vertex of the function is located at $x = \frac{-b}{2a}$ and $y = c - \frac{b^2}{4a}$.

Practice

1. Solve each equation.
   a. $0 = x^2 - 7x - 18$
   b. $x^2 + 10x = 39$
   c. $0 = x^2 - 10x + 12$
   d. $2x^2 + 4x = 0$
   e. $3x^2 - 22x + 7 = 0$
2. Determine the roots of the equation $y = x^2 + 9x + 3$. Check your solutions.
3. Consider the equation $y = 2x^2 + 10x - 8$.
   a. Graph the equation.
   b. Use the graph to estimate the solutions to the equation. Explain how you determined your answer.
   c. Two students completed the square to determine the solutions to this equation. Their work is shown. Who is correct? Explain your reasoning.

Student 1

$$y = 2x^2 + 10x - 8$$
$$2x^2 + 10x - 8 = 0$$
$$2x^2 + 10x = 8$$
$$2x^2 + 10x + 25 = 8 + 25$$
$$(2x + 5)^2 = 33$$
$$\sqrt{(2x + 5)^2} = \pm\sqrt{33}$$
$$2x + 5 = \pm\sqrt{33}$$
$$x = \frac{-5 \pm \sqrt{33}}{2}$$
$X \approx -5.372$ and $x \approx 0.372$

Student 2

$$y = 2x^2 + 10x - 8$$
$$2x^2 + 10x - 8 = 0$$
$$\frac{2x^2 + 10x - 8}{2} = 0$$
$$x^2 + 5x = 4$$
$$x^2 + 5x + \frac{25}{4} = 4 + \frac{25}{4}$$
$$\left(x + \frac{5}{2}\right)^2 = \frac{41}{4}$$
$$\sqrt{\left(x + \frac{5}{2}\right)^2} = \pm\sqrt{\frac{41}{4}}$$
$$x + \frac{5}{2} = \pm\frac{\sqrt{41}}{2}$$
$$x = \frac{-5 \pm \sqrt{41}}{2}$$
$x \approx -5.702$ and $x \approx 0.702$

   d. Compare the different solutions. Identify what the student who got the correct answer did that allowed him or her to correctly complete the square.
   e. Write a statement about the value of the coefficient of the x^2-term before you can complete the square.
4. Determine the roots of the equation $y = 3x^2 + 24x - 6$. Check your solutions.
5. Determine the roots and the location of the vertex of $y = x^2 + 20x + 36$. Write the zeros in terms of the axis of symmetry and the parabola.

Stretch

The function g is defined by $g(x) = x^2 - 3x - 10$. If $g(x + 3) = x^2 + bx - c$, what are the values of b and c? Show your work and justify your answer.

Review

1. For each quadratic function, determine if it has an absolute minimum or absolute maximum, if the graph opens upward or downward, and identify the y-intercept.
   a. $f(x) = 3x^2 + 6x - 72$.
   b. $f(x) = -\frac{1}{2}(x - 2)(x + 5)$.
2. Sketch a graph of each quadratic function. Determine the zeros of each function.
   a. $f(x) = (x + 6)^2$
   b. $f(x) = 3(x - \frac{9}{2})^2 - 5$
3. Write the equation of the function, $g(x)$, whose graph transforms the graph $f(x) = x^2$ by reflecting it across the x-axis, vertically compressing it by a factor of $\frac{1}{2}$, and moving it down 3 units.
4. Graph the function, $g(x)$, whose graph transforms the graph $f(x) = x^2$ by vertically stretching it by a factor of 3 and moving it up 4 units.

5

Ladies and Gents, Please Welcome the Quadratic Formula!

The Quadratic Formula

Warm Up

A bucket of paint falls from the top of a skyscraper that is 564 feet tall.

1. Write a quadratic function to represent the height of the can over time.
2. Use technology to graph the function.
3. How many seconds will it take for the can of paint to hit the ground?

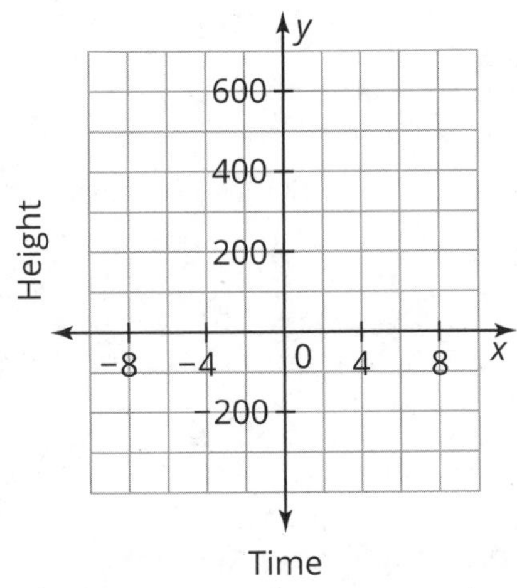

Learning Goals

- Derive the Quadratic Formula from a quadratic equation written in general form.
- Connect the Quadratic Formula to a graphical representation.
- Use the discriminant of the Quadratic Formula to determine the number of roots or zeros.
- Use the Quadratic Formula to determine roots and zeros.
- Determine whether a solution is rational or irrational when performing operations with rational and irrational numbers.

Key Terms

- Quadratic Formula
- discriminant

You know several strategies to solve quadratic equations, depending on the structure of the equation. Is there a single strategy that will work to solve any quadratic equation?

GETTING STARTED

Really, They Aren't the Same

Consider each graph.

Graph A

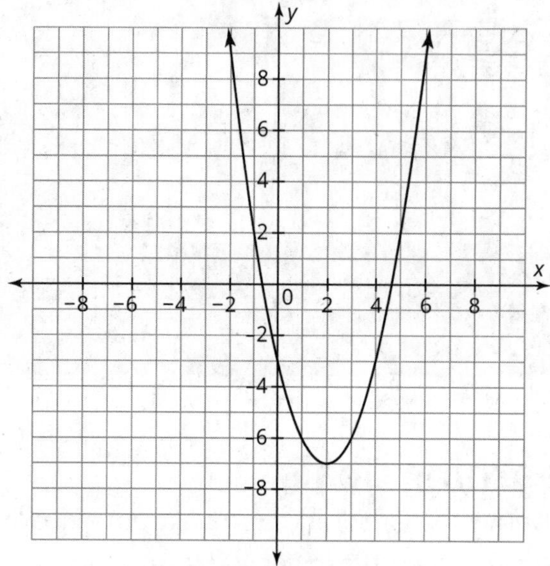

Graph B

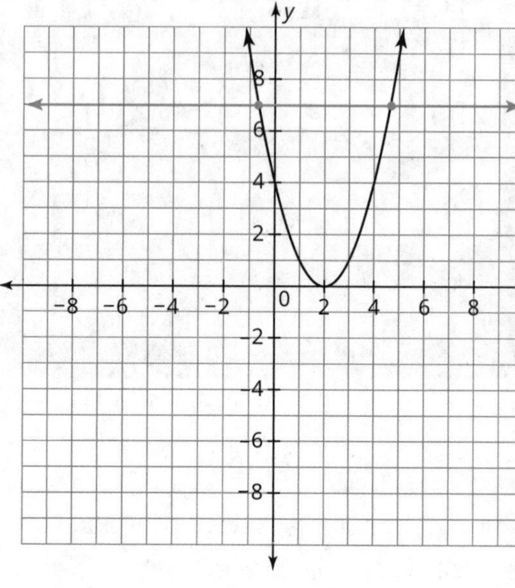

Graph C

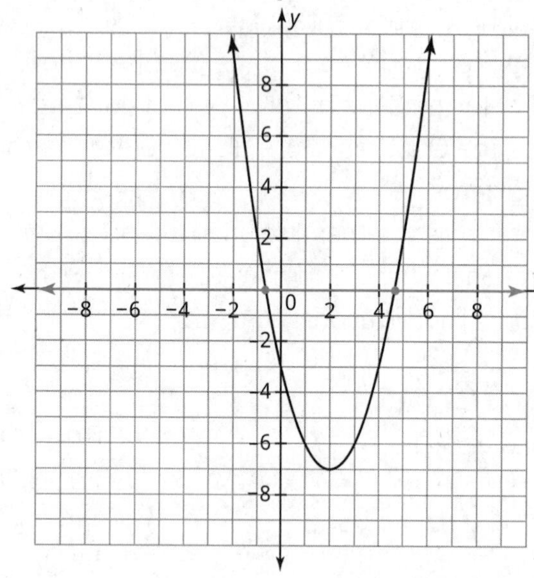

1. **Match each equation to its corresponding graph.**

   a. $(x - 2)^2 - 7 = 0$

   b. $y = (x - 2)^2 - 7$

   c. $(x - 2)^2 = 7$

2. **How do each of the graphs show solutions? How are the solutions related to the axis of symmetry?**

ACTIVITY

5.1

Introducing the Quadratic Formula

n the previous lesson, you took the general form of a quadratic equation, $y = ax^2 + bx + c$, and rewrote it in vertex form, $y = a\left(x + \frac{b}{2a}\right)^2 + \left(c - \frac{b^2}{4a}\right)$, by completing the square in order to determine the vertex and axis of symmetry for graphing purposes.

Now, let's take the general form of a quadratic equation, $y = ax^2 + bx + c$, and set $y = 0$ to determine the roots. You can complete the square in order to solve for the x-values when $y = 0$.

Worked Example

Write the equation in general form with $y = 0$.	$ax^2 + bx + c = 0$
Complete the square.	$ax^2 + bx = -c$ $x^2 + \frac{b}{a}x = -\frac{c}{a}$ $x^2 + \frac{b}{a}x + \left(\frac{b}{2a}\right)^2 = -\frac{c}{a} + \left(\frac{b}{2a}\right)^2$ $\left(x + \frac{b}{2a}\right)^2 = \left(\frac{b}{2a}\right)^2 - \frac{c}{a}$
Rewrite the right side of the equation.	$\left(x + \frac{b}{2a}\right)^2 = \frac{b^2}{4a^2} - \frac{c}{a}$ $\left(x + \frac{b}{2a}\right)^2 = \frac{b^2}{4a^2} - \frac{4ac}{4a^2}$ $\left(x + \frac{b}{2a}\right)^2 = \frac{b^2 - 4ac}{4a^2}$
Now that equation is written in the form $(x - c)^2 = q$, the square root can be taken on each side. Extract the square roots. Solve for x. These are the roots for the quadratic equation in the general form, $ax^2 + bx + c = 0$.	$x + \frac{b}{2a} = \pm\sqrt{\frac{b^2 - 4ac}{4a^2}}$ $x = -\frac{b}{2a} \pm \frac{\sqrt{b^2 - 4ac}}{2a}$ $x = \frac{-b}{2a} + \frac{\sqrt{b^2 - 4ac}}{2a}$ $\quad x = \frac{-b}{2a} - \frac{\sqrt{b^2 - 4ac}}{2a}$

This approach can be taken one step further and rewritten as a single fraction.

$$x = \frac{-b \pm \sqrt{b^2 - 4ac}}{2a}$$

So really, the Quadratic Formula is just taking the general form of a quadratic equation and isolating or solving for x.

This equation is known as the *Quadratic Formula*. The **Quadratic Formula**, $x = \frac{-b \pm \sqrt{b^2 - 4ac}}{2a}$, can be used to calculate the solutions to any quadratic equation of the form $ax^2 + bx + c = 0$, where a, b, and c represent real numbers and $a \neq 0$.

You can use the Quadratic Formula to determine the zeros of the function $f(x) = -4x^2 - 40x - 99$.

Worked Example

Rewrite the function as an equation to be solved for x when $y = 0$.	$-4x^2 - 40x - 99 = 0$
Determine the values of a, b, and c.	$a = -4, b = -40, c = -99$
Substitute the values into the Quadratic Formula.	$x = \frac{-(-40) \pm \sqrt{(-40)^2 - 4(-4)(-99)}}{2(-4)}$
Perform operations to rewrite the expression.	$x = \frac{40 \pm \sqrt{1600 - 1584}}{-8}$ $x = \frac{40 \pm \sqrt{16}}{-8}$ $x = \frac{40 \pm 4}{-8}$ $x = \frac{40 + 4}{-8}$ and $x = \frac{40 - 4}{-8}$ $x = \frac{44}{-8}$ and $x = \frac{36}{-8}$ $x = -5.5$ and $x = -4.5$
Interpret the solution.	The zeros of the function $f(x) = -4x^2 - 40x - 99$ are $x = -5.5$ and $x = -4.5$.

e Perris Pandas baseball team has a new promotional activity to courage fans to attend games: launching free T-shirts! They can launch -shirt in the air with an initial velocity of 91 feet per second from $5\frac{1}{2}$ feet the ground (the height of the team mascot).

Ask yourself:

What would a sketch showing the height of the T-shirt over time look like?

-shirt's height can be modeled with the quadratic function $= -16t^2 + 91t + 5.5$, where t is the time in seconds and $h(t)$ is the ight of the launched T-shirt in feet. They want to know how long it will e for a T-shirt to land back on the ground after being launched (if no s grab it before then!)

Why does it make sense to use the Quadratic Formula to solve this problem?

Use the Quadratic Formula to determine how long it will take for a T-shirt to land back on the ground after being launched.

Do you think an exact solution or approximate solution is more appropriate for this context?

Classify your solutions as rational or irrational.

ACTIVITY 5.2 Interpreting the Quadratic Formula Graphically

You used the Quadratic Formula to solve a quadratic equation. Let's connect the Quadratic Formula to the graph. Remember, the Quadratic Formula can be written to show two roots.

Think about:

How do the two roots relate to the graph?

$$x = \frac{-b}{2a} \pm \frac{\sqrt{b^2 - 4ac}}{2a}$$

$$x = \frac{-b}{2a} + \frac{\sqrt{b^2 - 4ac}}{2a} \qquad x = \frac{-b}{2a} - \frac{\sqrt{b^2 - 4ac}}{2a}$$

How do these roots, $x = \frac{-b}{2a} + \frac{\sqrt{b^2 - 4ac}}{2a}$ and $x = \frac{-b}{2a} - \frac{\sqrt{b^2 - 4ac}}{2a}$ relate to the graph?

1. **What does the first term of each root represent on the graph?**

2. **The second term of each root represents the distance the root lies from the axis of symmetry. Why is the second term in each root the same except for the sign?**

’s analyze how the structure of the Quadratic Formula is evident in the aphical representation of the zeros of a quadratic function.

Worked Example

Consider this graphical representation to determine the real roots of the quadratic equation $y = 2x^2 - x - 15$.

Steps	Graph
Set y equal to zero and identify the values of a, b, and c. $0 = 2x^2 - x - 15$ $a = 2 \quad b = -1 \quad c = -15 \quad a > 0$	$y = 0$
Identify the axis of symmetry and label the point where it intersects $y = 0$. $x = \frac{-(-1)}{2(2)} = \frac{1}{4}$	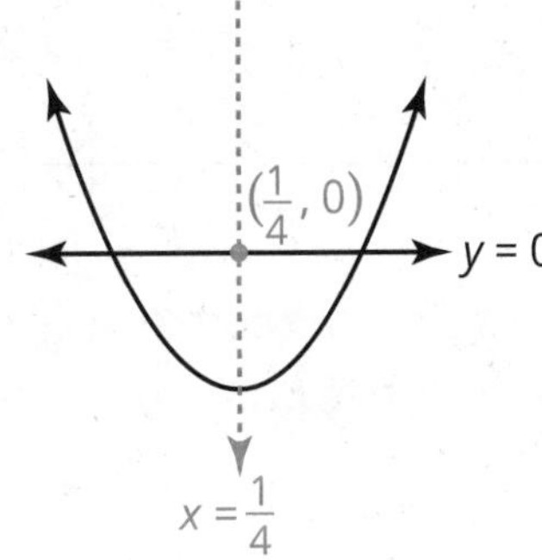
Identify the distance from the axis of symmetry to the parabola along $y = 0$. $+\frac{\sqrt{b^2 - 4ac}}{2a} =$ $\frac{\sqrt{(-1)^2 - 4(2)(-15)}}{2(2)} = \frac{\sqrt{121}}{4} = \frac{11}{4}$ $-\frac{\sqrt{b^2 - 4ac}}{2a} = -\frac{11}{4}$	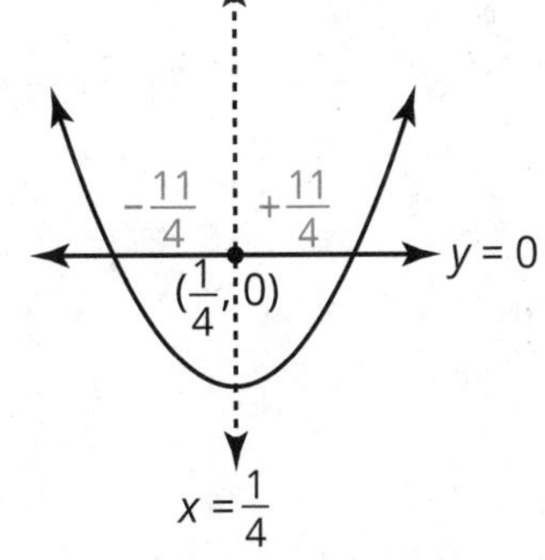
Identify the roots and label them on the graph. $\frac{1}{4} + \frac{11}{4} = \frac{12}{4} = 3$ $\frac{1}{4} - \frac{11}{4} = -\frac{10}{4} = -\frac{5}{2}$	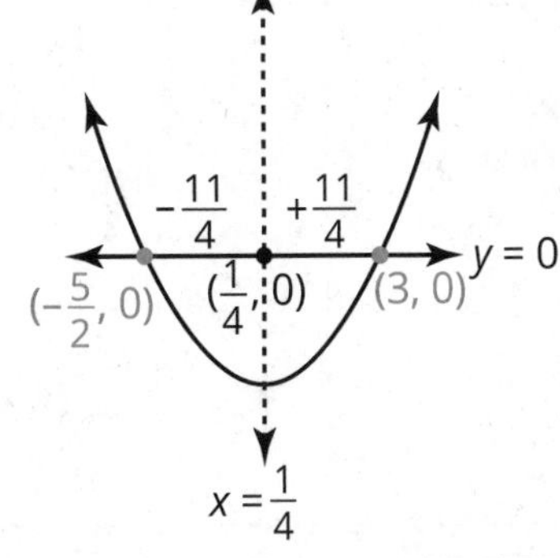
The real roots of $y = 2x^2 - x - 15$ are $x = 3$ and $x = -\frac{5}{2}$.	

3. **Repeat the process to determine the real roots of the equation $y = 2x^2 - 9x + 4$.**

Steps	Graph
a. **Let $y = 0$ and identify the values of a, b, and c.**	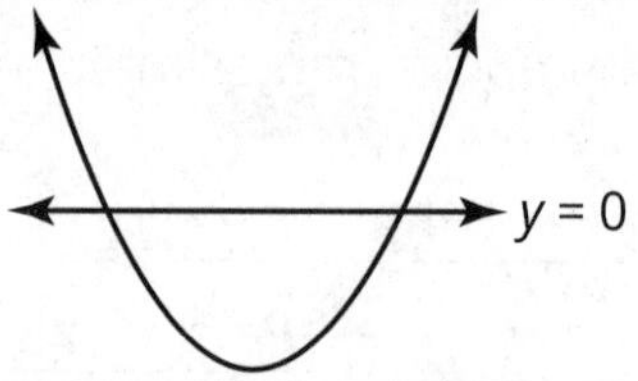 $y = 0$
b. **Identify the axis of symmetry and label the point where it intersects the x-axis.**	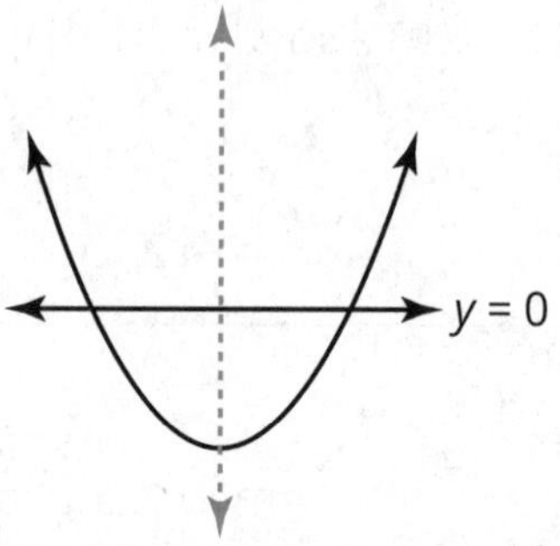 $y = 0$
c. **Identify the distance from the axis of symmetry to the parabola along $y = 0$.**	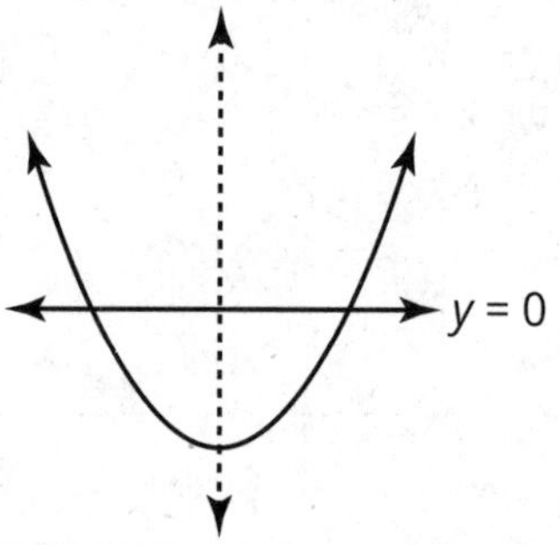 $y = 0$
d. **Identify the roots and label them on the graph.**	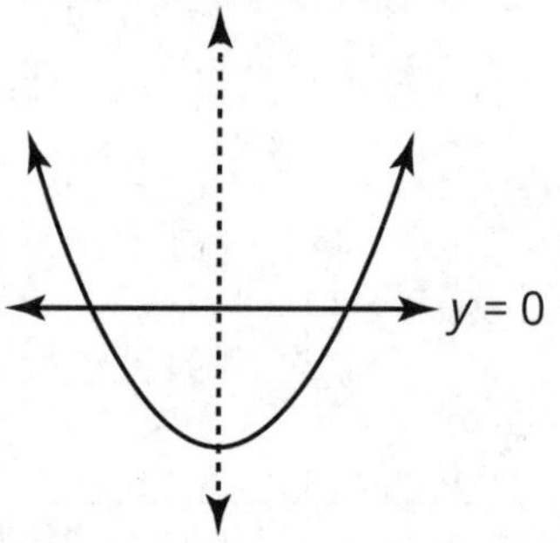 $y = 0$
e. **Summarize.**	

e graphs of quadratic equations are parabolas that have either an absolute ximum or an absolute minimum. A quadratic equation with two real roots sses the x-axis in two places. A quadratic equation with a double real root, one unique real root, touches the x-axis but does not cross it.

Quadratic Equations

With Two Real Roots **With Double Real Roots**

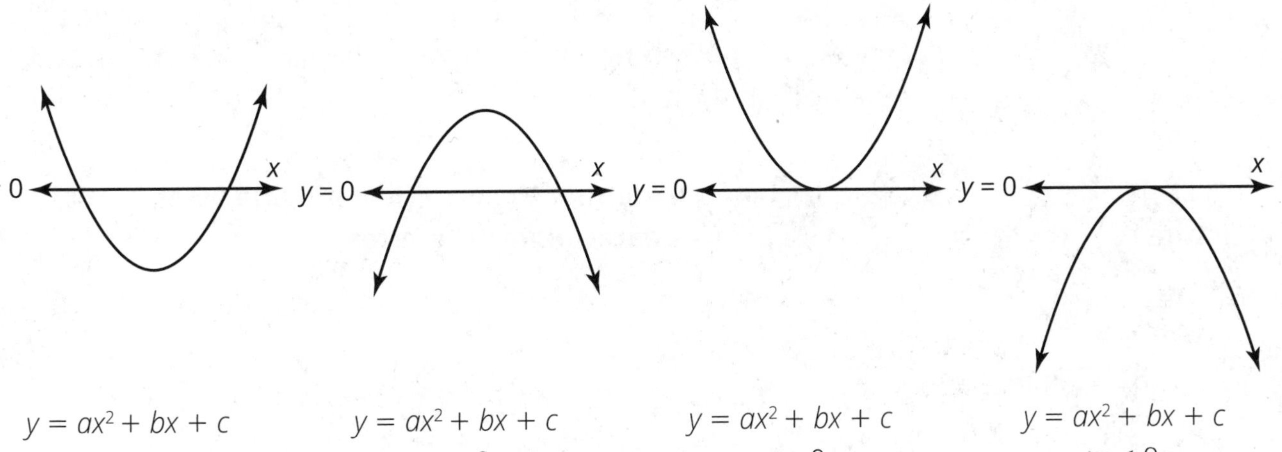

$y = ax^2 + bx + c$ $a > 0$

$y = ax^2 + bx + c$ $a < 0$

$y = ax^2 + bx + c$ $a > 0$

$y = ax^2 + bx + c$ $a < 0$

Draw and label the following components on each graph in terms of the equation $y = ax^2 + bx + c$.

a. vertex

b. axis of symmetry

c. intersection of the x-axis and line of symmetry

d. the distance represented by the expression $+\frac{\sqrt{b^2 - 4ac}}{2a}$

e. the distance represented by the expression $-\frac{\sqrt{b^2 - 4ac}}{2a}$

f. each root

ACTIVITY

5.3 Using the Quadratic Formula

Let's analyze the structure of the Quadratic Formula and examine commo student mistakes. Consider Javier's work.

1. Javier is determining the exact zeros for $f(x) = x^2 - 14x + 19$. His work is shown.

Javier

$f(x) = x^2 - 14x + 19$

$a = 1, b = -14, c = 19$

$x = \frac{-(-14) \pm \sqrt{(-14)^2 - 4(1)(19)}}{2(1)}$

$x = \frac{14 \pm \sqrt{196 - 76}}{2}$

$x = \frac{14 \pm \sqrt{120}}{2}$

$x = \frac{14 \pm \sqrt{30 \cdot 4}}{2}$

$x = \frac{14 \pm 2\sqrt{30}}{2}$

$x = 7 \pm 2\sqrt{30}$

a. Identify the error Javier made when determining the zeros.

b. Determine the correct zeros of the function.

"Leave the solutions in exact form" means not to estimate any radical values with rounded decimals.

2. Use the Quadratic Formula to determine the zeros for each function given. Leave the solutions in exact form and classify them as rational or irrational.

a. $f(x) = -2x^2 - 3x + 7$

b. $r(x) = -3x^2 + 19x - 7$

Lauren is solving the quadratic equation $x^2 - 7x - 8 = 3$. Her work is shown.

a. Identify Lauren's error.

b. Use the Quadratic Formula correctly to determine the solution to Lauren's quadratic equation. Classify the solutions as rational or irrational.

Lauren 

$x^2 - 7x - 8 = 3$

$a = 1, b = -7, c = -8$

$$x = \frac{-(-7) \pm \sqrt{(-7)^2 - 4(1)(-8)}}{2(1)}$$

$$x = \frac{7 \pm \sqrt{49 + 32}}{2}$$

$$x = \frac{7 \pm \sqrt{81}}{2}$$

$$x = \frac{7 \pm 9}{2}$$

$$x = \frac{7 + 9}{2} \text{ or } x = \frac{7 - 9}{2}$$

$$x = \frac{16}{2} = 8 \text{ or } x = \frac{-2}{2} = -1$$

The roots are 8 and −1.

c. Use technology to graph each side of the original quadratic equation $x^2 - 7x - 8 = 3$. Sketch your graph. Then interpret the meaning of the intersection points.

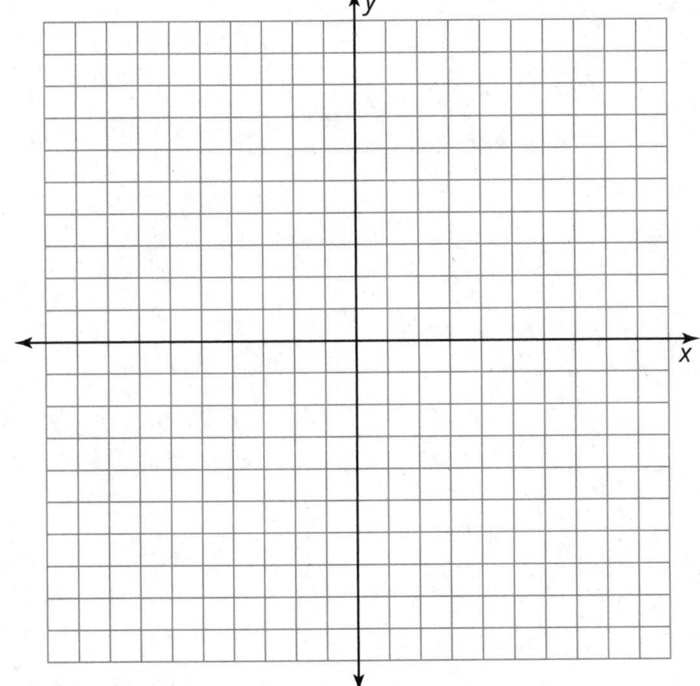

d. Next, rewrite the given quadratic equation so that one side of the equation is equal to zero. Use technology to graph each side of the quadratic equation. Sketch your graph. Interpret the meaning of the intersection points.

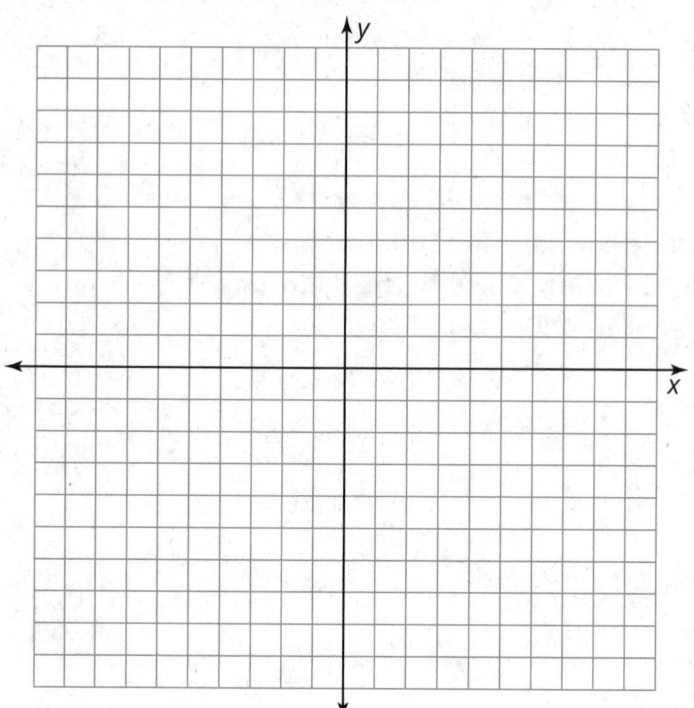

What does it mean to determine the solutions to a quadratic equation? What does it mean to determine the roots of a quadratic equation?

e. Compare the *x*-values of the intersection points from part (c), the *x*-values of the intersection points in part (d), and the solutions using the Quadratic Formula. What do you notice?

Use the Quadratic Formula to determine the zeros for each function. Round the solutions to the nearest hundredth and classify them as either rational or irrational.

a. $f(x) = 2x^2 + 10x - 1.02$

b. $h(x) = 3x^2 - 11x - 2$

Reflect on the different quadratic functions you have solved so far in this lesson.

a. How many zeros does each quadratic function in this lesson have?

b. Do all quadratic functions have two zeros? Explain why or why not.

yourself:

How can you use graphs to support your reasoning?

c. Do you think that a quadratic function could have no zeros? Explain why or why not.

d. Could a quadratic function have more than two zeros? Explain why or why not.

ACTIVITY 5.4

Making Sense of the Discriminant

A quadratic function can have one unique real zero, two real zeros, or at times, no real zeros. Let's investigate how the Quadratic Formula can infor you about different types of zeros.

Consider three quadratic equations and their graphs.

$y = x^2$

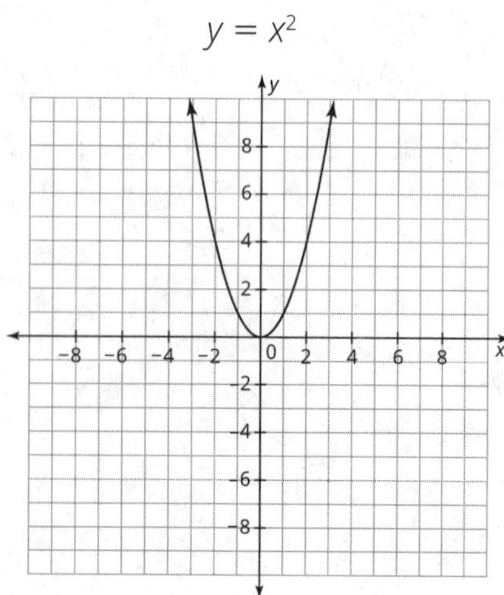

$y = x^2 - 1$

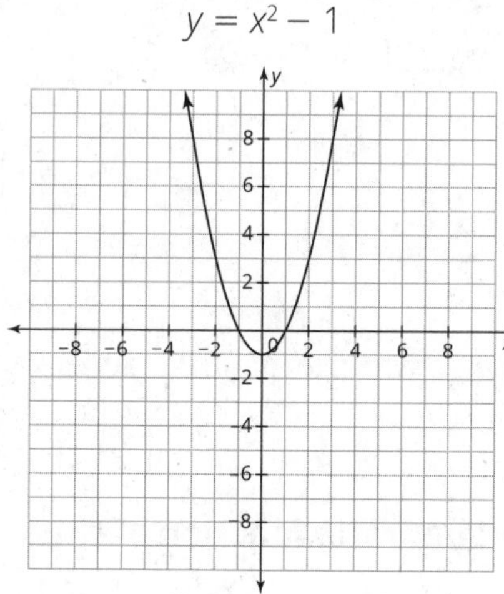

$y = x^2 + 1$

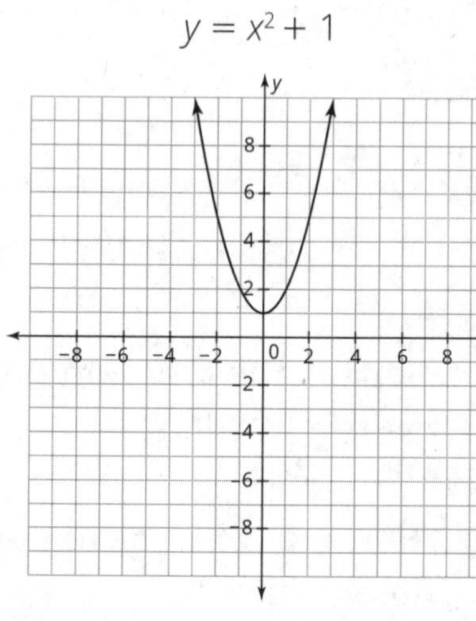

1. Use the Quadratic Formula to solve each quadratic equation. Show your work.

You have analyzed many graphs of quadratic equations. What do you know about the roots of a quadratic equation that touches but does not intersect the *x*-axis or intersects the *x*-axis at two points?

2. What do you notice about the relationship between the numbe of real roots, the graph, and the results of substituting the values *a*, *b*, and *c* into the Quadratic Formula?

cause this portion of the formula "discriminates" the number of real
os, or roots, it is called the **discriminant.**

3. Using the discriminant, write an inequality to describe when a quadratic function has each solution.

a. no real roots/zeros

b. one unique real root/zero

c. two unique real roots/zeros

Ask yourself:

How can you tell how many zeros a function will have by thinking about its graph before you use the Quadratic Formula?

e table shown summarizes the types of solutions for any quadratic
uation or function.

		Interpretation of the Solutions		
Equation/ Function	**Solutions**	**Number of Unique Real Zeros**	**Number of *x*-Intercepts**	**Sketch**
$x) = x^2$	$x = \frac{-0 \pm \sqrt{0^2 - 4(1)(0)}}{2(1)}$ $= \frac{0 \pm \sqrt{0}}{2}$ $= 0 \pm \sqrt{0}$	1	1	
$(x) = x^2 - 1$	$x = \frac{-0 \pm \sqrt{0^2 - 4(1)(-1)}}{2(1)}$ $= \frac{0 \pm \sqrt{4}}{2}$ $= 0 \pm 1$	2	2	
$(x) = x^2 + 1$	$x = \frac{-0 \pm \sqrt{0^2 - (4)(1)(1)}}{2(1)}$ $= \frac{0 \pm \sqrt{-4}}{2}$	0	0	

NOTES

Every quadratic equation with real coefficients has either 2 real roots or 0 real roots. However, if a graph of a quadratic equation has 1 x-intercep the equation *still* has 2 real roots. In this case, the 2 real roots are considered a double root.

4. Use the discriminant to determine the number of real roots f each equation. Then solve for the roots/zeros.

a. $y = 2x^2 + 12x - 2$

b. $0 = 2x^2 + 12x + 20$

c. $y = x^2 + 12x + 36$

d. $y = 3x^2 + 7x - 20$

e. $y = 4x^2 - 9$

f. $0 = 9x^2 + 12x + 4$

ACTIVITY

5.5 Operations with Rational and Irrational Numbers

n the previous activity, you used the discriminant of the Quadratic Formula to determine whether there were 2, 1, or 0 real roots to a quadratic equation. Remember that the set of real numbers is made up of the set of rational and the set of irrational numbers. Let's take a closer look at these two specific types of real numbers.

1. What characteristic of the discriminant determines whether the roots are rational or irrational?

2. Based on the number and nature of each of the roots, decide if the discriminant is positive, negative, or zero and if the discriminant is or is not a perfect square.

a. no real roots/zeros

b. one rational root/zero

c. two rational roots/zeros

d. two irrational roots/zeros

Throughout this lesson, you have solved quadratic equations with rational and irrational roots.

You have interpreted solutions as the sum or difference of a quantity from the axis of symmetry. In each case, the *c*-value that defines the axis of symmetry, $x = c$, is a rational number. In some cases, you added and subtracted a rational number. In other cases, you added and subtracted an irrational number.

Consider each equation and its corresponding roots.

$y = (x - 2)^2 - 9$
$x = 2 \pm 3$

$y = (x - 2)^2 - 7$
$x = 2 \pm \sqrt{7}$

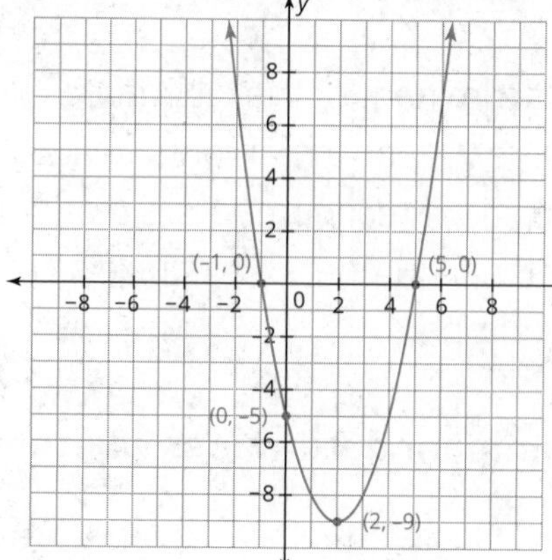

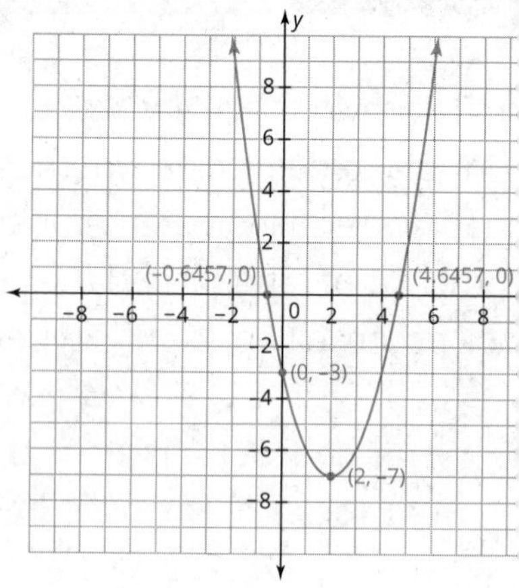

3. Describe the roots of each equation as rational or irrational.

4. Let m represent a nonzero rational number and let n represent an irrational number. Which expression could represent a rational number? Explain your reasoning and provide an example.

a. $m + n$

b. mn

c. $-n$

d. n^2

Consider a quadratic function with integer coefficients and two distinct zeros. If one zero is irrational, which statement is true about the other zero? Explain your reasoning and provide an example.

a. The other zero must be rational.

b. The other zero must be irrational.

c. The other zero can be either rational or irrational.

d. The other zero must be non-real.

Use the given values for *W*, *X*, *Y*, and *Z* to determine which expression results in a rational number. Explain your reasoning.

$W = \sqrt{4}$ $X = 2\sqrt{2}$ $Y = \sqrt{3}$ $Z = \sqrt{25}$

a. $W + X$

b. $X + Y$

c. $Y + Z$

d. $Z + W$

NOTES

TALK the TALK

Show Me the Ways

1. **Determine the real roots of the quadratic equation $y = 2x^2 + 4x - 6$ using the four methods you learned in this topic.**

Factoring	Completing the Square
Using the Quadratic Formula	**Graphing**

Assignment

Write

How can you determine the types of solutions when using the Quadratic Formula?

Remember

The Quadratic Formula, $x = \frac{-b \pm \sqrt{b^2 - 4ac}}{2a}$, can be used to calculate the solutions to any quadratic equation of the form $ax^2 + bx + c = 0$, where a, b, and c represent real numbers and $a \neq 0$.

On the graph of a quadratic function, $\pm\sqrt{b^2 - \frac{4ac}{2a}}$ is the distance from $\left(-\frac{b}{2a}, 0\right)$ to each root.

Practice

The formula shown can be used to calculate the distance, s, an object travels in t seconds. In this formula, u represents the initial velocity, and a represents a constant acceleration. Use this formula to answer each question.

$$S = ut + \frac{1}{2}at^2$$

1. Kian is driving 48 miles per hour and is starting to merge onto the highway; therefore, he must increase his speed. He gradually accelerates at a rate of 7 miles per hour for several seconds.
   a. Substitute the initial velocity and constant acceleration into the formula to write an equation to represent the distance Kian travels.
   b. Use the Quadratic Formula to determine the roots of the equation. What do the roots represent in the context of the problem situation? Explain your reasoning.
2. Sonja is driving her car 32 miles per hour when she passes Dominique's house. She then accelerates at a rate of 3 miles per hour for several minutes until she passes the movie theater. Sonja knows that the movie theater is 2.9 miles from Dominique's house.
   a. Substitute the initial velocity, constant acceleration, and distance into the formula to write an equation represent the distance Sonja travels.
   b. Use the Quadratic Formula to determine the roots of the equation you wrote in part (a). What do the roots represent in the context of the problem situation? Explain your reasoning.
3. Use the discriminant to determine the number of real roots for each equation. Then solve the quadratic equations with real roots.
   a. $4x^2 + 8x - 12 = 0$
   b. $x^2 + 2x - 10 = 0$
   c. $9x^2 - 12x + 4 = 0$
   d. $3x^2 - 4 = 0$
   e. $3x^2 + 2x - 2 = 0$
   f. $x^2 - 3x + 5 = 0$

Stretch

Consider the function $f(x) = -2x^2 + bx - 5$. Determine the b-value(s) that would ensure the function has two real roots. Explain your reasoning.

Review

1. Analyze each pair of representations. Then, answer each question and justify your reasoning.

   a. Which function has a greater y-intercept?

A	B
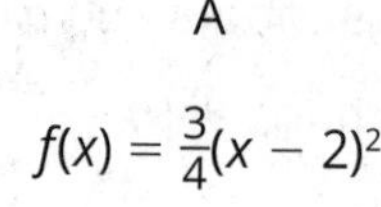 $f(x) = \frac{3}{4}(x - 2)^2$	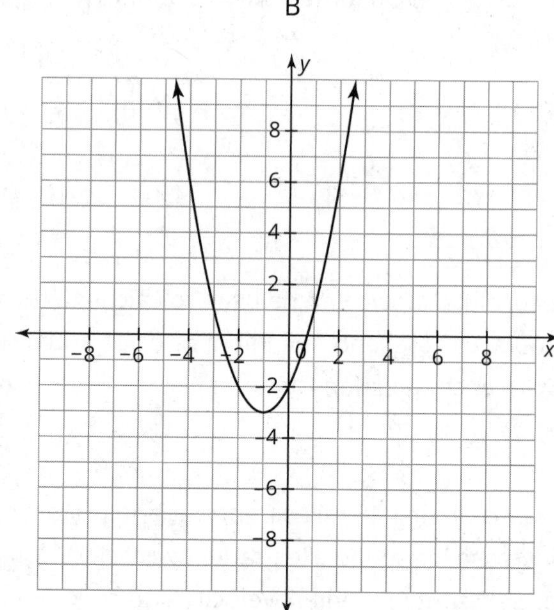

   b. Which function has a greater absolute maximum?

A

x	y
0	24
3	25
6	24

B

$f(x) = -2x^2 + 15x - 4$

2. Complete the square to determine the roots of each equation. Show your work.

   a. $y = 2x^2 + 5x - 14$

   b. $y = -3x^2 - 6x + 10$

3. Consider the function $f(x) = (x + \frac{1}{2})(x - \frac{3}{4})$.

   a. Identify the form of the function as factored, general, or vertex.

   b. Identify the zeros and axis of symmetry of the function.

Solving Quadratic Equations Summary

KEY TERMS

- polynomial
- monomial
- binomial
- trinomial
- degree of a polynomial
- closed, closure
- difference of two squares
- perfect square trinomial
- principal square root
- double root
- Zero Product Property
- completing the square
- Quadratic Formula
- discriminant

LESSON 1

This Time, With Polynomials

Linear and quadratic expressions are part of a larger group of expressions known as polynomials. A **polynomial** is an expression involving the sum of powers in one or more variables multiplied by coefficients. A polynomial in one variable is the sum of terms of the form ax^k where a, called the coefficient, is a real number and k is a non-negative integer. A polynomial is written in general form when the terms are in descending order, starting with the term with the greatest degree and ending with the term with the least degree.

$$a_1x^k + a_2x^{k-1} + \ldots a_nx^0$$

Each product in a polynomial is called a term. Polynomials are named according to the number of terms: **monomials** have exactly 1 term, **binomials** have exactly 2 terms, and **trinomials** have exactly 3 terms.

The exponent of a term is the degree of the term, and the greatest exponent in a polynomial is th **degree of the polynomial**.

The characteristics of the polynomial $13x^3 + 5x + 9$ are shown in the chart.

	1st term	2nd term	3rd term
Term	$13x^3$	$5x$	9
Coefficient	13	5	9
Power	x^3	x^1	x^0
Exponent	3	1	0

This trinomial has a degree of 3 because 3 is the greatest degree of the terms in the trinomial.

When an operation is performed on any of the numbers in a set and the result is a number that is also in the same set, the set is said to be **closed** (or to have **closure**) under that operation. The definition of closure can also be applied to polynomials.

Polynomials can be added or subtracted by identifying the like terms of the polynomial functions, using the Associative Property to group the like terms together, and combining the like terms to simplify the expression.

For example, to add the polynomial expressions $(7x^2 - 2x + 12)$ and $(8x^3 + 2x - 3x)$, use the Associative Property to combine the like terms.

$$(7x^2 - 2x + 12) + (8x^3 + 2x - 3x)$$
$$8x^3 + (7x^2 + 2x^2) + (-2x - 3x) + 12$$
$$8x^3 + 9x^2 - 5x + 12$$

The product of 2 binomials can be determined by using a multiplication table, or area model, which organizes the two terms of the binomials as factors of multiplication expressions.

$$(9x - 1)(5x + 7)$$

·	**9x**	**−1**
5x	$45x^2$	$-5x$
7	$63x$	-7

$$(9x - 1)(5x + 7) = 45x^2 - 5x + 63x - 7$$
$$= 45x^2 + 58x - 7$$

The Distributive Property can also be used to multiply polynomials. Depending on the number of terms in the polynomials, the Distributive Property may need to be used multiple times.

For example, to multiply the polynomials $x + 5$ and $x - 2$, first, use the Distributive property to multiply each term of $x + 5$ by the entire binomial $x - 2$.

$(x + 5)(x - 2) = (x)(x - 2) + (5)(x - 2)$

Next, distribute x to each term of $x - 2$ and distribute 5 to each term of $x - 2$.

$x^2 - 2x + 5x - 10$

Finally, collect the like terms and write the solution in general form.

$x^2 + 3x - 10$

There are special products of degree 2 that have certain characteristics. The **difference of two squares** is an expression in the form $a^2 - b^2$ that has factors $(a + b)(a - b)$. A **perfect square trinomial** is formed by multiplying a binomial by itself. It is an expression in the form $a^2 + 2ab + b^2$ or in the form $a^2 - 2ab + b^2$. A perfect square trinomial can be written as the square of a binomial. In these cases, the factors are $(a + b)^2$ and $(a - b)^2$, respectively.

LESSON 2 Solutions, More or Less

A quadratic function is a function of degree 2 because the greatest power for any of its terms is 2. This means that it has at most 2 zeros, or at most 2 solutions, at $y = 0$.

The two solutions of a quadratic function can be represented as square roots of numbers. Every positive number has two square roots, a positive square root, which is also called the **principal square root**, and a negative square root. To solve the equation $x^2 = 9$, take the square root of both sides of the equation.

$$\sqrt{x^2} = \sqrt{9}$$
$$x = \pm 3$$

You can solve $x^2 = 9$ on a graph by looking for the points of intersection between $y = x^2$ and $y = 9$. The solutions are both 3 units from the axis of symmetry, $x = 0$.

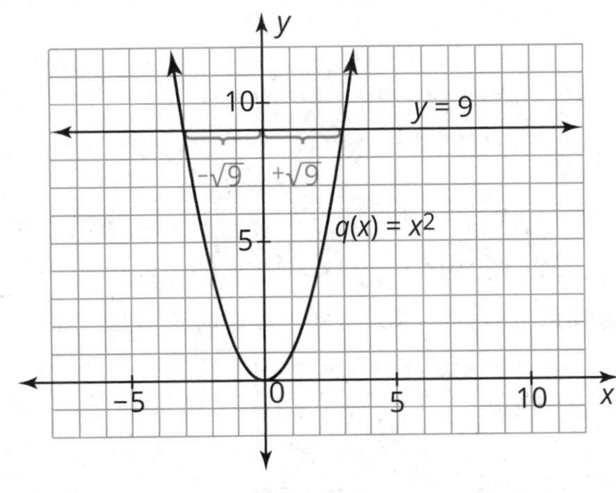

The x-intercepts of a graph of a quadratic function are called the zeros of the quadratic function. The zeros are called the roots of the quadratic equation.

The x-coordinates of the x-intercepts of a graph of a quadratic function are called the zeros of the quadratic function. The zeros are called the roots of the quadratic equation.

The quadratic function $q(x) = x^2$ has two solutions at $y = 0$. Therefore, it has 2 zeros: $x = +\sqrt{0}$ and $x = -\sqrt{0}$, so the function $q(x) = x^2$ is said to have a **double root**.

When you encounter solutions that are not perfect squares, you can either determine the approximate value of the radical or rewrite it in an equivalent radical form.

To approximate a square root, determine the perfect square that is closest to, but less than, the given value and the perfect square that is closest to, but greater than, the given value. You can use these square roots to approximate the square root of the given number.

For example, the approximate value of $\sqrt{40}$ falls between $\sqrt{36}$, or 6, and $\sqrt{49}$, or 7. Since $6.3^2 = 39.69$ and $6.4^2 = 40.96$, the approximate value of $\sqrt{40}$ is 6.3.

To rewrite a square root in equivalent radical form, first rewrite the product of the radicand to include any perfect square factors. Then extract the square roots of those perfect squares.

$$\sqrt{27} = \sqrt{9 \cdot}$$
$$= \sqrt{9} \cdot$$
$$= 3\sqrt{3}$$

A quadratic function written in factored form is in the form $f(x) = a(x - r_1)(x - r_2)$, where $a \neq 0$. In factored form, r_1 and r_2 represent the x-intercepts of the graph of the function. The x-intercepts of the graph of the quadratic function $f(x) = ax^2 + bx + c$ and the zeros of the function are the same the roots of the equation $ax^2 + bx + c = 0$.

To write a quadratic function in factored form, first determine the zeros of the function $f(x) = x^2 -$ set the trinomial expression equal to 0, and solve for x.

$$0 = x^2 - 9$$
$$9 = x^2$$
$$\sqrt{9} = \sqrt{x^2}$$
$$\pm 3 = x$$

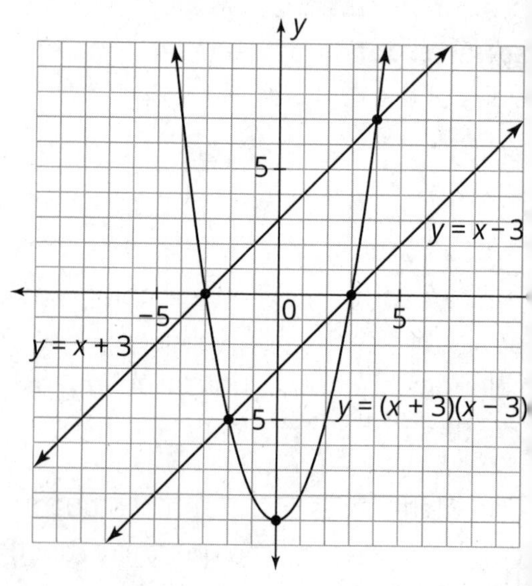

You can then use the zeros to write the function in factored form, $f(x) = (x + 3)(x - 3)$.

The Zero Product Property states that if the product of two or more factors is equal to zero, then at least one factor must be equal to zero. You can see from the graph that the zeros of the function $f(x) = x^2 - 9$ occur where either $y = x + 3$ or $y = x - 3$ are zero.

LESSON 3

Transforming Solutions

'he solutions to any quadratic equation are located on the parabola, equidistant from the axis of symmetry.

quadratic function in vertex form $f(x) = a(x - h)^2 + k$ is translated horizontally h units, dilated ertically by the factor a, and translated vertically k units.

or the equation $f(x) = (x - c)^2$, the solutions can be represented by $c \pm \sqrt{y}$. For the equation $(x) = a(x - c)^2$, the solutions can be represented by $c \pm \sqrt{\frac{y}{a}}$. For the equation $f(x) = a(x - c)^2 + d$, he solutions can be represented by $c \pm \sqrt{\frac{y - d}{a}}$.

or example, consider the equation $2(x - 1)^2 + 2 = 20$.

$$x = 1 \pm \sqrt{\frac{20 - 2}{2}}$$
$$= 1 \pm \sqrt{9}$$
$$= 1 \pm 3$$

The solutions to the equation are 3 units away from the axis of symmetry, $x = 1$. The solutions are $x = -2$ and $x = 4$.

LESSON 4

The Missing Link

You can factor trinomials by rewriting them as the product of two linear expressions.

For example, to factor the trinomial $x^2 + 10x + 16$, determine the factor pairs of the constant term. The factors of 16 are (1)(16), (2)(8), and (4)(4). Then, determine the pair whose sum is the coefficient of the middle term, 10.

•	**x**	**8**
x	x^2	$8x$
2	$2x$	16

The sum of $2x$ and $8x$ is $10x$. So, $x^2 + 10x + 16 = (x + 2)(x + 8)$.

You can use factoring and the Zero Product Property to solve quadratics in the form $y = ax^2 + bx +$

For example, you can solve the quadratic equation $x^2 - 4x = -3$.

$$x^2 - 4x = -3$$
$$x^2 - 4x + 3 = -3 + 3$$
$$x^2 - 4x + 3 = 0$$
$$(x - 3)(x - 1) = 0$$

$$(x - 3) = 0 \quad \text{or} \quad (x - 1) = 0$$
$$x - 3 + 3 = 0 + 3 \quad \text{or} \quad x - 1 + 1 = 0 + 1$$
$$x = 3 \quad \text{or} \quad x = 1$$

For a quadratic function that has zeros but cannot be factored, there is another method for solvin the quadratic equation. **Completing the square** is a process for writing a quadratic expression ir vertex form, which then allows you to solve for the zeros.

For example, you can calculate the roots of the equation $x^2 - 4x + 2 = 0$.

Isolate $x^2 - 4x$.

$$x^2 - 4x + 2 - 2 = 0 - 2$$
$$x^2 - 4x = -2$$

Complete the square and rewrite this as a perfect square trinomial.

Determine the constant term that would complete the square.

$$x^2 - 4x + ? = -2 + ?$$

Add this term to both sides of the equation.

$$x^2 - 4x + 4 = -2 + 4$$
$$x^2 - 4x + 4 = 2$$

Factor the left side of the equation.

Determine the square root of each side of the equation.

$$(x - 2)^2 = 2$$
$$\sqrt{(x - 2)^2} = \sqrt{2}$$
$$(x - 2) = \pm\sqrt{2}$$

Set the factor of the perfect square trinomial equal to each square root of the constant and solve for x.

$$x - 2 = \sqrt{2} \quad \text{or} \quad x - 2 = -\sqrt{2}$$
$$x = 2 + \sqrt{2} \quad \text{or} \quad x = 2 - \sqrt{2}$$

$$x \approx 3.41 \quad \text{or} \quad x \approx 0.59$$

The roots are approximately 3.41 and 0.59.

Completing the square can also be used to identify the axis of symmetry and the vertex of any quadratic function written in standard form.

When a function is written in standard form, $ax^2 + bx + c$, the axis of symmetry is $x = -\frac{b}{2a}$.

Given a quadratic equation in the form $y = ax^2 + bx + c$, the vertex of the function is located at $x = -\frac{b}{2a}$ and $y = c - \frac{b^2}{4a}$.

LESSON
5

Ladies and Gents, Please Welcome the Quadratic Formula!

The **Quadratic Formula**, $x = \frac{-b \pm \sqrt{b^2 - 4ac}}{2a}$, can be used to calculate the solutions to any quadratic equation of the form $ax^2 + bx + c = 0$, where a, b and c represent real numbers and $a \neq 0$.

For example, given the function $f(x) = 2x^2 - 4x - 3$ you can identify the values of a, b and c.

$$a = 2;\ b = -4;\ c = -3$$

Then you use the quadratic formula to solve.

$$x = \frac{-(-4) \pm \sqrt{(-4)^2 - 4(2)(-3)}}{2(2)}$$

$$x = \frac{4 \pm \sqrt{16 - 24}}{4}$$

$$x = \frac{4 \pm \sqrt{40}}{4}$$

$$x \approx \frac{4 + 6.325}{4} \approx 2.581 \quad \text{or} \quad x \approx \frac{4 - 6.325}{4} \approx -0.581$$

The roots are approximately 2.581 and −0.581.

A quadratic function can have one real zero, two real zeros, or at times, no real zeros.

You can use the part of the Quadratic Formula underneath the square root symbol to identify the number of real zeros or roots. Because this portion of the formula "discriminates" the number of real zeros or roots, it is called the **discriminant**.

If the discriminant is positive, the quadratic has two real roots.
If the discriminant is negative, the quadratic has no real roots.
If the discriminant is 0, the quadratic has a double real root.

You can also use the discriminant to describe the nature of the roots. If the discriminant is a perfe
square, then the roots are rational. If the discriminant is not a perfect square, then the roots are irrational.

Rational numbers are closed under addition and multiplication. A rational number plus an irration
number is an irrational number. A rational number times an irrational number is an irrational number. An irrational number times an irrational number can have an irrational or rational produc

OPIC 2

Applications of Quadratic Equations

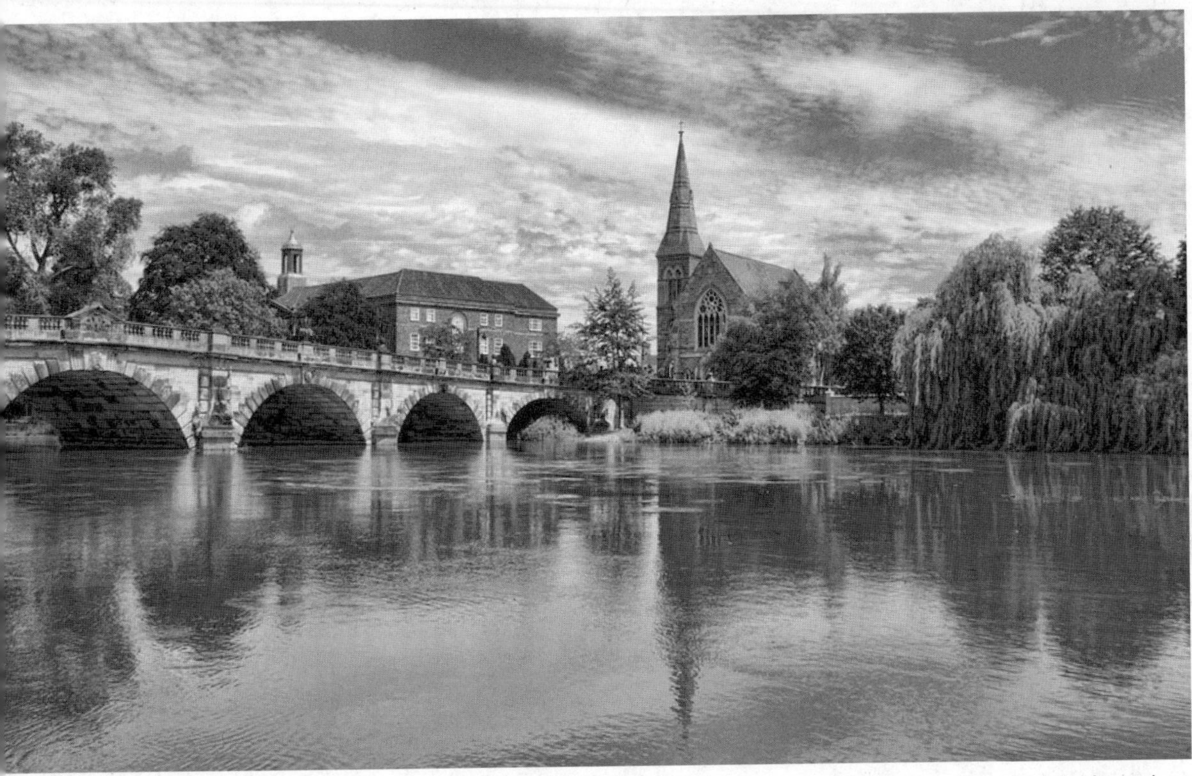

keystone is the wedge-shaped stone at the top of an arch that locks the other stones in place. If an arch is shaped e a parabola, the vertex (maximum) will be somewhere on the keystone.

Module 4: Seeing Structure

TOPIC 2: APPLICATIONS OF QUADRATIC EQUATIONS

This topic provides students with an opportunity to use what they have learned to model and solve problems in situations involving quadratics. Students start by exploring the complex plane and imaginary numbers. They then investigate a real-world problem that can be modeled by a quadratic inequality. From there, students are given a scenario that can be modeled by a system comprised of a quadratic function and a linear function. They use technology to graph the system and determine the solutions. Students are presented with a real-world situation and use familiar strategies to fit a quadratic regression.

Where have we been?

Students have graphed and solved linear inequalities in one variable and in two variables, as well as systems of linear inequalities. They will use these skills to graph and solve quadratic inequalities, interpreting the solution set in the same way. Students know that a graph represents the solutions to the function it models and that the intersection point(s) of two graphs represent the solution(s) shared by both functions.

Where are we going?

This topic provides students with an opportunity to bring together the advanced techniques that they have learned throughout this course and the previous course. When students move into the next course, their knowledge of first- and second-degree polynomials will be used and expanded upon as they encounter cubics, quartics, rational functions, and logarithmic functions. Modeling advanced scenarios will be heavily used by students who continue on to calculus and post-secondary mathematics.

Quadratic Inequalities

To solve a quadratic inequality, such as $x^2 - 4x + 3 < 0$, you can first solve the corresponding quadratic equation: $x^2 - 4x + 3 = 0$, which will give you the roots $x = 1$ or $x = 3$. Plot the roots to create intervals on the x-axis.

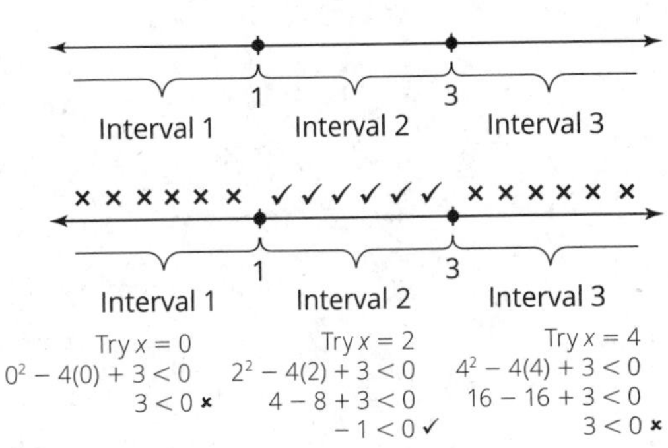

Interval 2 satisfies the original inequality, so the solution includes all numbers between 1 and 3.

Baby, You're a Firework

Many historians believe fireworks were first created and used in China during the 7th century. To these ancient people, fireworks were a way to scare spirits away—a tradition that is still used for Chinese New Year festivities. Also in this modern time, fireworks are often used during celebrations, and they come in many different shapes and colors. Many aerial fireworks burst at different heights and can travel anywhere from 300 to about 1300 feet in the air!

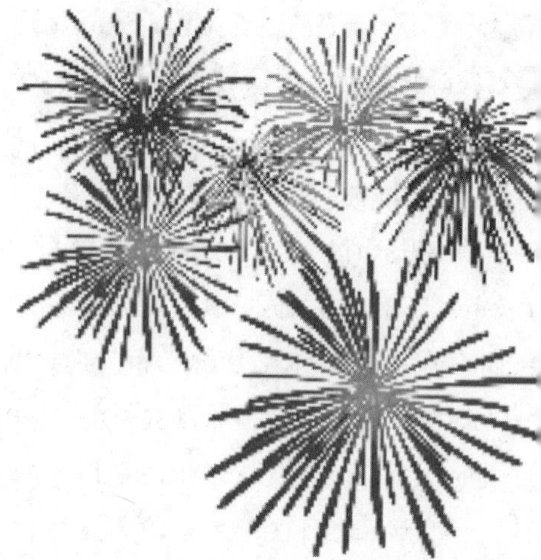

Talking Points

It can be helpful to understand imaginary and complex numbers for college admissions tests.

Here is an example of a sample question:

Simplify: $\sqrt{-3} + \sqrt{-9} + \sqrt{-16}$.

To solve this problem, you need to understand imaginary numbers and square roots. The imaginary number i is equal to $\sqrt{-1}$. You can rewrite expressions with i just as with any variable.

So, $\sqrt{-3} = \sqrt{(3)(-1)}$, or $\sqrt{3}i$. The sum can be written as

$$\sqrt{3}i + 3i + 4i, \text{ or } (7 + \sqrt{3})\,i$$

Key Terms

Fundamental Theorem of Algebra

The Fundamental Theorem of Algebra states that any polynomial equation of degree n must have, with multiplicity, exactly n complex roots or solutions.

one-to-one function

A function is a one-to-one function if both the function and its inverse are functions.

1

i Want to Believe

Imaginary and Complex Numbers

Warm Up

Determine the zeros of each function.

1. $f(x) = x^2 - 4x + 4$

2. $g(x) = x^2 - 25$

3. $h(x) = (x - 1)^2 - 9$

4. $j(x) = 2x^2 + 8x + 5$

Learning Goals

- Simplify expressions involving negative roots using *i*.
- Simplify expressions involving imaginary numbers.
- Understand properties of the set of complex numbers.
- Determine the sets to which numbers belong.
- Calculate complex roots of quadratic equations and complex zeros of quadratic functions.
- Interpret complex roots of quadratic equations and complex zeros of quadratic functions.
- Determine whether a function has complex solutions from a graph and from an equation in radical form.
- Determine the number of roots of a quadratic equation from a graph and from an equation in radical form.

Key Terms

- the number *i*
- imaginary roots
- imaginary zeros
- imaginary numbers
- pure imaginary number
- complex numbers
- real part of a complex number
- imaginary part of a complex number
- Fundamental Theorem of Algebra

You have solved quadratic equations with real number solutions. How can you solve a quadratic equation that has a solution that is not real?

GETTING STARTED

Did I Cross the Line?

1. Consider the quadratic functions and their graphs shown.

$f(x) = x^2 - 10x + 25$

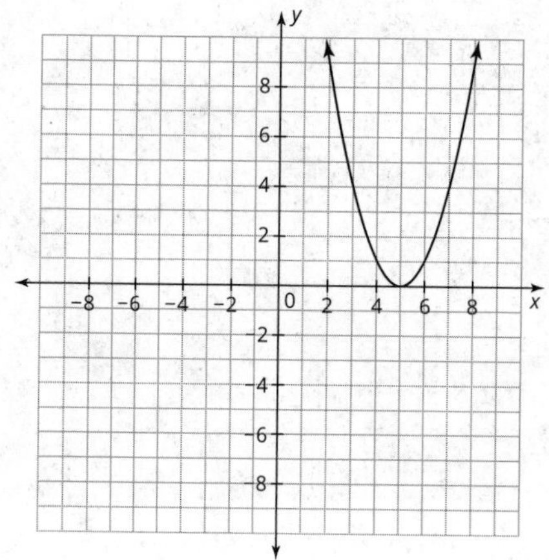

$c(x) = -x^2 + 6x$

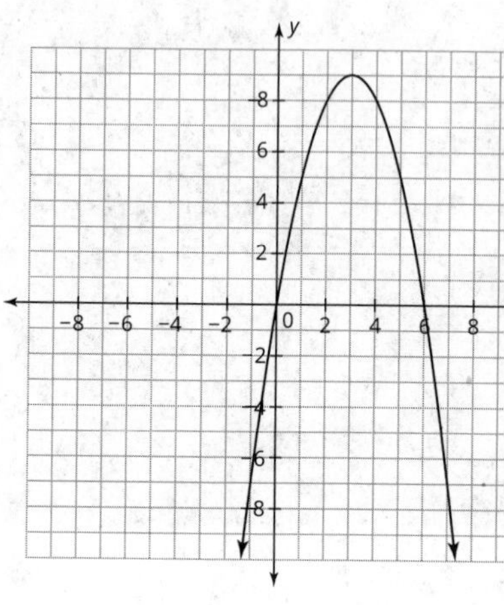

$p(x) = x^2 + 1$

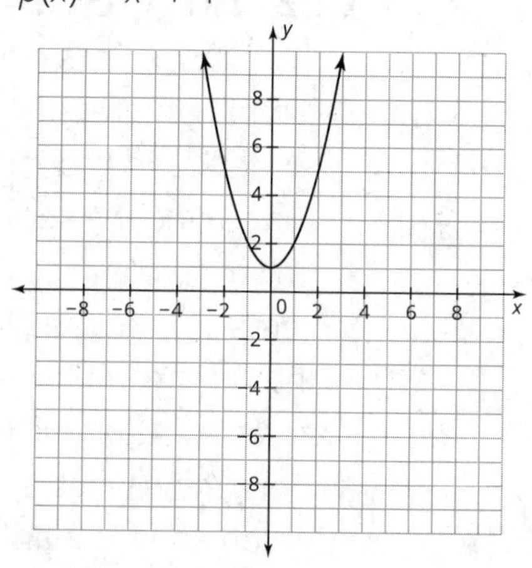

a. List all the key characteristics you know about each function. Be sure to include the number of zeros, the *x*-intercept(s), the *y*-intercept, the axis of symmetry, and the vertex.

b. Compare the three functions. What do they have in common? What is different about the functions?

ACTIVITY 1.1

The Number i

Consider the function $p(x) = x^2 + 1$ and its graph from the Getting Started.

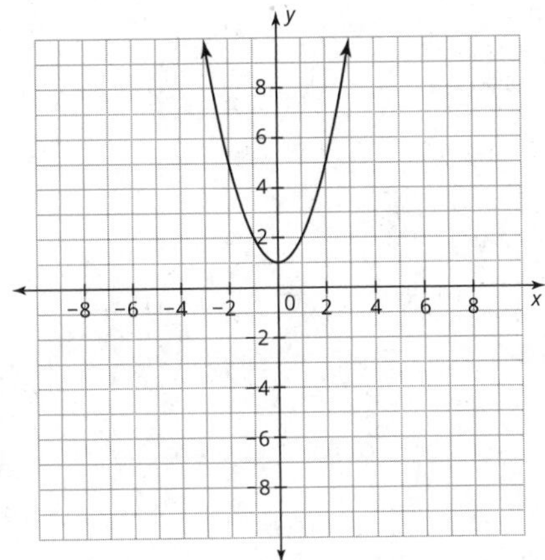

Elena and Mark determined the zeros of the function.

Elena

$x^2 + 1 = 0$

$x^2 = -1$

$x = \pm\sqrt{-1}$

Mark

$x^2 + 1 = 0$

$x^2 = -1$

$x = \pm 1$

1. What did Mark do wrong? Use the graph to justify your answer.

2. Consider Elena's solution. Does the solution fall within the real number system? Explain your reasoning.

In order to calculate the square of any real number, there must be some way to calculate the square root of a negative number. That is, there must be a number such that when it is squared, it is equal to a negative numbe For this reason, mathematicians defined what is called *the number i*. **The number *i*** is a number such that $i^2 = -1$. The number i is also called the imaginary identity.

The number i is similar to the number π: even though they are both numbers, each is special enough that it gets its very own symbol.

3. If $i^2 = -1$, then what is the value of i?

4. Recall the function $p(x) = x^2 + 1$. Write the zeros of the function in terms of i.

Functions and equations that have solutions requiring i have **imaginary zeros** or **imaginary roots.**

5. How can you tell from the graph of a quadratic equation whethe or not it has real solutions or imaginary solutions?

6. Do you think you can determine the imaginary solutions by examining the graph? Explain your reasoning.

ACTIVITY 1.2

The Complex Number System

e set of **complex numbers** is the set of all numbers written in the form + *bi*, where *a* and *b* are real numbers. The term *a* is called the **real part of a mplex number**, and the term *bi* is called the **imaginary part of a complex umber**. The set of complex numbers is represented by the notation $\mathbb{C}$.

e set of **imaginary numbers** is the set of all numbers written in the rm $a + bi$, where *a* and *b* are real numbers and *b* is not equal to 0. The set imaginary numbers is represented by the notation $\mathbb{I}$. A **pure imaginary umber** is a number of the form $a + bi$, where *a* is equal to 0 and *b* is not qual to 0.

Complex Numbers
$\mathbb{C}$
$a + bi$ where $a, b \in \mathbb{R}$

Real Numbers
$\mathbb{R}$
$a + bi$ where $b = 0$

Imaginary Numbers
$\mathbb{I}$
$a + bi$ where $b \neq 0$

Rational Numbers
$\mathbb{Q}$

Irrational Numbers
$\mathbb{R} - \mathbb{Q}$

Integers
$\mathbb{Z}$

Whole Numbers
$\mathbb{W}$

Natural Numbers
$\mathbb{N}$

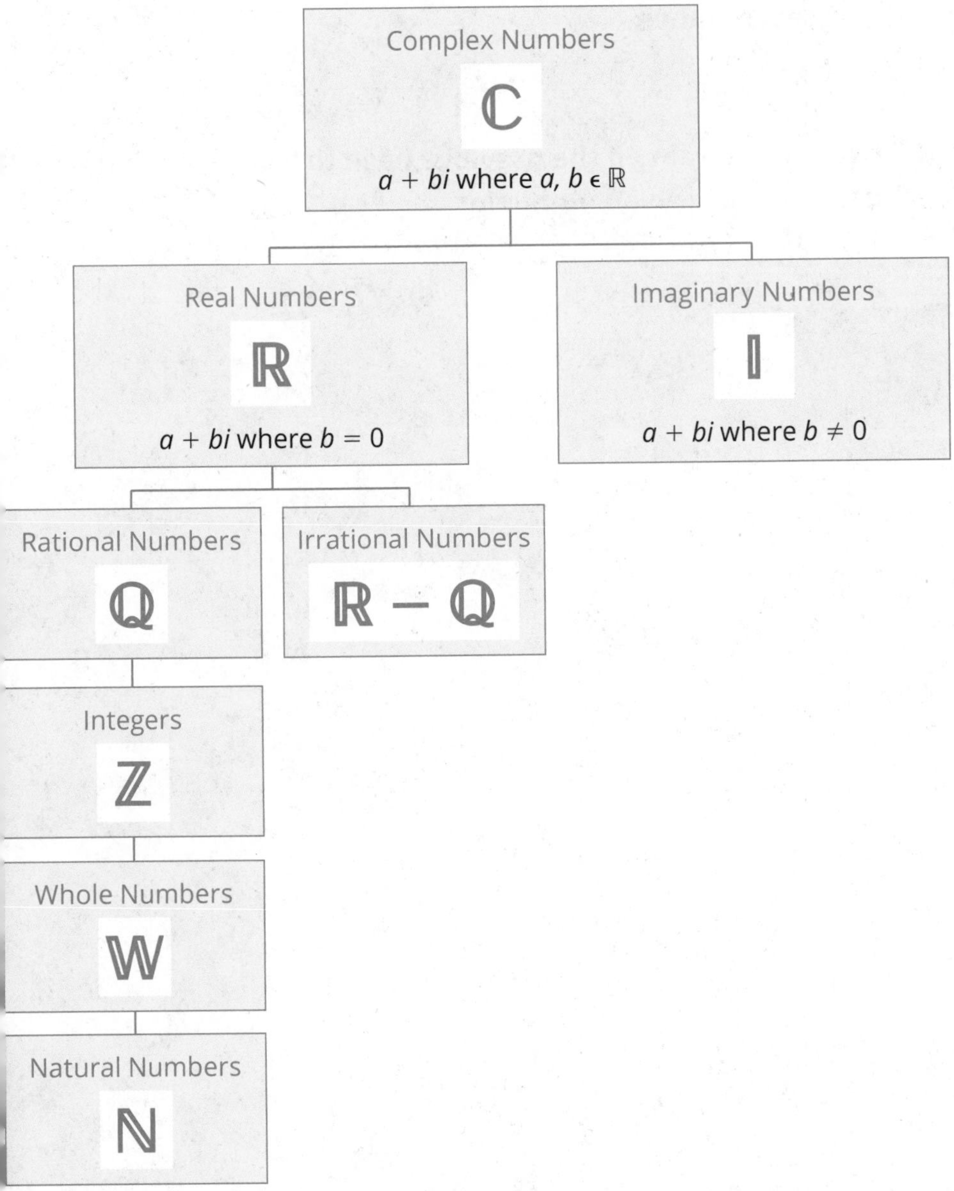

The $\in$ symbol means "an element of". Therefore, "$a, b \in \mathbb{R}$" means that the values for *a* and *b* are elements of the set of real numbers.

1. **Complete each statement with *always, sometimes*, or *never*.**

   a. **If a number is an imaginary number, then it is __________ a complex number.**

   b. **If a number is a complex number, then it is __________ an imaginary number.**

   c. **If a number is a real number, then it is __________ a complex number.**

   d. **If a number is a real number, then it is __________ an imaginary number.**

   e. **If a number is a complex number, then it is __________ a real number.**

2. **Use the diagram on the previous page to list *all* number sets t describe each given number.**

   a. 3

   b. $\sqrt{7}$

   c. $3i$

   d. $5.\overline{45}$

   e. $\frac{7}{8}$

   f. $6 - i$

u can rewrite expressions involving negative roots by using *i*.

Worked Example

You can use the number *i* to rewrite $\sqrt{-25}$.

Factor out −1. $\sqrt{-25} = \sqrt{(-1)(25)}$

Rewrite the radical expression. $= \sqrt{-1} \cdot \sqrt{25}$

Apply the square root on $\sqrt{25}$. $= 5\sqrt{-1}$

Rewrite $\sqrt{-1}$ as *i*. $= 5i$

So, $\sqrt{-25}$ can be rewritten as $5i$.

Rewrite each expression using *i*.

a. $\sqrt{-4}$

b. $\sqrt{-12}$

c. $5 + \sqrt{-50}$

d. $\frac{6 - \sqrt{-8}}{2}$

ACTIVITY 1.3

Add, Subtract, and Multiply Complex Numbers

A complex number can be represented on the complex plane. The x-axis of th complex plane contains all the real numbers, and the y-axis contains all of the imaginary numbers.

The complex number $2 + 3i$ can be represented as shown.

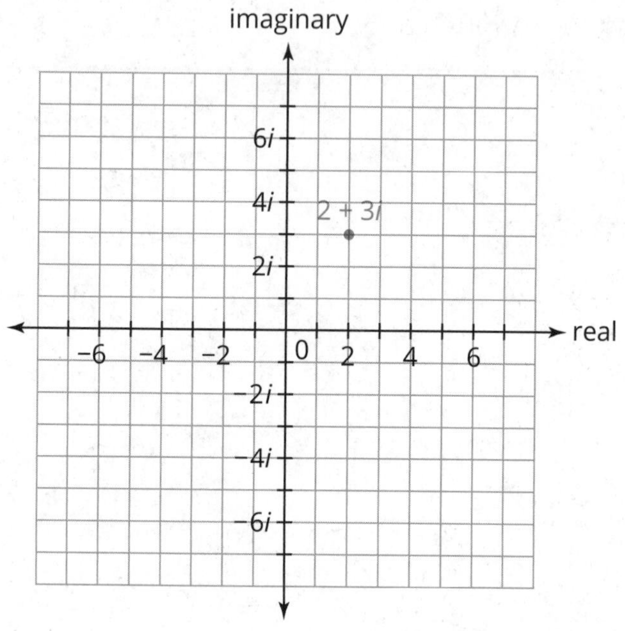

1. Plot and label each of these complex numbers on the complex plane shown.

a. $5 - 3i$

b. $-3 + 4i$

c. $8 + 6i$

d. $-6i$

e. -7

f. i

g. $5 + 3\sqrt{-1}$

h. $-3\sqrt{-1} + 3$

i. $-4\sqrt{-1} - 3$

2. Describe the process you can use to plot a complex number $a + bi$ on the complex plane.

:'s consider the sum of two complex numbers.

e complex plane shows the sum of $(2 + 3i) + (-5 + i)$.

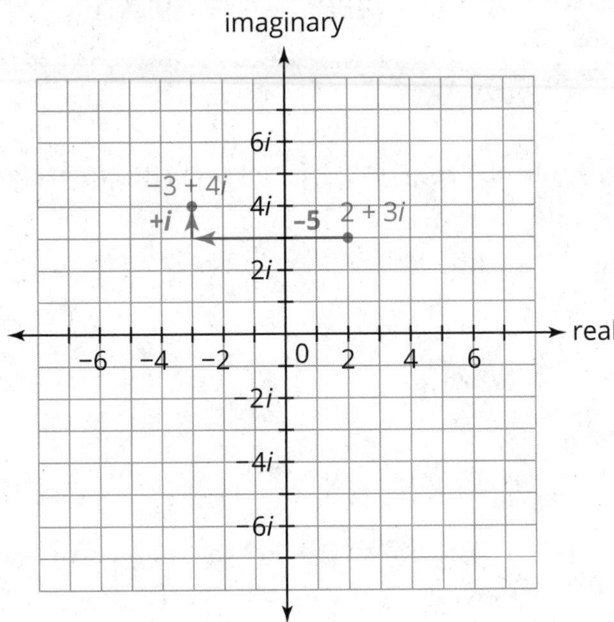

Suppose you start at the point $(-5 + i)$ and add $(2 + 3i)$.

a. Show how to determine the sum on the complex plane.

b. What do you notice about the sum? What does it suggest about the Commutative Property and complex numbers?

Kimani

To add two complex numbers, you can add their real parts separately, then add their imaginary parts separately, and then combine the results into the form a + bi.

Subtracting a number is the same as adding its negative.

4. Explain why Kimani's reasoning is correct. Illustrate your answ with an example.

5. Is $(-3 + 4i) - (-5 + i)$ equal to $2 + 3i$? Use the complex plane to confirm your answer.

6. Suppose you start at the point 2, or $2 + 0i$, and add $3i + (-5 + i)$

a. Show how to determine the sum on the complex plan

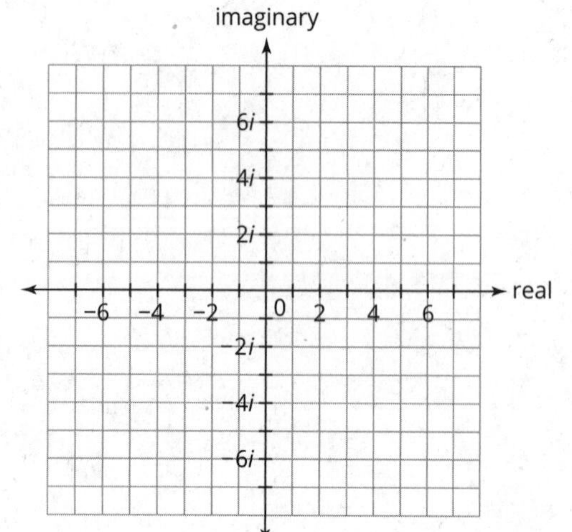

b. Compare the sum with $(2 + 3i) + (-5 + i)$. What do yo notice? What does it suggest about the Associative Property and complex numbers?

u can multiply complex numbers by real numbers. Multiplying by a al number, k, results in a dilation of the point on the complex plane: $+ bi) = ka + kbi$.

Consider the complex numbers plotted and labeled. Four different products can be represented. Complete each product and explain your answers.

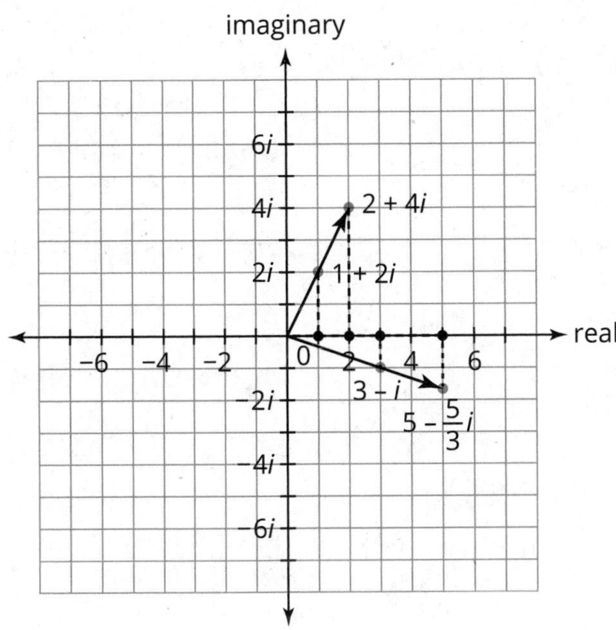

a. (__________)$(1 + 2i) = (2 + 4i)$

b. (__________)$(2 + 4i) = (1 + 2i)$

c. (__________)$(3 - i) = (5 - \frac{5}{3}i)$

d. (__________)$(5 - \frac{5}{3}i) = (3 - i)$

What do these products suggest about the Distributive Property and complex numbers?

ACTIVITY

1.4 Operations with Complex Numbers

When operating with complex numbers involving i, combine like terms by treating i as a variable (even though it is a constant)

1. Perform each operation. Show your work.

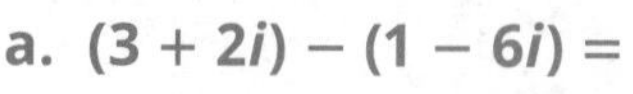

a. $(3 + 2i) - (1 - 6i) =$

b. $4i + 3 - 6 + i - 1 =$

c. $5i(3 - 2i) =$

d. $(5 + 3i)(2 - 3i) =$

Remember:

The value of i^2 is -1.

2. Determine each product.

a. $(2 + i)(2 - i) =$

b. $(\frac{1}{2} + i)(\frac{1}{2} - i) =$

c. $(3 + 2i)(3 - 2i) =$

d. $(1 - 3i)(1 + 3i) =$

e. What do you notice about each product?

What effect does multiplying a complex number by *i* have on the location of the point on the complex plane? Use examples to justify your thinking.

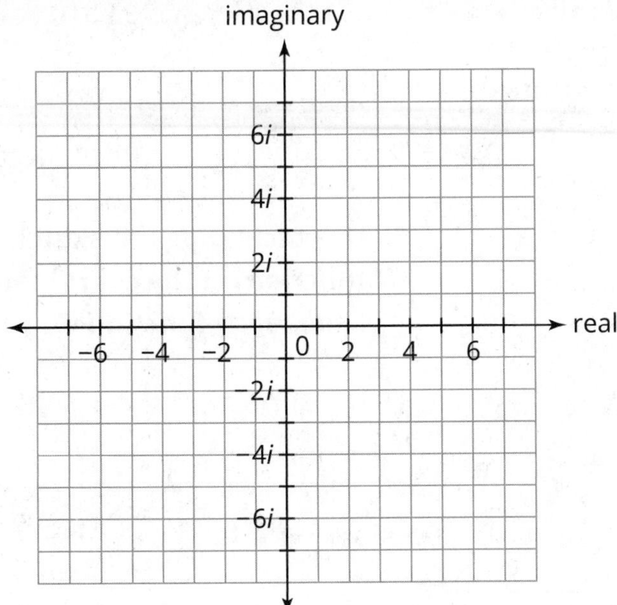

ACTIVITY 1.5 Solving Quadratics with Imaginary Zeros

Consider each quadratic function.

$f(x) = x^2 + 9$ $\quad$ $g(x) = (x - 2)^2 + 1$ $\quad$ $h(x) = x^2 - 2x + 2$

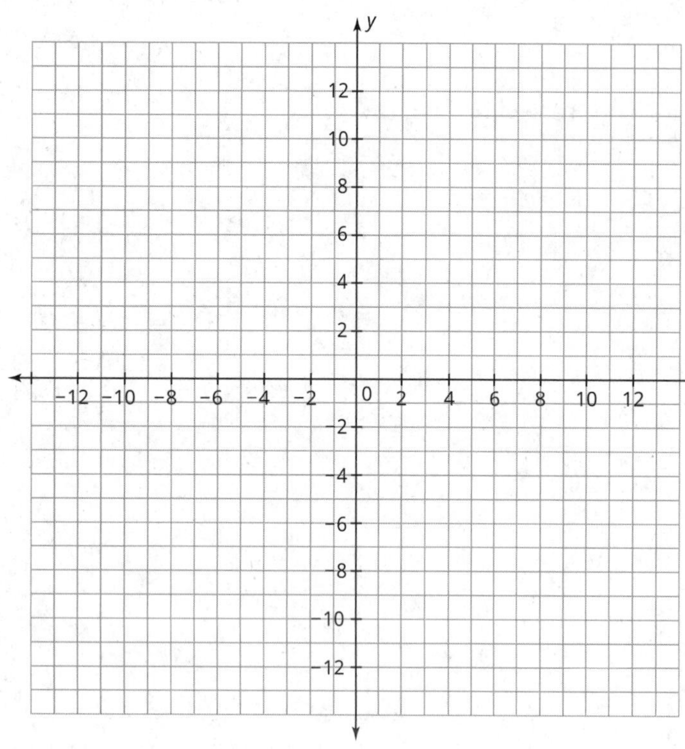

1. Use technology to sketch each function on the coordinate plane. Label each function on your graph.

2. What do the solutions of the three functions have in common?

3. Consider the function $f(x) = x^2 + 9$.

a. Describe the structure of the function. How does it compare to the function $q(x) = x^2 - 9$?

b. Consider an equation written in the form $ax^2 + c = 0$. Complete the table to show when the solutions of a function are real or imaginary.

	c is positive	*c* is negative
a is positive		
a is negative		

c. If the factored form of a difference of squares is $a^2 - b^2 = (a - b)(a + b)$, what is the factored form of a sum of squares, $a^2 + b^2$?

d. What are the solutions to $f(x) = x^2 + 9$?

Consider the function $g(x) = (x - 2)^2 + 1$.

a. How can you use the structure of the function to determine whether its zeros are real or imaginary?

Will the graph of the function pass through the x-axis?

b. What is the solution to $(x - 2)^2 + 1 = 0$?

Consider the function $h(x) = x^2 - 2x + 2$.

a. What is the most efficient method to determine the zeros? Explain your reasoning.

The discriminant of the function is $b^2 - 4ac$.

b. Determine the discriminant of the function. How can you use the discriminant to know whether the solutions are real or imaginary?

c. What is the solution to $x^2 - 2x + 2 = 0$?

d. Describe how you can check your solutions.

You can apply the Distributive Property to determine whether an equation in factored form is equivalent to an equation in general form.

Worked Example

Consider the expression $(x - i)(x + i)$.

Multiply binomials.	$(x - i)(x + i) = x^2 + xi - xi - i^2$
Group like terms.	$= x^2 + (xi - xi) - i^2$
Combine like terms.	$= x^2 - i^2$
Use the powers of i to rewrite i^2 as -1.	$= x^2 - (-1)$
Rewrite.	$= x^2 + 1$

So, $(x - i)(x + i) = x^2 + 1$.

Recall that a quadratic function in factored form is written in the form $y = a(x - r_1)(x - r_2)$.

6. **Use your answer to Question 5 part (c) to write the function $h(x) = x^2 - 2x + 2$ in factored form.**

7. **Explain why the function you wrote in factored form is equivalent to $h(x) = x^2 - 2x + 2$.**

Use any method to solve each function.

a. $f(x) = -x^2 - 8x - 18$

b. $g(x) = 2x^2 - 2x + 3$

c. $h(x) = -3x^2 - 4x - 4$

TALK the TALK

Beyond Imagination

The **Fundamental Theorem of Algebra** states that any polynomial equation of degree n must have exactly n complex roots or solutions. Any root may be a multiple root.

1. **Complete the table to determine the number of real and imaginary roots for different quadratic equations.**

Location of Vertex	Concavity	Sketch	Number of x-Intercepts	Number and Type of Roots
Above the x-axis	Up	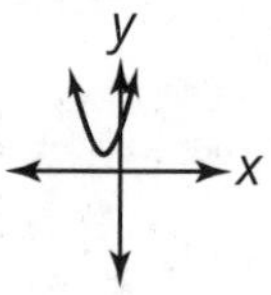	0	2 imaginary roots
	Down	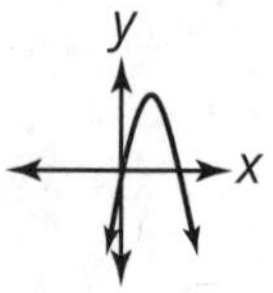		
Below the x-axis	Up	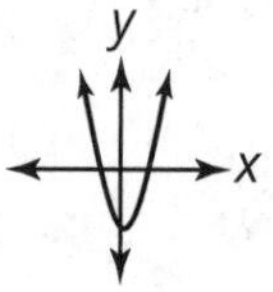		
	Down	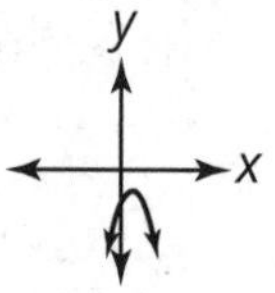		
On the x-axis	Up	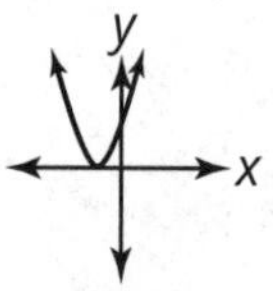		
	Down	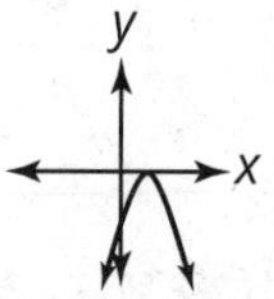		

NOTES

2. Casey says that any quadratic equation has only one of these 3 types of solutions:

- 2 unique real number solutions
- 2 equal real number solutions (a double root)
- 1 real and 1 imaginary solution

Brandon says that any quadratic equation has only one of these 3 types of solutions:

- 2 unique real number solutions
- 2 equal real number solutions (a double root)
- 2 imaginary solutions

Karl says that any quadratic equation has only one of these 4 types of solutions:

- 2 unique real number solutions
- 2 equal real number solutions (a double root)
- 2 imaginary solutions
- 1 real and 1 imaginary solution

Who's correct? Explain your reasoning.

3. Explain why it is not possible for a quadratic equation to have 2 equal imaginary solutions (double imaginary root).

Assignment

Write

Match each definition to the corresponding term.

1. the set of all numbers written in the form $a + bi$, where a and b are real numbers
2. the set of all numbers written in the form $a + bi$, where a and b are real numbers and b is not equal to 0
3. the term bi in a complex number written as $a + bi$
4. a number equal to $\sqrt{-1}$
5. solutions to functions and equations that have a negative value for the discriminant
6. a number of the form bi where b is a real number and is not equal to 0
7. the term a in a complex number written as $a + bi$

a. imaginary roots (imaginary zeros)
b. the number i
c. imaginary numbers
d. pure imaginary number
e. complex numbers
f. real part of a complex number
g. imaginary part of a complex number

Remember

The set of complex numbers is the set of all numbers written in the form $a + bi$, where a and b are real numbers. Imaginary numbers are complex numbers where b is not equal to 0 and real numbers are complex numbers where b is equal to 0.

Practice

1. Rewrite each radical using i.

   a. $\sqrt{-16}$ b. $\sqrt{-27}$ c. $\sqrt{-200}$ d. $5 + \sqrt{-20}$

2. Classify each number according to its most specific number set.

   a. $\frac{-4}{\sqrt{9}}$ b. $\frac{\sqrt{-4}}{9}$ c. $9 - \sqrt{-4}$ d. $-4 - \sqrt{9}$

3. Mr. Hilbert writes the expression $(3 + i)(7 - 2i)$ on the board and asks his students to rewrite it using the Distributive Property. The work of two students is shown below. Which student simplified the expression correctly? What mistake did the other student make?

Student 1

$$\begin{aligned}(3 + i)(7 - i) &= 21 - 3i + 7i - i^2 \\ &= 21 + 4i + 1 \\ &= 22 + 4i\end{aligned}$$

Student 2

$$\begin{aligned}(3 + i)(7 - i) &= 21 - 3i + 7i - i^2 \\ &= 21 + 4i - 1 \\ &= 20 + 4i\end{aligned}$$

4. Francois claims that $\sqrt{-16} \cdot \sqrt{-4}$ is equal to 8. Jeanette claims that $\sqrt{-16} \cdot \sqrt{-4}$ is equal to -8. Who is correct? What mistake did the other student make? Support your answer with work.
5. Erika identifies $\frac{6i}{4}$ as an imaginary number and a rational number. Is Erika correct? Explain how you determined your answer.
6. Consider the functions $g(x) = x^2 - 8x - 26$ and $h(x) = x^2 - 8x + 26$ and their graphs.
   a. Describe each function. Be sure to include the number of zeros, the x-intercept(s), the y-intercept, the axis of symmetry, and the vertex.
   b. Compare the functions and their graphs. Identify any similarities and differences.
   c. Determine the zeros of both functions. Show your work.
   d. How do your answers in parts (a) and (c) compare?

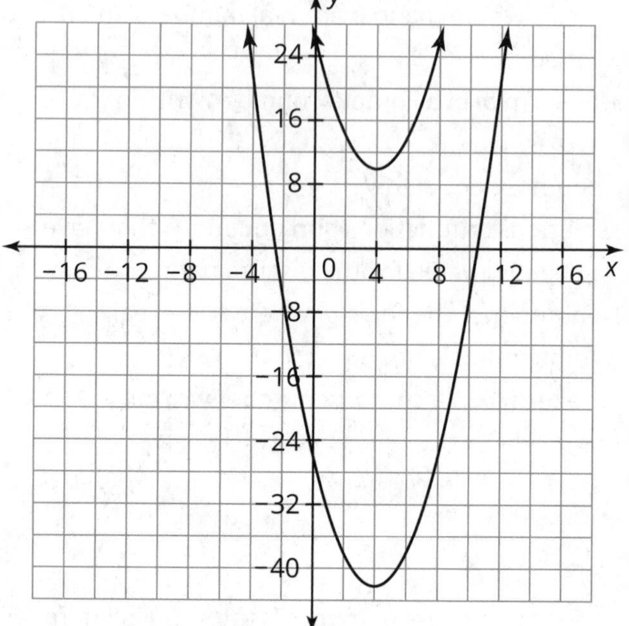

Stretch

How could you use your knowledge of quadratic functions to solve for a quadratic inequality by graphing?

Review

1. Factor each trinomial.
   a. $x^2 - 2x - 15$
   b. $x^2 + 2x - 15$
2. Write each function in factored form and determine its roots.
   a. $f(x) = 4x^2 + 8x - 12$
   b. $g(x) = 15x^2 - 35x + 20$
3. Consider the function $f(x) = 3x^2 - 4$.
   a. How many zeros does the function have?
   b. What are the zeros of the function?

2

Ahead of the Curve

Solving Quadratic Inequalities

Warm Up

Determine the solution of each quadratic equation.

1. $x^2 - 100 = -64$

2. $x^2 + 3x + 5 = 15$

3. $4x^2 + 12x = 7$

4. $x^2 + 4x - 3 = 5$

Learning Goals

- Solve a quadratic inequality by calculating the roots of the quadratic equation which corresponds to the inequality and testing values within intervals determined by the roots.
- Connect the graphical representation of a quadratic function and the solution to a corresponding quadratic inequality represented on a number line.
- Use interval notation to record the solutions to quadratic inequalities.

You have interpreted the solution sets to linear inequalities on a coordinate plane. You have also solved quadratic equations using a variety of methods. How can you interpret the solutions sets to quadratic inequalities on a coordinate plane using what you know about solving quadratic equations?

GETTING STARTED

It Has Its Ups and Downs

A vertical motion model is a quadratic equation of the form $y = -16t^2 + v_0 t + h_0$.

A firework is shot straight up into the air with an initial velocity of 500 feet per second from 5 feet off the ground. The graph of the function that represents this situation is shown.

1. **Use the graph to approximate when the firework will be at each given height off the ground.**

   a. **0 feet**

   b. **1000 feet**

   c. **2500 feet**

   d. **3900 feet**

2. **Describe any patterns you notice for the number of times the firework reaches a given height.**

3. **Draw a horizontal line on the graph to represent when the firework is 2000 feet off the ground.**

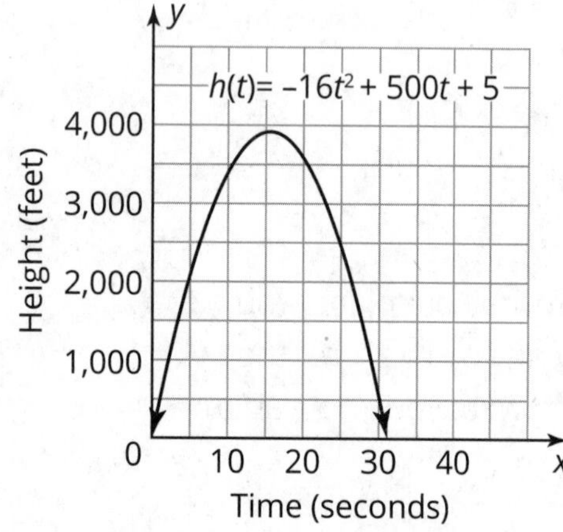

   a. **When is the firework higher than 2000 feet? Circle this portion of the graph.**

   b. **When is the firework below 2000 feet? Draw a box around this portion of the graph.**

   c. **Write a quadratic inequality that represents the times when the firework is below 2000 feet.**

ACTIVITY

2.1

Solving Quadratic Inequalities

ust like with the other inequalities you have studied, the solution to a quadratic inequality is the set of values that satisfy the inequality.

Worked Example

Let's determine the solution of the quadratic inequality $x^2 - 4x + 3 < 0$.

Write the corresponding quadratic equation. $x^2 - 4x + 3 = 0$

Calculate the roots of the quadratic equation using an appropriate method.

$$(x - 3)(x - 1) = 0$$
$$(x - 3) = 0 \quad \text{or} \quad (x - 1) = 0$$
$$x = 3 \quad \text{or} \quad x = 1$$

Plot the roots to divide the number line into three regions.

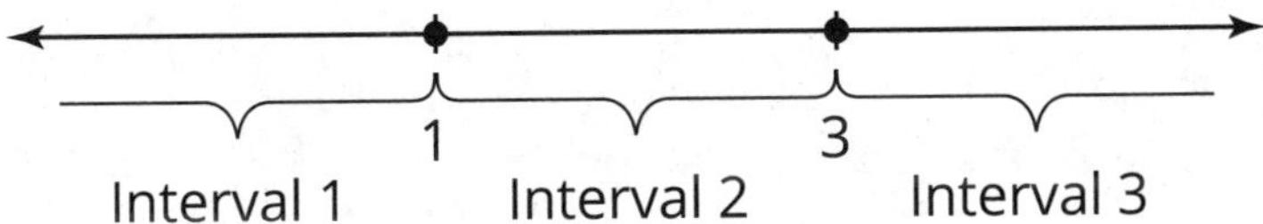

Choose a value from each interval to test in the original inequality.

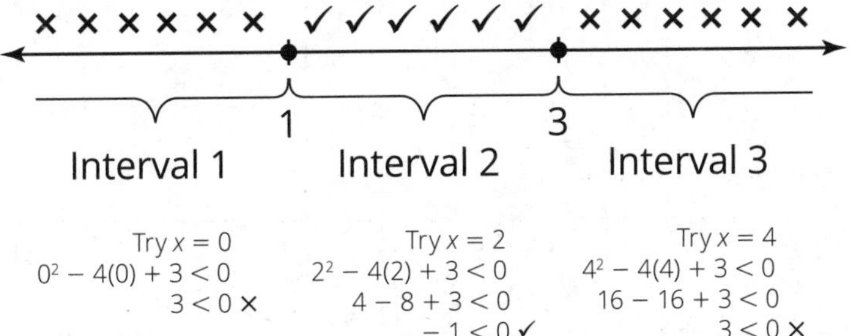

Try $x = 0$	Try $x = 2$	Try $x = 4$
$0^2 - 4(0) + 3 < 0$	$2^2 - 4(2) + 3 < 0$	$4^2 - 4(4) + 3 < 0$
$3 < 0$ ✗	$4 - 8 + 3 < 0$	$16 - 16 + 3 < 0$
	$-1 < 0$ ✓	$3 < 0$ ✗

Identify the solution set as the interval(s) in which your test value satisfies the inequality.

Interval 2 satisfies the original inequality, so the solution includes all numbers between 1 and 3.

Solution: $x \in (1, 3)$

The symbol $\in$ is read "is an element of," "is in," or "belongs to." The notation $x \in (1, 3)$ means the same as $1 < x < 3$.

1. **Analyze the worked example.**

The notation $x \in [1, 3]$ means the same as $1 \leq x \leq 3$.

a. **How would the solution set change if the inequality was less than or equal to? Explain your reasoning.**

b. **How would the solution set change if the inequality was greater than or equal to? Explain your reasoning.**

2. **Graph $y = x^2 - 4x + 3$ on the coordinate plane shown and label the roots of the equation and the vertex. Then describe how the graph supports that the solution set for the associated quadratic inequality $x^2 - 4x + 3 < 0$ is $1 < x < 3$.**

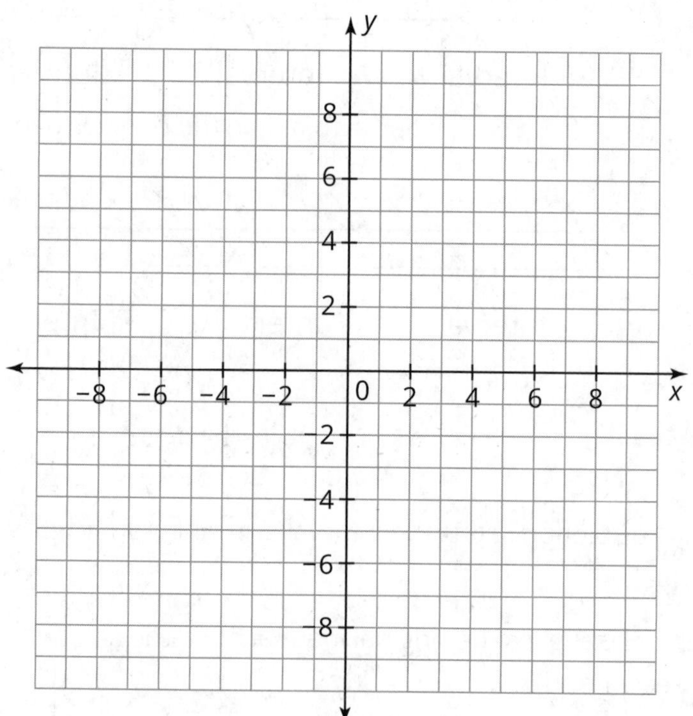

correctly determined the roots of the quadratic inequality $- 14x + 27 \geq 7$ to be $x = 5$ and $x = 2$. However, he incorrectly [de]termined the solution set. His work is shown.

Jeff

$2x^2 - 14x + 27 = 7$
$2x^2 - 14x + 20 = 0$
$2(x^2 - 7x + 10) = 0$
$2(x - 5)(x - 2) = 0$
$x = 5$ or $x = 2$

$x = 1$	$x = 3$	$x = 6$
$2(1)^2 - 14(1) + 27 \geq 7$	$2(3)^2 - 14(3) + 27 \geq 7$	$2(6)^2 - 14(6) + 27 \geq 7$
$2 - 14 + 27 \geq 7$	$18 - 42 + 27 \geq 7$	$72 - 84 + 27 \geq 7$
$15 \geq 7$ ✓	$3 \geq 7$ ✗	$15 \geq 7$ ✓

Solution: $x \in (-\infty, 1]$ or $x \in [6, \infty)$

Describe Jeff's error. Then, determine the correct solution set for the inequality.

When testing values from each interval, could you use the factored form of the inequality rather than the original inequality?

ACTIVITY
2.2

Modeling Quadratic Inequalities

A water balloon is launched from a machine upward from a height of 10 f[eet] with an initial velocity of 46 feet per second.

1. **Identify the variables and write a quadratic function to represent this situation.**

2. **Use technology to sketch the graph of the function.**

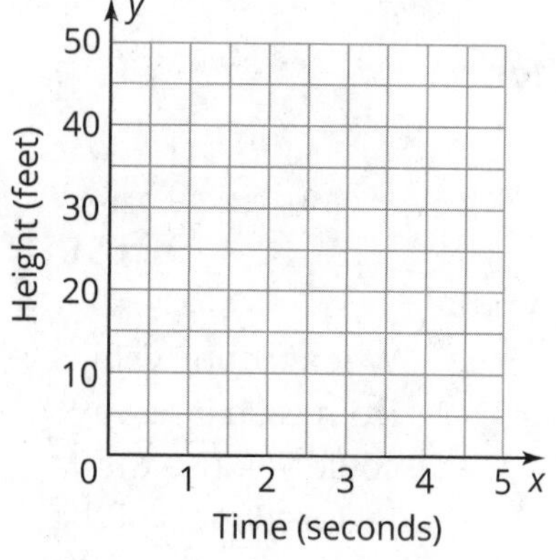

3. **Draw a horizontal line on the graph to represent when th[e] balloon is 30 feet off the ground.**

   a. **Circle the portion of the graph that represents when th[e] balloon is above 30 feet.**

   b. **Write and solve an inequality to determine when the balloon is above 30 feet. Use the graph to explain your solution.**

4. **Determine when the balloon is at or below 43 feet. Interpret your solution in terms of the model you graphed.**

ALK the TALK

Boom! Boom!

n the Getting Started activity, a firework was shot straight up into the ir with an initial velocity of 500 feet per second from 5 feet off the round. The function representing the situation was identified as $(t) = -16t^2 + 500t + 5$. You determined the firework would be above 000 feet between about 5 seconds and 27 seconds.

uppose a second firework was shot straight up into the air with an nitial velocity of 500 feet per second from the ground.

. **Predict whether the second firework will be above 2000 feet for more time, less time, or the same amount of time as the first firework.**

. **Write a quadratic inequality to represent when the second firework will be above 2000 feet.**

. **Determine when the second firework will be above 2000 feet.**

NOTES

NOTES

4. **Was your prediction made in Question 1 correct?**

5. **Use technology to compare the graph of the first firework to the graph of the second firework. What do you notice?**

Assignment

Write

Describe the difference between the solutions of a quadratic equation and the solutions of a quadratic inequality.

Remember

The solution set of a quadratic inequality is determined by first solving for the roots of the quadratic equation, then determining which interval(s) created by the roots satisfy the inequality.

Practice

1. A nutrition company has determined that the fixed cost associated with producing cases of its special health bars is \$1000. The variable cost is $\frac{3}{4}x + 25$ dollars per case that they produce. The selling price of the cases of health bars is $135 - \frac{1}{4}x$ per case that they sell.
   a. Determine the cost function $C(x)$ for this product based on the number of cases, x, that they produce and sell. Simplify if necessary.
   b. Determine the revenue function $R(x)$ for this product based on the number of cases, x, that they produce and sell. Simplify if necessary.
   c. The profit that a company makes is the difference between the revenue and the cost. Determine the profit function $P(x)$ for this product.
   d. Determine when the company will break even.
   e. If they make and sell fewer than 10 cases of health bars, will they have a positive or negative profit? Explain your reasoning.
   f. If they make and sell more than 100 cases of health bars, will they have a positive or negative profit? Explain your reasoning.
   g. Determine how many units the company must produce and sell to make a profit of at least \$1800.
2. Solve each inequality.
   a. $2y^2 + 2y - 12 > 0$
   b. $x^2 + 6x \leq 0$
   c. $4b^2 + 14b + 16 < 10$
   d. $a^2 \geq 4(2a - 3)$
   e. $2t^2 > 9t + 18$
   f. $k^2 + 3k + 2 < -3(k + 2)$

Stretch

1. Marelby and Merily both started their own companies with \$3000. Marelby's profits can be represented as $g(x) \geq x^2 - 5x + 3$. Merily's profits can be represented by $h(x) \leq -x^2 + 5x + 3$. Graph the solutions to the quadratic inequalities and state what the shaded region means in regards to Marelby and Merily's profits.

Review

1. Determine each product.

   a. $(3x - 9)^2$ b. $(6x^2 + 5x + 4)(-x - 3)$

2. Solve each equation.

   a. $x^2 = 5x - 4$ b. $x^2 + 9x - 23 = 0$

3. Determine the roots of each function.

   a. $f(x) = (x + 5)^2 + 9$ b. $g(x) = x^2 - 3x + 5$

3

All Systems Are Go!

Systems of Quadratic Equations

Warm Up

Solve each system of equations.

1. $\begin{cases} y = 2x - 5 \\ y = x - 1 \end{cases}$

2. $\begin{cases} y = -3x + 2 \\ y = 5x - 6 \end{cases}$

3. $\begin{cases} y = -2x + 7 \\ y = -4x + 3 \end{cases}$

4. $\begin{cases} y = 3x + 7 \\ y = x + 1 \end{cases}$

Learning Goals

- Solve systems of a linear equation and a quadratic equation.
- Solve systems of two quadratic equations.

You have solved systems of linear equations graphically by determining the point of intersection and algebraically using substitution. How can you use these same methods to solve systems involving a linear and a quadratic equation or systems of two quadratic equations?

GETTING STARTED

Block That Kick!

A punter kicks a football. The height of the football, in meters, is modeled the function $h(t) = -4.9t^2 + 20t + 0.75$, where t represents time, in secon A blocker can only attempt to knock down the football as it travels upwar from the punter's foot. The height in meters of the approaching blocker's hands is modeled by the function $h(t) = -0.6t + 3$, where t represents th same time. Can the blocker knock down the football?

1. **Describe the shape of the functions that model the football's height over time and the height of the blocker's hands over tim**

2. **Sketch a graph of the situation. Do you think it is possible for th blocker to knock down the football? Explain your reasoning.**

ACTIVITY **3.1**

Modeling a System with a Linear and a Quadratic Equation

system of equations can involve nonlinear equations, such as quadratic quations. The scenario described in the previous activity models the elationship between a quadratic and a linear equation.

1. **Use technology to sketch the graph of the system described in the previous activity.**

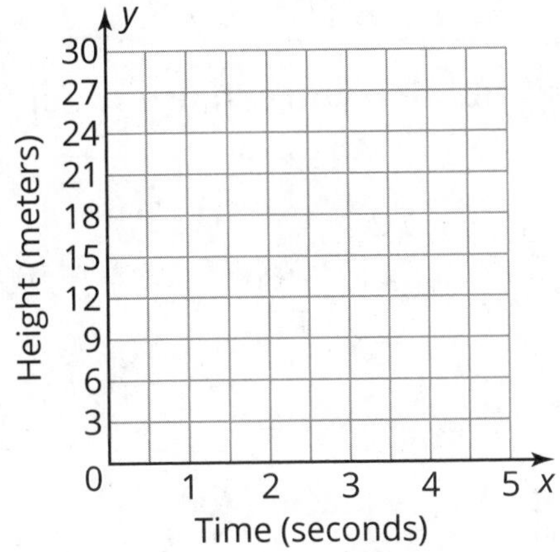

2. **How many solutions does the system have? Explain your reasoning.**

3. **Does every solution make sense in the context of the problem situation? Explain your reasoning.**

4. **Use the graph to approximate at what point the blocker can block the football. Interpret your solution in the context of the problem.**

ACTIVITY 3.2

Solving a System With a Linear and a Quadratic Equation

Methods for solving a system of non-linear equations can be similar to methods for solving a system of linear equations.

1. Consider the system of a linear equation and a quadratic equation shown.

$$\begin{cases} y = 2x + 7 \\ y = x^2 + 4 \end{cases}$$

Since y is equal to two different expressions, can you set the expressions equal to each other?

a. Write a new equation you can use to solve this system.

b. Solve the resulting equation for x.

c. Calculate the corresponding values for y.

d. Identify the solution(s) to the system of equations.

e. Graph each equation of the system and calculate the points of intersection.

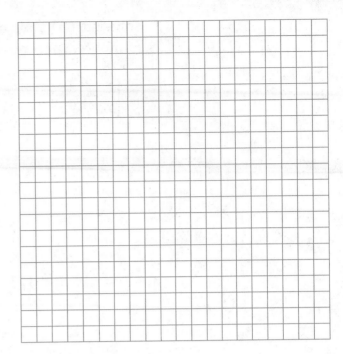

f. What do you notice about the solutions you calculated algebraically and graphically?

Think about the graphs of a linear equation and a quadratic equation. Describe the different ways in which the two graphs can intersect and provide a sketch of each case.

3. **Solve each system of equations algebraically over the set of re[al] numbers. Then verify the solution graphically.**

a. $\begin{cases} y = -2x + 4 \\ y = 4x^2 + 2x + 5 \end{cases}$

b. $\begin{cases} y = -4x - 7 \\ y = 3x^2 + x - 3 \end{cases}$

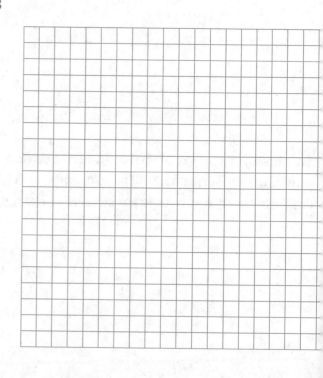

ACTIVITY

3.3

Solving a System of Two Quadratic Equations

You have solved quadratic equations and systems of linear and quadratic equations. In this activity, you will apply your knowledge of these concepts to solve a system of two quadratic equations.

1. **Consider the system of two quadratic equations.**

$$\begin{cases} y = x^2 + 3x - 5 \\ y = -x^2 + 10x - 1 \end{cases}$$

   a. **Use substitution to solve the system algebraically.**

   b. **Solve the system graphically. Graph each equation of the system and determine the points of intersection.**

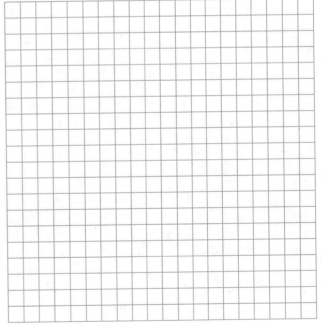

   c. **What do you notice about the solutions you calculated algebraically and graphically?**

2. **Think about the graphs of two quadratic equations. Describe the different ways in which the two graphs can intersect and provide a sketch of each case.**

3. **Solve each system of equations algebraically over the set of rea numbers. Then verify the solution graphically.**

a. $\begin{cases} y = x^2 + 2x + 1 \\ y = 2x^2 - x - 3 \end{cases}$

b. $\begin{cases} y = 2x^2 - 7x + 6 \\ y = -2x^2 + 5x - 3 \end{cases}$

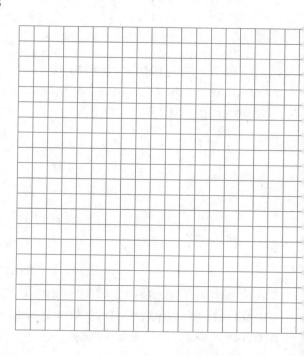

c. $\begin{cases} y = x^2 + 5x + 4 \\ y = -x^2 - 5 \end{cases}$

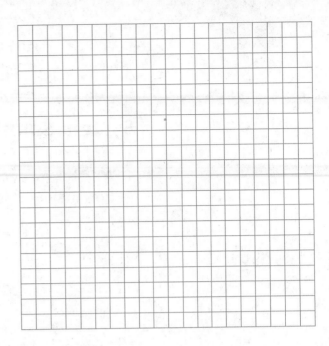

d. $\begin{cases} y = x^2 + 4x + 4 \\ y = x^2 + 2x + 6 \end{cases}$

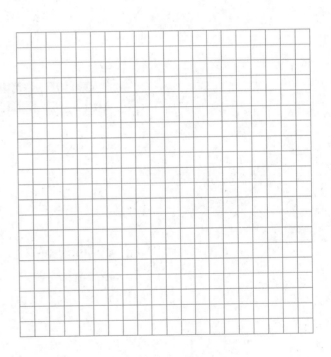

NOTES

TALK the TALK 

System Solutions

1. A system of equations consisting of two linear equations has how many possible solutions?

2. A system of equations consisting of two quadratic equations has how many possible solutions?

3. A system of equations consisting of a linear equation and a quadratic equation has how many possible solutions?

4. Explain why a system of equations consisting of a linear equation and a quadratic equation cannot have an infinite number of solutions.

Assignment

Write

escribe how a graph can e used to determine the olutions to a system of onlinear equations in your wn words.

Remember

A system of equations consisting of a linear and a quadratic equation can have no solution, one solution, or two solutions. A system of equations consisting of two quadratic equations can have no solution, one solution, two solutions, or an infinite number of solutions.

Practice

. The Fandango Bike Company specializes in children's bikes. Each month, the company must keep track of their costs and revenue. Their costs consist of fixed costs that include rent, utilities, and workers' salaries, as well as the variable cost to make the bikes. The company's costs can be represented by the function $C(x) = 25x + 900$. The company's revenue for every bike sold can be represented by the function $R(x) = 100x - x^2$.
   a. Determine the break-even point(s) for the month.
   b. What is the solution to this system of equations? Explain what the solution means in terms of the problem.
   c. Verify the solution by graphing both the cost and the revenue equations and interpreting the points of intersection.
2. Due to the rising costs of running a business, the Fandango Bike Company anticipates fixed costs in the next year to be \$1800 per month, whereas the cost to make each bike will stay at \$25 per bike.
   a. Determine the number of bikes the company will now need to make for one month to break even if the revenue from selling bikes remains the same.
   b. Verify the solution by graphing both the revenue and the cost equations.
   c. What does the company need to do to be able to break even for the month?
3. The company decides to change its location to a new building that is more energy efficient in order to help decrease fixed costs. It also invests in new machinery to reduce the number of employee hours needed to make a bike. The new monthly cost equation is represented by $C = 0.4x^2 + 15x + 400$. The company then decides to sell the bikes strictly online. The new monthly revenue equation becomes $R = 100x + 0.6x^2$.
   a. Determine the break-even point(s) for the company for each month.
   b. Verify the solution by graphing both the revenue and the cost equations and interpreting the points of intersection.

Stretch

Graph the inequalities given and describe what the double shaded region means in your own words.

$$\begin{cases} y > 2x + 5 \\ y \le -3x^2 + 15x \end{cases}$$

Review

1. Rewrite the radical $\sqrt{72}$ by extracting a perfect square.
2. Solve $x^2 - 12 = 5$.
3. Perform each operation.
   a. $(7x^3 + 5x^2 - 8x) + (3x^3 - 4x^2 + 11)$
   b. $(6x - 2y) - (3x - 5y)$.
4. A soccer ball is kicked up off a 5-meter-high platform with an initial velocity of 27 meters per second.
   a. Write an inequality to represent when the soccer ball will be above 40 meters.
   b. Graph the inequality and state when the soccer ball will be above 40 meters.

4

Model Behavior

Using Quadratic Functions to Model Data

Warm Up

1. Determine a linear regression equation that best models the data.

x	y
1	32
2	35
3	34
4	35
5	39
6	38
7	40
8	42
9	41

Learning Goals

- Use a quadratic function to model data.
- Interpret characteristics of a quadratic function in terms of a problem situation.
- Use graphs of quadratic functions to make predictions.
- Interpret the inverse of a function in terms of a problem situation.
- Determine the inverse of a quadratic function using a graph.
- Determine the equation of the inverse of a quadratic function.
- Determine whether given functions are one-to-one functions.
- Identify function types that are always, sometimes, or never one-to-one functions.

Key Terms

- restrict the domain
- one-to-one function

You know how to model data with regression equations and how to write inverses of linear functions. How can you determine whether a quadratic regression equation may best model the data, and whether the inverse of a quadratic function is also a function?

GETTING STARTED

That Might Be a Bad Idea. . .

A 12-ounce can of soda was put into a freezer. The table shows the volum
of the soda in the can, measured at different temperatures.

The first step of the modeling process is to notice and wonder. What do you notice about the data? Is there a question it brings to mind that you wonder about?

Temperature of Can (°F)	Soda Volume cm^3
68.0	355.51
50.0	354.98
42.8	354.89
39.2	354.88
35.6	354.89
32.0	354.93
23.0	355.13
14.0	355.54

1. Describe the data distribution.

2. Create a scatter plot of the data. Sketch the plot of points on th coordinate plane shown.

The second step of the modeling process is to organize and mathematize. The scatter plot is a way to organize the data.

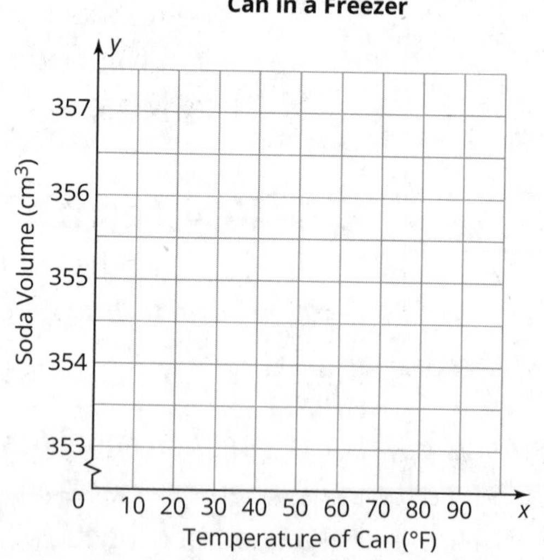

ACTIVITY 4.1

Using Quadratic Functions to Model Data

Let's continue to analyze the data and make some predictions about the volume of soda at different temperatures.

1. **Use technology to calculate the regression equation that best models the data in the previous activity. Sketch the graph of the regression equation on the coordinate plane on which you created your scatter plot. Explain why the regression equation best models the data.**

You can mathematize the data by modeling it with an appropriate regression equation.

2. **State the domain and range of your function. How do they compare to the domain and range of this problem situation?**

3. **Use the regression equation to answer each question.**

   a. **Determine the *y*-intercept and interpret its meaning in terms of this problem situation.**

   b. **Determine the *x*-intercepts, and interpret the meaning of each in terms of this problem situation.**

The third step of the modeling process is to predict and analyze and the fourth step is to test and interpret. These questions focus on these two steps of the process.

4. Predict the volume of the soda can when the temperature is:

a. 20°F.

b. 60°F.

5. Write a summary of the problem situation, your model as the solution, and any limitations of your model.

ACTIVITY 4.2

Analyzing a Quadratic Model and Its Inverse

rlen City Police Department is offering special classes for interested high chool students this summer. Elsa decides to enroll in an introductory orensic science class. On the first day, Dr. Suarez tells Elsa's class that rime scenes often involve speeding vehicles which leave skid marks n the road as evidence. Taking into account the road surface, weather onditions, the percent grade of the road, and vehicle type, they use his function:

$$f(s) = 0.034s^2 + 0.96s - 26.6$$

o determine the length in feet of skid marks left by a vehicle ased on its speed, s, in miles per hour.

25	
30	
45	
55	
60	
75	
90	
100	
110	

1. **Complete the table based on $f(s)$. Label the column titles with the independent and dependent quantities and their units.**

2. **According to the table, what are the domain and range for the problem situation?**

3. **Graph the table values and sketch the graph of $f(s)$ on the grid shown. Label the axes.**

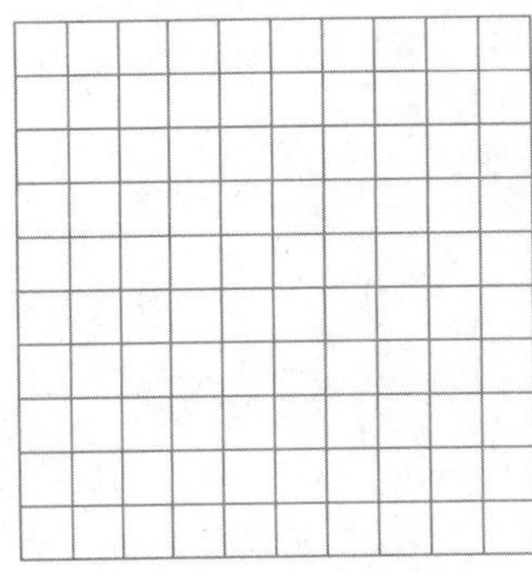

During another class period, Dr. Suarez takes Elsa's class to a mock crime scene to collect evidence.

4. One piece of evidence is a skid mark that is 300 feet long.

a. Use the graph to estimate the speed of the vehicle that created this skid mark. Explain your process.

How do these data differ from the data in the table?

b. Determine the exact speed of the vehicle that created this skid mark. Show your work.

5. Describe a new function that Elsa can use to determine the speed of a vehicle given the length of a skid mark it created. In your description, include information about the independent and dependent variables, and the domain and range of this problem situation.

Predict what you think the graph of the new function will look like and sketch the graph on the grid shown.

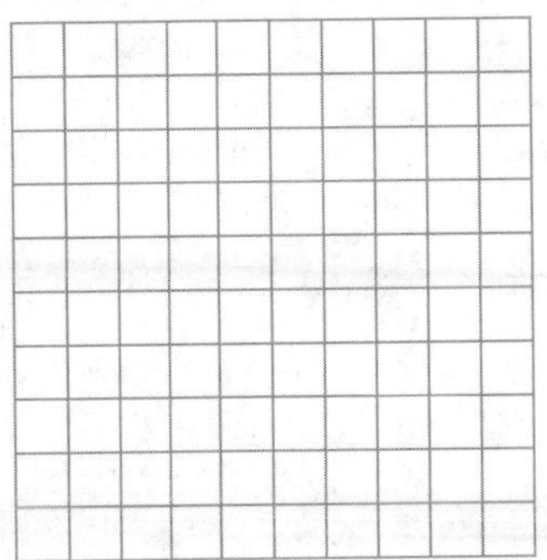

Use your graph to estimate the car's speed before stopping for each given skid mark length.

a. 50 feet

b. 175 feet

c. 350 feet

Write a report about the length of skid marks left by vehicles and vehicle speeds. Discuss possible factors that would affect the length of the skid marks left by a vehicle, and what effect these factors would have on the graph of *f*(*s*) and the graph of its inverse.

ACTIVITY 4.3 Exploring Inverses of Quadratics

You have determined inverses of linear functions by reflecting a function across the line $y = x$. Consider the basic quadratic function $f(x) = x^2$.

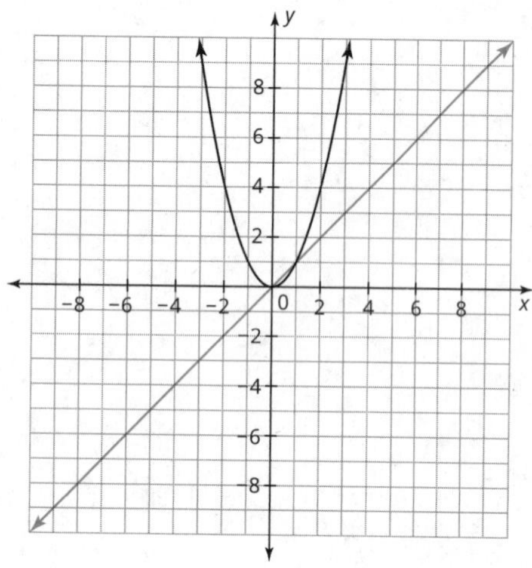

1. Use patty paper to reflect $f(x)$ across the line $y = x$ graph its inverse.

2. Explain why the inverse is not a function based on its graph.

3. What is the domain and range of the function? What the domain and range of the inverse of the function?

You can determine the equation of the inverse of the basic quadratic function $f(x) = x^2$ the same way you determined the equation of the inverse of a linear function.

Determining the equations of the inverses of exponential and linear absolute value functions is a bit more complicated, and beyond the scope of this course.

Worked Example

$$f(x) = x^2$$

Step 1: Replace $f(x)$ with y. $\quad y = x^2$

Step 2: Switch the x and y variables. $\quad x = y^2$

Step 3: Solve for y. $\quad \pm\sqrt{x} = y$

So, the equation of the inverse is $y = \pm\sqrt{x}$.

4. Explain why the inverse is not a function based on its equation.

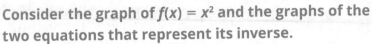

u know that the inverse of $f(x) = x^2$ is not a function. However, u can *restrict the domain* of this function so that the inverse also a function. To **restrict the domain** of a function means define a new domain for the function that is a subset of the ginal domain.

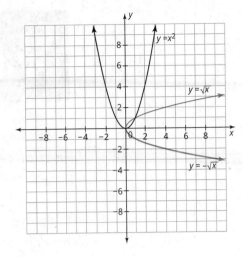

Consider the graph of $f(x) = x^2$ and the graphs of the two equations that represent its inverse.

a. Identify the restrictions of $f(x) = x^2$ to produce the inverse equations $y = \sqrt{x}$ and $y = -\sqrt{x}$. Then state the domain and range of each inverse.

Restrictions for $y = x^2$ | $y = \sqrt{x}$

Domain: __________ | **Domain:** __________

Range: __________ | **Range:** __________

Restrictions for $y = x^2$ | $y = -\sqrt{x}$

Domain: __________ | **Domain:** __________

Range: __________ | **Range:** __________

b. How does the domain and range of the inverse relate to the restricted domain and range of the original function?

c. Do all the graphs represent functions? Explain your reasoning.

ACTIVITY

4.4

More with Inverses of Quadratics

Marissa is competing in the Egg Drop Competition at her school's Science Fair. Competitors in the Egg Drop Competition are required to create a container in which they place a raw egg, and then drop the container from various heights to see if the egg breaks. The winner of the contest is the person whose container is dropped from the greatest height without breaking the egg.

Marissa is testing a container she built for the competition. She placed an egg in her container and dropped it from the roof of a building. The height of the egg can be modeled by the function $f(x) = -16x^2 + 64$, where x represents the time in seconds.

1. **Define the independent and dependent quantities of $f(x)$.**

2. **What is the domain and range of $f(x)$ based on its equation?**

3. **Determine any restrictions on the domain of $f(x)$ based on this problem situation. Explain your reasoning.**

Graph $f(x) = -16x^2 + 64$ with the restricted domain based on this problem situation. Be sure to label your graph.

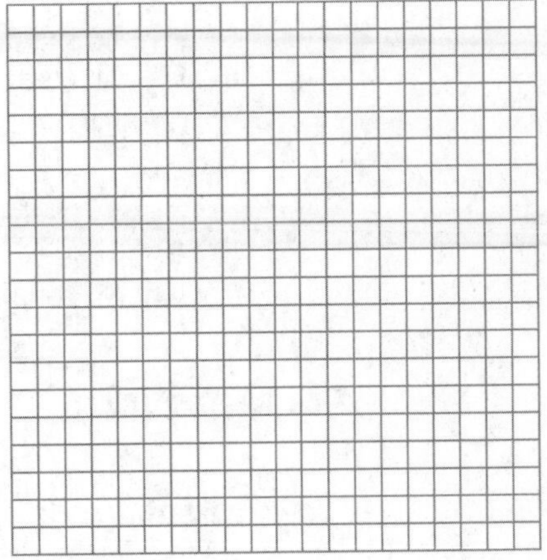

Define the independent and dependent quantities of the inverse of $f(x)$.

What is the domain and range of the inverse of $f(x)$ with the restricted domain?

Graph the inverse of $f(x)$ with the restricted domain. You may use different bounds than you used in Question 4.

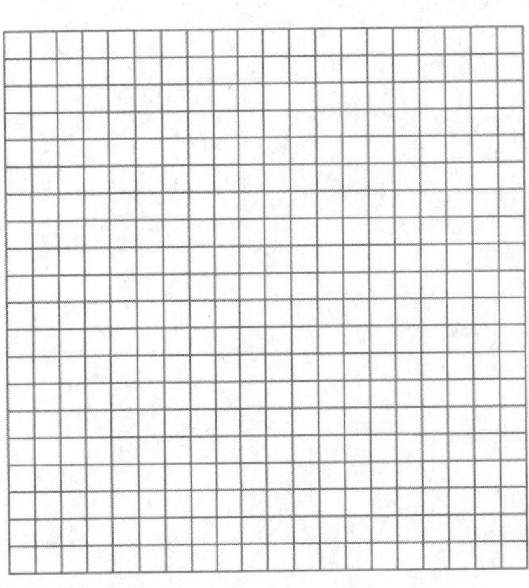

8. Explain why the inverse of $f(x)$ with the restricted domain is a function. Then, write an equation for the inverse.

9. Explain what the inverse models in terms of this problem situation.

10. After 1.5 seconds, what is the egg's height? Explain which function you used and how you determined your answer.

11. After how many seconds is the egg at a height of 55 feet? Expla which function you used and how you determined your answe

NOTES

ALK the TALK

-2-1

a previous lesson, you determined the inverses of linear functions. ou also determined whether the inverses were also functions.

function is a **one-to-one function** if both the function and its inverse re functions.

. Adam and Stacey are working on a homework assignment in which they must identify all functions that are one-to-one functions. Adam says that all linear functions are one-to-one functions, so they don't even need to look at the linear functions. Stacey disagrees, and says that not all linear functions are one-to-one functions. Who is correct? Explain how you determined which student is correct.

. Complete each sentence with *always*, *sometimes*, or *never*.

a. A linear function is ____________________ a one-to-one function.

b. An exponential function is ____________________ a one-to-one function.

c. A quadratic function is ____________________ a one-to-one function.

d. A linear absolute value function is ____________________ a one-to-one function.

Assignment

Write

Write a definition for each term in your own words.

1. restricted domain
2. one-to-one function

Remember

Quadratic regression equations can be used to model real-world situations.

Algebraically determining the inverse of a quadratic function is the same process as determining the inverse of a linear function.

Practice

1. The table shows the percent of public schools with internet access from 1994 to 2005. (The largest growth years are shown in the table.)
   a. Predict whether a linear or quadratic regression equation will best fit the data. Explain your reasoning.
   b. Create a scatter plot of the data.
   c. Does your scatter plot change or support your answer to part (a)? Explain your reasoning.
2. Andrew thinks a quadratic regression equation would best fit the data.
   a. Calculate the quadratic regression equation of the data. Do you agree with Andrew? Explain your reasoning.
   b. Year 2004 is missing from the data. Calculate the percent of public schools with internet access in 2004. Does your answer make sense in terms of the problem situation? Explain your reasoning.
   c. Calculate the percent of public schools with internet access in 2020. Does your answer make sense in terms of the problem situation? Explain your reasoning.
   d. What are the *x*-intercepts and what do they mean in terms of the problem situation?
   e. In what year does the percent of public schools with internet access begin to decline? Explain how you determined your answer.
   f. Do you think it is likely that the percent of public schools with internet access will decline? Explain your reasoning.

Year	Percent of Public Schools with Internet Access
1994	35
1995	50
1996	65
1997	78
1998	89
1999	95
2000	98
2001	99
2002	99
2003	100
2005	100

3. The number of catfish in Lake Paul is growing in a way that can be represented by the quadratic function $c(x) = 2x^2 + 50$, where x represents the number of months since the initial number of catfis was counted.
   a. Determine any restrictions on the domain of $c(x)$ based on the problem situation. Explain your reasoning.
   b. Graph $c(x)$ with the restricted domain based on the problem situation. Be sure to label your graph
   c. What is the domain and range of the inverse of $c(x)$ with the restricted domain?
   d. Graph the inverse of $c(x)$ with the restricted domain. Be sure to label your graph.
   e. Explain why the inverse of $c(x)$ with the restricted domain is a function. Then, write an equation for its inverse.
   f. If there are 178 catfish in the lake, how many months have gone by since the initial number of catfish was counted? Explain your reasoning.
   g. Five months have gone by since the initial counting of the catfish. How many catfish are in Lake Paul now? Explain your reasoning.
4. Determine the inverse of each function.
   a. $y = x^2 - 9$
   b. $y = (x + 4)^2$
   c. $y = (x - 3)^2 + 7$
   d. $y = x^2 + 5$

Stretch

1. The base of a triangle is represented as $6x$. The height of a triangle is represented as $4x$.
   a. What is the equation for the inverse of the area of the triangle? Explain your reasoning.
   b. If the area of the triangle is 108 meters, what is the value of the inverse of the function? Explain your reasoning.

Review

1. Consider the each function shown.
   $t(x) = (x - 3)^2$
   $w(x) = 3(x - 3)^2$
   $z(x) = 3(x - 3)^2 + 1$
   a. Graph each function on the same coordinate plane.
   b. Describe how functions w and z have been transformed from function t.
2. Consider the function $f(x) = x^2 - 2x - 2$.
   a. Graph the function.
   b. Describe the key characteristics of the graph.
3. The cost of producing chapter books for a company is $C(x) = 6x + 81$. The company's revenue for every chapter book sold is $R(x) = 36x - x^2$.
   a. What is the company's break-even point for the production and sales of chapter books?
   b. What does the solution mean?
   c. Show the solution graphically.

Applications of Quadratic Equations Summary

KEY TERMS

- the number i
- imaginary roots
- imaginary zeros
- complex numbers
- real part of a complex number
- imaginary part of a complex number
- imaginary numbers
- pure imaginary number
- Fundamental Theorem of Algebra
- restrict the domain

LESSON 1 — i Want to Believe

n order to calculate the square root of any real number, there must be some way to calculate the square root of a negative number. That is, there must be a number such that when it is squared, it is equal to a negative number. For this reason, mathematicians defined what is called **the number *i*.** The number i is a number such that $i^2 = -1$.

For example, you can rewrite the expression $\sqrt{-25}$ by using i.

Factor out −1.	$\sqrt{-25} = \sqrt{(-1)(25)}$
Rewrite the radical expression.	$= \sqrt{-1} \cdot \sqrt{25}$
Apply the square root on $\sqrt{25}$.	$= 5\sqrt{-1}$
Rewrite $\sqrt{-1}$ as i.	$= 5i$

So, $\sqrt{-25}$ can be rewritten as $5i$.

Functions and equations that have imaginary solutions have **imaginary roots** or **imaginary zer**
which are the solutions.

The set of **complex numbers** is the set of all numbers written in the form $a + bi$, where a and b a
real numbers. The term a is called the **real part of a complex number,** and the term bi is called
the **imaginary part of a complex number**.

The set of **imaginary numbers** is a subset of the set of complex numbers. A **pure imaginary number** is a number of the form $a + bi$, where b is not equal to 0.

When operating with complex numbers involving i, combine like terms by treating i as a variable (even thought it is a constant).

For example, consider the sum of $(2 + 3i) + (-5 + i)$.

$$\begin{aligned}(2 + 3i) + (-5 + i) &= (2 + (-5)) + (3i + i)\\ &= -3 + 4i\end{aligned}$$

You can also multiply complex numbers using the Distributive Property.

For example, consider the product of $(2 + i)(2 - i)$.

$$\begin{aligned}(2 + i)(2 - i) &= 2(2) + 2(-i) + i(2) + i(-i)\\ &= 4 - 2i + 2i - i^2\\ &= 4 - i^2\\ &= 4 - (-1) = 5\end{aligned}$$

You can use the same methods you used to solve quadratic equations with real solutions to solve quadratic equations with imaginary solutions.

For example, consider the function $f(x) = x^2 - 2x + 2$

$$x = \frac{-(-2) \pm \sqrt{(-2)^2 - 4(1)(2)}}{2(1)}$$

$$x = \frac{2 \pm \sqrt{4 - 8}}{2}$$

$$x = \frac{2 \pm \sqrt{-4}}{2}$$

$$x = \frac{2 \pm 2i}{2}$$

$$x = 1 \pm i$$

he **Fundamental Theorem of Algebra** states that any polynomial equation of degree n must ave, exactly n complex roots or solutions.

ny root may be a multiple root. The table shows the number of real and imaginary roots for ifferent quadratic equations.

Location of Vertex	Concavity	Sketch	Number of x-Intercepts	Number and Type of Roots
Above the x-axis	Up	y x	0	2 imaginary roots
	Down	y x	2	2 real roots
Below the x-axis	Up	y x	2	2 real roots
	Down	y x	0	2 imaginary roots
On the x-axis	Up	y x	1	1 unique root
	Down	y x	1	1 unique root

LESSON 2

Ahead of the Curve

Just like with the other inequalities you have studied, the solution to a quadratic inequality is the s of values that satisfy the inequality.

For example, consider the inequality $x^2 - 4x + 3 < 0$.

Write the corresponding quadratic equation. $x^2 - 4x + 3 = 0$

Calculate the roots of the quadratic equation using an appropriate method.

$(x - 3)(x - 1) = 0$

$(x - 3) = 0$ or $(x - 1) = 0$

$x = 3$ or $x = 1$

Plot the roots to divide the number line into three regions.

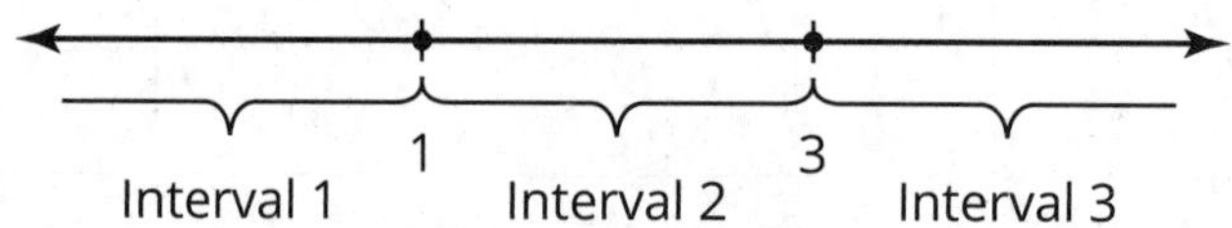

Choose a value from each interval to test in the original inequality. Identify the solution set as the interval(s) in which your test value satisfies the inequality.

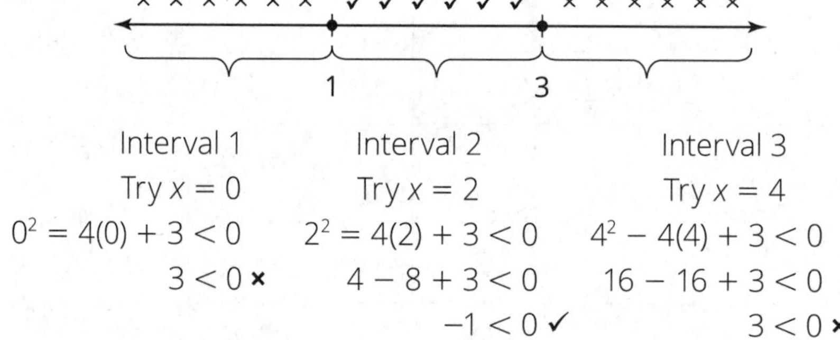

Interval 1	Interval 2	Interval 3
Try $x = 0$	Try $x = 2$	Try $x = 4$
$0^2 = 4(0) + 3 < 0$	$2^2 = 4(2) + 3 < 0$	$4^2 - 4(4) + 3 < 0$
$3 < 0$ ×	$4 - 8 + 3 < 0$	$16 - 16 + 3 < 0$
	$-1 < 0$ ✓	$3 < 0$ ×

Interval 2 satisfies the original inequality, so the solution includes all numbers between 1 and 3. Solution: $x \in (1, 3)$, or $1 < x < 3$.

LESSON

3

All Systems Are Go!

The graph of a linear equation and the graph of a quadratic equation can intersect at two points, at one point, or not at all. The graphs of two quadratic equations can intersect at two points, at one point, at an infinite number of points, or not at all.

The method to determine the solution or solutions of a system involving quadratic equations is similar to solving a system of linear equations. First, substitute one equation into the other. Then, solve the resulting equation for x and calculate the corresponding values for y. These values represent the point(s) of intersection. Finally, graph each equation of the system to verify the points of intersection.

$y = 5x^2 + 8x + 6$

$y = x^2 - 4x - 3$

$$x^2 - 4x - 3 = 5x^2 + 8x + 6$$
$$0 = 4x^2 + 12x + 9$$
$$0 = (2x + 3)(2x + 3)$$

$2x + 3 = 0$

$2x = -3$

$x = -\frac{3}{2}$

$y = \left(-\frac{3}{2}\right)^2 - 4\left(-\frac{3}{2}\right) - 3$

$= 5\frac{1}{4}$

The system has one solution: $\left(-\frac{3}{2}, 5\frac{1}{4}\right)$.

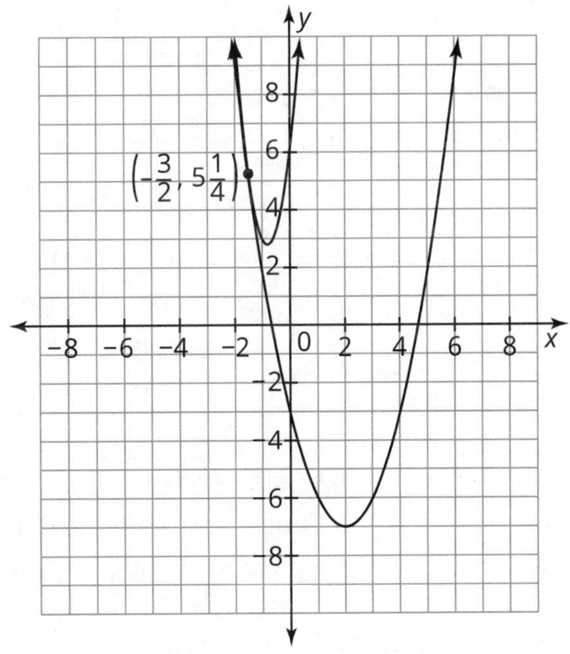

LESSON 4

Model Behavior

Quadratic regression equations can be used to model real-world situations and make predictions.

For example, as vans, trucks, and SUVs have increased in popularity, the fuel consumption of these types of vehicles has also increased.

Years Since 1980	Fuel Consumption (billions of gallons)
0	23.8
5	27.4
10	35.6
15	45.6
19	52.8

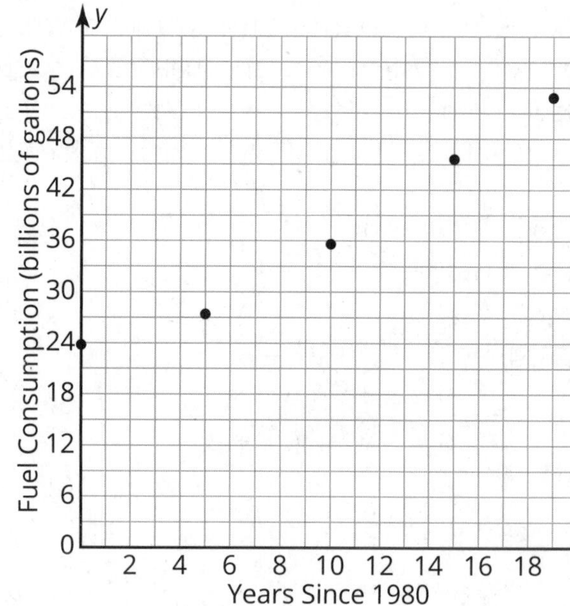

The quadratic regression equation that best fits the data is $y = 0.0407x^2 + 0.809x + 23.3$. The r^2 value for the quadratic regression fit is 0.996. Just as with linear and exponential regressions, the equation can be used to make predictions for the data.

For example, you can predict the fuel consumption in the year 2020 by substituting $x = 40$ into the regression equation.

$y = 0.0407(40)^2 + 0.809(40) + 23.3$
$y \approx 121$

In 2020, fuel consumption will be about 121 billion gallons.

Depending on the information given in a problem situation, a function or its inverse could be used to draw conclusions from the data.

linear and exponential function are always one-to-one functions, but a quadratic function is not. herefore, you need to restrict the domain of the original quadratic function so that the inverse s also a function. To **restrict the domain** of a function means to define a new domain for the unction that is a subset of the original domain.

or example, you can determine the equation of the inverse of the basic quadratic function $(x) = x^2$ by first restricting the domain to $x > 0$, replacing $f(x)$ with y, switching the x and y variables, nd solving for y.

$$f(x) = x^2$$
$$y = x^2$$
$$x = y^2$$
$$y = \sqrt{x}$$

he inverse of $f(x) = x^2$ is $f^{-1}(x) = \sqrt{x}$ for $x > 0$.

OPIC 3

ircles on a Coordinate Plane

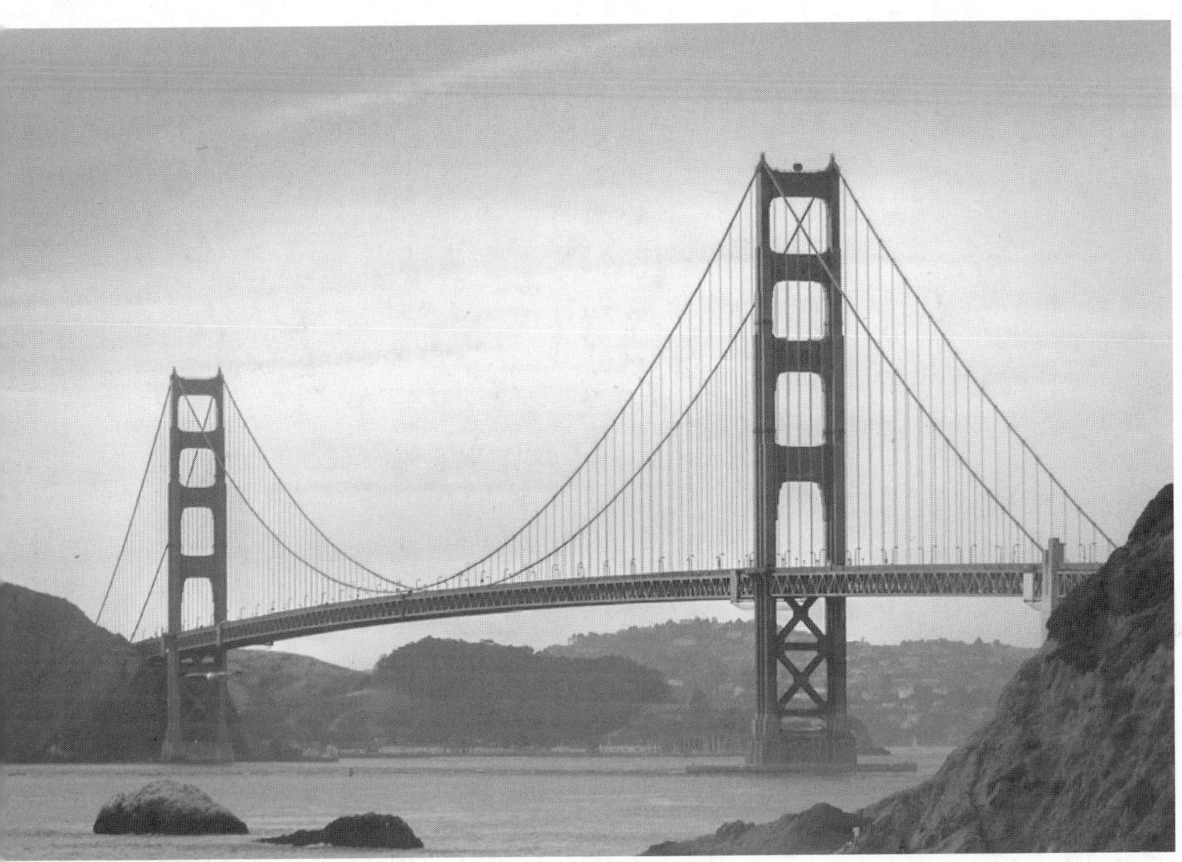

Golden Gate Bridge is one of the most famous suspension bridges in the world. The cables of a suspension bridge m a parabolic shape.

Module 4: Seeing Structure

OPIC 3: CIRCLES ON A :OORDINATE PLANE

his topic explores circles and parabolas on ne coordinate plane. Equations for these eometric figures can be written using their ey characteristics. Students begin by using ne Distance Formula to derive equations or a circle centered at the origin and a circle entered at point (h, k). Students explore ow to use the Pythagorean Theorem, ne Distance Formula, and symmetry to etermine whether a given point lies on a ircle centered on or off the origin. Finally, ne focus and directrix of a parabola are ntroduced through an exploratory activity.

Where have we been?

Students first learned the Pythagorean Theorem in middle school. They have used it to solve for distances on the coordinate plane, to derive the Distance Formula, and to verify properties of triangles and quadrilaterals on a coordinate plane. Development of the Pythagorean Identity recalls students' understanding of trigonometric ratios.

Where are we going?

In more advanced mathematics, students will study ellipses, of which circles are a special case, and hyperbolas. Together with parabolas, these conic sections will be useful in studying three-dimensional geometry. Conic sections model important physical processes in nature, including the trajectories of objects in space and of charged particles, making them an important tool not only in mathematics but also in physics, astronomy, and engineering.

Deriving the Equation for a Circle

right triangle can be situated at the origin of a coordinate plane. As the reference angle θ hanges, the end of the hypotenuse can trace out a circle. The coordinates of this endpoint are lways ($r \cdot \cos\theta$, $r \cdot \sin\theta$), where r is the radius of the circle.

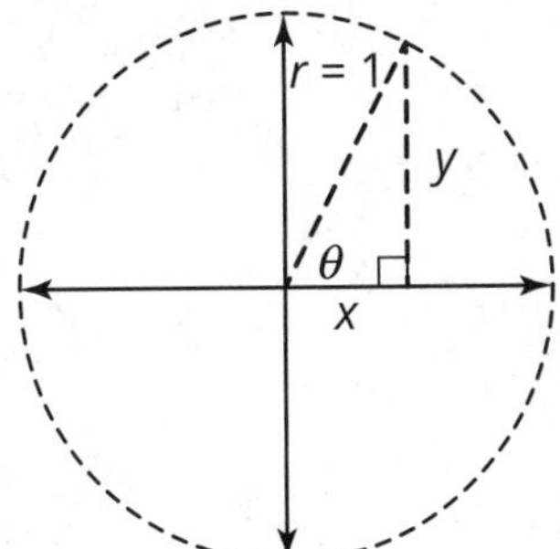

When r is 1, as it is in the unit circle, then the Pythagorean Theorem tells us that $\cos^2\theta \cdot \sin^2\theta = 1$.

Take Us to Your Leader!

Scientists explore deep space by using large antennas to listen for distant radio waves. Parabol antennas amplify faint signals by using the propertie of parabolas to focus them onto a receiver. The worldwide Deep Space Network also helps to keep track of exploratory spacecraft like the two Voyager spacecrafts, which have left our Solar System!

Talking Points

It can be helpful to understand concepts involved in circles on a coordinate plane for college admissions tests.

Here is an example of a sample question:

$$x^2 + (y + 1)^2 = 4$$

The graph of the equation above on the coordinate plane is a circle. If the center of the circle is translated 2 units down and the radius is increased by 1, what is the equation of the resulting circle?

A circle with its center at (h, k) is described by the equation $(x - h)^2 + (y - k)^2 = r^2$, where r is the radius. So, the center of the original circle is at $(0, -1)$ and it has a radius of 2. The new center will be at $(0, -3)$ and its radius will be 3.

So, the equation for the resulting circle will be $x^2 + (y + 3)^2 = 9$.

Key Terms

Pythagorean identity

A Pythagorean identity is a trigonometric equation that expresses the Pythagorean Theorem in terms of trigonometric ratios.

focus of a parabola

A parabola is the set of all points in a plane that are equidistant from a fixed point and a fixed line. The focus of a parabola is the fixed point.

directrix of a parabola

A parabola is the set of all points in a plane that are equidistant from a fixed point and a fixed line. The directrix of a parabola is the fixed line.

concavity

The concavity of a parabola describes the orientation of the curvature of the parabola.

X^2 Plus Y^2 Equals Radius²

1

Deriving the Equation for a Circle

Warm Up

Determine each unknown side length. Write your answers in radical notation.

1.

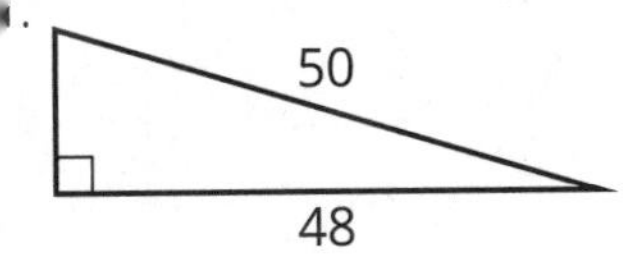

2.

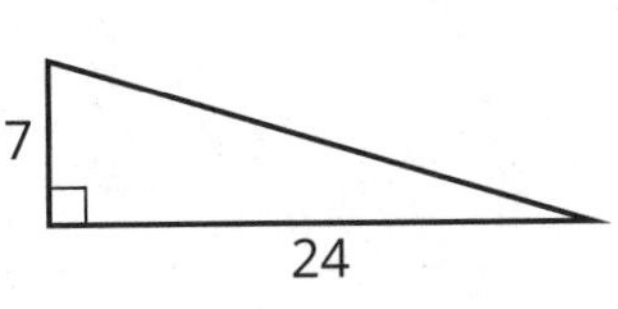

3.

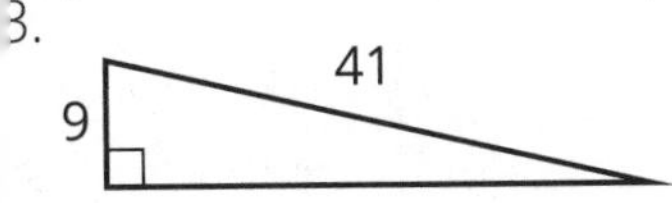

Learning Goals

- Use the Pythagorean Theorem to derive the equation of a circle given the center and radius.
- Distinguish between the equation of a circle written in general form and the equation of a circle written in standard form (center-radius form).
- Complete the square to determine the center and the radius of a circle.

You have graphed linear and quadratic functions and written equations for their graphs. How can you write the equation for a circle and graph it?

GETTING STARTED

Spinning Right Triangles

Recall that a circle is the set of points on a plane equidistant from a given point. If the circle shown is drawn on a coordinate plane, it is possible to write an algebraic equation for the circle.

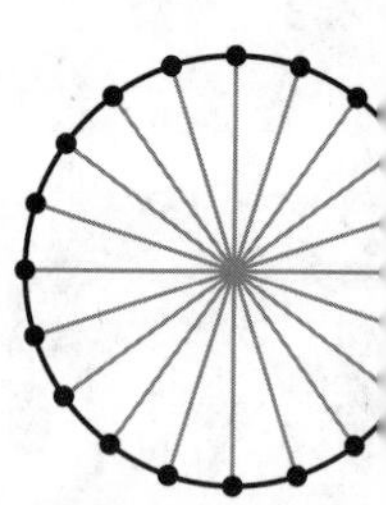

1. Follow the steps to write an equation for each circle shown.

a. Consider a circle drawn with its center located at (0, 0) and a point (*x*, *y*) on the circle. Label the sides of the right triangle formed. Then, use the Pythagorean Theorem to solve for r^2.

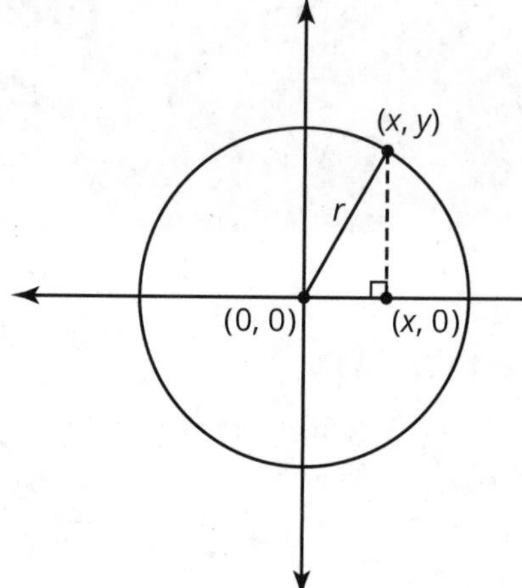

Because your equation is true for every point on the circle, it can be used as the equation of a circle centered at the origin.

b. Next, consider a circle with its center located at point (*h*, *k*) and a point (*x*, *y*) on the circle. Label the sides of the right triangle formed. Then, use the Pythagorean Theorem to solve for r^2.

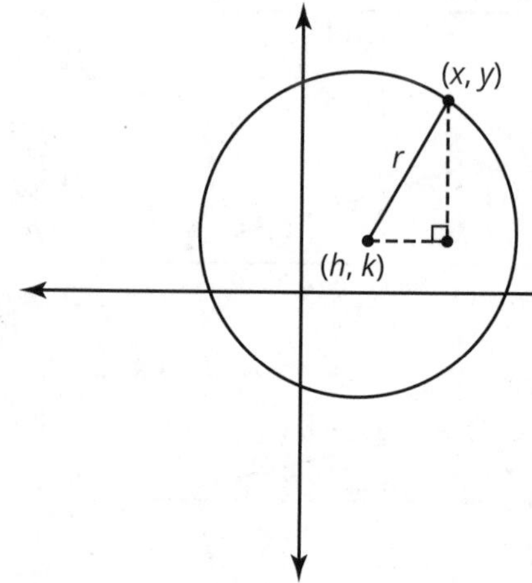

Think about:

The vertical height of the triangle can be expressed in the form $y_2 - y_1$. The horizontal length of the triangle can be expressed in the form $x_2 - x_1$.

2. How does the equation you wrote with a center at (*h*, *k*) also describe a circle with its center point at the origin? Explain your reasoning.

ACTIVITY 1.1

The Equation for a Circle

he standard form of the equation of a circle centered at (h, k) with radius f length r can be expressed using the equation shown.

$$(x - h)^2 + (y - k)^2 = r^2$$

Pay attention to the form of the equation. The coefficients of both x and y are 1.

. **Write an equation for each description.**

a. **A circle with center at the origin and $r = 8$**

b. **A circle with center $(3, -5)$ and $r = 6$**

Is a circle a function?

c. **Circle *P***

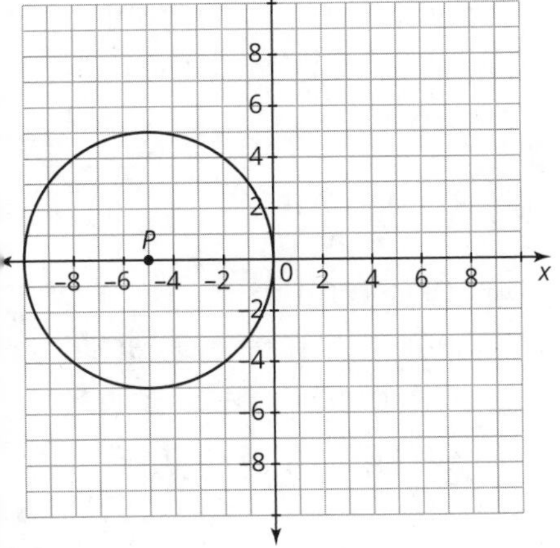

d. **Circle *Q***

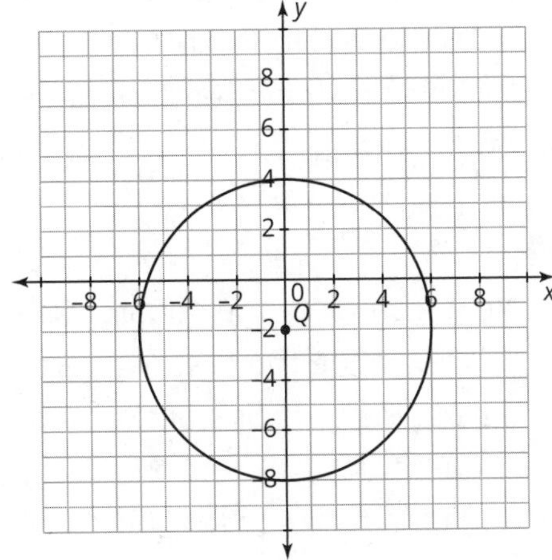

ACTIVITY

1.2

Completing the Square to Determine the Center

The variables h and k are constants; they represent the center of the circle.

By expanding the binomial terms of the standard form of a circle, $(x - h)^2 + (y - k)^2 = r^2$, the equation can be written as

$$x^2 - 2hx + h^2 + y^2 - 2ky + k^2 = r^2, \text{ or}$$
$$x^2 + y^2 - 2hx - 2ky + h^2 + k^2 = r^2$$

The equation for a circle in general form is $Ax^2 + Cy^2 + Dx + Ey + F = 0$, where A, C, D, E, and F are constants, $A = C$, and $x \neq y$.

To identify the center and radius of a circle written in general form, you nee to rewrite the equation in standard form. It is often necessary to use completing the square to rewrite the equation in standard form.

Worked Example

You can rewrite $x^2 + y^2 - 4x - 6y + 9 = 0$ in standard form by completing the square.

First, use an algebraic transformation to remove the constant term from the variable expression. Write the resulting equation grouping the x-terms together and the y-terms together using sets of parentheses.

$$(x^2 - 4x) + (y^2 - 6y) = -9$$

Next, complete the square within each pair of parentheses. To do this, examine the first two terms of each quadratic expression and determine the constant term to rewrite each expression as a perfect square trinomial. Add those constant terms to both sides of the equation. Write the resulting equation.

$$(x^2 - 4x + 2^2) + (y^2 - 6y + 3^2) = -9 + 2^2 + 3^2$$

Finally, rewrite the left side of the equation as the sum of the perfect squares.

$$(x - 2)^2 + (y - 3)^2 = 4$$

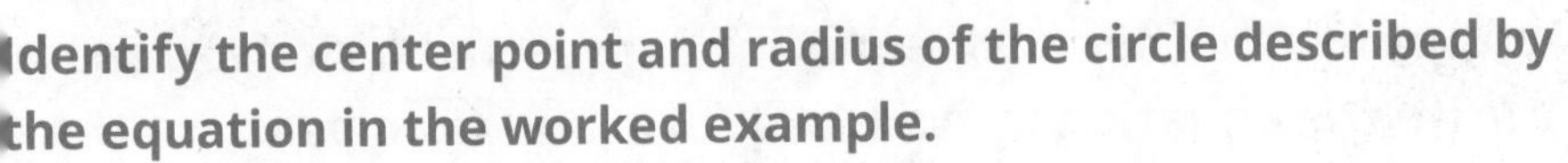

Identify the center point and radius of the circle described by the equation in the worked example.

Consider the general form of the equation $2x^2 + 2y^2 - x + 4y + 2 = 0$.

a. How do the coefficients of the squared terms in this equation differ from the equation in the worked example? How can you tell this equation represents a circle?

b. How does this general form of a circle equation change your strategy to rewrite it in standard form?

c. Rewrite the equation in standard form.

3. Determine whether each equation represents a circle. If so, rewrite the equation in standard form and then describe the location of the center and the length of the radius.

a. $x^2 + y^2 - 2x + 4y + 4 = 0$

b. $x^2 + 4y^2 - 24y + 32 = 0$

c. $x^2 + y^2 - 10x + 12y + 51 = 0$

d. $2x^2 + 2y^2 - 5x + 8y + 10 = 0$

ACTIVITY

1.3

Doubling and Tripling Circumference and Area

et's consider what happens to the equation of a circle when its ircumference or area is changed.

. **Circle *P* is represented by the equation $(x - 4)^2 + (y + 1)^2 = 36$.**

a. **Determine the equation of a circle that has the same center as circle *P* but whose circumference is twice that of circle *P*.**

b. **Determine the equation of a circle that has the same center as circle *P* but whose circumference is three times that of circle *P*.**

c. **Determine the equation of a circle that has the same center as circle *P* but whose area is twice that of circle *P*.**

d. **Determine the equation of a circle that has the same center as circle *P* but whose area is three times that of circle *P*.**

2. **Complete the table. Then, identify any pattern(s) you notice.**

Equation of Circle P	$r = 6$	$(x - 4)^2 + (y + 1)^2 = 36$
2 Times the Circumference of Circle P		
3 Times the Circumference of Circle P		
4 Times the Circumference of Circle P		
5 Times the Circumference of Circle P		
n Times the Circumference of Circle P		

3. **Complete the table. Then, identify any pattern(s) you notice.**

Equation of Circle P	$r = 6$	$(x - 4)^2 + (y + 1)^2 = 36$
2 Times the Area of Circle P		
3 Times the Area of Circle P		
4 Times the Area of Circle P		
5 Times the Area of Circle P		
n Times the Area of Circle P		

NOTES

Circle *F* is represented by the equation $x^2 + (y - 3)^2 = 25$.

a. Determine the equation of a circle that has the same center as circle *F* but whose circumference is 10 times that of circle *F*.

b. Determine the equation of a circle that has the same center as circle *F* but whose area is 10 times that of circle *F*.

TALK the TALK 

Match Game

Cut out each circle equation located at the end of the lesson. Then tape each equation into the table with its corresponding center and radius.

Radius Length	Center at (0, 2)	Center at (1, 2)	Center at (1, −2)	Center at (−1, 2)
5				
10				
$\sqrt{5}$				
$\sqrt{10}$				

rcle Equations

A $x^2 + (y - 2)^2 + 5 = 10$	**B** $(x + 1)^2 + (y - 2)^2 = 25$
C $(x - 1)^2 + (y + 2)^2 = 10$	**D** $x^2 + y^2 - 4y + 4 = 100$
E $(x - 1)^2 + (y - 2)^2 = 25$	**F** $x^2 + y^2 - 2x + 4y = 0$
G $x^2 + y^2 - 2x - 4y - 95 = 0$	**H** $x^2 + y^2 + 2x - 4y = 5$
I $(x - 1)^2 + (y + 2)^2 = 25$	**J** $x^2 + (y - 2)^2 = 10$
K $(x + 1)^2 + (y - 2)^2 = 100$	**L** $(x - 1)^2 + (y - 2)^2 = 5$
M $x^2 + y^2 - 2x - 4y - 5 = 0$	**N** $(x - 1)^2 + (y + 2)^2 = 100$
O $(x + 1)^2 + (y - 2)^2 = 5$	**P** $x^2 + y^2 - 4y - 21 = 0$

Assignment

Write

Describe how the graph of $(x - h)^2 + (y - k)^2 = r^2$ is related to the graph of $x^2 + y^2 = r^2$.

Remember

Circle with center at origin and radius *r*	**Circle with center at (*h*, *k*) and radius *r***
y, x, (x, y), r, $(0, 0)$	y, x, (x, y), r, (h, k)
Center: (0, 0) Radius: *r*	Center: (*h*, *k*) Radius: *r*
$x^2 + y^2 = r^2$	$(x - h)^2 + (y - k)^2 = r^2$

Practice

1. Write an equation in standard form given circle *M*.

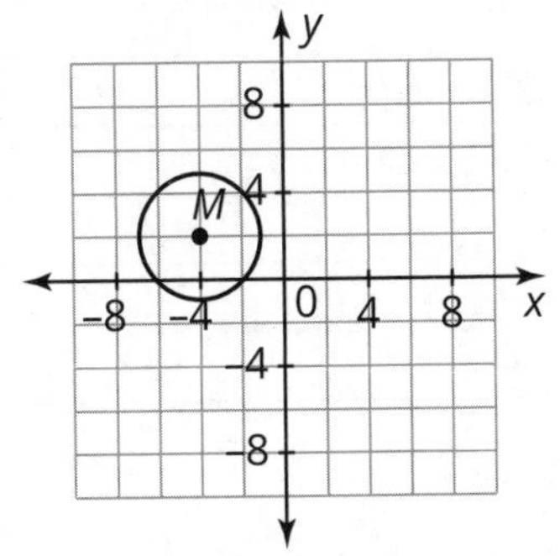

a. A circle with a center at *M* (−4, 2) and a radius of 3.

b. A circle with the same center as the circle *M*, but whose circumference is 20 times that of circle *M*.

2. Write an equation in standard form given circle *M*.

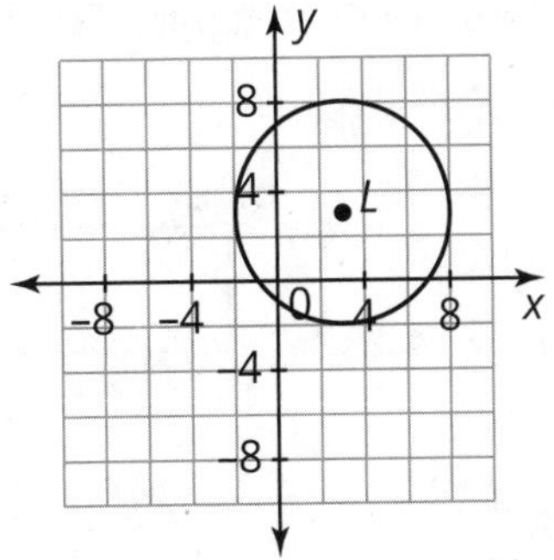

a. A circle with center at *L* (3, 3) and a radius of 5.

b. A circle with the same center as the circle *L*, but whose area is 20 times that of circle *L*.

3. Determine whether each equation represents a circle. If so, describe the location of the center and radius.

   a. $x^2 + y^2 - 4x + 6y + 9 = 0$

   b. $4x^2 + 4y^2 - 8x - 20y - 30 = 0$

   c. $3x^2 + y^2 + 3x + 9y + 15 = 0$

Stretch

1. Determine whether the point (1, 1) is inside, outside, or on the circle that is represented by the equation $x^2 + y^2 + 4x - 8y = 5$. Explain your reasoning.
2. Determine the radius of the circle given the location of the center of the circle and a point on the circle. Then, write the equation of the circle in standard form.
   a. A circle with a center at (0, 0) and the point (0, 3) on the circle
   b. A circle with a center at (1, 1) and the point (1, 5) on the circle
   c. A circle with a center at (−2, 5) and the point (−2, 7) on the circle

Review

1. Determine the inverse of $y = (x + 9)^2$.
2. The table shows temperatures recorded during a winter storm. Determine the regression equation that best models the data set. Include the correlation coefficient.

Time Since Start of Snow Storm (hours)	Temperature (°F)
1	25
2	22
3	18
4	16
5	12
6	13
7	15
8	20
9	23
10	27

3. Rewrite each expression. Show your work.

   a. $6i(-7 - i)$

   b. $(5 - 12i) - (3 + 2i)$

4. Determine the perimeter of each figure. The sides are measured in inches.

   a. $x^3 + 2x - 4$; $3x^3 + x^2 + 6x + 7$; $-3x^2 - 8$

   b. $3x^3 + 8x^2 - 13$; $9x^3 - 4x + 7$

2

A Blip on the Radar

Determining Points on a Circle

Warm Up

Write the equation of each circle using the information given.

1. center at the origin, radius of 2

2. center at (5, −10), radius of 10

3. radius of 5, points on the circle at (3, 2) and (3, −8)

Learning Goals

- Use the Pythagorean Theorem to determine whether a point lies on a circle on the coordinate plane given the circle's center at the origin or not at the origin, the radius of the circle, and the coordinates of the point.
- Use rigid motion to transform a circle about the coordinate plane to determine whether a point lies on a circle's image given the pre-image's center, radius, and the coordinates of the point.
- Determine the coordinates of a point that lies on a circle given the location of the center point and the radius of the circle.

You have determined the equation for a circle centered at the origin and not centered at the origin. How can you determine the coordinates of points on the circumference of a circle?

GETTING STARTED

Peripheral Vision

In a video game, the locations of objects are tracked by "radar" using coordinates.

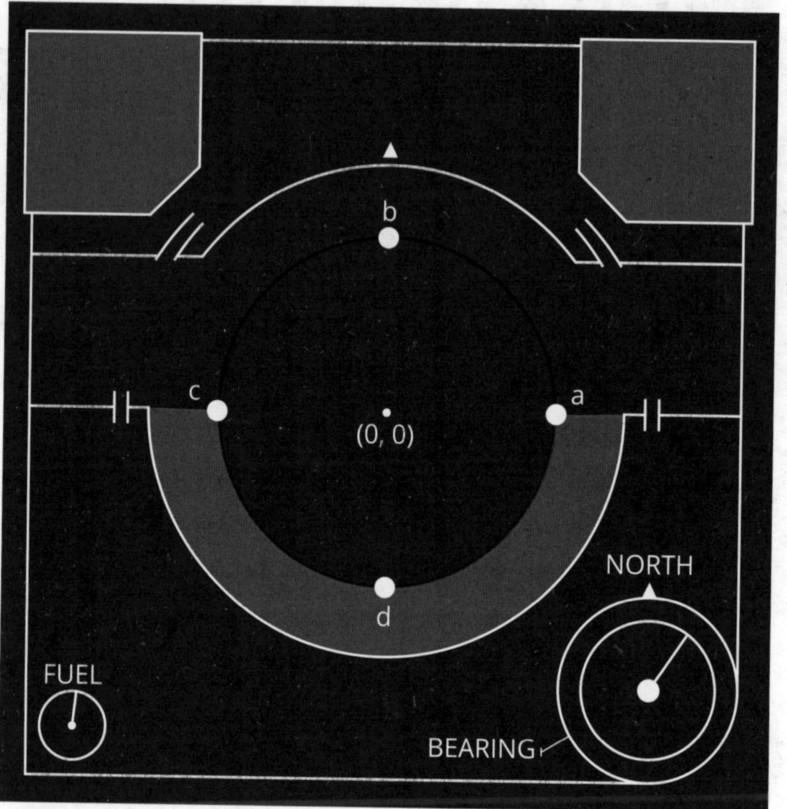

1. **Four objects are represented on the circumference of the blue circle, which has a radius of 10 units. Label the objects with their coordinates. Explain how you know the coordinates of the objects.**

2. **Consider an object on the circumference of the blue circle which is not located at one of the four points shown in the diagram. What is the minimum information you need to determine the coordinates of the point? Justify your answer.**

ACTIVITY

2.1 Identifying Points on a Circle

et's continue to explore the connection between the Pythagorean heorem and circles.

onsider circle *A* with its center point located at the origin and point (5, 0) on the circle.

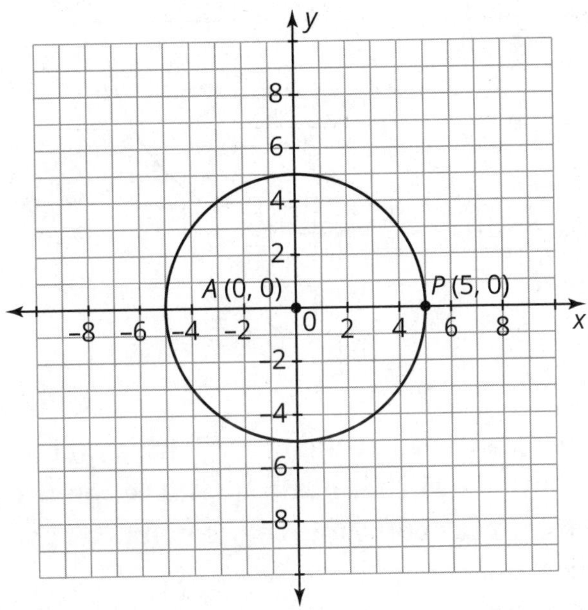

1. **Use the axes to plot three additional points on circle *A* and label the coordinates for each point.**

There are an infinite number of points located on circle *A*. To determine the coordinates of other points located on circle *A*, you can use the Pythagorean Theorem.

2. **Use the Pythagorean Theorem to determine whether point *B* (4, 3) lies on circle *A*, and then explain your reasoning.**

3. Consider circle *D* centered at the origin with a diameter of 16 uni Determine whether point *H* $(5, \sqrt{38})$ lies on circle *D*. If so, then us symmetry to determine 3 more points on circle *D*. If not, explain your reasoning.

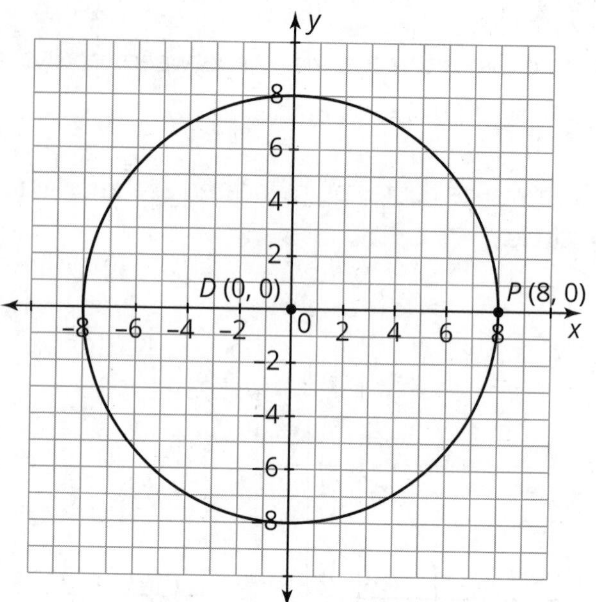

4. Consider circle *E* centered at the origin with a diameter of 34 units. Determine whether point *J* (8, 15) lies on circle *E*. If so, then use symmetry to determine 3 more points on circle *E*. If not, explain your reasoning.

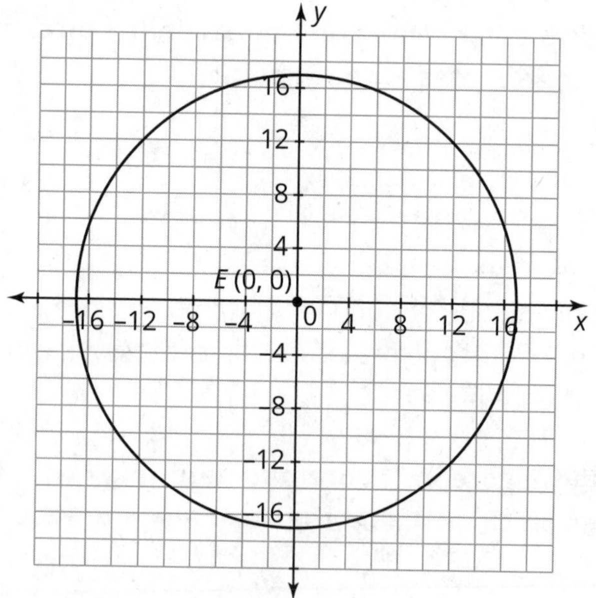

ACTIVITY

2.2

The Center Is Not at the Origin

ow can you identify points on a circle when the center is not located at ie origin?

. **Consider circle *G* with its center point located at (3, 0) and point *M* (3, 2) on the circle. Determine whether each point lies on circle *G*, and then explain your reasoning.**

How does your strategy change when the center of the circle is not on the origin?

a. $J\left(4.5, \frac{\sqrt{3}}{2}\right)$

b. $P(4, \sqrt{3})$

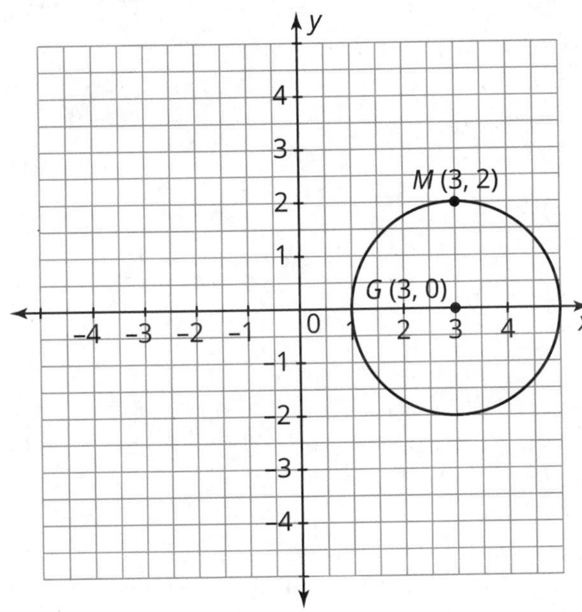

Consider Elizabeth's statement about additional points on circle *G*.

Elizabeth

Only one of those points is located on circle G. I can use that point and what I know about symmetry in a circle to identify other points on circle G.

2. Justify Elizabeth's reasoning and identify additional points on circle *G*.

A figure can be in any of the four quadrants of a coordinate plane—and sometimes a figure is in multiple quadrants. This is also true of circles.

3. **Circle K has its center at $(-2, -3)$, and contains point N $(-4, -1.5$**
Point C is at $(-2, -5.5)$.

   a. **Describe what method(s) you can use to determine whethe**
   point C lies on circle K.

   b. **Determine whether point C lies on circle K. Describe how yo**
   determined your answer.

ACTIVITY
2.3

Reasoning with Circle Symmetry

Scientists are working on a new circular mirror for an orbiting telescope. They must install eight mounting brackets at equal intervals around the mirror. Once ready, the mirror will be launched into space and astronauts will be required to install the mirror with bolts.

There is no room for error on this job. So use exact values, not approximations.

1. Circle *C* with its center point located at (1, 5) and a radius of 3 units represents the telescope's new mirror. The location of one of the mounting brackets is shown.

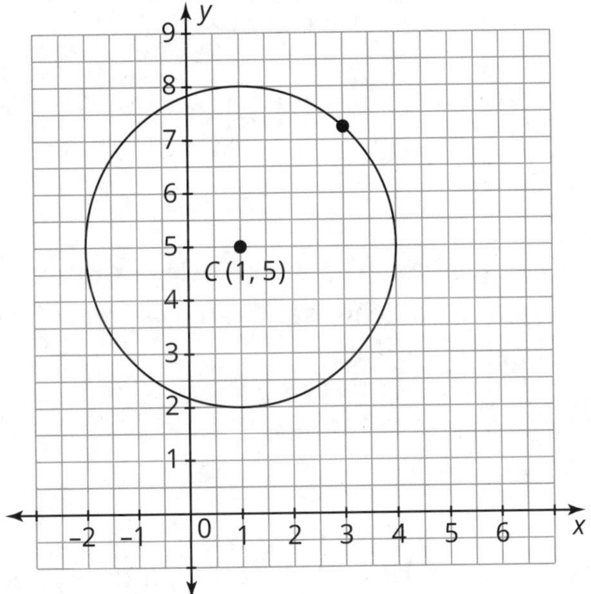

a. Determine the coordinates of the mounting bracket shown.

b. Use symmetry to identify the locations of the other seven mounting brackets on the mirror.

2. Sal listens to two radio stations. Station WPOP plays Top 40 hits. Station WREQ, located 50 miles due east of Station WPOP, plays oldies. Each radio station has a circular broadcast range, and Sal lives on the very edge of both of the stations' ranges. Sal's house is 24 miles north and 32 miles east of Station WPOP.

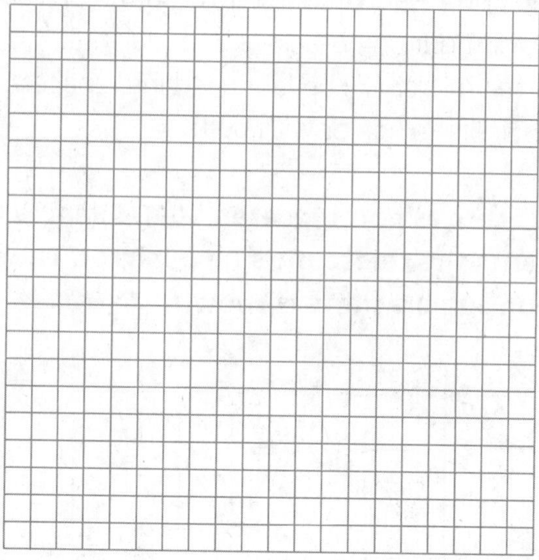

a. Let Station WPOP be located at the origin. Plot the location of each station and Sal's house. Then, graph each station's broadcast range.

b. Use symmetry to describe the location of the other point that is on the very edge of both of the radio stations' broadcast ranges.

c. What area is covered by each station's broadcast range? Show your work.

ACTIVITY
2.4

Circle Problems

ircles and polygons located on a coordinate plane enable you to calculate istances, slopes, and equations of lines.

. **Lauren and Jamie were practicing their discus throws. They each spun around in a circle to gain speed and then released their discus at a tangent to the circular spin. Jamie is left-handed, so she spun clockwise and released her discus at point *T* shown. Lauren is right-handed. She spun counterclockwise and released at point *N*. Both of the girls' throws landed at point *A*. Who made the longer throw? Justify your answer.**

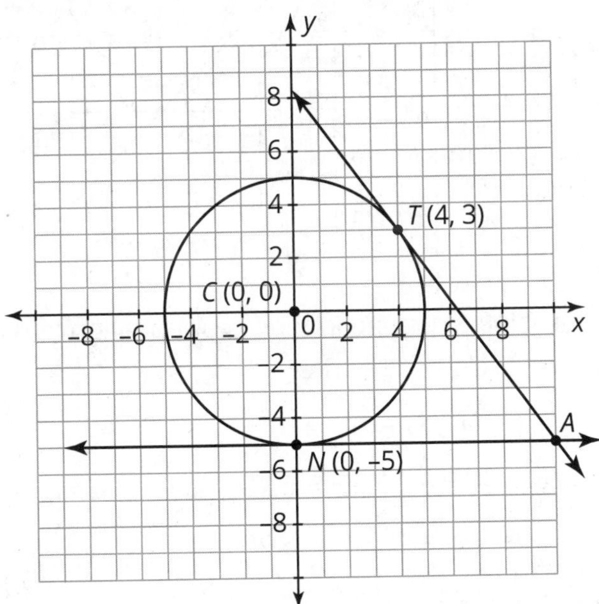

You can determine the intersection points of a circle and a line using a system of equations.

Worked Example

Consider the graph of a line and a circle.

The line has a slope of −1 and a y-intercept of 5.5, so the equation for the line is $y = -x + 5.5$.

The circle is centered at (5, 3) and has a radius of 2.5, so the equation for the circle is $(x - 5)^2 + (y - 3)^2 = 6.25$.

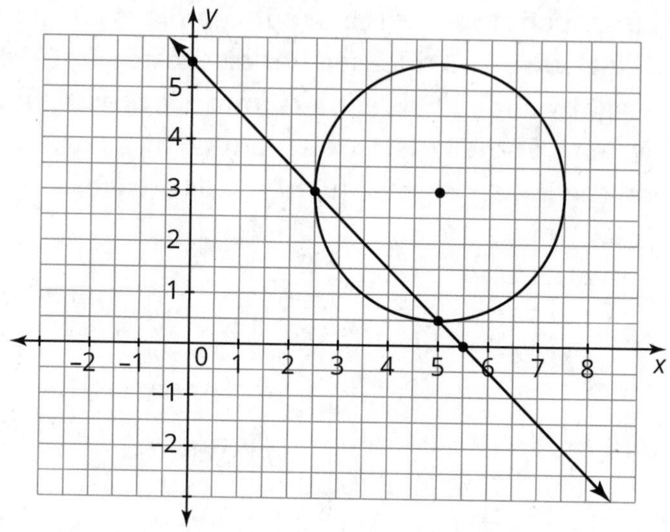

Substitute the value of y given in the linear equation into the equation for the circle and rewrite.

$$(x - 5)^2 + (-x + 5.5 - 3)^2 = 6.25$$

$$x^2 - 10x + 25 + x^2 - 5x + 6.25 = 6.25$$

$$2x^2 - 15x + 31.25 = 6.25$$

$$2x^2 - 15x + 25 = 0$$

$$(2x - 5)(x - 5) = 0$$

$$x = 5 \text{ and } x = 2.5$$

The points of intersection are (5, 0.5) and (2.5, 3).

Remember:

You can also use the Quadratic Formula to solve any quadratic equation.

2. How were the points of intersection determined in the worked example?

Determine the intersection point(s) for each system.

a. $\begin{cases} x^2 + y^2 = 100 \\ y = 2x - 20 \end{cases}$

b. $\begin{cases} (x + 5)^2 + y^2 = 64 \\ y = x - 3 \end{cases}$

c. $\begin{cases} (x - 1)^2 + (y + 2)^2 = 25 \\ y = -x - 5 \end{cases}$

d. $\begin{cases} (x + 3)^2 + (y - 1)^2 = 36 \\ y = -x + 7 \end{cases}$

4. **In the video game you saw previously, the locations of aerial targets are shown using coordinates. The blue circle represents the perimeter of home base. At what approximate coordinates will the targets breach the perimeter of the home base? Show your work.**

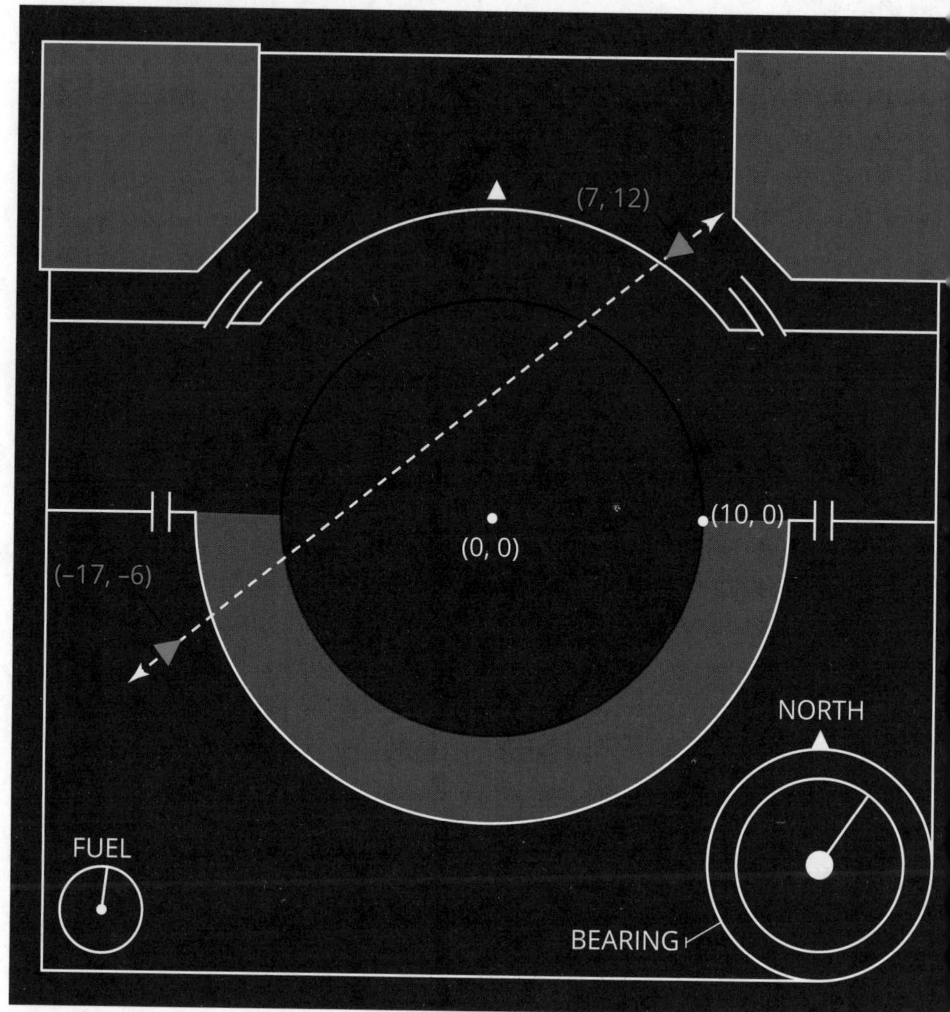

NOTES

TALK the TALK

Algebra and Geometry, Together Again

1. Given circle A with radius AB and radius AC, and $\overline{AB} \perp \overline{DC}$ at point D, determine the coordinates of point C.

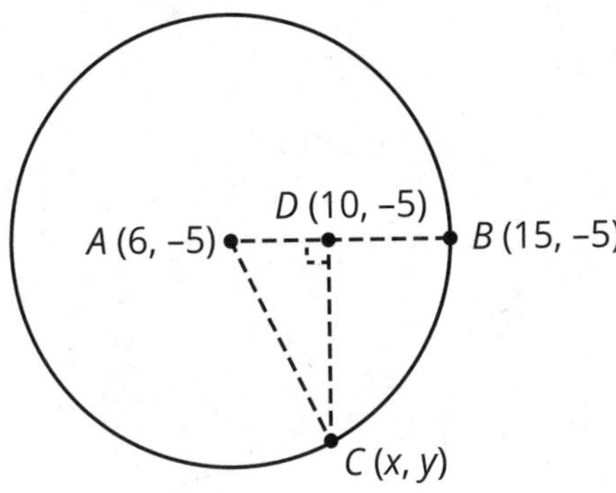

2. Determine the equation of a line tangent to circle C whose center point is the origin if the point of tangency is (6, 4).

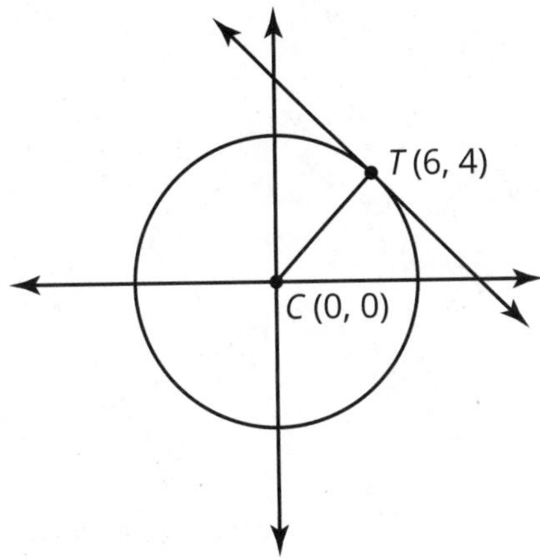

Assignment

Write

xplain how to determine the ocations of other points on a circle iven the coordinates of one point. Draw an example.

Remember

You can use the Pythagorean Theorem, the Distance Formula, and symmetry to determine whether a point lies on a circle given the coordinates of the center point at the origin or not at the origin and the coordinates of a point on the circle.

Practice

. Consider circle P centered at the origin with a radius of 4 units as shown.

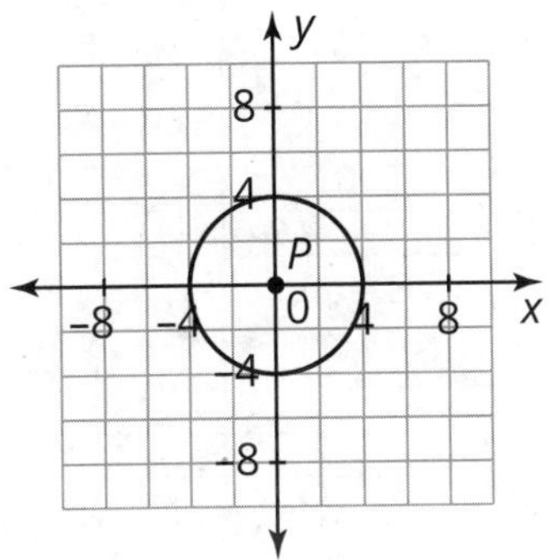

a. Verify that point $K(1, \sqrt{15})$ lies on circle P.

b. Use symmetry to determine three more points on circle P.

2. Consider circle T with its center point located at (2, 3) with a radius of $3\sqrt{2}$ units as shown.

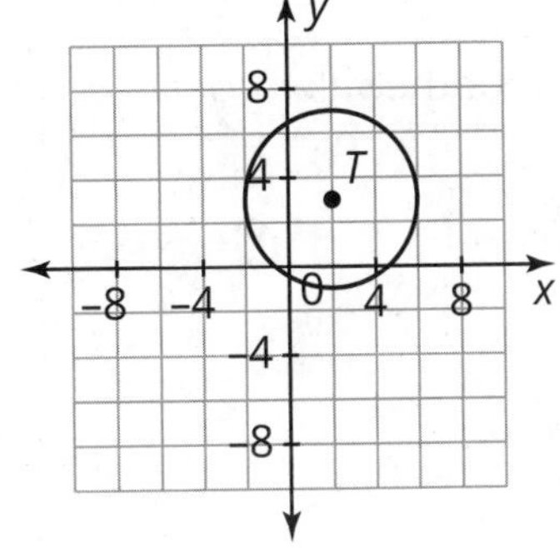

a. Verify that point $R(5, 0)$ lies on circle T.

b. Use symmetry to determine three more points on circle T.

3. Maddie brought home a new puppy, Ralph, which she needs to introduce to her current dog, Ellie. She ties Ellie in the middle of her backyard. She ties a shorter rope, exactly 4 feet to the east and 4 feet north of Ellie's rope, for her new puppy, Ralph. Based upon the graph, the dogs can meet at the point (3, 4).

a. Graph the range each dog will be able to travel on their rope. Use the origin as the place where Ellie is tied down. Show your work.

b. Use symmetry to describe the location of the other point that is on the very edge of both of the dogs' ranges.

4. Determine the intersection point(s) for each system.

a. $\begin{cases} (x-3)^2 + (y-1)^2 = 25 \\ y = x + 3 \end{cases}$

b. $\begin{cases} (x+4)^2 + (y)^2 = 100 \\ y = 2x \end{cases}$

c. $\begin{cases} x^2 + y^2 = 41 \\ y = x + 4 \end{cases}$

Stretch

1. Consider circle S with its center point located at (4, 3) with a radius of $2\sqrt{5}$ units as shown. If the x-coordinate of a point on the circle is 6, what are the possible values for the y-coordinate?

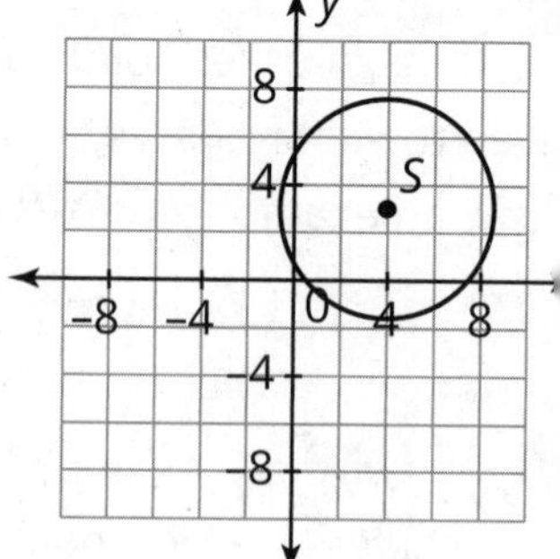

2. The circle shown is centered at the origin with a radius of 4.
   a. Determine the coordinates of the vertices for $\triangle AMC$.
   b. Determine $\sin\theta$, $\cos\theta$, and $\tan\theta$ for $\triangle AMC$ using the coordinates of the vertices.
   c. Determine the coordinates of the vertices for $\triangle BMD$.
   d. Determine $\sin\theta$, $\cos\theta$, and $\tan\theta$ for $\triangle BMD$ using the coordinates of the vertices.
   e. What do you notice about the values of $\sin\theta$, $\cos\theta$, and $\tan\theta$ for the two triangles?

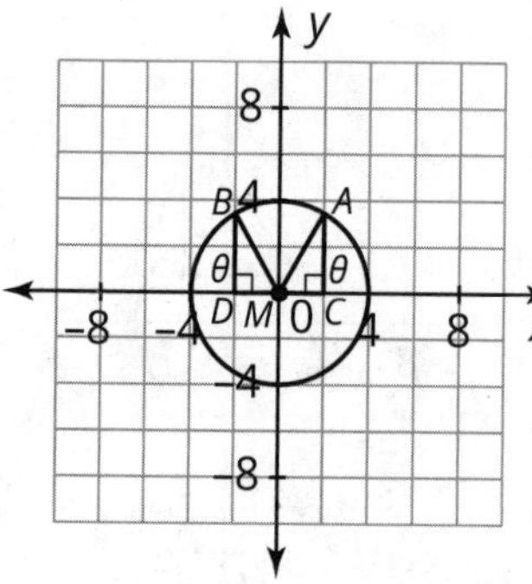

Review

1. Write an equation in standard form for each description.
   a. A circle with a center at M (1,−4) and a radius of 7
   b. A circle with the same center as circle M, but whose circumference is 10 times that of circle M
2. Determine whether $x^2 + y^2 + 6x + 8y + 9 = 0$ represents a circle. If so, write the equation in standard form and then describe the location of the center and radius.
3. Rewrite each complex expression. Show your work.
   a. $(-1 - i)^2$
   b. $-i(7i)(5i)$
4. Factor each trinomial.
   a. $2x^2 + 7x - 15$
   b. $8y^2 + 2y - 3$

3

$\text{Sin}^2\ \theta$ Plus $\text{Cos}^2\ \theta$ Equals 1^2

The Pythagorean Identity

Warm Up

Determine the value for each.

1. sin 45°

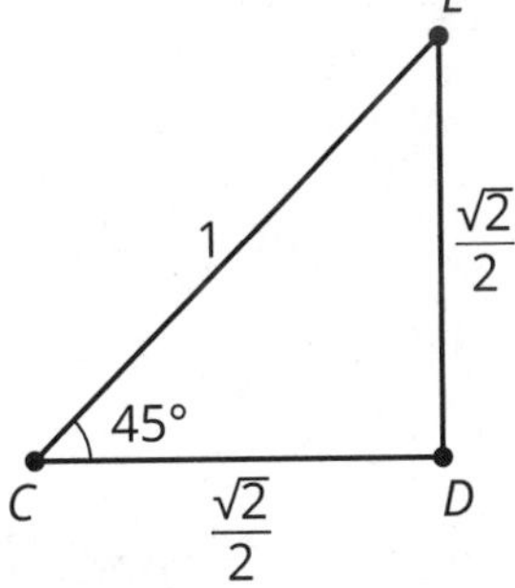

2. cos 30°

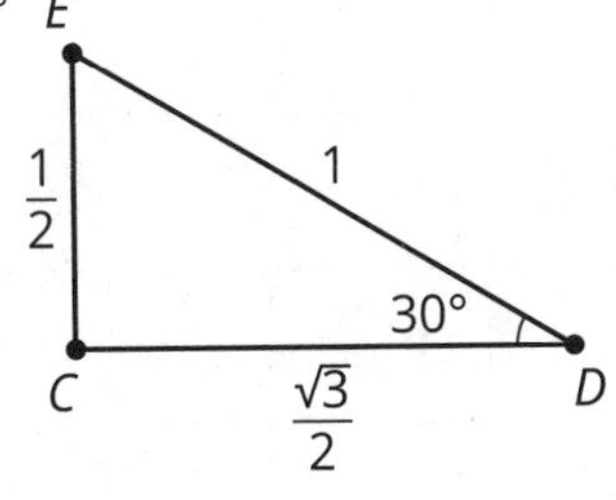

Learning Goals

- Prove the Pythagorean identity $\sin^2\theta + \cos^2\theta = 1$.
- Use the Pythagorean identity to determine the sine, cosine, or tangent of an angle measure in a given quadrant.

Key Term

- Pythagorean identity

You have learned about right-triangle ratios such as sine, cosine, and tangent and about the Pythagorean Theorem. How is the Pythagorean Theorem related to these trigonometric ratios?

GETTING STARTED

Round the Unit Circle

The trigonometric ratios sine, cosine, and tangent can have different sign negative or positive, depending on which quadrant of the coordinate pla the angle and right triangle are in.

A unit circle is a circle with a radius of 1.

Consider the unit circle shown.

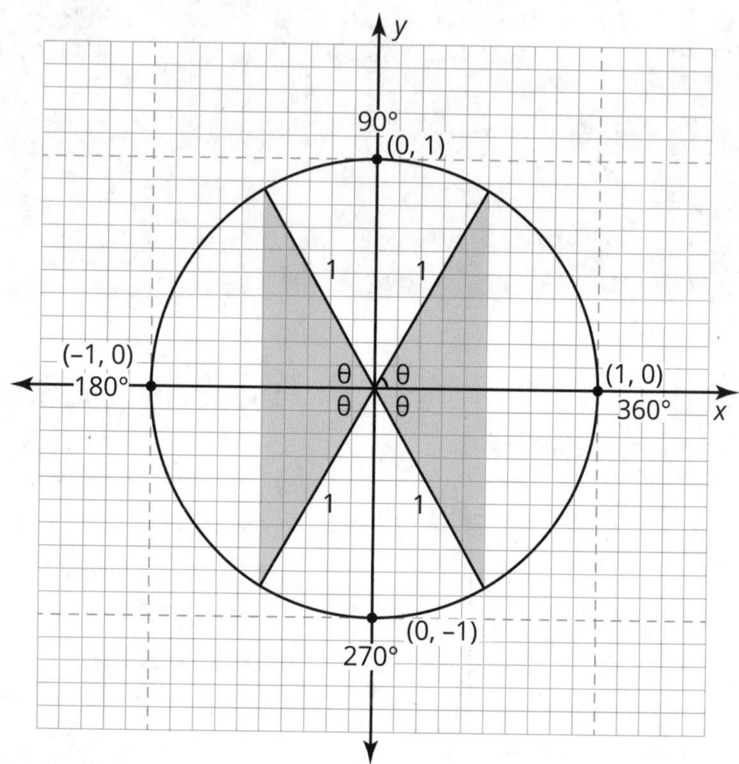

In Quadrant II, the horizontal side of the right triangle has a negative value, and the vertical side has a positive value.

1. Complete the table. Determine the sign of each trigonometric rat in the given quadrant of the coordinate plane.

	Sign (+/−)			
	Quadrant I	Quadrant II	Quadrant III	Quadrant I
Sine		+		
Cosine		−		
Tangent				

ACTIVITY

3.1 Pythagorean Identity

Pythagorean identity is a trigonometric identity that expresses ıe Pythagorean Theorem in terms of trigonometric ratios. The basic ɛlationship between the sine and cosine is given by the Pythagorean lentity $(\sin \theta)^2 + (\cos \theta)^2 = (1)^2$. The symbol θ represents an angle ıeasure.

This Pythagorean identity can also be written as $\sin^2 \theta + \cos^2 \theta = 1$.

ou can prove this Pythagorean identity using your knowledge of the unit rcle and the Pythagorean Theorem.

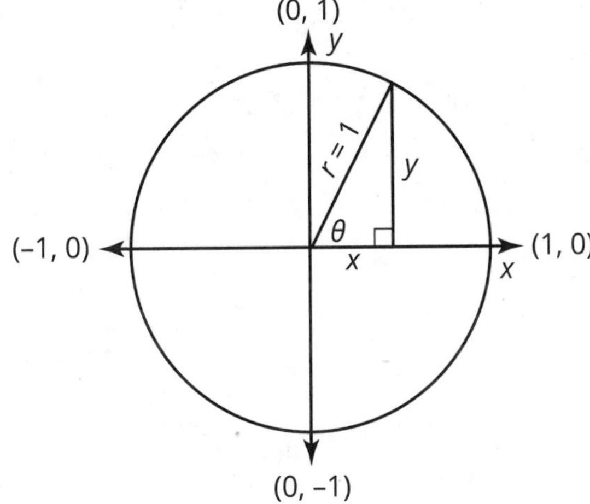

. **Demonstrate how the Pythagorean identity follows from the Pythagorean Theorem.**

a. **Given the unit circle and the angle θ, label the side lengths of the right triangle in terms of sin θ and cos θ.**

b. **State the Pythagorean Theorem.**

c. **Use substitution to demonstrate how the Pythagorean identity follows from the Pythagorean Theorem.**

2. **Write the Pythagorean identity $\sin^2 \theta + \cos^2 \theta = 1$ in two other forms.**

   a. **Solve for $\sin^2 \theta$.**

   b. **Solve for $\cos^2 \theta$.**

ACTIVITY

3.2 Determining Sine and Cosine in All Four Quadrants

ou can use the Pythagorean identity $\sin^2 \theta + \cos^2 \theta = 1$ and what ou know about solutions in different quadrants to determine values f trigonometric functions.

Worked Example

Determine the exact value of $\cos \theta$ in Quadrant II, given $\sin \theta = \frac{2}{3}$.

You can use a Pythagorean identity to determine $\cos \theta$.

$$\sin^2 \theta + \cos^2 \theta = 1$$
$$\left(\frac{2}{3}\right)^2 + \cos^2 \theta = 1$$
$$\frac{4}{9} + \cos^2 \theta = 1$$
$$\cos^2 \theta = \frac{5}{9}$$
$$\cos \theta = \pm\frac{\sqrt{5}}{3}$$

The solution is $\cos \theta = -\frac{\sqrt{5}}{3}$ because the solution is in Quadrant II $\left(\frac{\pi}{2} \le \theta \le \pi\right)$.

How does solving this equation relate to solving simple quadratic equations?

. **Given $\sin \theta = \frac{3}{5}$ in Quadrant II, determine $\cos \theta$.**

. **Given $\cos \theta = -\frac{12}{13}$ in Quadrant III, determine $\sin \theta$.**

. **Given $\cos \theta = \frac{1}{4}$ in Quadrant IV, determine $\sin \theta$.**

. **Given $\sin \theta = -\frac{1}{10}$ in Quadrant IV, determine $\cos \theta$.**

ACTIVITY

3.3

Determining Tangent in All Four Quadrants

You can also solve for the tangent of an angle in all four quadrants, using what you know about trigonometric ratios.

1. Consider this diagram from a previous activity and how you labeled the right triangle. Write tan θ in terms of sine and cosine. Explain your reasoning.

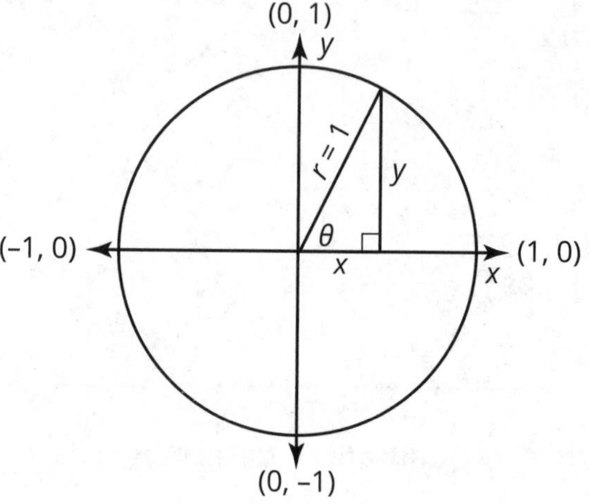

2. Given $\sin\theta = -\frac{1}{4}$ in Quadrant III, determine tan θ.

3. Given $\cos\theta = \frac{9}{10}$ in Quadrant IV, determine tan θ.

4. Given $\sin\theta = \frac{3}{5}$ in Quadrant II, determine tan θ.

TALK the TALK

360 Degrees of Trig

A unit circle is shown.

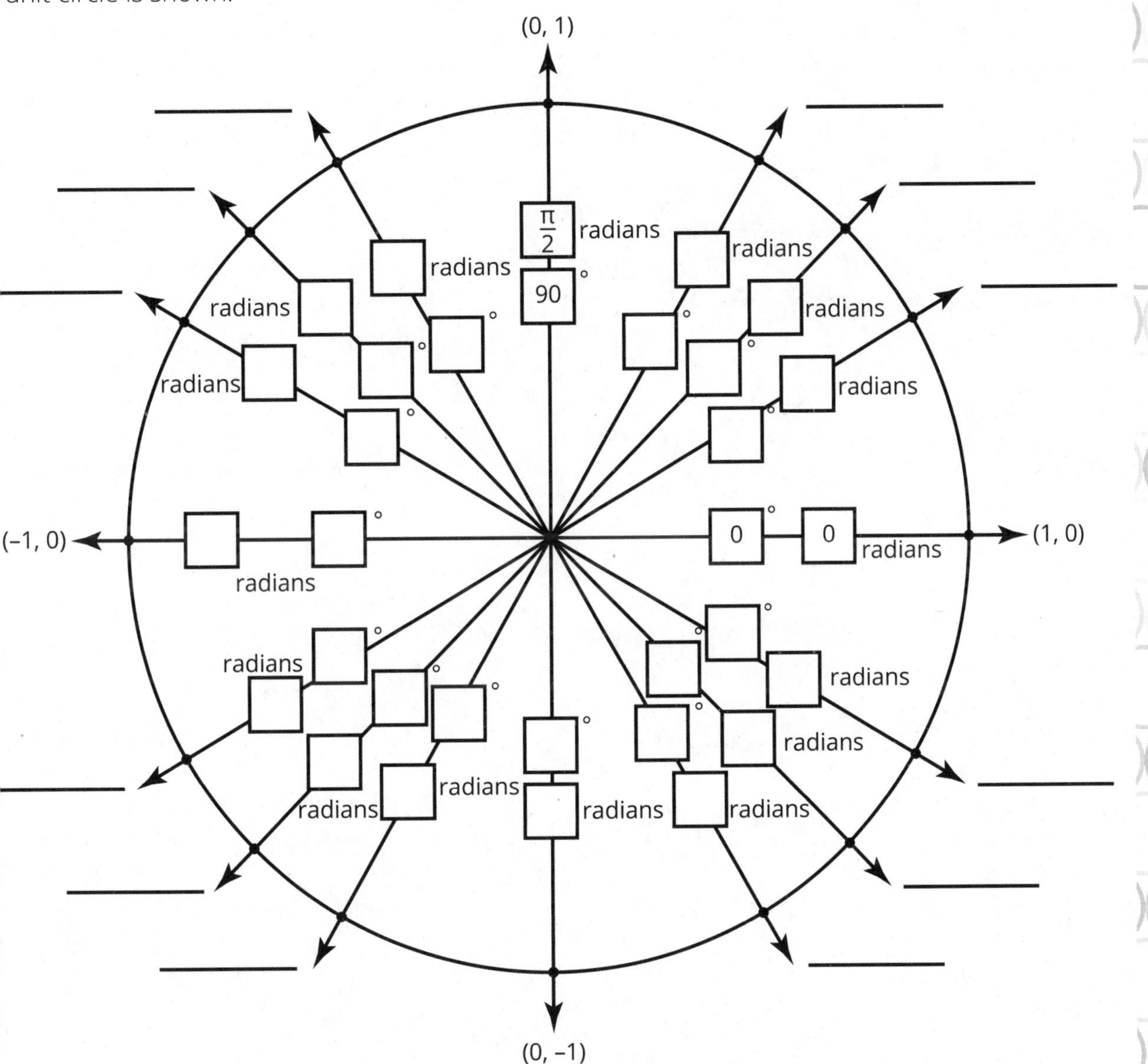

1. **Measure the angles. Write each angle measure in degrees and in radians.**

2. **Label the coordinates of the points on the unit circle.**

Assignment

Vrite

xplain in your own words how the Pythagorean identity follows from the Pythagorean Theorem.

Remember

ne Pythagorean identity states that $\sin^2\theta + \cos^2\theta = 1$.

ne trigonometric ratios sine, cosine, and tangent can have different signs, negative or positive, epending on what quadrant of the coordinate plane the angle and right triangle are in.

Practice

se the Pythagorean identity $\sin^2\theta + \cos^2\theta = 1$ to determine the value of each trigonometric function.

. Given $\sin\theta = \frac{5}{13}$ in Quadrant I, determine $\cos\theta$.

. Given $\cos\theta = -\frac{7}{25}$ in Quadrant III, determine $\sin\theta$.

. Given $\sin\theta = -\frac{1}{3}$ in Quadrant IV, determine $\cos\theta$.

. Given $\cos\theta = -\frac{2}{3}$ in Quadrant II, determine $\sin\theta$.

. Given $\sin\theta = \frac{1}{6}$ in Quadrant II, determine $\cos\theta$ and $\tan\theta$.

Stretch

1. Rewrite the Pythagorean identity $\sin^2\theta + \cos^2\theta = 1$ as an identity with $\tan\theta$ and $\sec\theta$. Show your work.

2. Rewrite the Pythagorean identity $\sin^2\theta + \cos^2\theta = 1$ as an identity with $\cot\theta$ and $\csc\theta$. Show your work.

Review

1. Consider circle J centered at the origin with a radius of 6 units as shown.

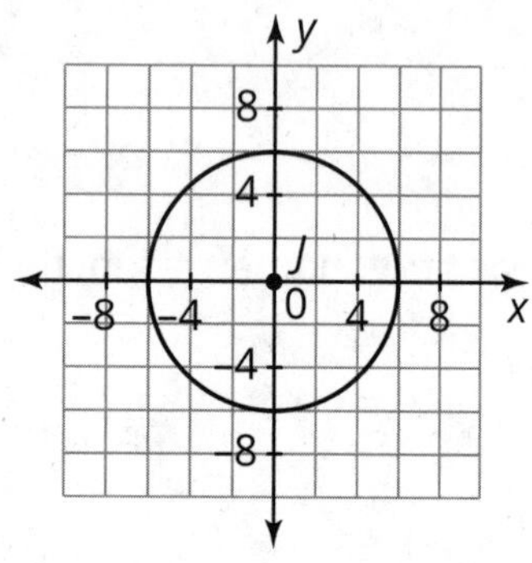

   a. Verify that point $A\ (-2, 4\sqrt{2})$ lies on circle J.

   b. Use symmetry to determine three more points on circle J.

2. Determine the inverse of each function.

   a. $y = x^2 - 7$

   b. $y = (x - 2)^2 + 9$

3. Determine each difference.

   a. $(-7x^3 + 9x^2 - 25x + 11) - (-15x^3 + 19x^2 + 15x + 18)$

   b. $(10x^3 - 8x^2 + 7x - 15) - (-3x^3 + 21x - 3)$

4

Going the Equidistance

Equation of a Parabola

Varm Up

Jse graphing technology to graph each quation and its inverse. Determine the ertex and axis of symmetry of each graph.

. $x^2 = 8y$

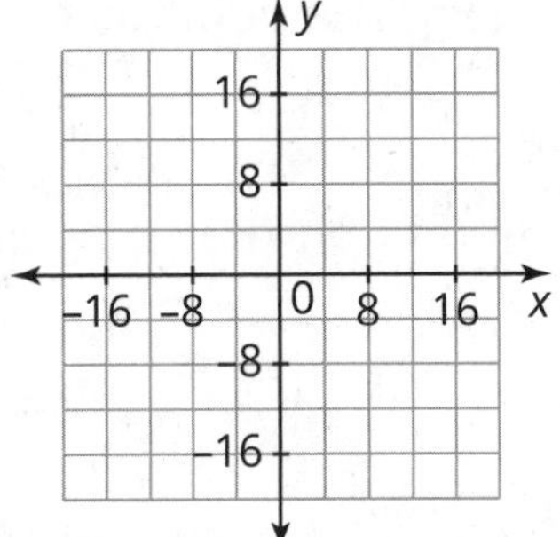

!. $-x^2 = 8y$

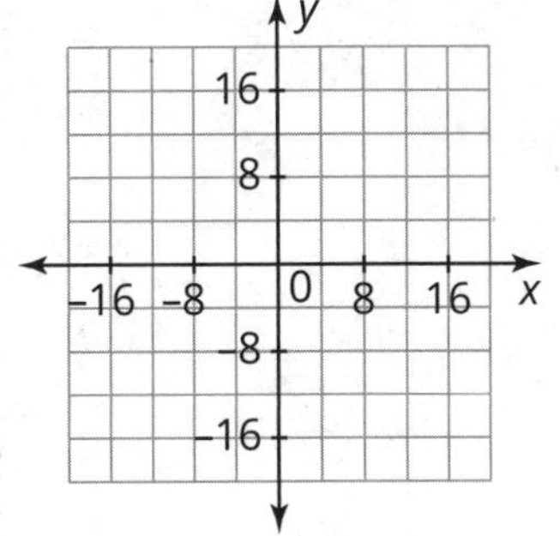

Learning Goals

- Derive the equation of a parabola given the focus and the directrix.
- Solve problems using characteristics of parabolas.

Key Terms

- conic section
- nappes
- locus of points
- parabola
- focus
- directrix
- vertex of a parabola
- concavity
- general form of a parabola
- standard form of a parabola

'ou have studied parabolas as quadratic functions. What are the characteristics of a parabola letermined by the set of points equidistant from both a given point and a given line?

GETTING STARTED

Hocus Pocus . . . Make the Locus!

Consider the grid with the plotted point and graphed line. Can you create a set of points that are the same distance from both the point and the line?

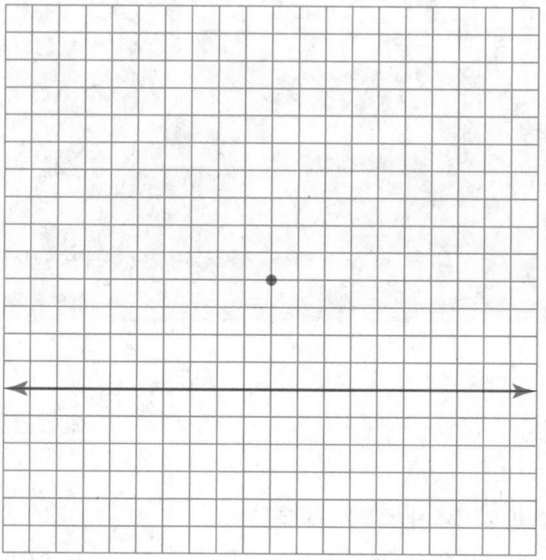

1. Construct a circle with a radius of 1 unit using the point as the circle's center.

a. What is the relationship between the points on the circle and the plotted point?

b. Are any of the points on the circle the same distance from the plotted point and the graphed line? Explain your reasoning.

2. Construct a circle with a radius of 2 units using the point as the circle's center.

a. Are any of the points on the circle the same distance from the plotted point and the graphed line? Explain your reasoning.

b. Plot a point on the circle that is the same distance from the circle's center and the line.

Continue to construct a total of eight concentric circles using the point as the center with the radius of each successive circle increasing by 1 unit.

a. How can you determine which points on each new circle are the same distance from the circle's center and the line?

b. Plot the points on each circle that are the same distance from the circle's center and the line.

Think about:

Will any of the points be below the graphed line?

Connect the points you plotted with a smooth curve.

a. What shape did you draw?

b. What do all the points on the curve have in common?

ACTIVITY
4.1 A Parabola as a Locus of Points

Everything you already know about parabolas remains true. The axis of symmetry of a parabola is a line that passes through the parabola and divides it into two symmetrical parts that are mirror images of each other.

You previously studied parabolas as quadratic functions and recognized the equation of a parabola as $y = x^2$. You analyzed equations and graphe parabolas based on the position of the vertex and additional points determined by using x-values on either side of the axis of symmetry.

A parabola can also be described as a *conic section*. A **conic section** is a curve obtained as the intersection of the surface of a double-napped cor with a plane. The upper and lower cones are called **nappes**. When a plan intersects one nappe of the double-napped cone parallel to the edge of t cone, the curve that results is a parabola.

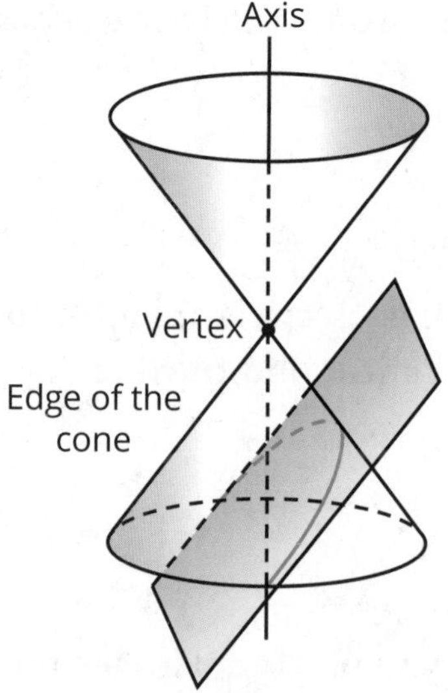

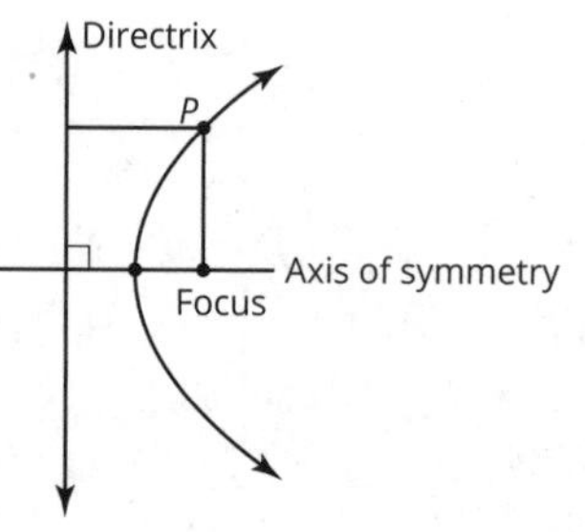

In this lesson, you will explore a *parabola* as a *locus of points* to determine more information about the parabola. A **locus of points** is a set of points that share a property. A **parabola** is the set of all points in a plane that are equidistant from both a *focus* and a *directrix*. The **focus** is a point which lies inside the parabola on the axis of symmetry. The **directrix** is a line that is perpendicular to the axis of symmetry and lies outside the parabola and do not intersect the parabola.

Create a parabola by folding patty paper.

a. Take a piece of patty paper. Near the bottom of the paper, draw a line (the directrix). Draw a point (the focus) above the line and label it point *F*.

b. Fold the patty paper so that point *F* and the line meet and make a crease. Next, slide point *F* along the line continuing to crease the patty paper. Repeat this process for at least 30 points along the line.

c. What conic section is formed by the folds? Outline the shape.

e **concavity** of a parabola describes the orientation of the curvature the parabola. A parabola can be concave up, concave down, concave ht, or concave left, as shown. The **vertex of a parabola** is the point on e axis of symmetry which is exactly midway between the focus and the ectrix. It is also the point where the parabola changes direction.

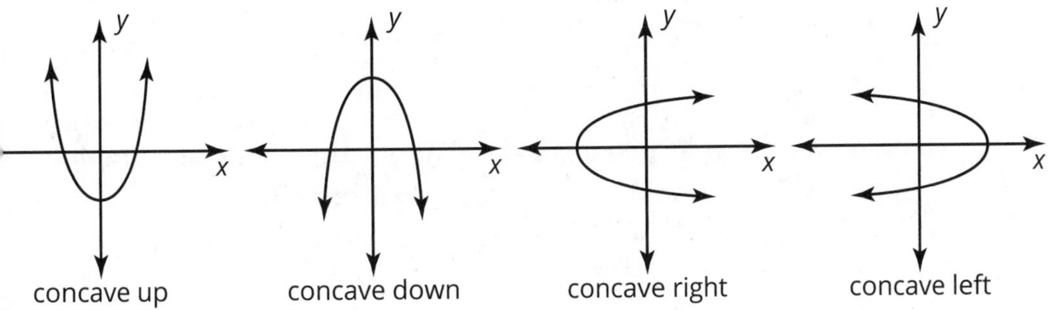

Label the vertex of the parabola you constructed.

3. Investigate the parabola you constructed using patty paper.

a. Draw a point on the directrix and label it point *D*. Draw a line from point *F*, the focus, to point *D*. Fold the paper so points *F* and *D* meet. What is the relationship between the line formed by the crease and $\overline{FD}$?

b. Draw a line perpendicular to the directrix through point *D*. Label the point where the perpendicular line intersects the crease as point *P*. Where does point *P* lie?

c. What is true about the distances from point *P* to point *F* and to point *D*? How do you know this is true?

d. Draw two additional points on the directrix and repeat parts (a) through (c). What do you notice?

4. Summarize what you discovered about the distance from any point on a parabola to the focus and directrix.

ACTIVITY

4.2 Equations of a Parabola

he parabola shown is defined such that all points on he parabola are equidistant from the point (0, 2) and he line $y = -2$. One point on the parabola is labeled s (x, y).

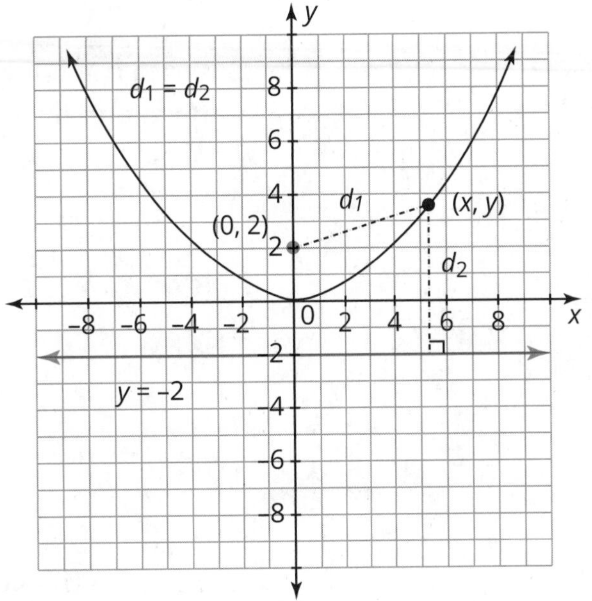

. **Determine the equation of the parabola by completing the steps.**

a. Let d_1 represent the distance from (x, y) to (0, 2). Write an equation using the Distance Formula to represent d_1. Simplify the equation.

b. Let d_2 represent the distance from (x, y) to the line $y = -2$. Write an equation using the Distance Formula to represent d_2. Simplify the equation.

c. What do you know about the relationship between d_1 and d_2?

d. Write an equation for the parabola using Question 1, parts (a) through (c). Simplify the equation so that one side of the equation is x^2.

The **general form of a parabola** with a vertex at the origin is an equatic of the form $Ax^2 + Dy = 0$ or $By^2 + Cx = 0$.

The **standard form of a parabola** with a vertex at the origin is an equation of the form $x^2 = 4py$ or $y^2 = 4px$, where p represents the distanc from the vertex to the focus.

2. **Write the equation of the parabola from Question 1 in general form and in standard form.**

3. **What are the coordinates for the intercept(s) of the parabola?**

4. **Describe the symmetry of the parabola.**

5. **Calculate the coordinates of the point that has an *x*-coordinate of 4.**

6. **Use symmetry to determine which other point on the parabola has a *y*-coordinate of 2. Explain your reasoning.**

7. **Calculate the coordinates of each point that has a *y*-coordinate of 4.5.**

How can you determine the points on the parabola that have a y-coordinate of −4.5 graphically and algebraically?

Consider the parabola represented by the equation $y^2 = 2x$.

a. Sketch the parabola using the table of values.

x	y
8	−4
2	−2
0	0
2	2
8	4

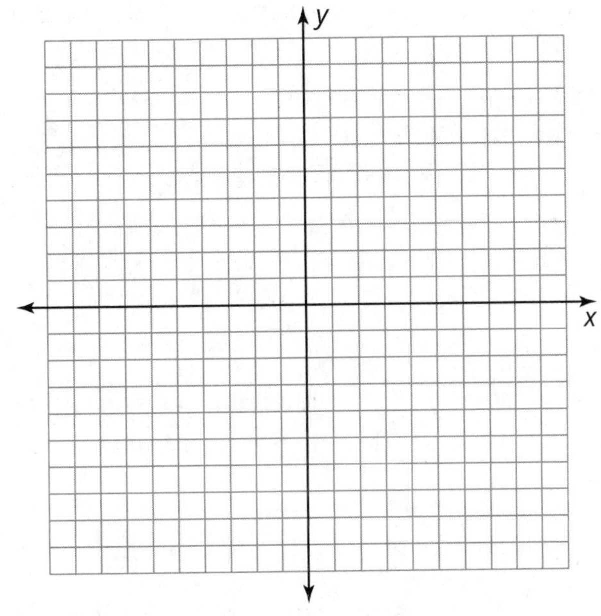

What does the form of the equation tell you about the shape of the parabola?

b. What is the relationship between the axis of symmetry and the equation of the parabola?

c. What are the coordinates of the vertex?

d. How is the concavity of the parabola related to the orientation of the parabola?

10. Consider the parabola represented by the equation $x^2 = 9y$.

a. Complete the table of values for the equation. Sketch the parabola using the coordinates from the table.

x	y
−6	
−3	
0	
3	
6	

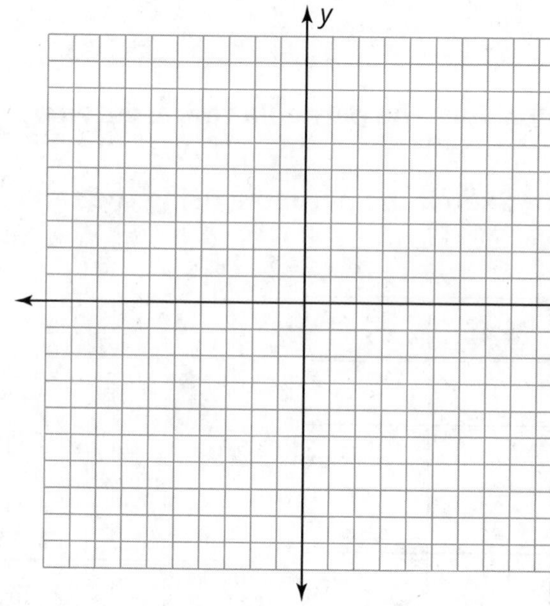

b. What is the relationship between the axis of symmetry and the equation of the parabola?

c. What are the coordinates of the vertex?

d. How is the concavity of the parabola related to the orientation of the parabola?

11. The standard form of a parabola with its vertex at the origin is an equation of the form $x^2 = 4py$ or $y^2 = 4px$.

a. What is the standard form of a parabola with an axis of symmetry parallel to the y-axis?

b. What is the standard form of a parabola with an axis of symmetry parallel to the *x*-axis?

c. What is the equation of the axis of symmetry for a parabola with a vertical orientation?

d. What is the equation of the axis of symmetry for a parabola with a horizontal orientation?

e. Is the concavity of a parabola with a vertical orientation described as concave up/down or concave right/left?

f. Is the concavity of a parabola with a horizontal orientation described as concave up/down or concave right/left?

ACTIVITY

4.3 Making Sense of the Constant p

You have learned that the standard form of a parabola with a vertex at the origin is an equation of the form $x^2 = 4py$ or $y^2 = 4px$, where p represents the distance from the vertex to the focus. What is the significance of the value $4p$ in each equation?

1. Consider the sketch of the parabola. Let p represent the distance from the vertex to the focus.

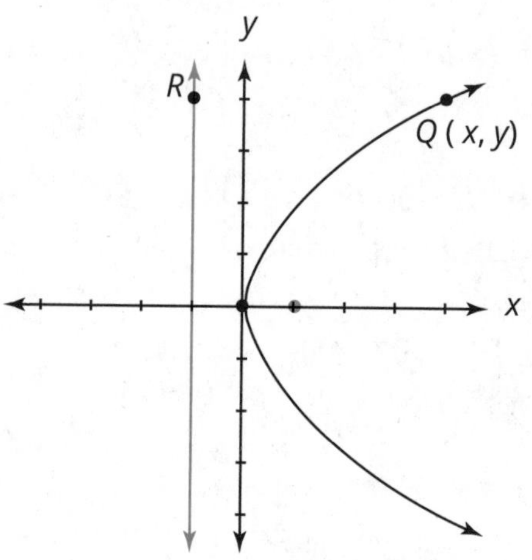

a. Label the vertex with its coordinates.

b. Label the distance, p, on the graph.

What is the relationship between the directrix and the axis of symmetry?

c. Label the focus with its coordinates.

d. Label the directrix with the equation for its line. Explain your reasoning.

e. What is the distance from the focus to the directrix? Label this distance on the graph.

Write an equation for the parabola.

a. Let d_1 represent the distance from point Q on the parabola to the focus. Write an equation using the Distance Formula to represent d_1. Simplify the equation.

b. Line segment QR represents the perpendicular distance from point Q on the parabola to the directrix. Draw line segment QR. What are the coordinates of point R? Label the coordinates on the graph.

c. Let d_2 represent the distance from point Q to point R. Write an equation using the Distance Formula to represent d_2. Simplify the equation.

d. Write an equation for the parabola using parts (a) through (c). Simplify the equation so that one side of the equation is the squared term.

e. Describe the significance of the equation derived in part (d).

ACTIVITY 4.4 Using the Constant p to Graph a Parabola

Let's investigate different equations to understand the relationships between the structure of the equation and its graph.

What does the form of the equation tell you? What do you think the graph will look like?

1. Consider the parabola represented by the equation $y^2 = 20x$.

a. Identify the coordinates of the vertex and the equation of th line of symmetry.

b. Determine the value of p. Then determine the coordinates of the focus and the equation of the directrix. Justify your reasoning.

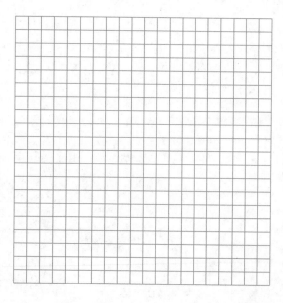

c. Graph the parabola. Then describe the concavity of the parabola. Justify your reasoning.

Consider the parabola represented by the equation $x^2 = -12y$.

a. Identify the coordinates of the vertex and the equation of the line of symmetry.

b. Determine the value of p. Then determine the coordinates of the focus and the equation of the directrix. Justify your reasoning.

c. Graph the parabola. Then describe the concavity of the parabola. Justify your reasoning.

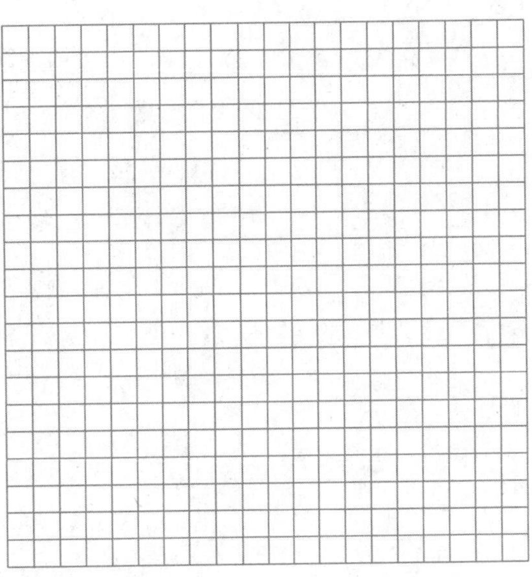

3. Consider the parabola represented by the equation $x^2 = 28y$.

a. Identify the coordinates of the vertex and the equation of the line of symmetry.

b. Determine the value of p. Then determine the coordinates of the focus and the equation of the directrix. Justify your reasoning.

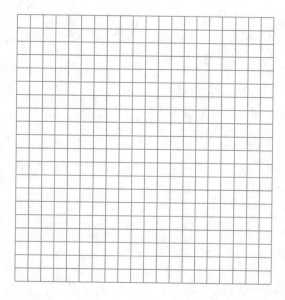

c. Graph the parabola. Then describe the concavity of the parabola. Justify your reasoning.

4. Consider the parabola represented by the equation $y^2 = -10x$.

a. Identify the coordinates of the vertex and the equation of the line of symmetry.

b. Determine the value of p. Then determine the coordinates of the focus and the equation of the directrix. Justify your reasoning.

c. Graph the parabola. Then describe the concavity of the parabola. Justify your reasoning.

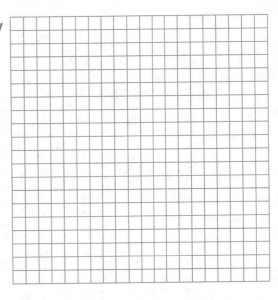

5. **Analyze each equation and its corresponding graph in Questions 1 through 4. Describe the relationship between the sign of the constant *p* and the concavity of each parabola.**

6. **Complete the table.**

Parabola Centered at Origin		
Graph	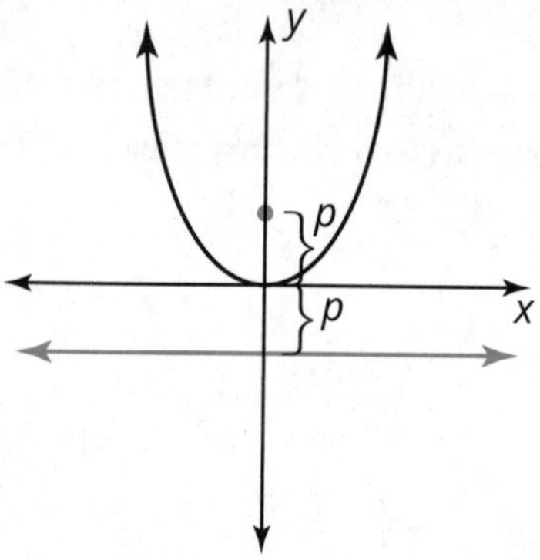 *y*, *p*, *p*, *x*	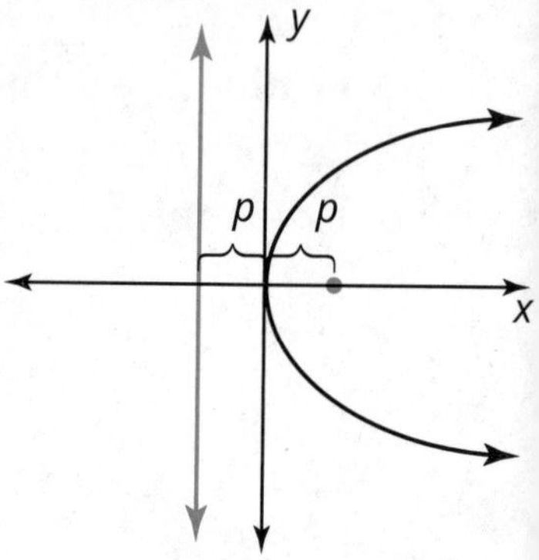 *y*, *p*, *p*, *x*
Equation of Parabola		
Orientation of Parabola		
Axis of Symmetry		
Coordinates of Vertex		
Coordinates of Focus		
Equation of Directrix		
Concavity		

ACTIVITY

4.5

Writing an Equation Given a Focus and a Directrix

n this activity, you will use the Distance Formula to determine the quation of points that are equidistant from a given point (the focus) nd a given line (the directrix) where the vertex is a point other than he origin.

. **Consider the graph shown.**

a. **Determine an equation for all the points equidistant from the point (−3, −5) and the line $y = 3$.**

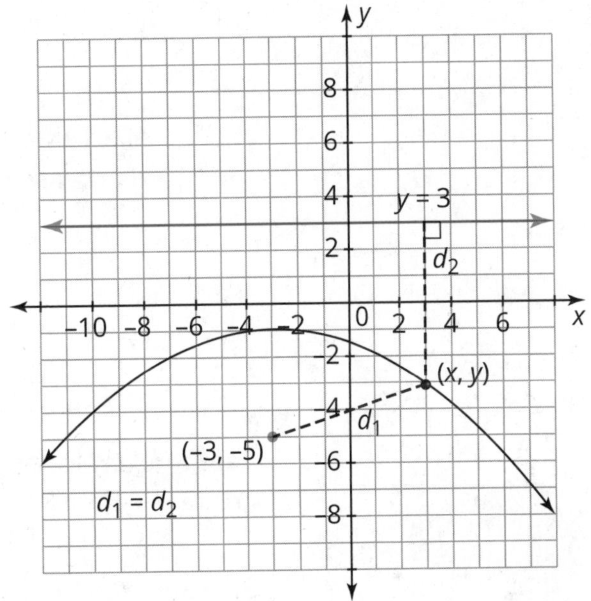

b. **Determine the coordinates of the vertex and equation of the axis of symmetry of the parabola. Explain your reasoning.**

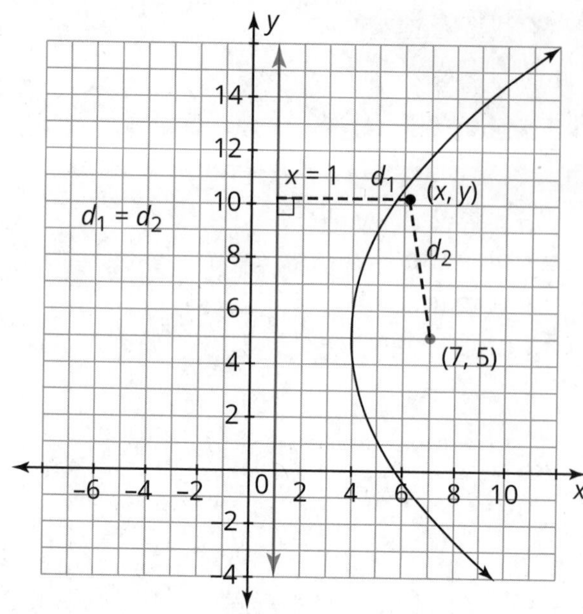

2. Consider the graph shown.

a. Determine the equation for all the poi[nts] equidistant from the point (7, 5) and th[e] line $x = 1$.

b. Determine the coordinates of the vertex and equation of th[e] axis of symmetry of the parabola. Explain your reasoning.

The standard forms of parabolas with vertex at (h, k) are $(x - h)^2 = 4p(y - k$ and $(y - k)^2 = 4p(x - h)$.

How do these equations compare with the standard form of the equation of a circle: $(x - h)^2 + (y - k)^2 = r^2$?

3. Rewrite the equations from Questions 1 and 2 in one of these forms.

Rewrite each equation in standard form. Determine the value of *p*, the coordinates of the vertex and focus, and the equations of the directrix and the axis of symmetry. Then sketch the graph of the parabola with the focus and directrix and describe the concavity.

a. $y^2 + 8y + 8x + 16 = 0$

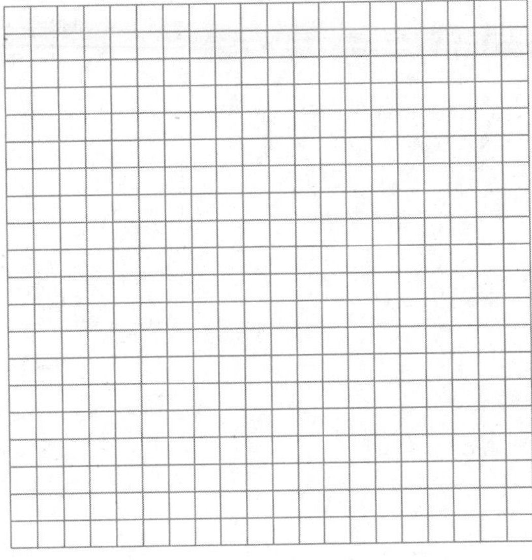

b. $4x^2 - 40x + 48y + 4 = 0$

5. **Write an equation in standard form for each parabola. Then, graph and label the parabola.**

a. **A parabola with a vertex at (3, 2) and a focus at (3, 4).**

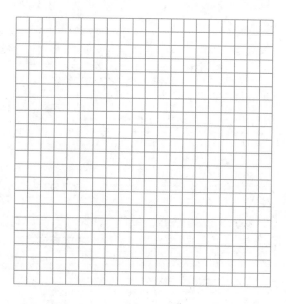

b. **A parabola with a vertex at (4, 1) and a directri at $x = 2$.**

Complete the table.

Parabola		
Graph	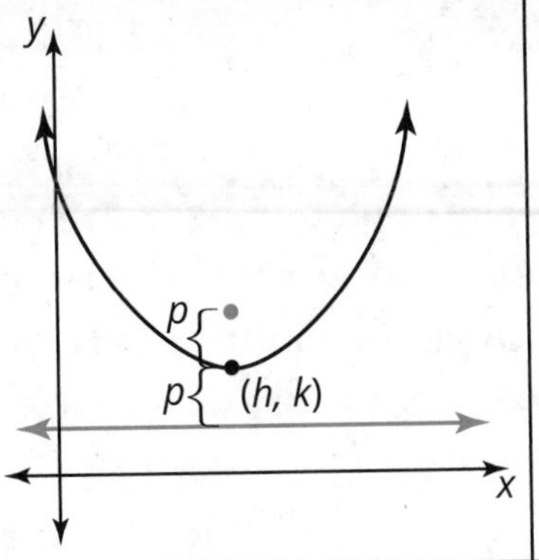	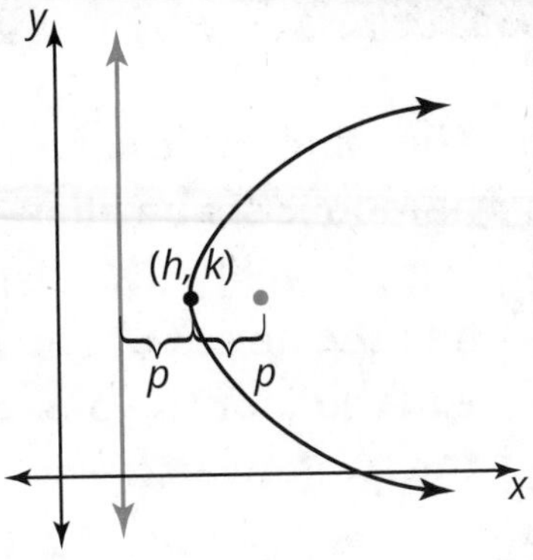
Equation of Parabola	$(x - h)^2 = 4p(y - k)$	$(y - k)^2 = 4p(x - h)$
Orientation of Parabola		
Axis of Symmetry		
Coordinates of Vertex		
Coordinates of Focus		
Equation of Directrix		
Concavity		

ACTIVITY

4.6

Applications of Parabolas

1. **The main cables of a suspension bridge are parabolic. The parabolic shape allows the cables to bear the weight of the bridge evenly. The distance between the towers is 900 feet and the height of each tower is about 75 feet. Write an equation for the parabola that represents the cable between the two towers.**

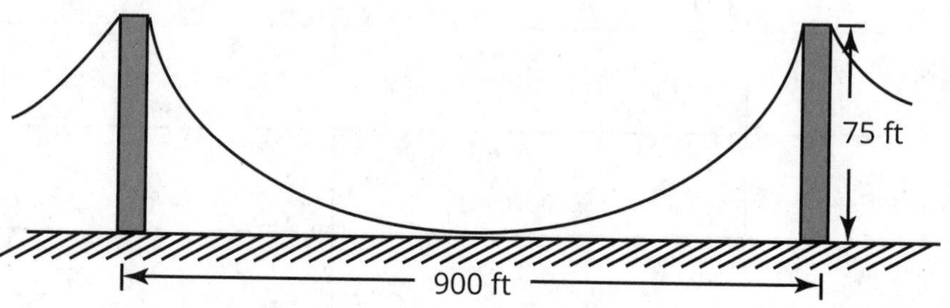

2. **A cross section of a satellite dish is a parabola. The satellite dish is 5 feet wide at its opening and 1 foot deep. The receiver of the satellite dish should be placed at the focus of the parabola. How far should the receiver be placed from the vertex of the satellite dish?**

Many carnivals and amusement parks have mirrors that are parabolic. When you look at your reflection in a parabolic mirror, your image appears distorted and makes you look taller or shorter depending on the shape of the mirror. The focal length of a mirror is the distance from the vertex to the focus of the mirror. Consider a mirror that is 72 inches tall with a vertex that is 6 inches from the top and bottom edges of the mirror. What is the focal length of the mirror?

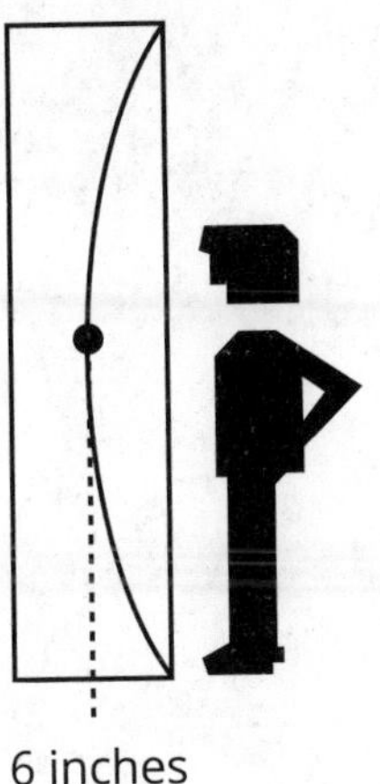

NOTES

TALK the TALK 

Simply Parabolic

Graph each parabola. Label the vertex, the focus, and the directrix. Then describe the concavity.

1. $x^2 = 18y$

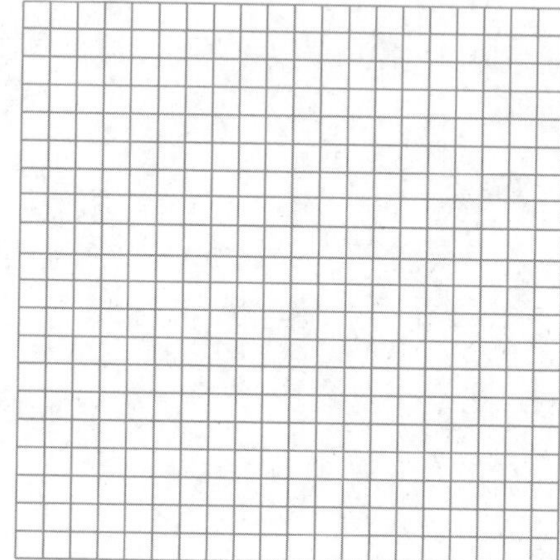

2. $y^2 + 44x = 0$

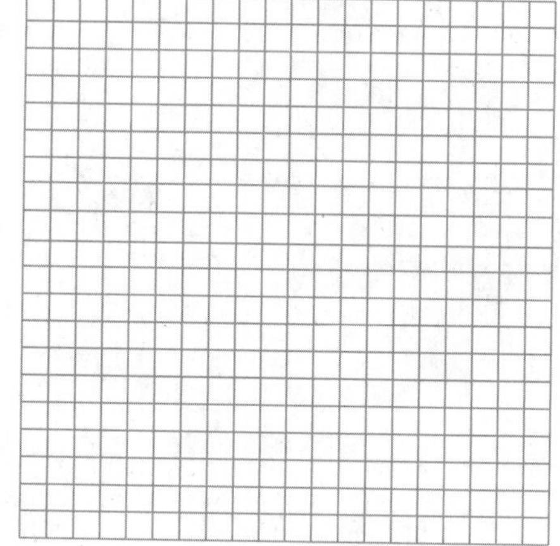

Assignment

Write

Match each term with its definition.

1. locus of points
2. parabola
3. focus
4. directrix
5. general form of a parabola
6. standard form of a parabola
7. vertex of a parabola
8. concavity

a. $Ax^2 + Dy = 0$ or $By^2 + Cx = 0$

b. $x^2 = 4py$ or $y^2 = 4px$

c. describes the orientation of the curvature of the parabola

d. a set of points in a plane that are equidistant from a fixed point and a fixed line

e. The maximum or minimum point of a parabola

f. a set of points that share a property

g. the fixed point from which all points of a parabola are equidistant

h. the fixed line from which all points of a parabola are equidistant

Remember

A parabola is the set of all points in a plane that are equidistant from a fixed point, the focus, and a fixed line, the directrix. A parabola has an axis of symmetry, a vertex, and concavity. A parabola can be concave up, concave down, concave right, or concave left.

The general form of a parabola centered at the origin is an equation of the form $Ax^2 + Dy = 0$ or $By^2 + Cx = 0$. The standard form of a parabola centered at the origin is an equation of the form $x^2 = 4py$ or $y^2 = 4px$. The standard forms of parabolas with vertex (h, k) are $(x - h)^2 = 4p(y - k)$ and $(y - k)^2 = 4p(x - h)$.

Practice

1. For each equation, determine the value of p, the coordinates of the vertex and focus, and the equations of the axis of symmetry and the directrix. Then graph the parabola and describe the concavity.
   a. $x^2 = 3y$
   b. $2y^2 = x$
   c. $x = -(y - 2)^2 + 3$
   d. $x^2 - 8x - 4y - 4 = 0$

2. Determine the equation of each parabola with the given focus and directrix. Let (x, y) represent a point on the parabola.
   a. focus: (0, 3); directrix: $y = -3$
   b. focus: (−4, 0); directrix: $x = 4$
   c. focus: (7, 0); directrix: $x = -7$
3. Write an equation in standard form for each parabola. Then graph and label the parabola.
   a. A parabola with a vertex of (8, 6) and a focus of (6, 6).
   b. A parabola with a vertex of (1, 0) and a directrix of $y = -3$.

Stretch

The finish line of a 5K race is an archway of balloons. The archway is formed by two parabolas, one representing the top of the archway and one representing the bottom of the archway as shown.

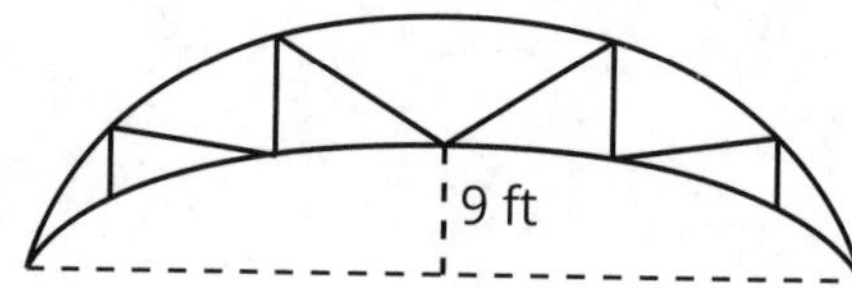

The width of the archway on the ground is 60 feet. The height of the top of the archway is 18 feet. The height of the bottom of the archway is 9 feet. The framework of the archway consists of vertical posts 10 feet apart with posts connecting the tops and bottoms of adjacent vertical posts. Calculate the sum of the lengths of the posts.

Review

1. Given $\cos\theta = -\frac{5}{13}$ in Quadrant III, use the Pythagorean identity to determine $\sin\theta$.
2. Given $\cos\theta = \frac{2}{9}$ in Quadrant IV, determine $\sin\theta$ and $\tan\theta$.
3. Solve each system of equations.
   a. $\begin{cases} y = x^2 + 3x - 7 \\ x + y = -2 \end{cases}$
   b. $\begin{cases} y = x^2 + 3x + 2 \\ y = 2x + 4 \end{cases}$
4. Determine each product.
   a. $(x^3 - 6x + 5)(-2x^2 - 8x + 4)$
   b. $(2x^3 - 5x^2 - 7x + 12)(-11x^2 + 12x - 1)$

Circles on a Coordinate Plane Summary

KEY TERMS

- conic section
- nappes
- Pythagorean identity
- locus of points
- parabola
- focus
- directrix
- vertex of a parabola
- concavity
- general form of a parabola
- standard form of a parabola

LESSON 1 X^2 plus Y^2 Equals Radius^2

The equation of a circle centered at the origin is $x^2 + y^2 = r^2$ where r is the radius of the circle.

The standard form of the equation of a circle centered at (h, k) with radius r can be expressed as $(x - h)^2 + (y - k)^2 = r^2$.

For example, a circle with a center at (2, 3) and a radius of 5 has the equation $(x - 2)^2 + (y - 3)^2 = 25$.

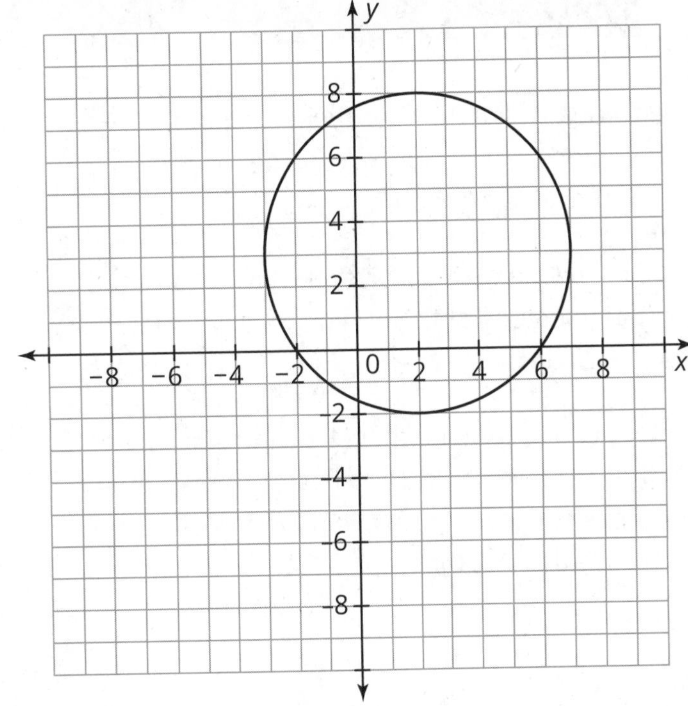

The equation for a circle in general form is $Ax^2 + Cy^2 + Dx + Ey + F = 0$, where A, C, D, and E are constants, $A = C$, and $x \neq y$.

To identify the center and the radius of a circle written in general form, it is necessary to rewrite the equation in standard form. Completing the square can be used to rewrite the equation.

For example, rewrite $x^2 + y^2 - 4x - 6y + 9 = 0$ in standard form by completing the square.

First, use an algebraic transformation to remove the constant term from the variable expression. Write the resulting equation grouping the x-terms together and the y-terms together using sets of parenthes

$$(x^2 - 4x) + (y^2 - 6y) = -9$$

Next, complete the square within each parentheses. To do this, examine the first two terms of each quadratic expression. Determine what the constant term would be if each expression were a perfec square trinomial. Add those constant terms to each side of the equation. Write the resulting equatic

$$(x^2 - 4x + 4) + (y^2 - 6y + 9) = -9 + 4 + 9$$

Finally, factor the left side of the equation, which should be a perfect square trinomial. Write the resulting equation.

$$(x - 2)^2 + (y - 3)^2 = 4$$

The center of this circle is (2, 3) and the radius is 2.

LESSON **2**

A Blip on the Radar

To determine the coordinates of points located on a circle, you can use the Pythagorean Theorem.

For example, consider circle A with its center point located at the origin and point P (5, 0) on the circle as shown.

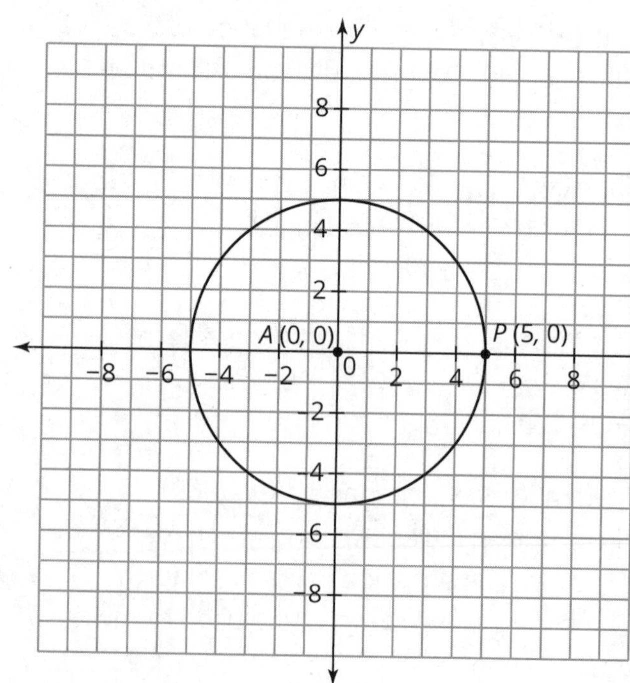

We can determine that (4, 3) is on the circle because we can enter it into our equation for a circle, knowing that the radius is 5 and the center is at (0, 0).

$$x^2 + y^2 = 25$$

$$4^2 + 3^2 = 25$$

$$25 = 25$$

his method also works when the center of the circle is not at the origin. If you are given the center f a circle and a point that lies on the circle, you can determine whether other points lie on the circle s well. First, determine the radius using the Distance Formula. Then repeat the method that was hown in the example above and substitute the center and the point in the equation for a circle.

ircles and polygons located on a oordinate plane enable you to calculate istances, slopes, and equations of lines.

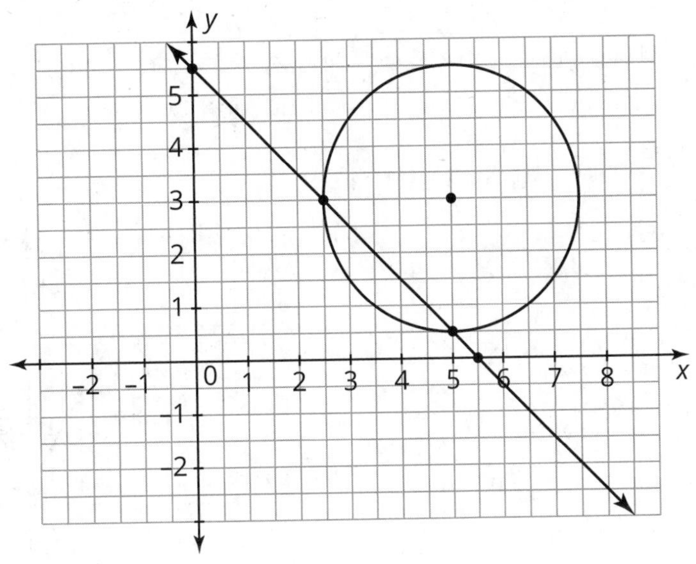

or example, consider the graph of the ircle and the line shown. The line has a lope of −1 and a y-intercept of 5.5, so the quation for the line is $y = -x + 5.5$.

he circle is centered at (5, 3) and has a adius of 2.5, so the equation for the circle s $(x - 5)^2 + (y - 3)^2 = 6.25$.

ubstitute the value of y given in the linear quation into the equation for the circle nd rewrite.

$$(x - 5)^2 + (-x + 5.5 - 3)^2 = 6.25$$

$$x^2 - 10x + 25 + x^2 - 5x + 6.25 = 6.25$$

$$2x^2 - 15x + 31.25 = 6.25$$

$$2x^2 - 15x + 25 = 0$$

$$(2x - 5)(x - 5) = 0$$

$$x = 5 \text{ and } x = 2.5$$

The points of intersection are (5, 0.5) and (2.5, 3).

LESSON 3

$\text{Sin}^2\,\theta$ Plus $\text{Cos}^2\,\theta$ Equals 1^2

The trigonometric ratios sine, cosine, and tangent can have different signs. They can be negative o positive, depending on what quadrant of the coordinate plane the angle and right triangle are in.

Consider the unit circle shown.

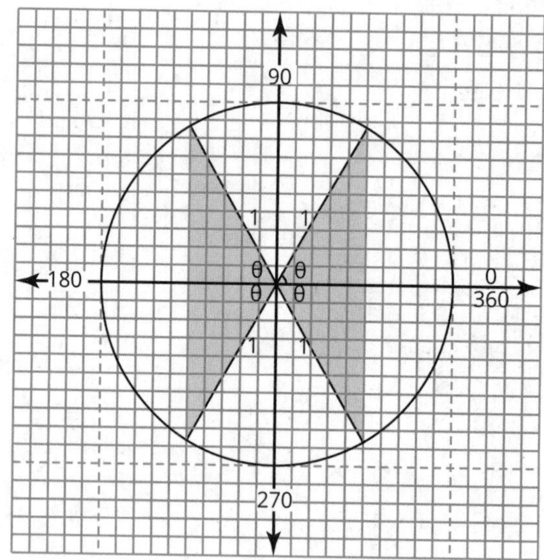

	Sign (+/–)			
	Quadrant I	**Quadrant II**	**Quadrant III**	**Quadrant IV**
Sine	+	+	–	–
Cosine	+	–	–	+
Tangent	+	–	+	–

A **Pythagorean identity** is a trigonometric identity that expresses the Pythagorean Theorem in terms of trigonometric ratios. The Pythagorean identity states that $(\sin\theta)^2 + (\cos\theta)^2 = (1)^2$. The symbol θ represents an angle measure.

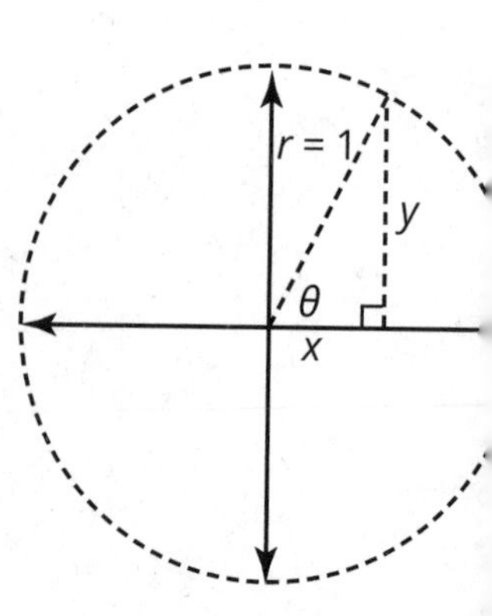

You can use the Pythagorean identity and what you know about solutions in different quadrants to determine values of trigonometric functions.

For example, to determine the exact value of $\cos\theta$ in Quadrant II, given $\sin(\theta) = \frac{2}{3}$, use a Pythagorean identity to determine $\cos\theta$.

$$\sin^2\theta + \cos^2\theta = 1$$

$$\left(\frac{2}{3}\right)^2 + \cos^2\theta = 1$$

$$\frac{4}{9} + \cos^2\theta = 1$$

$$\cos^2\theta = \frac{5}{9}$$

$$\cos\theta = \pm\frac{\sqrt{5}}{3}$$

he solution is $\cos\theta = -\frac{\sqrt{5}}{3}$ because the solution is in Quadrant II.

ou can also solve for the tangent of an angle in all four quadrants using what you know about rigonometric ratios.

$$\tan\theta = \frac{y}{x}$$

$$\tan\theta = \frac{\sin\theta}{\cos\theta}$$

Jsing sine, cosine and tangent you can complete a unit circle.

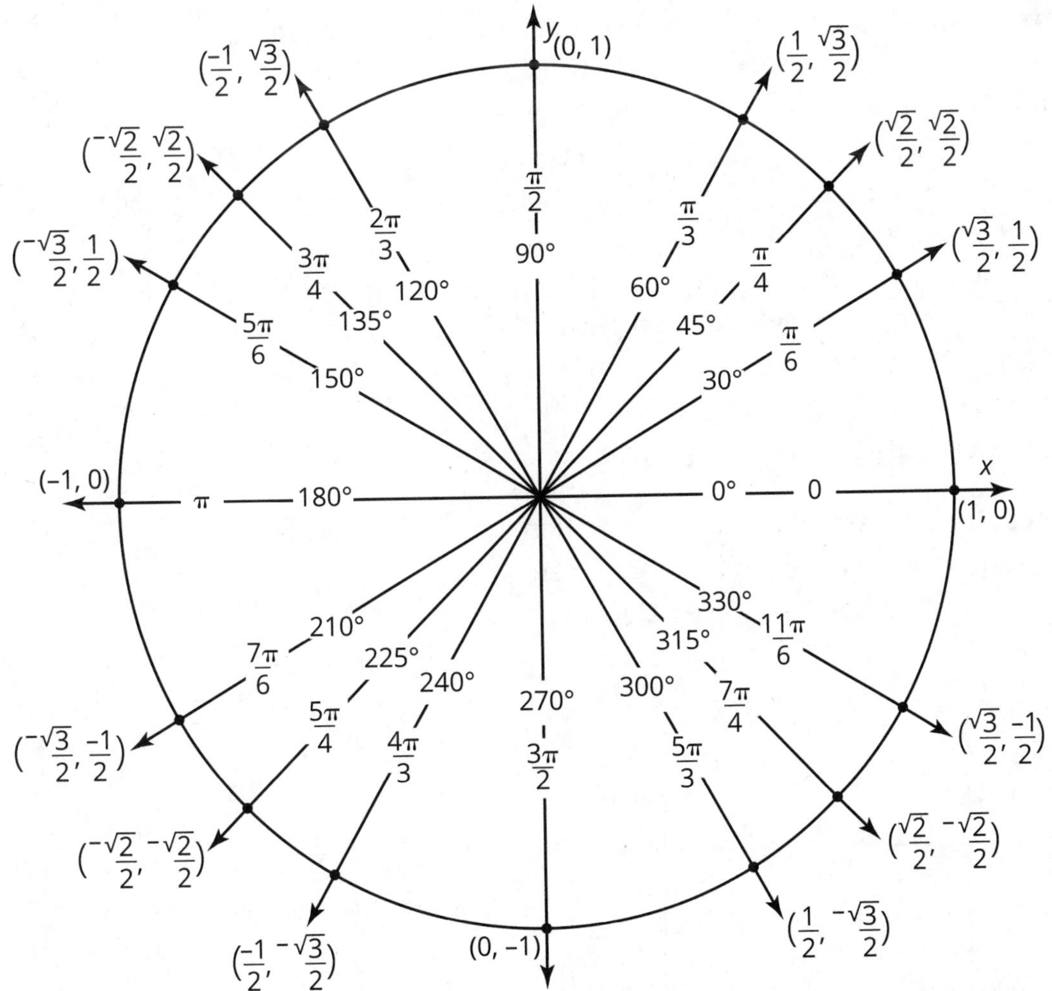

LESSON 4

Going the Equidistance

You previously studied parabolas as quadratic functions. You analyzed equations and graphed parabolas based on the position of the vertex and additional points determined using x-values on either side of the axis of symmetry.

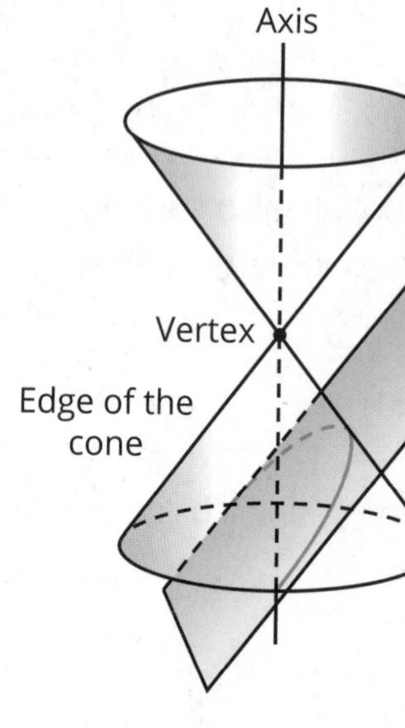

A parabola can also be described as a conic section. A **conic section** is a curve obtained as the intersection of the surface of a double-napped cone with a plane. The upper and lower cones are called **nappes**. When a plane intersects one nappe of the double-napped cone parallel to the edge of the cone, the curve that results is a *parabola*.

A **locus of points** is a set of points that share a property. A **parabola** is the set of all points in a plane that are equidistant from a focus and a directrix. The **focus** is a point which lies inside the parabola on the axis of symmetry. The **directrix** is a line that is perpendicular to the axis of symmetry and lies outside the parabola and does not intersect the parabola. Thus, a parabola is equidistant from the focus and the directrix. The **vertex of a parabola** is the point on the axis of symmetry which is exactly midway between the focus and the directrix. It is also the point where the parabola changes direction.

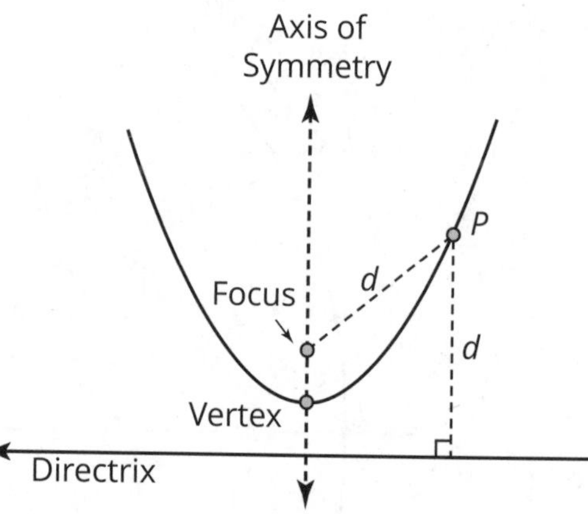

The **concavity** of a parabola describes the orientation of the curvature of the parabola. A parabola can be concave up, concave down, concave right, or concave left, as shown.

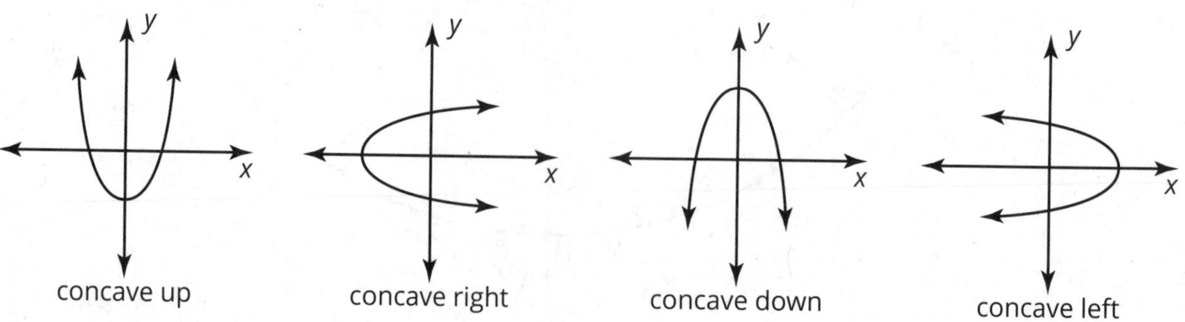

ne **general form of a parabola** centered at the origin is an equation of the form $Ax^2 + Dy = 0$ or $y^2 + Cx = 0$. The **standard form of a parabola** centered at the origin is an equation of the form $= 4py$ or $y^2 = 4px$, where p represents the distance from the vertex to the focus.

Parabola		
Graph		
Equation of Parabola	$x^2 = 4py$	$y^2 = 4px$
Orientation of Parabola	vertical	horizontal
Axis of Symmetry	y-axis	x-axis
Coordinates of Vertex	(0, 0)	(0, 0)
Coordinates of Focus	$(0, p)$	$(p, 0)$
Equation of Directrix	$y = p$	$x = p$
Concavity	up or down	right or left

he standard forms of parabolas with a vertex at (h, k) are $(x - h)^2 = 4p(y - k)$ and $(y - k)^2 = 4p(x - h)$.

Parabola		
Graph		
Equation of Parabola	$(x - h)^2 = 4p(y - k)$	$(y - k)^2 = 4p(x - h)$
Orientation of Parabola	vertical	horizontal
Axis of Symmetry	$x = h$	$y = k$
Coordinates of Vertex	(h, k)	(h, k)
Coordinates of Focus	$(h, k + p)$	$(h + p, k)$
Equation of Directrix	$y = k - p$	$x = h - p$
Concavity	up or down	right or left

A

MAKING INFORMED DECISIONS

B

e lessons in this module expand on your experiences with simple and compound obabilities. You will learn how to determine when two events have no effect upon each other d how to calculate probabilities when they do. You will use what you know about two-way equency tables to organize sample spaces and calculate probabilities of compound events. u will learn strategies for counting the number of outcomes in a sample space and use this owledge to solve problems and make decisions.

ɔPIC 1

ndependence and Conditional robability

es the probability of bad weather affect the probability of your flight being delayed?

Module 5: Making Informed Decisions

TOPIC 1: INDEPENDENCE AND CONDITIONAL PROBABILITY

In this topic, students investigate compound probability with an emphasis toward modeling and analyzing sample spaces to determine rules for calculating probabilities in different situations. Students explore various probability models and calculate compound probabilities with independent and dependent events in a variety of problem situations. Students use technology to run experimental probability simulations.

Where have we been?

In grade 7, students learned about probability involving simple events and described the probabilities of those events both informally and formally. Students have also explored both experimental and theoretical probability and sample spaces for compound events.

Where are we going?

Students formalize notions about probability and broaden the complexity of their understanding of both probability and samples spaces to include combinations, permutations, and expected value. Probabilistic reasoning is an important component of statistical reasoning as students work with randomness in more advanced courses.

Using a Tree Diagram to Determine a Sample Space

A tree diagram can be used to determine a sample space for compound events. For example, at Mario's Pizzeria, you can choose a round or square pizza, thick crust or thin crust, a large size or small size, and pepperoni or mushrooms.

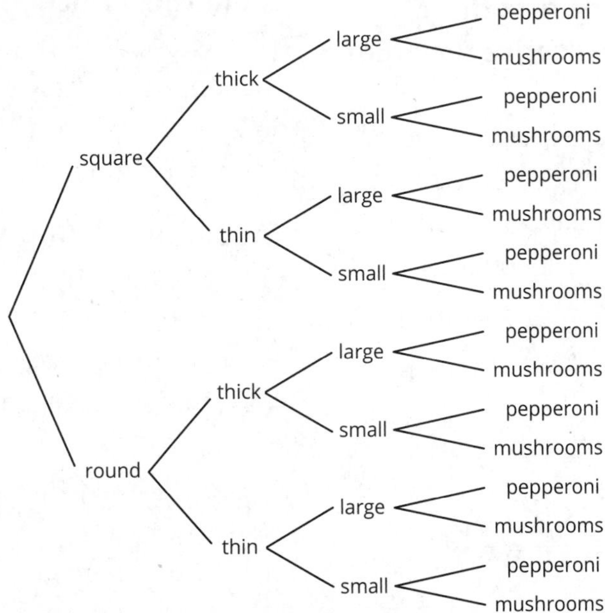

Let's Make a Deal!

There are three doors. Behind one door is a prize. Behind the other two doors are donkeys. You choose one door. The game show host opens one of the doors that you did not choose to reveal a donkey. Then, the host asks you if you would like to stay on the door you chose or switch to the other unopened door. Should you stay or switch? Or does it matter?

This famous probability problem is known as the Monty Hall problem—named after the host of the game show Let's Make a Deal, which featured this problem.

Can you figure out what you should do? What if you had 100 doors to choose from and, after you made your choice, the game show host opened 98 doors to reveal 98 donkeys?

Talking Points

It can be helpful to understand probability for college admissions tests.

Here is an example of a sample question:

A teacher hands out gumballs from a jar randomly to her class. If the jar has 50 gumballs in all—15 licorice, 10 banana, 20 watermelon, and 5 grapefruit— what is the probability that the first three gumballs picked out are licorice flavored?

The probability of choosing a licorice-flavored gumball on the first draw is $\frac{15}{50}$. On the next draw, there are 49 gumballs and 14 licorice-flavored ones, so the probability on the second draw is $\frac{14}{49}$. The probability on the third draw is $\frac{13}{48}$.

We can see that this is "and" probability, so multiply all the probabilities:

$$\frac{15}{50} \times \frac{14}{49} \times \frac{13}{48} = \frac{2730}{117{,}600} = \frac{13}{560}$$

Key Terms

uniform probability model
In a uniform probability model, the probabilities for each outcome are equal.

non-uniform probability model
When the probabilities of the outcomes are not all equal, the model is a non-uniform probability model.

Counting Principle
The Counting Principle states that if an action *A* can occur in *m* ways and for each of these *m* ways an action *B* can occur in *n* ways, then actions *A* and *B* can occur in $m \cdot n$ ways.

Addition Rule for Probability
The Addition Rule for Probability states that the probability that Event *A* occurs or Event *B* occurs is the probability that Event *A* occurs plus the probability that Event *B* occurs minus the probability that both *A* and *B* occur.

1

What Are the Chances?

Compound Sample Spaces

Varm Up

onsider the 7 days of a week. uppose the name of each day is ritten on a separate piece of folded aper and placed into a bag. You each into the bag and choose one iece of paper.

etermine each probability.

. Randomly choosing a day that begins with the letter S
. Randomly choosing a weekday
. Randomly choosing Wednesday

Learning Goals

- List the sample space for situations involving probability.
- Construct a probability model for a situation.
- Differentiate between uniform and non-uniform probability models.
- Develop a rule to determine the total number of outcomes in a sample space without listing each outcome.
- Classify events as independent or dependent.
- Use the Counting Principle to calculate the size of sample spaces.

Key Terms

- outcome
- sample space
- event
- probability
- probability model
- uniform probability model
- non-uniform probability model
- complement of an event
- tree diagram
- organized list
- set
- element
- disjoint sets
- intersecting sets
- union of sets
- independent events
- dependent events
- Counting Principle

n previous courses you have explored simple and compound probabilities. How are the possible utcomes of an experiment affected by the types of events and sets in the experiment?

GETTING STARTED

Take a Spin

A sample space is typically enclosed in braces, { }, with commas between the outcomes.

An **outcome** is a result of an experiment. The **sample space** is the set c all the possible outcomes of an experiment. An **event** is an outcome or s of outcomes in a sample space.

The **probability** of an event is the ratio of the number of desired outcon to the total number of possible outcomes. The probability of event A is

$$P(A) = \frac{\text{number of outcomes in } A}{\text{total possible outcomes}}$$

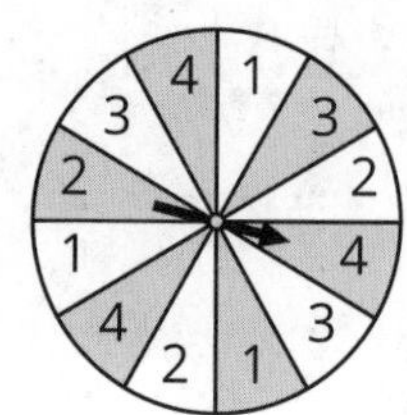

1. A board game includes the spinner shown that players must us to advance a game piece around the board.

a. What is the sample space if a player spins the spinner show one time?

b. What is the probability of spinning the number 3, $P(3)$?

c. What is the probability of spinning a number greater than 1

In a probability model, the sum of the probabilities must equal 1.

It is often helpful to construct a model when analyzing situations involvin probability. A **probability model** lists the possible outcomes and the probability for each outcome.

In a **uniform probability model**, the probabilities for each outcome are equal. When the probabilities of the outcomes are not all equal, the model is a **non-uniform probability model**.

2. Consider the spinner.

a. Complete the probability model for spinning the spinner.

Outcomes	1	2	3	4
Probability				

b. Is this a *uniform probability model* or a *non-uniform probabilit model*? Explain how you know.

What is the probability of a spin not resulting in a 3?

his game, players can earn different types of tokens as they move und the board. If a player lands on certain spaces, the player can domly choose a token from a box. token is then replaced before the t player's turn.

6 tokens 4 tokens 2 tokens

The **complement of an event** is an event that contains all the outcomes in the sample space that are not outcomes in the event. If E is an event, then the complement of E is often denoted as $\overline{E}$ or E^c.

Robert and Larissa each determined the sample space for choosing a token.

Robert: Cylinder, Cube, Pyramid

Larissa: Cylinder, Cylinder, Cylinder, Cylinder,
Cylinder, Cylinder
Cube, Cube, Cube, Cube
Pyramid, Pyramid

Who determined the sample space correctly? Explain your reasoning.

Consider the choice of tokens.

a. What is the probability of choosing a pyramid, *P*(pyramid)? A cube, *P*(cube)?

b. Construct the probability model for choosing one of the tokens.

Outcomes	cylinder	cube	pyramid
Probability			

c. Is this a uniform probability model or a non-uniform probability model? Explain how you know.

d. What is the probability of choosing a token that is not a cylinder?

ACTIVITY 1.1

Sample Space for Pizza Special

Mario's Pizzeria advertises special deals in the newspaper.

Today's Special at Mario's Pizzeria

Large one-topping pizza $9.00
Small one-topping pizza $6.50
Choose either a square or a round pizza with thick or thin crust.
Available toppings: pepperoni or mushrooms
Enjoy a fresh-baked pizza!!!

A **tree diagram** is a visual model for determining the sample space of multiple events.

Amaliya and Romeo sketched tree diagrams to show the possible pizza specials at Mario's Pizzeria.

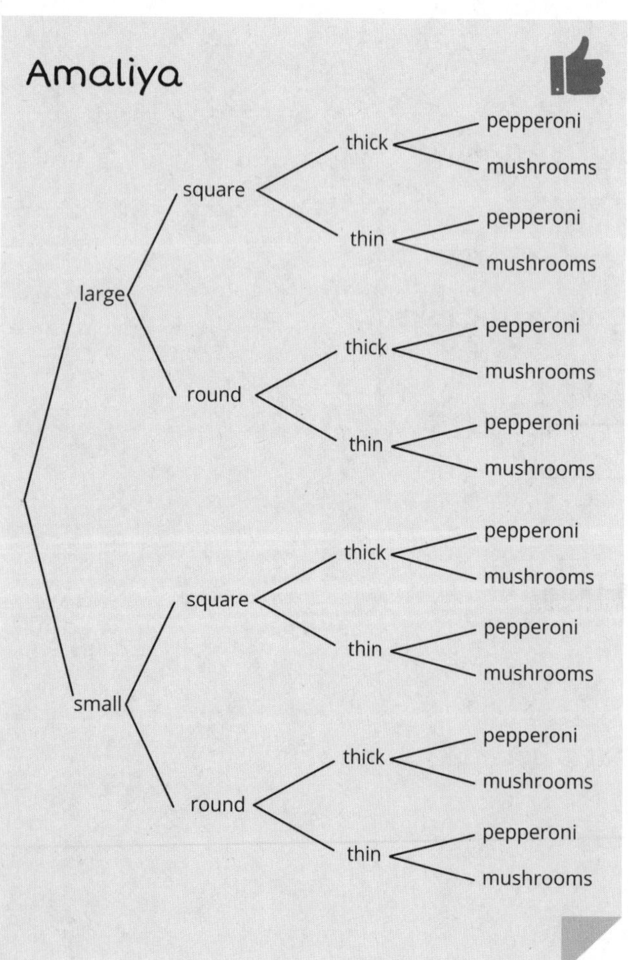

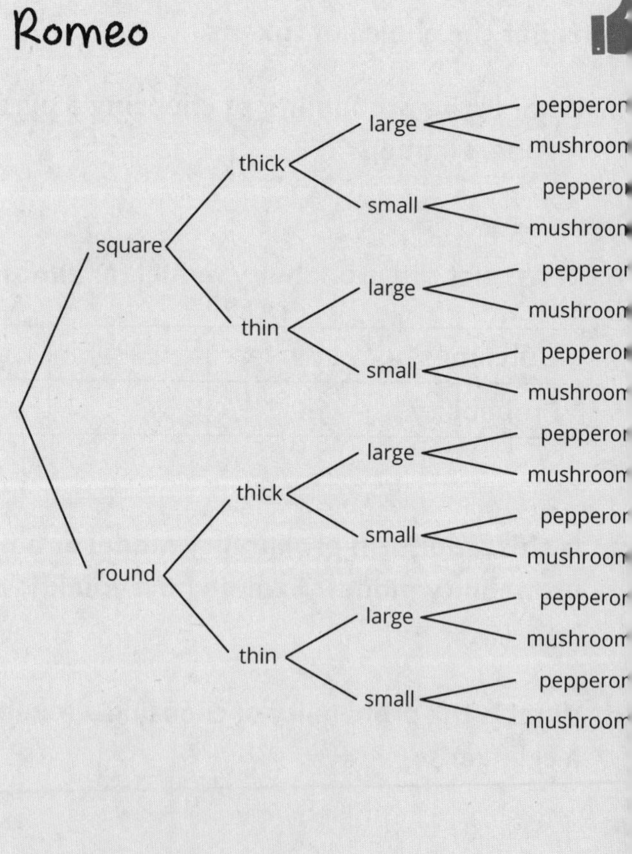

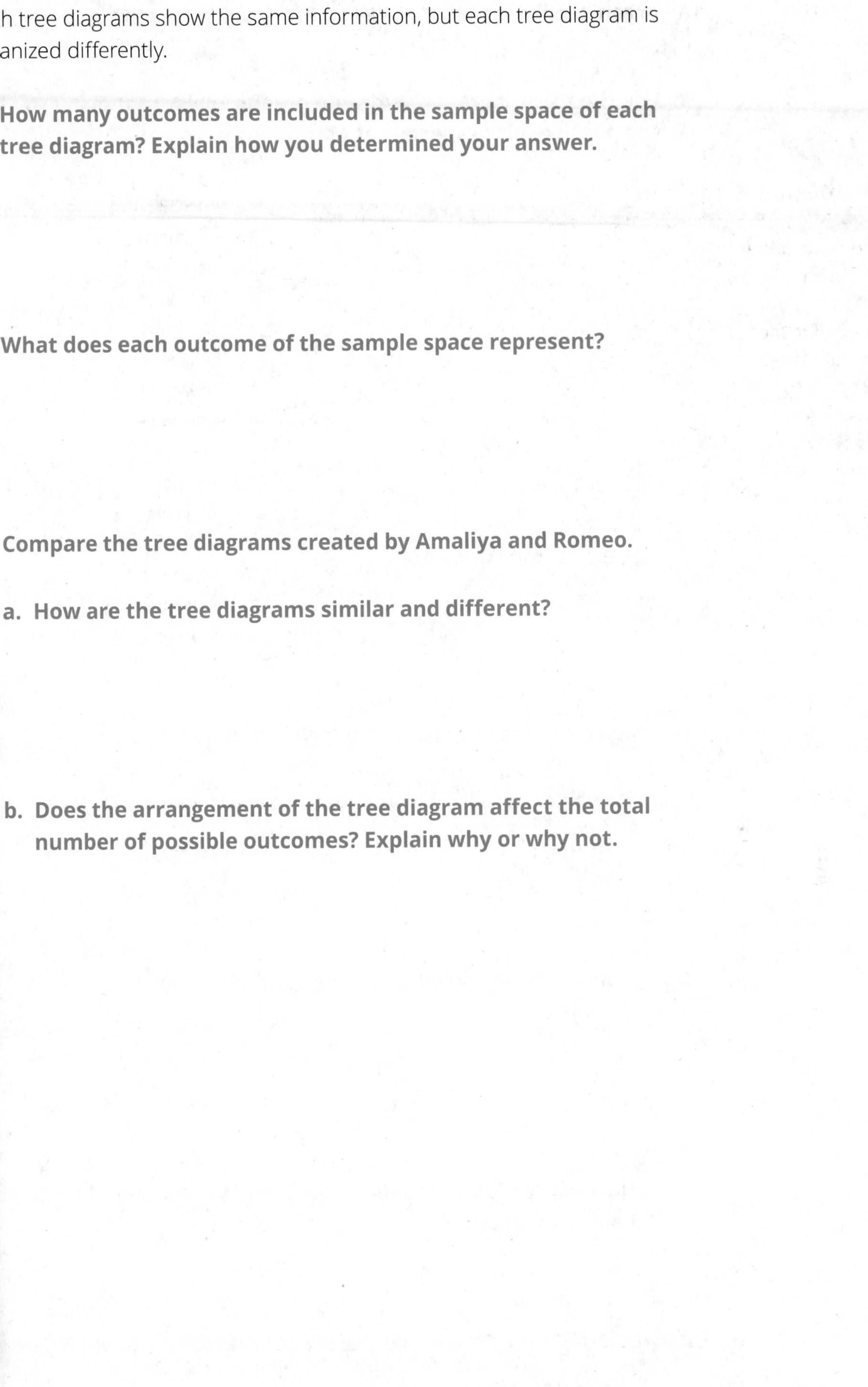

h tree diagrams show the same information, but each tree diagram is anized differently.

How many outcomes are included in the sample space of each tree diagram? Explain how you determined your answer.

What does each outcome of the sample space represent?

Compare the tree diagrams created by Amaliya and Romeo.

a. How are the tree diagrams similar and different?

b. Does the arrangement of the tree diagram affect the total number of possible outcomes? Explain why or why not.

An **organized list** is a visual model for determining the sample space of events.

There are descriptions that begin with the same letter. If you are abbreviating the names, what makes sense? Be sure to include a key so others know what you mean.

4. Use the tree diagram to write an organized list that displays al the possible pizza specials at Mario's Pizza.

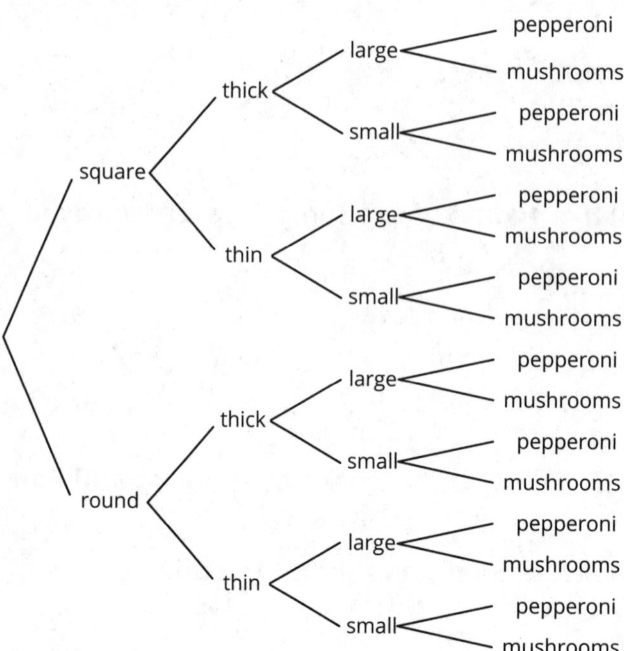

5. Analyze the sample space to answer each question.

a. How many possible round pizza specials can you order?

b. How many possible thick and round pizza specials can you order?

c. How many of the possible pizza choices are square but do nc have mushrooms?

ACTIVITY

1.2

Sample Space for Student Council Election

rdan, Gray, Kelly, Morgan, and Taylor are running for student council ffices. The student with the greatest number of votes is elected resident, and the student receiving the next greatest number of votes is ected vice president.

. **Create a tree diagram to represent the possible outcomes for the election.**

. **What does each level in your diagram represent? Does order matter? Explain your reasoning.**

. **Write the sample space as an organized list.**

. **Analyze the sample space to answer each question.**

a. **How many outcomes result in Gray being elected president or vice president?**

b. **How many outcomes result in Taylor not being elected president?**

c. **How many outcomes result in Jordan or Kelly as president and Taylor or Gray as vice president?**

5. Bentley used the first initial of each student's name as an abbreviation in his sample space. He included both JM and MJ different outcomes. Kaleb says these two outcomes mean the same thing and only one should be included in the sample spa Who's correct? Explain your reasoning.

6. Can you rearrange the tree diagram to produce a different number of total possible outcomes for the election? Explain wh or why not.

7. Consider your sample spaces from *Pizza Special* and *Student Council Election.*

a. Does choosing a topping for a pizza at Mario's Pizzeria affec any of the other choices you have? Does choosing a size affe any of the other choices? Explain your reasoning.

b. Does electing the student council president affect the choic for vice president? Explain your reasoning.

ACTIVITY 1.3

Categorizing Scenarios Involving Events

set is a collection of items. If x is a member of set B, then x is an ement of set B.

onsider the examples of disjoint sets, intersecting sets, and the union sets.

Two or more sets are **disjoint sets** if they do not have any common elements.

Two or more sets are **intersecting sets** if they do have common elements.

The **union of sets** is a set formed by combining all the members of the sets. A member is listed only once.

Worked Example

Disjoint Sets

Let N represent the set of 9th grade students. Let T represent the set of 10th grade students.

The set of 9th grade students and the set of 10th grade students are disjoint because the two sets do not have any common elements. Any student can be in one grade only.

Intersecting Sets

Let V represent the set of students who are on the girls' volleyball team. Let M represent the set of students who are in the math club. Julia is on the volleyball team and belongs to the math club.

The set of students who are on the girls' volleyball team and the set of students who are in the math club are intersecting because we know they have at least one common element, Julia.

The Union of Sets

Let B represent the set of students in the 11th grade band. Let C represent the set of students in the 11th grade chorus. The union of these two sets would be all the students in the 11th grade band or the 11th grade chorus. A student in both would be listed only once.

. **Identify the sets in each scenario in the previous two activities. Then, determine whether the sets are disjoint or intersecting. Explain your reasoning.**

a. ***Pizza Special***

b. ***Student Council Election***

2. **Determine whether each set is disjoint or intersecting. Explain your reasoning.**

   a. **Let *E* represent the set of even integers. Let *O* represent the set of odd integers.**

   b. **Let *T* represent the set of multiples of 2. Let *F* represent the set of multiples of 5.**

Independent events are events for which the occurrence of one event has no impact on the occurrence of the other event.

Dependent events are events for which the occurrence of one event has an impact on the occurrence of subsequent events.

3. **Consider the letters in the words *crafty* and *crate*.**

   a. **What set would be formed by taking the intersection of the letters in the two words?**

   b. **What set would be formed by taking the union of the letters in the two words?**

Consider the examples of independent events and dependent events.

Worked Example

A jar contains 1 blue marble, 1 green marble, and 2 yellow marbles.

Independent Events

You randomly choose a yellow marble, replace the marble in the jar, and then randomly choose a yellow marble again.

The event of choosing a yellow marble first does not affect the event of choosing a yellow marble second because the yellow marble chosen first is replaced in the jar.

The events of randomly choosing a yellow marble first and randomly choosing a yellow marble second are independent events because the first yellow marble was replaced in the jar.

You can see this visually using a tree diagram.

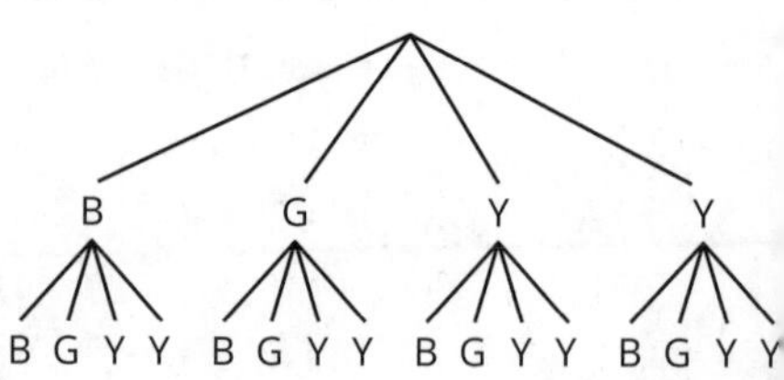

Vorked Example

ependent Events

jar contains 1 blue marble, 1 green marble, and 2 yellow marbles. You randomly choose a ellow marble without replacing the marble in the jar, and then randomly choose a yellow narble again.

he event of choosing a yellow marble first does affect the vent of choosing a yellow marble second because the ellow marble chosen first is not replaced in the jar.

he events of randomly choosing a yellow marble first nd randomly choosing a yellow marble second are lependent events because the first yellow marble was ot replaced in the jar.

You can see this visually using a tree diagram.

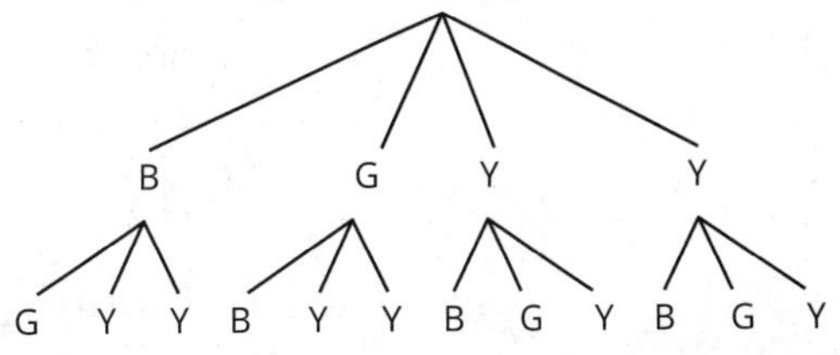

Explain why Sia's statement is incorrect.

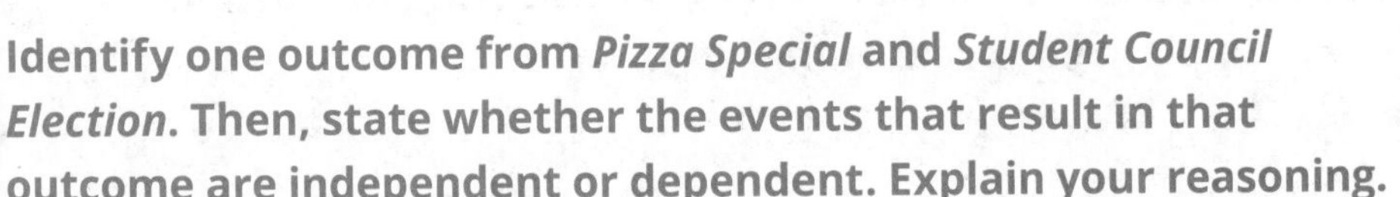

Sia
think that choosing the first marble and choosing the
second marble are dependent events.

Identify one outcome from *Pizza Special* and *Student Council Election*. Then, state whether the events that result in that outcome are independent or dependent. Explain your reasoning.

a. *Pizza Special*

b. *Student Council Election*

ACTIVITY 1.4

The Counting Principle

Paula's aunt owns an ice cream shop. She offers her customers a choice chocolate, vanilla, or strawberry ice cream in a cone or cup with or witho sprinkles. Her aunt was trying to determine the number of ways that a customer could order ice cream. Paula said, "There are 12 ways!" Paula used a mathematical principle called the *Counting Principle*. The principle used to determine the number of outcomes in the sample space.

The **Counting Principle** states: "If an action A can occur in m ways and for each of these m ways an action B can occur in n ways, then actions and B can occur in $m \cdot n$ ways."

Think about:

What is the difference between an event and an action?

The Counting Principle can be generalized to more than two actions th happen in succession. If for each of the m and n ways A and B occur the is also an action C that can occur in s ways, then Actions A, B, and C can occur in $m \cdot n \cdot s$ ways.

1. Devin has an all-day pass for Scream amusement park. His favorite rides are the Bungee-Buggy, Head Rush roller coaste Beep Beep go-karts, and Tsunami Slide water roller coaster. H never rides any other rides, and he can ride each of his favori rides as many times as he wants.

A situation can involve independent events from disjoint sets, independent events from the same set with repetitions allowed, or dependent events from the same set without repetitions.

a. Describe the type of event for selecting ride order. Explain your reasoning.

b. Use the Counting Principle to determine the number of possible ride orders for Devin's next two rides. Explain your reasoning.

c. How many ride order possibilities are there for Devin's nex five rides?

Sherry stayed home from school Wednesday because she was ill. She watched a television program from 12:00 PM until 12:30 PM, and another program from 12:30 PM until 1:00 PM From 12:00 PM until 12:30 PM, her program choices were the news, cartoons, or a talk show. From 12:30 PM until 1:00 PM, her program choices were a comedy, a soap opera, a game show, or a cooking show.

a. Describe the type of event for Sherry's television program selections. Explain your reasoning.

b. How many program selections can Sherry watch from 12:00 PM until 1:00 PM?

A student's daily schedule includes math, English, science, social studies, foreign language, art, and physical education. Students are enrolled in each class for one period per day.

a. Describe the type of event for creating a student's daily schedule. Explain your reasoning.

b. Determine how many different orders the classes can be arranged to fill a seven-period daily schedule.

c. Lunch period is directly after fourth period. How many different class schedule arrangements are possible before lunch period? Explain your reasoning.

4. The cell phone PIN to access voicemail is a 4-digit number. Each digit can be a number from 0 to 9, including 0 and 9.

   a. How many 4-digit numbers are possible? Repetition of numbers is allowed. Explain your calculation.

   b. If repeating digits is not permitted, how many different 4-digit PINs are possible?

5. A typical license plate number for a car consists of three lett followed by four numbers ranging from 0 through 9, includin 0 and 9.

   a. How many different license plate numbers are possible if letters and numbers can be repeated? Explain your calculation.

   b. How many different 3-letter, 4-digit license plate numbers are possible if letters and digits cannot be repeated?

NOTES

ALK the TALK

ounting Without Counting

e Counting Principle is used to determine the number of outcomes in sample space. The calculations vary depending upon the situation.

. **For each given type of event and type of set, write a scenario and sample space calculation that represents the type of event and type of set.**

Type of Event (independent or dependent)	Type of Set (disjoint or intersecting)	Scenario	Sample Space Calculation
independent	three disjoint sets		
dependent	intersecting sets		
dependent	two disjoint sets		

NOTES

2. **Efi and Areti each describe a scenario with a sample space of $4 \cdot 3 \cdot 2 = 24$.**

> Efi
> The scenario has independent events and disjoint sets.

> The scenario has dependent events and intersecting sets.

a. **Based on Efi's description, write an example scenario involving 3 disjoint sets and 24 outcomes in the sample space.**

b. **Based on Areti's description, write an example scenario involving 3 intersecting sets and 24 outcomes in the sample space.**

3. **Describe how to calculate the number of outcomes in the sample space of situations involving either independent or dependent events.**

4. **List advantages and disadvantages of using a tree diagram or an organized list to represent a sample space.**

Assignment

Vrite

A ____________________ is a collection or group of items and each item within it is called an ____________________.

The ____________________ is a set formed by combining all the members of the sets, such that all the members are only listed once.

Sets that do not have common elements are called ____________________.

Sets that do have common elements are called ____________________.

____________________ and ____________________ are two types of visual models that display sample space.

. Events for which the occurrence of one event has no impact on the occurrence of the other event are ____________________.

Events for which the occurrence of one event has an impact on the following events are ____________________.

. The ____________________ states that if an action *A* can occur in *m* ways and for each of these *m* ways, an action *B* can occur in *n* ways, then Actions *A* and *B* can occur in $m \cdot n$ ways.

Remember

he Counting Principle states: "If an action *A* can occur in *m* ways and for each of these *m* ways, an ction *B* can occur in *n* ways, then actions *A* and *B* can occur in $m \cdot n$ ways." The values for *m* and *n* are etermined by whether the events are independent or dependent events.

Practice

. Suppose you roll a number cube once.

a. Identify the sample space.

b. What is the probability of rolling a 5, *P*(5)?

c. What is the probability of rolling an even number, *P*(even)?

d. What is the probability of rolling a number greater than 2, *P*(greater than 2)?

e. Construct the probability model for rolling a number cube.

Outcomes						
Probability						

f. Is the probability model from part (e) a uniform or non-uniform probability model? Explain your reasoning.

g. What is the probability of rolling a number that is not a multiple of 3, *P*(not a multiple of 3)?

2. For each scenario,
   - Determine the actions.
   - Determine the outcomes of each action.
   - Determine whether the outcomes of each action belong to disjoint sets or intersecting sets. Explain your reasoning.
   - Sketch a tree diagram or write an organized list to represent the sample space.
   - Determine whether the events in each outcome of the sample space are independent or dependent.
   - Determine the size of the sample space using the Counting Principle. Show your calculation.

   Deck A

Lose a Turn	Take 2 Tokens	Take an Extra Turn

   Deck B

Go Back 2 Spaces	Go Back 1 Space	Go Ahead 2 Spaces	Go Ahead 1 Space

   a. While playing a board game, a player randomly chooses one card from each of the two decks, and then replaces the cards in the decks.
   b. Amanda randomly chooses a card from a deck of six cards, without replacing it, then chooses another card. The cards are numbered 1 through 6.

Stretch

1. Jacinta rolls two number cubes. Both number cubes are numbered from 1 to 6.
   a. What are the actions?
   b. What are the outcomes of each action?
   c. Determine the size of the sample space using the Counting Principle. Show your calculation.
   d. Write an organized list that represents the sample space.
   e. What is the probability of rolling two dice with a sum greater than 9, *P*(sum greater than 9)?
2. Jalen rolls a number cube that is numbered 1 through 6. He then flips a coin with heads on one side and tails on the other side.
   a. Are the events in each outcome of the sample space independent or dependent? Explain.
   b. Write an organized list that represents the sample space.
   c. What is the probability that the number on the cube is even and the result of the coin flip is tails, *P*(even number and tails)?
   d. If just the cube is rolled, what is the probability that the number rolled on the cube is an even number, *P*(even number)?
   e. If just the coin is flipped, what is the probability that it is tails, *P*(tails)?
   f. How do the answers to parts (c), (d), and (e) relate to each other?

Review

Determine the vertex, axis of symmetry, the value of p, the directrix, the focus, and the concavity for the parabola $(x - 1)^2 = 8(y + 3)$. Then graph the parabola.

Determine the equation of the parabola with focus $(0, -1)$ and directrix $y = 3$. Let (x, y) represent a point on the parabola.

Write an equation in standard form for each.

a. A circle with a center at $M(-2, 15)$ and a radius of $\sqrt{11}$

b. A circle with the same center as circle M, but whose area is 3 times that of circle M

Given $\sin \theta = \frac{\sqrt{2}}{2}$ in Quadrant II, use the Pythagorean identity to determine $\cos \theta$.

Use a trigonometric ratio to solve for the value of x. Round your answer to the nearest tenth.

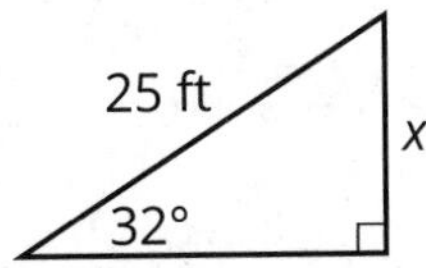

2

And?

Compound Probability with *And*

Warm Up

Determine each product.

1. $\frac{4}{5} \cdot \frac{1}{4}$

2. $\frac{1}{6} \cdot \frac{3}{5}$

3. $\frac{5}{8} \cdot \frac{3}{7}$

4. $\frac{1}{4} \cdot \frac{2}{3} \cdot \frac{1}{2}$

Learning Goals

- Determine the probability of two or more independent events.
- Determine the probability of two or more dependent events.

Key Terms

- compound event
- Rule of Compound Probability involving *and*
- conditional probability

You have used tree diagrams and organized lists to determine the sample space and calculate the probability of events. How can you calculate the probability of compound events that are combined by the word *and* using a mathematical rule?

GETTING STARTED

Frundaes!

Stan's Frozen Yogurt Shop offers frundaes, which are frozen yogurt sundaes. The shop advertises different frundae options for customers.

BUILD YOUR OWN FRUNDAE

Choose one yogurt flavor and one topping.

Frozen Yogurt Flavors	**Toppings**
vanilla	nuts
chocolate	sprinkles
strawberry	granola
peach	

1. **Write the sample space of different frundae options consisting one yogurt flavor and one topping using an organized list.**

2. **How many different frundaes can be created by first selecting one frozen yogurt flavor and then one topping?**

Alec and Ella each order a single flavor cone with no toppings.

3. **Write an organized list for the sample space of the single flavor cones that Alec and Ella could buy. Describe the sample space.**

A Triple-Decker Froyanza is a frozen yogurt cone with three servings of yogurt. Tamara orders a Triple-Decker Froyanza with one serving of chocolate, one serving of vanilla, and one serving of strawberry frozen yogurt.

a. Write an organized list for the sample space that represents the order in which the server could stack the three servings of frozen yogurt on Tamara's cone.

b. How many different stacking orders are possible for the frozen yogurt flavors of Tamara's Triple-Decker Froyanza? Explain how you determined your answer.

Compare and contrast the sample spaces from Questions 1, 3, and 4.

a. How are the sample spaces alike?

b. How is Question 1 and its sample space different from Question 3 and its sample space?

c. How is Question 4 and its sample space different from Questions 1 and 3 and their sample spaces?

ACTIVITY
2.1

Exploring Compound Events with *And*

Frozen Yogurt Flavors
vanilla
chocolate
strawberry
peach

Toppings
nuts
sprinkles
granola

A **compound event** is an event that consists of two or more events.

1. **Consider the different ordering situations of frozen yogurt fro[m] the Getting Started.**

   a. **Which situations represent compound events? Explain your reasoning.**

   b. **Describe the events that make up the compound event in ordering a frundae. Then list the outcomes for each event.**

Suppose you decide to build your next frundae by randomly selecting a yogurt flavor and topping.

How can you use the sample spaces you created to determine each probability?

2. **What is the probability of choosing a frundae that does not hav[e] chocolate yogurt and does have a granola topping?**

   a. **Let *A* represent the event of choosing a flavor that is not chocolate. What is *P*(*A*), the probability of choosing a flavor that is not chocolate?**

   b. **Let *B* represent the event of choosing granola as a topping. What is *P*(*B*), the probability of choosing granola as a topping?**

c. What is *P*(*A* and *B*), the probability of choosing a flavor other than chocolate that has granola as a topping? Explain how you determined your answer.

P(*A* and *B*) can be written as *P*($A \cap B$), where $A \cap B$ represents an intersection of Events *A* and *B*. The intersection of Events *A* and *B* is the set of all of the outcomes where both Event *A* and Event *B* occur.

What is the probability of choosing a frundae with chocolate flavored yogurt and a topping that is not granola?

a. Let *A* represent the event of choosing a frundae with chocolate flavored yogurt. What is *P*(*A*), the probability of choosing a frundae with chocolate flavored yogurt?

b. Let *B* represent the event of choosing a topping that is not granola. What is *P*(*B*), the probability of choosing a topping that is not granola?

c. What is *P*(*A* and *B*), the probability of choosing a frundae with chocolate flavored yogurt and a topping that is not granola? Explain how you determined your answer.

NOTES

4. **Compare the probabilities you determined in Questions 2 and 3. What mathematical relationship exists between *P*(*A*), *P*(*B*), and *P*(*A* and *B*)?**

5. **Why do you think that the probability of both events occurring is less than the probability of either event occurring by itself?**

6. **Why do you think multiplication is performed in compound probability problems using the word *and*?**

ACTIVITY

2.2

Calculating Compound Probabilities with *And*

ou just calculated probabilities for a compound event comprised of two vents. Now, let's consider a compound event comprised of more than vo events.

Suppose you flip 3 coins and record the result of each flip.

a. What is the probability that all 3 coins land heads up?

b. What is the probability that the first 2 coins land heads up and the third coin lands tails up?

c. What is the probability of the second coin landing tails up? Explain how you determined your answer.

d. What is the probability of flipping heads on the first coin and tails on the third coin? Explain how you determined your answer.

Some calculators display a maximum of 10 digits. Very large numbers are often displayed using scientific notation.

2. **Suppose you flip 50 coins. What is the probability of flipping heads on the first and second coins? Derrick and Sarina each answered this question differently.**

> **Derrick**
>
> To calculate the number of total possible outcomes, I multiply 2 by itself 50 times, which is 2^{50}, or 1,125,899,906,842,624. There is 1 desired outcome for each of the first 2 coins, or 1×1. For the other 48 coins, there are 2 desired outcomes, because they can be heads or tails. This is 2^{48}. So, the number of desired outcomes is $1 \times 1 \times 2^{48}$, or 281,474,976,710,656.
>
> The probability of flipping heads on the first and second coins, then, is
> $\frac{281{,}474{,}976{,}710{,}656}{1{,}125{,}899{,}906{,}842{,}624} = \frac{2^{48}}{2^{50}} = \frac{1}{2^2} = \frac{1}{4}$.

> **Sarina**
>
> I only need to do calculations with the probabilities for the first 2 coins because the probabilities for the other 48 coins are each $\frac{2}{2}$, or 1.
>
> The probability of flipping heads on the first two of 50 coins is $\frac{1}{2} \times \frac{1}{2}$, or $\frac{1}{4}$.

Which strategy is more efficient? Why?

If Events A and B are independent, does the occurrence of Event A affect the probability of the occurrence of Event B?

The **Rule of Compound Probability involving *and*** states: "If Event A and Event B are independent events, then the probability that Event A happens and Event B happens is the product of the probability that Event A happens and the probability that Event B happens, given that Event A has happened."

$$P(A \text{ and } B) = P(A) \cdot P(B)$$

ACTIVITY

2.3

Dependent Events with *And*

You have 2 red, 1 blue, and 3 green socks in a drawer.

You can use small numbers called subscripts to indicate the different red or green socks. For example, R_1 and R_2 can represent the two red socks.

Suppose you reach into the drawer without looking and choose a sock, replace it, and then choose another sock. You choose a total of 2 socks.

1. Use this information to answer each question.

a. Does the action "choosing the first sock" affect the outcomes of "choosing the second sock"? If so, how? Explain your reasoning.

b. Use a tree diagram or organized list to represent the sample space for this situation.

c. How can you use the Counting Principle to determine the total number of possible outcomes? Explain your reasoning.

d. Calculate the probability of choosing:

- **A blue sock and then a red sock.**

- **A red sock and then a sock that is not blue.**

- **Two socks with the first sock being green.**

How can a tree diagram or organized list be used to check your answers?

Suppose you reach into the drawer without looking and choose a sock, do not replace it, and then choose another sock. You choose a total of 2 socks. Remember, there are 2 red, 1 blue, and 3 green socks in a drawer.

2. Use this information to answer the questions.

a. Does the action "choosing the first sock" affect the outcomes of "choosing the second sock"? If so, how? Explain your reasoning.

b. Use a diagram or organized list to represent the sample space for this situation.

c. How can you use the Counting Principle to determine the tota[l] number of possible outcomes? Explain your reasoning.

d. Calculate the probability of choosing:

- **A blue sock and then a red sock.**

- **A red sock and then a sock that is not blue.**

- **Two socks with the first sock being green.**

3. What's different about the probability calculations in Question 1[,] part (d) and Question 2, part (d)?

vent A and Event B are dependent, then the probability that Event A ppens and Event B happens is the product of the probability that nt A happens and the probability that Event B happens, given that nt A has already occurred.

vents A and B are dependent, then the probability of Event B occurring ffected by the occurrence of the first event. Therefore, the notation the Rule of Compound Probability involving *and* now states that and $B) = P(A) \cdot P(B|A)$.

Conditional probability is the probability of an event which assumes the occurrence of some other event. $P(B|A)$ means "the probability of the occurrence of Event B given the occurrence of Event A."

Two red socks, 1 blue sock, and 3 green socks are in a drawer. One sock is randomly chosen without replacing it in the drawer, then a second sock is randomly chosen. What is the probability that the second sock is red?

Juan explained his solution method.

Juan

We want the second sock to be red, but the first sock can be red or not red. The desired outcomes are "red and red" or "not red and red."

There are two cases that you should consider, depending on whether the first sock was red or not.

Calculate the probability of choosing a red sock second.

Two red socks, 1 blue sock, and 3 green socks are in a drawer. One sock is randomly chosen without replacing it in the drawer, and then a second sock is randomly chosen. Use Juan's method to answer each question.

a. What is the probability that the second sock is blue? Explain your reasoning.

b. What is the probability that the second sock is green? Explain your reasoning.

NOTES

TALK the TALK

That Depends

Consider the situations that you analyzed in this lesson.

1. **Compare the methods you used to determine the compound probability of two independent events both occurring and the compound probability of two dependent events both occurring. Describe the similarities and differences between the methods.**

2. **What rules could you write to determine the compound probability of three or more independent events? Three or more dependent events? Include examples to support your conclusions.**

Assignment

Vrite

escribe the difference between the Rule Compound Probability involving *and* for dependent and dependent events in your wn words.

Remember

A compound event is an event that consists of two or more events. If the events are combined by the word *and*, you can multiply the probability of each event to determine the compound probability.

ractice

Suppose a player chooses cards from the two decks shown. The subsets of cards are labeled C1 to C7 (see figure).

a. A player chooses one card from Deck A and one card from Deck B.
What is the probability that the player will choose cards C1 and C4?

b. A player chooses one card from Deck A and replaces it. Then the next player chooses one card from Deck A. What is the probability that both players will choose a C2 card?

c. A player chooses two cards at the same time from Deck B. What is the probability that the player will choose two C5 cards?

d. A player chooses one card from Deck A and one card from Deck B. What is the probability of not choosing a C1 card from Deck A and the probability of not choosing a C7 card from Deck B?

e. A player chooses one card from Deck A and then, without replacing it, chooses another card from Deck A. What is the probability that the first card will be a C2 and the second card will not be a C2?

Deck A

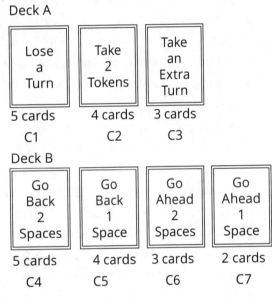

Lose a Turn	Take 2 Tokens	Take an Extra Turn
5 cards	4 cards	3 cards
C1	C2	C3

Deck B

Go Back 2 Spaces	Go Back 1 Space	Go Ahead 2 Spaces	Go Ahead 1 Space
5 cards	4 cards	3 cards	2 cards
C4	C5	C6	C7

2. The board game includes both the spinner and the set of tokens shown in the figure.

a. A player spins the spinner once and then randomly chooses a token. What is the probability that the spinner will land on a 4 and the player will choose a cube token?

b. A player spins the spinner twice. What is the probability that the second spin will land on a 3?

c. A player chooses a token from the set, replaces it, and then chooses another token from the set. What is the probability that the first token chosen will be a cube and the second will be a disk?

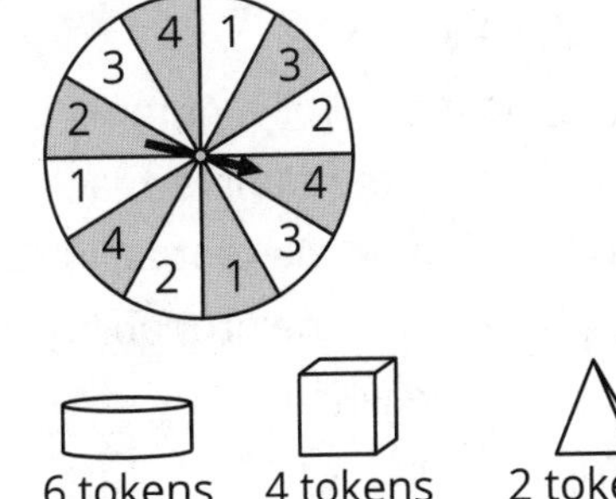

d. A player chooses two tokens from the set at the same time. What is the probability that both will be pyramids?

e. A player spins the spinner once and then randomly chooses a token. What is the probability that the spinner will not land on a 3 and the player will choose a disk token?

f. A player randomly chooses three tokens at once from the set. What is the probability that the first two tokens are cubes?

Stretch

1. A batch of 100 calculators are manufactured in a day on a factory line. There are 5 calculators that are defective in the batch. On another line, a batch of 5000 computers are manufactured. There are 50 computers that are defective in the batch. On the third line, a batch of 1000 fitness watches are manufactured. There are 25 watches that are defective in the batch.
   a. A quality control inspector randomly picks a calculator, a computer, and a fitness watch from the three batches. What is the probability all of them are defective?
   b. A quality control inspector randomly picks 3 calculators from the batch without replacing any of them. What is the probability the first is defective and the second two are not defective?
   c. A quality control inspector randomly picks 2 calculators, 1 computer, and 2 watches without replacing any of them. What is the probability none of the products are defective?
2. Tushar has a bag of candy that contains 4 lollipops, 8 chocolate bars, and 5 pieces of taffy.
   a. If Tushar randomly picks a piece of candy, what is the probability it is a lollipop?
   b. If Tushar randomly picks a piece of candy, what is the probability it is a chocolate bar?
   c. If Tushar randomly picks a piece of candy, what is the probability it is a lollipop or a chocolate bar?
   d. What is the mathematical relationship between the answers to parts (a), (b), and (c)?

Review

1. Suppose you roll a number cube once. The number cube is numbered 1 through 10.
   a. Identify the sample space.
   b. Determine the probability of rolling an odd number, *P*(odd).
   c. Determine the probability of rolling a number that is not a multiple of 5, *P*(not a multiple of 5).
2. Determine whether $4x^2 + 4y^2 - 16x - 24y + 16 = 0$ represents a circle. If so, describe the location of the center and radius.
3. Write an equation in standard form for a parabola with a vertex of $(-2, 3)$ and a focus of $(-2, 1)$. Then graph and label the parabola.
4. Write the equation for the function that results when the basic function $f(x) = x^2$ is translated up four units and is vertically stretched by a factor of 3.
5. Determine the solutions for $x^2 + 13x - 20 = 0$.

3

Or?

Compound Probability with *Or*

Warm Up

Determine the value of each expression.

1. $\frac{1}{2} + \frac{1}{3} - \frac{1}{4}$
2. $\frac{1}{6} + \frac{3}{4} - \frac{2}{5}$
3. $\frac{2}{3} + \frac{1}{8} - \frac{1}{2}$

Learning Goals

- Determine the probability of one or another independent event.
- Determine the probability of one or another dependent event.

Key Term

- Addition Rule for Probability

You have determined the probability of compound events related by the word *and*. How do the methods for determining the probability of compound events related by the word *or* compare?

GETTING STARTED

Making Heads or Tails of It

Suppose you flip two coins. What is the probability of the first coin landir
heads up or the second coin landing tails up?

1. Describe the events in this probability situation.

2. Complete the table to construct the sample space for this situatic

		Second Coin	
		H	T
First Coin	H		
	T		

a. Draw a circle around the outcomes that match the first ever

b. Draw a rectangle around the outcomes that match the second event.

3. How can you describe the outcome that is circled and has a rectangle around it in the sample space?

Kirk and Damon described the probability of a heads up result for the first coin or a tails up result for the second coin.

irk

circled 2 outcomes and drew a ectangle around 2 outcomes, and here are 4 possible outcomes. So, he probability of flipping a heads on the first coin or a tails on the second is

$\frac{2+2}{4} = \frac{4}{4} = 1.$

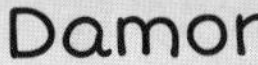

Damon

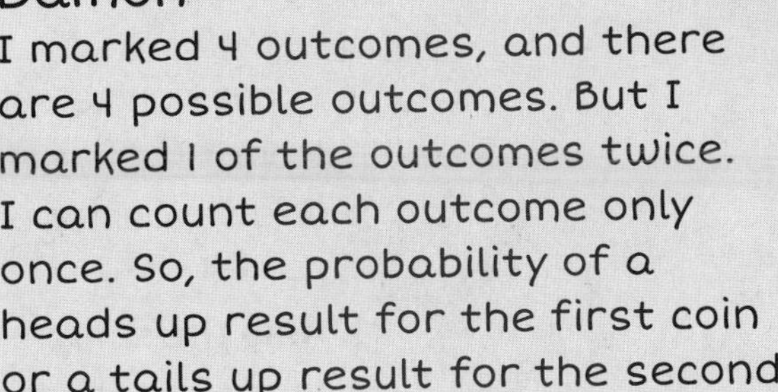

I marked 4 outcomes, and there are 4 possible outcomes. But I marked 1 of the outcomes twice. I can count each outcome only once. So, the probability of a heads up result for the first coin or a tails up result for the second coin is $\frac{3}{4}$.

Explain in your own words why Damon is correct and Kirk is incorrect.

ACTIVITY 3.1	Exploring Compound Events with *Or*

In a compound event that is related by the word *or*, there can be possible outcomes that are in the sample space for each event. These outcomes should be counted only once when determining the compound probability

1. **Use the sample space and what you know about probability to answer each question.**

   a. **What is the probability of a heads up result for flipping the first coin, *P*(*A*)?**

   b. **What is the probability of a tails up result for flipping the second coin, *P*(*B*)?**

   c. **What is the probability of a heads up result for the first coin flip AND a tails up result for the second coin flip, *P*(*A* and *B*)?**

   d. **What is the probability of a heads up result for the first coin flip OR a tails up result for the second coin flip *P*(*A* or *B*)?**

2. **Create a formula you could use to relate the probability of each event by itself, *P*(*A*), *P*(*B*), and the probability of the first event O the second event *P*(*A* or *B*). Explain why your formula works.**

ACTIVITY 3.2

Calculating Compound Probabilities with *Or*

new holiday—Probability Day—is going to be celebrated at your school. may be celebrated on any of the first 3 days of any month. The problem ow is to choose which day it will fall on. Of course, the day will be elected at random. First the month will be selected and then the day.

. How many dates for Probability Day are in the sample space? Explain how you determined the answer.

. Construct a model to represent the sample space for this situation.

. Determine the probability that each day is randomly chosen. Explain your reasoning.

a. January 3rd

b. May 2nd

c. Any specific day and month

The summer months are June, July, and August.

4. **Study the sample space. Let $P(A)$ represent the probability of randomly choosing a summer month, and let $P(B)$ represent th probability of randomly choosing the first day of the month.**

   a. **Calculate $P(A)$.**

   b. **Calculate $P(B)$.**

   c. **Calculate $P(A \text{ and } B)$.**

   d. **Calculate $P(A \text{ or } B)$. Use the organized list you created to explain your answer.**

$P(A \text{ or } B)$ is also known as $P(A \cup B)$, where $A \cup B$ represents a union of Events A and B. The union of Events A and B is the set all of the outcomes where Event A or Event B occurs.

5. **Use your answers from Question 4. Describe how you can calculate the probability of randomly choosing a summer mont or the first day of a month without using a tree diagram or organized list.**

The **Addition Rule for Probability** states: "The probability that Event *A* occurs or Event *B* occurs is the probability that Event *A* occurs plus the probability that Event *B* occurs minus the probability that both *A* and *B* occur."

$$P(A \text{ or } B) = P(A) + P(B) - P(A \text{ and } B)$$

What is the probability of randomly choosing a summer month or a winter month?

The winter months are December, January, and February.

7. Jereld says that because the summer month outcomes and the winter month outcomes are disjoint sets, the probability that one event or the other occurs is just the sum of the probabilities. It's not necessary to subtract the probability of both events. Is Jereld correct? Explain why or why not.

Remember:

Disjoint sets are sets with no outcomes in common.

ACTIVITY

3.3 Dependent Events with *Or*

You have seen that you can use the Addition Rule for Probability to determine the probability that one or another of two independent events occurs. Can you also use this rule to determine the probability of one or another of two dependent events occurring? Let's find out!

Suppose six cards are taken from a set of cards and that 3 of the cards ha a yellow dot on the back, 1 of the cards has a purple dot on the back, and 2 of the cards have a blue dot on the back. You are asked to randomly select two cards, one at a time.

1. **Does the action "choosing the first card" affect the action of "choosing the second card"? If so, how? Explain your reasoning.**

2. **Write an organized list to represent the sample space for this situation.**

3. **Use the sample space to determine the probability of randomly choosing a yellow card first or a blue card second.**

   a. **Describe the events in this probability situation.**

b. Draw a circle around the outcomes that match the first event and a rectangle around the outcomes that match the second event. How can you describe the outcomes that are circled and have a rectangle around them in the sample space?

c. What is the probability of randomly choosing a yellow card first, *P*(*A*)?

If only the second event is specified, you can consider it as an independent event and determine its probability without considering the first event.

d. What is the probability of randomly choosing a blue card second, *P*(*B*)?

e. What is the probability of randomly choosing a yellow card first AND a blue card second, *P*(*A* and *B*)?

f. What is the probability of randomly choosing a yellow card first OR a blue card second, *P*(*A* or *B*)?

4. **Beth wrote an explanation for randomly choosing a blue card second. Explain why Beth's reasoning is incorrect.**

> **Beth**
>
> Because the actions are dependent in this problem, the probability of choosing a blue card second is $\frac{2}{5}$. There are 5 cards left after the first pick, and 2 of the cards left are blue.

5. **Pedro wrote an explanation for randomly choosing a yellow card first and a blue card second. Explain why Pedro's reasoning is incorrect.**

> **Pedro**
>
> In this problem, the probability of choosing a yellow card first is $\frac{1}{2}$, and the probability of choosing a blue card second is $\frac{1}{3}$. So, the probability of choosing both a yellow card first and a blue card second is $\frac{1}{2} \times \frac{1}{3} = \frac{1}{6}$.

6. Calculate the probability of randomly choosing a yellow card first or a blue card second, *P*(*A* or *B*), using the Addition Rule. Compare this to your answer in Question 3, part (f). What do you notice?

7. Determine the probability of choosing a yellow card first or a yellow card second using the Addition Rule. Verify your answer using the sample space in Question 2.

Does the Addition Rule apply to independent events as well as dependent events? Explain your reasoning.

NOTES

TALK the TALK

Don't Compound the Problem

In this lesson and the previous lesson, you investigated the probabilitie of different kinds of compound events.

1. Complete the graphic organizer to record examples of the types of compound events you have studied. For each type of compound event, describe the methods you used to determine the probability.

COMPOUND EVENTS

Independent Events
$P(A \text{ and } B)$

Scenario:

Question:

Method:

Independent Events
$P(A \text{ or } B)$

Scenario:

Question:

Method:

Dependent Events
$P(A \text{ and } B)$

Scenario:

Question:

Method:

Dependent Events
$P(A \text{ or } B)$

Scenario:

Question:

Method:

Assignment

/rite

In symbols, what is the Addition Rule for Probability?

When should you use the Addition Rule for Probability?

Remember

If two compound events are combined by the word *or*, you can add the probabilities of each event occurring separately and subtract the probability of both events occurring.

ractice

Two decks of cards are used for a game.

a. A player chooses one card from Deck A and one card from Deck B. What is the probability that the player will choose a C2 card from the first deck or a C6 card from the second deck?

b. A player chooses one card from Deck A and one card from Deck B. What is the probability that the player will choose a C3 card from the first deck or a C5 card from the second deck?

c. A player chooses two cards from Deck A. What is the probability that the player will choose a C1 card first or a C2 card second?

d. A player chooses two cards from Deck B. What is the probability that the player will choose a C5 card first or a C4 card second?

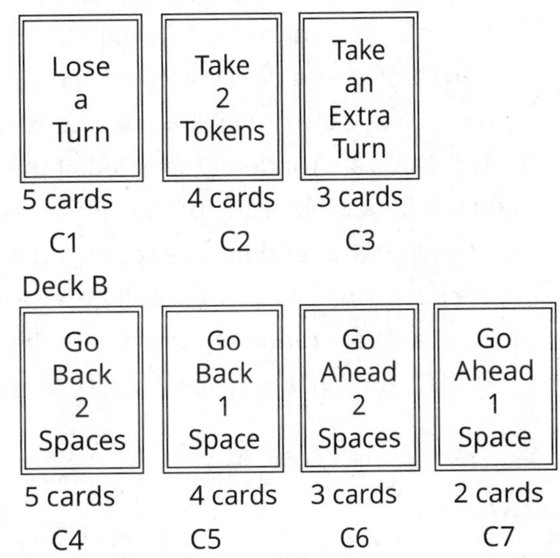

Consider the spinner and the set of tokens shown in the figure.

a. A player spins the spinner one time and then randomly chooses a token. What is the probability that the spinner will land on a 2 or the player will choose a pyramid?

b. A player spins the spinner two times. What is the probability that the spinner will land on a number greater than 1 the first time or on a number greater than 2 the second time?

c. A player spins the spinner one time and then randomly chooses a token. What is the probability that the spinner will not land on a 2 or the player will not choose a disk?

d. A player spins the spinner two times. What is the probability that the spinner will land on a 1 the first time or on a 4 the second time?

e. A player spins the spinner one time and then randomly chooses a token. What is the probability that the spinner will land on a 2 or the player will choose a cube?

Stretch

1. Two decks of cards are used for a game.
   a. A player chooses one card from Deck A and one card from Deck B. Write an organized list to represent the sample space in this situation.
   b. Use the sample space to determine the probability that a Queen is selected from Deck A or a 10 is selected from Deck B.
   c. Use the Addition Rule for Probability to determine the probability that a Queen is selected from Deck A or a 10 is selected from Deck B. Show your work.

Deck A

K	Q	J
3 cards	2 cards	1 ca

Deck B

10	9
3 cards	2 cards

2. A deck of cards contains only face cards. There are four kings, four queens, and four jacks.
   a. A card is randomly selected. What is the probability the card is a queen?
   b. Two cards are randomly selected. If the first card selected is a queen and the card is replaced in the deck, what is the probability the second card is a queen?
   c. Two cards are randomly selected. If the first card selected is a queen and the card is not replacec in the deck, what is the probability the second card is a queen?
   d. Two cards are randomly selected. If the first card selected is a queen and the card is replaced in the deck, what is the probability the second card is a king?
   e. Two cards are randomly selected. If the first card selected is a queen and the card is not replaced in the deck, what is the probability the second card is a king?

Review

1. A board game includes a spinner and a deck of cards. A player spins the spinner once and then randomly chooses a card. What is the probability that the spinner will land on a 3 and the player will choose a card that says, "Go Back 1 Space"?

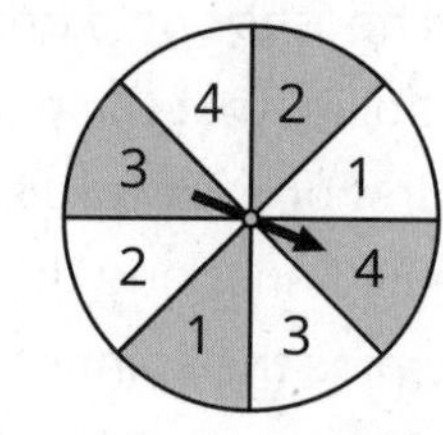

PICK A CARD	LOSE A TURN	GO BACK 1 SPACE	GO AHEAD 1 SPAC
6 cards	4 cards	3 cards	2 card

2. A school district has two schools, School A and School B. The drawing shows the number of students in each class that had perfect attendance last year. The superintendent of the schools randomly chooses two students from School B. What is the probability that both students are from Class 6?

School A

Class 1	Class 2	Class 3
7 students	5 students	4 students

School B

Class 4	Class 5	Class 6	Class 7
8 students	6 students	3 students	2 student

Given $\sin \theta = -\frac{5}{8}$ in Quadrant III, determine $\cos \theta$ and $\tan \theta$.

Given the equation $x = 2(y + 1)^2 - 4$. Determine the value of p, the coordinates of the vertex and focus, and the equations for the axis of symmetry and directrix. Then graph the parabola and describe the concavity.

Determine the solution(s) for each equation.

a. $2w^2 + 7w + 6 = 0$

b. $x^2 - 8x - 9 = 0$

4

And, Or, and More!

Calculating Compound Probability

Warm Up

The local diner serves five different kinds of pie: apple, blueberry, lemon, rhubarb, and peach.

They serve four flavors of ice cream: vanilla, strawberry, chocolate, and tangerine.

1. What is the probability of a customer ordering peach pie and ordering vanilla ice cream?

2. What is the probability of a customer ordering peach pie or ordering vanilla ice cream?

Learning Goals

- Calculate compound probabilities with and without replacement.
- Interpret probabilities in terms of real-world situations.

You have calculated compound probabilities for compound events combined by the word *and* and the word *or*. How can you determine when compound events are independent or dependent events in order to correctly calculate compound probabilities?

GETTING STARTED

It's All in the Cards

You will often see the phrases "with replacement" and "without replacemer in probability problems. These phrases refer to whether or not the total sample space changes from the first to the last event.

For example, if you draw a marble from a bag, record the color, and then replace the marble, the sample space for the next event remains the sam If you do not replace it, then the sample space decreases.

A standard deck of playing cards contains 52 cards. There are 4 suits: spad clubs, hearts, and diamonds. Each suit contains 13 cards: an ace, the numb 2–10, and three face cards, which are the Jack, Queen, and King.

A pair is 2 cards with the same number or face. Two aces is an example o pair. A three of a kind is 3 cards with the same number or face. Three Jack is an example of a three of a kind.

1. **Calculate each of the following probabilities for randomly drawin 2 cards from a standard deck of playing cards, one at a time, *with* replacement. Explain your reasoning.**

   a. **An ace first and a ten second**

   b. **An ace first or a ten second**

   c. **Two diamonds**

   d. **Any pair**

Calculate each probability for drawing 2 cards, one at a time, *without* replacement.

a. An ace first and a ten second

b. An ace first or a ten second

c. Two diamonds

d. Any pair

ACTIVITY **4.1**

More Than Two Compound Events

You can use the same methods to calculate the probabilities for more th
two compound events.

1. **Calculate each of the following probabilities for drawing 3 card one at a time, *with* replacement.**

   a. **Three of a kind**

   b. **Three Kings**

Calculate each of the following probabilities for drawing 3 cards, one at a time, *without* replacement.

a. Three of a kind

b. Three Kings

What kinds of events generally correspond to situations "with replacement"? "Without replacement"? Why?

ACTIVITY

4.2

Compound Events Without Repetition

A homeowner's association has 25 members. The association needs to establish a three-member committee.

You can assume that, in this situation, every member of the homeowner's association has a different first name.

1. **Calculate the probability that Bill, George, and Rio are random selected to serve on the committee.**

2. **Calculate the probability that Bill is randomly selected as president, George as vice president, and Rio as treasurer.**

3. **What is the difference between the situations in Questions 1 and**

Calculate the probability of five particular members being chosen to serve on a five member committee.

Calculate the probability of a particular member of the homeowner's association being chosen to serve as one of five officers.

ACTIVITY
4.3 *And or Or*

The menu at a local restaurant offers the items shown. A dinner consists of one selection from each category.

Appetizers: Shrimp, Veggies, Avocado Dip, Soup, Stuffed Mushrooms
Salads: Garden, Caesar, Pasta, House
Entrées: Steak, Pizza, Ravioli, Meatloaf, Chicken, Flounder, Spaghetti, Pork, Ham, Shrimp
Desserts: Ice Cream, Cookies, Fruit, Chocolate Cake, Pie, Cheese Cake, Sorbet

1. **How many different dinners exist?**

2. **What is the probability that a patron selects chicken?**

3. **What is the probability that a patron selects meatloaf and chocolate cake?**

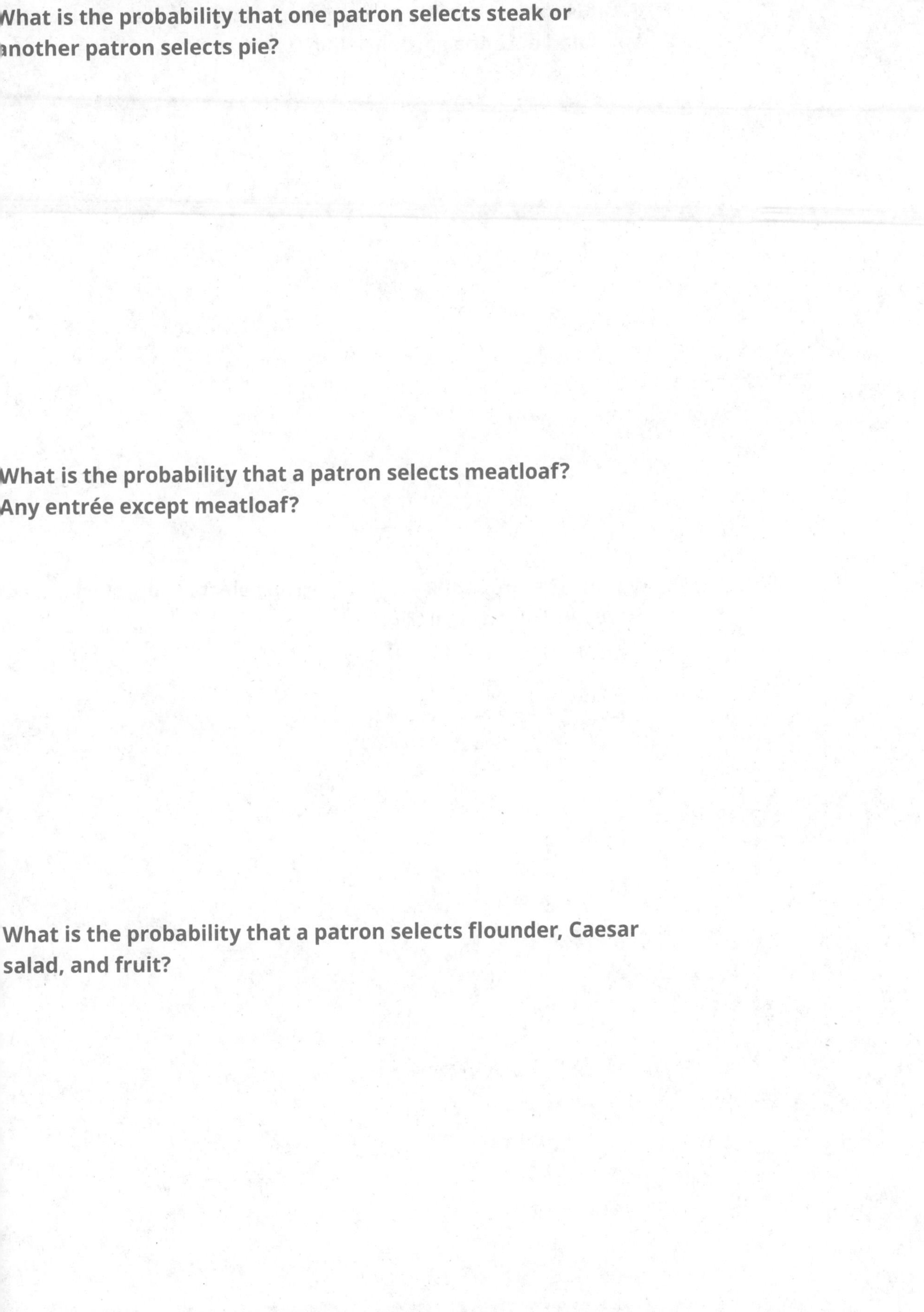

What is the probability that one patron selects steak or another patron selects pie?

What is the probability that a patron selects meatloaf? Any entrée except meatloaf?

What is the probability that a patron selects flounder, Caesar salad, and fruit?

7. **What is the probability that a patron selects pizza, cookies, an any salad except a garden salad?**

8. **What is the probability that a patron selects soup, chicken, any salad, and any dessert?**

ALK the TALK

o You Get It?

pack of 200 trivia cards is divided evenly into five categories: sports, usic, movies, books, and occupations.

Suppose you randomly choose one card. What is the probability of selecting a card in the sports category?

. Suppose you randomly choose two cards with replacement. What is the probability of choosing two cards in the sports category?

NOTES

NOTES

3. Suppose you choose three cards without replacement. What is the probability of drawing three cards in the sports category?

Assignment

Vrite

escribe in your own words the effects of ne phrases "with replacement" and "without eplacement" on sample space in a compound robability problem.

Remember

Situations "with replacement" generally involve independent events. In this type of situation, the first event does not affect subsequent events. Situations "without replacement" generally involve dependent events. In this type of situation, the first event affects each subsequent event.

Practice

. A game includes a deck of cards with an animal picture on each card. The table shows the numbers of each type of card. Suppose each time a card is chosen, the card is replaced before another card is chosen.

Number of Cards	Animal on Card
8	lion
6	giraffe
10	monkey
12	elephant
4	panda bear

a. A child draws out two cards. What is the probability that the first card will have a monkey on it and the second card will have an elephant on it?

b. A child draws out two cards. What is the probability that the first card will have a lion on it or the second card will have a giraffe on it?

c. A child draws out two cards. What is the probability that the second card will have a panda bear on it?

d. A child draws out three cards. What is the probability that the first card will have a lion on it, and the third will have a monkey on it?

e. A child draws out five cards. What is the probability that they will all have a different animal on them?

. Consider the same game and deck of cards from Question 1. This time when a card is chosen, it is not replaced in the deck.

a. A child draws out two cards. What is the probability that the first card will have an elephant on it and the second card will have a lion on it?

b. A child draws out two cards. What is the probability that the first card will have a monkey on it or the second card will have a panda bear on it?

c. A child draws out three cards. What is the probability that the second card will have a lion on it?

d. A child draws out two cards. What is the probability that the first card will have a panda bear on it or the second card will have a giraffe on it?

e. A child draws out three cards. What is the probability that the second and third cards will display elephants?

f. A child draws out two cards. What is the probability that the first card will have a lion on it or the second card will have a monkey on it?

Stretch

1. A game includes a deck of cards with a color on each card. The table shows the numbers of each type of card. When a card is chosen, it is not replaced in the deck.
   a. A player draws out ten cards. What is the probability that all the cards are red except the last card, which is teal?
   b. A player draws out five cards. What is the probability that none of the cards are orange?

Number of Cards	Color on Card
15	red
12	yellow
10	green
14	blue
16	orange
15	purple
20	teal

Review

1. Consider the spinner and the set of cards shown in the figure. A player spins the spinner one time and then randomly chooses a card. What is the probability that the spinner will land on the letter B or the player will choose a blue card?

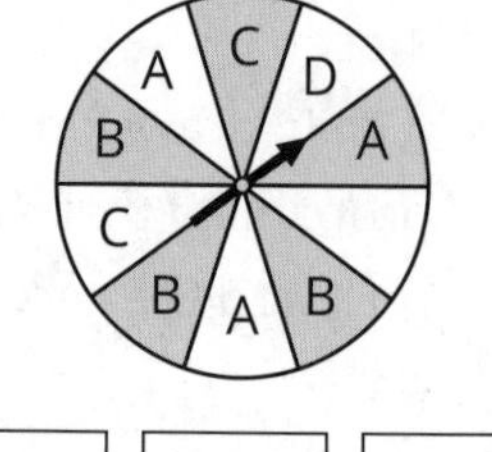

red	blue	green
5 cards	4 cards	3 cards

2. Two bags of marbles with the given contents are used for a game.
   Bag A: 6 red, 5 blue, 4 white
   Bag B: 6 green, 5 orange, 4 purple, 3 black
   A player chooses two marbles from Bag B. What is the probability that the player will choose an orange marble first or a black marble second?
3. Consider circle P with its center point located at $(-2, -3)$ with a radius of $3\sqrt{5}$ units as shown.
   a. Verify that point $H(-8, 0)$ lies on circle P.
   b. Use symmetry to determine three more points on circle P.

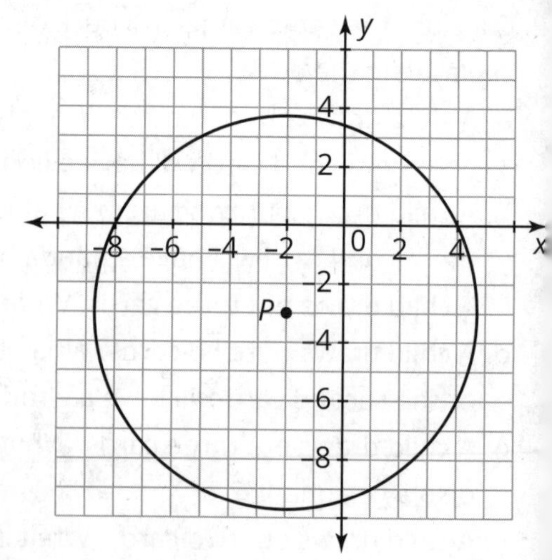

4. Determine whether each quadratic equation is in factored, general or vertex form.
   a. $y = -2(x - 4)(x + 5)$
   b. $y = 3(x + 1)^2 - 10$

ndependence and Conditional Probability Summary

KEY TERMS

- outcome
- sample space
- event
- probability
- probability model
- uniform probability model
- non-uniform probability model
- complement of an event
- tree diagram
- organized list
- set
- element
- disjoint sets
- intersecting sets
- union of sets
- independent events
- dependent events
- Counting Principle
- compound event
- Rule of Compound Probability involving *and*
- conditional probability
- Addition Rule for Probability

LESSON 1

What Are the Chances?

n **outcome** is a result of an experiment. The **sample space** is the set of all the possible outcomes of an experiment. An **event** is an outcome or set of outcomes in a sample space.

he **probability** of an event is the ratio of the number of desired outcomes to the total number of ossible outcomes. The probability of event A is $P(A) = \frac{\text{desired outcomes}}{\text{possible outcomes}}$.

t is often helpful to construct a model when analyzing situations involving probability. A **probability nodel** lists the possible outcomes and the probability for each outcome.

In a probability model, the sum of the probabilities must equal 1. In a **uniform probability mod** the probabilities for each outcome are equal. When the probabilities of the outcomes are not all equal, the model is a **non-uniform probability model**.

For example, consider the spinner shown. For the experiment of spinning the spinner, the numbers on the sections of the spinner are the outcomes. The sample space of spinning the spinner is {1, 2, 3, 4}. The probability of spinning the number 1 is $P(1) = \frac{3}{12} = \frac{1}{4}$. The uniform probability model shows the probability of each outcome.

Outcomes	1	2	3	4
Probability	$\frac{1}{4}$	$\frac{1}{4}$	$\frac{1}{4}$	$\frac{1}{4}$

The **complement of an event** is an event that contains all the outcomes in the sample space th are not outcomes in the event. If E is an event, then the complement of E is often denoted as $\overline{E}$ or

For example, the probability of rolling a 1 or a 2 on a six-side number cube is $P(1, 2) = \frac{1}{3}$. The complement of rolling a 1 or a 2 on a six-sided number cube is rolling a 3, 4, 5, or 6, so $P(1, 2^c) = \frac{2}{3}$.

A **tree diagram** is a visual model for determining the sample space of multiple events. For examp consider the following menu.

For example, the sample space for all of the possible types of pizza specials that can be made at a pizzeria is be modeled by the tree diagram shown.

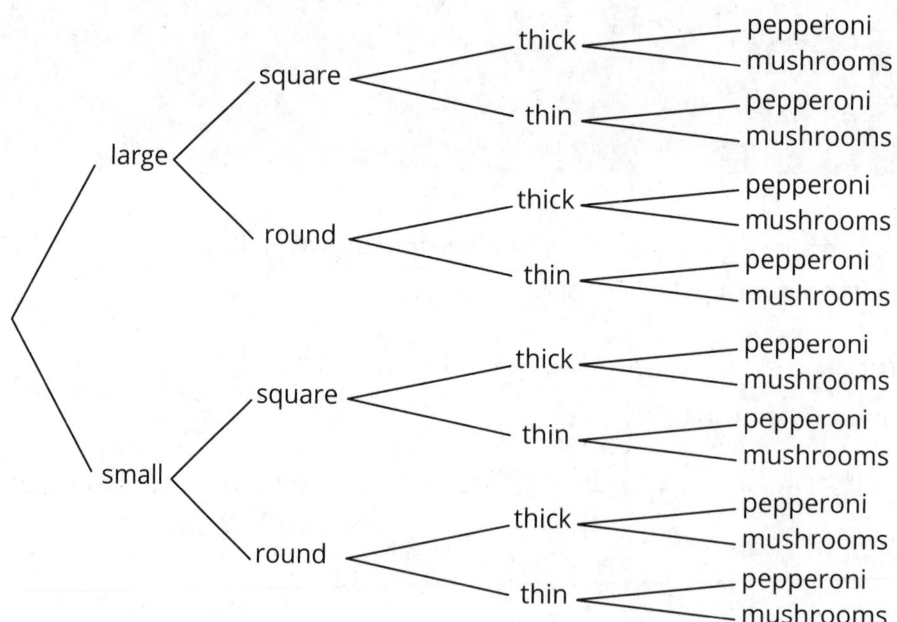

ı **organized list** is a visual model for determining the sample space of events. You can abbreviate ıe names of the outcomes as long as a key is provided.

ɔr example, an organized list for the pizza tree diagram could use the abbreviation key: lg-large, n-small, sq-square, ro-round, thk-thick, thn-thin, pepp-pepperoni, mush-mushroom. The resulting st would be as follows:

_g-sq-thk-pepp	Lg-ro-thk-pepp	Sm-sq-thk-pepp	Sm-ro-thk-pepp
_g-sq-thk-mush	Lg-ro-thk-mush	Sm-sq-thk-mush	Sm-ro-thk-mush
_g-sq-thn-pepp	Lg-ro-thn-pepp	Sm-sq-thn-pepp	Sm-ro-thn-pepp
_g-sq-thn-mush	Lg-ro-thn-mush	Sm-sq-thn-mush	Sm-ro-thn-mush

set is a collection of items. If *x* is a member of set *B*, then *x* is an **element** of set *B*. Two or ıore sets are **disjoint sets** if they do not have any common elements. Two or more sets are **ıtersecting sets** if they do have common elements. The **union of sets** is a set formed by ombining all the members of the sets. A member may be listed only once.

or example, consider the following sets.

isjoint Sets:
et *N* represent the set of 9th grade students. Let *T* represent the set of 10th grade students. The et of 9th grade students and the set of 10th grade students are disjoint because the two sets do ot have any common elements. Any student can be in one grade only.

ntersecting Sets:
et *V* represent the set of students who are on the girls' volleyball team. Let *M* represent the set of tudents who belong to the math club. Julia is on the volleyball team and belongs to the math club. he set of students who are on the girls' volleyball team and the set of students who are in the math lub are intersecting because you know they have at least one common element, Julia.

The Union of Sets:
et *B* represent the set of students in the 11th grade band. Let *C* represent the set of students in the 1th grade chorus. The union of these two sets would be all the students in the 11th grade band or he 11th grade chorus. A student in both would only be listed once.

ndependent events are events for which the occurrence of one event has no impact on the ɔccurrence of the other event.

Dependent events are events for which the occurrence of one event has an impact on the ɔccurrence of subsequent events.

For example, consider a jar which contains 1 blue marble, 1 green marble, and 2 yellow marbles.

Independent Events:
You randomly choose a yellow marble, replace the marble in the jar, and then randomly choose a yellow marble again. The event of choosing a yellow marble first does not affect the event of choosing a yellow marble second because the yellow marble chosen first is replaced in the jar. The events of randomly choosing a yellow marble first and randomly choosing a yellow marble second are independent events.

Dependent Events:
You randomly choose a yellow marble without replacing the marble in the jar, and then randomly choose a yellow marble again. The event of choosing a yellow marble first does affect the event of choosing a yellow marble second because the yellow marble chosen first is not replaced in the jar. The events of randomly choosing a yellow marble first and randomly choosing a yellow marble second are dependent events.

The Counting Principle is used to determine the number of outcomes in the sample space. The **Counting Principle** states that if an action *A* can occur in *m* ways and for each of these *m* ways an action *B* can occur in *n* ways, then actions *A* and *B* can occur in $m \cdot n$ ways. The Counting Principle can be generalized to more than two actions that happen in succession. If for each of th *m* and *n* ways *A* and *B* occur there is also an action *C* that can occur in *s* ways, then Actions *A*, *B*, and *C* can occur in $m \cdot n \cdot s$ ways.

For example, if you were to visit an ice cream store that sells either chocolate, vanilla, or strawberry ice cream in a cone or cup with or without sprinkles, you would have $3 \cdot 2 \cdot 2 = 12$ possible outcomes.

And?

A **compound event** is an event that consists of two or more events.

The **Rule of Compound Probability involving *and*** states: "If Event *A* and Event *B* are independe events, then the probability that Event *A* happens and Event *B* happens is the product of the probability that Event *A* happens and the probability that Event *B* happens, given that Event *A* has happened." $P(A \text{ and } B) = P(A) \cdot P(B)$

If Event *A* and Event *B* are dependent, then the probability that Event *A* happens and Event *B* happens is the product of the probability that Event *A* happens and the probability that Event *B* appens, given that Event *A* has already happened. If two or more of the sets are disjoint, then their robability will be zero as the two sets will have no elements in common.

or example, suppose you have 2 red, 1 blue, and 3 green socks in a drawer. You reach into the rawer without looking and choose a sock, replace it, and then choose another sock. You choose a otal of 2 socks.

hese are independent events, so use the rule of compound probability to calculate.
(green and red) = *P*(green) · *P*(red) = $\frac{3}{6} \cdot \frac{2}{6} = \frac{6}{36} = \frac{1}{6}$

Jow suppose you reach into the drawer without looking and choose a sock, do not replace it, and hen choose another sock. You choose a total of 2 socks.

hese are dependent events, so *P*(*A* and *B*) = *P*(*A*) · *P*(*B*, given *A*). Therefore, *P*(green and red) = $\frac{3}{6} \cdot \frac{2}{5} = \frac{6}{30} = \frac{1}{5}$.

conditional probability is the probability of event *B*, given that event *A* has already occurred. onsider a number cube that is rolled. The probability of rolling a 4 or less on the second roll of the umber cube (*B*), given that a 5 is rolled first (*A*), is an example of a conditional probability.

he notation for conditional probability is *P*(*B*|*A*), which reads, "the probability of event *B*, given event *A*."

LESSON 3

Or?

n a compound event that is related by the word *or*, there can be possible outcomes that are in the sample space for each event. These outcomes should only be counted once when determining the compound probability.

The **Addition Rule for Probability** states: "The probability that Event *A* occurs or Event *B* occurs is the probability that Event *A* occurs plus the probability that Event *B* occurs minus the probability that both *A* and *B* occur."

$$P(A \text{ or } B) = P(A) + P(B) - P(A \text{ and } B)$$

Keeping in mind that if two events are disjoint, then their probability will be *P*(*A* or *B*) = *P*(*A*) + *P*(*B*).

For example, consider determining the probability of drawing a jack or a club from a deck of cards. Let A = a jack and B = a club.

$$P(\text{jack or club}) = P(\text{jack}) + P(\text{club}) - P(\text{jack and club}) = \frac{4}{52} + \frac{13}{52} - \frac{1}{52} = \frac{16}{52} = \frac{4}{13}$$

LESSON 4

And, Or, and More!

You can use the same methods to calculate the probabilities for more than two compound events.

You will often see the phrases "with replacement" and "without replacement" in probability problems. These phrases refer to whether or not the total sample space changes from the first to the last event. For example, if you draw a marble from a bag, record the color, and then replace it, the sample space for the next event remains the same. If you do not replace it, then the sample space decreases.

For example, the probability for drawing 3 of a kind from a deck of cards with replacement is

$P(\text{3 of a kind}) = \frac{4}{52} \cdot \frac{4}{52} \cdot \frac{4}{52} = \frac{1}{2197}.$

The probability of drawing 3 of a kind without replacement is

$P(\text{3 of a kind}) = \frac{4}{52} \cdot \frac{3}{51} \cdot \frac{2}{50} = \frac{1}{5525}.$

TOPIC 2

Computing Probabilities

‑ darts, players score points by throwing darts inside the scoring area. A dart that lands outside the scoring area ‑cores no points.

Module 5: Making Informed Decisions

OPIC 2: COMPUTING ROBABILITIES

this topic, students apply and extend e probability concepts they learned in e previous topic to explore expected alue and conditional probability. They so use combinatorial techniques, such as ombinations and permutations, to construct nd reason with large sample spaces. tudents consider simple and complex event teractions in this topic and organize them order to derive information from them bout probabilities.

Where have we been?

In the previous topic, students revisited simple probability and deepened their understanding of compound probability in preparation for this topic. The Counting Principle was introduced in the previous topic as a precursor to combinations and permutations introduced in this topic.

Where are we going?

Combinations and permutations used to construct large sample spaces are widely used concepts in a variety of mathematical subfields, including number theory and computer science. Conditional probability and expected value are important concepts in fields such as economics and statistics.

Jsing a Two-Way Table to Determine a Sample Space

two-way table can be used to determine a sample space for compound events. For example, the able shown can organize the outcomes when two number cubes are rolled and summed.

1st Number Cube \ 2nd Number Cube	1	2	3	4	5	6
1	2	3	4	5	6	7
2	3	4	5	6	7	8
3	4	5	6	7	8	9
4	5	6	7	8	9	10
5	6	7	8	9	10	11
6	7	8	9	10	11	12

None of the Above

One good thing about a multiple choice question is that you can always make an educated guess. This can be a good strategy, especially if you're not 100% sure about the solution.

On the flip side, relying too much on guessing means you may not have been prepared for the questions. Remember, a little extra preparation can go a long way!

Have you thought about the chances of guessing the correct answer to a multiple choice question? What about the chances of guessing the correct answers to a bunch of multiple-choice questions?

QUESTIONS

1- (A) B C D
2- A B C (D)
3- A (B) C D
4- A (B) C D
5- A B (C) D
6- (A) B C D

Talking Points

It can be helpful to understand combinations and permutations for college admissions tests.

Here is an example of a sample question:

A committee of 10 people will elect three representatives. How many different groups of three representatives can they choose?

It is possible to choose two groups of the same three people, which only differ by the order they were chosen. Those groups would be permutations of each other. But what we want are combinations—where no two groups have the same people.

There is a formula for choosing *r* combinations from a set of *n* elements: $\frac{n!}{(n-r)!r!}$. So, the number of different groups of three representatives that can be chosen is:

$$\frac{10!}{(10-3)! \cdot 3!} = \frac{3{,}628{,}800}{30{,}240} = 120$$

Key Terms

contingency table
A two-way frequency table, also called a contingency table, shows the number of data points and their frequencies for two variables.

relative frequency
A relative frequency is the ratio of occurrences within a category to the total number of occurrences.

conditional probability
A conditional probability is the probability of Event *B*, given that Event *A* has already occurred.

factorial
The factorial of *n*, which is written with an exclamation mark as *n*!, is the product of all non-negative integers less than or equal to *n*.

Table Talk

Compound Probability for Data Displayed in Two-Way Tables

Warm Up

A quiz in a magazine contains 5 true-false questions. The questions are written in a language you do not recognize.

1. What is the probability of guessing the correct answers to all 5 questions?
2. What is the probability of guessing only one question correctly?

Learning Goals

- Determine probabilities of compound events for data displayed in two-way tables.
- Determine relative frequencies of events.

Key Terms

- two-way table
- frequency table
- two-way frequency table
- contingency table
- categorical data
- qualitative data
- relative frequency
- two-way relative frequency table

You have previously learned how to calculate probability as the ratio of desired outcomes divided by total outcomes. You have also calculated the probability for compound events that are independent and dependent. How can you determine both simple and compound probabilities from data relayed by a two-way table?

GETTING STARTED

Some Sum

When playing board games, it is common to roll two number cubes and calculate their sum.

1. **Determine the number of possible outcomes when two number cubes are rolled once. Explain your conclusion.**

2. **Write the sample space for rolling two number cubes one time.**

A **two-way table** shows the relationship between two data sets; one data set is organized in rows and the other data set is organized in columns.

3. **Complete the two-way table to represent all the possible sums that result from rolling two number cubes one time.**

		2nd Number Cube					
		1	2	3	4	5	6
1st Number Cube	1						
	2						
	3						
	4						
	5						
	6						

4. **What are the possible sums? Explain your reasoning.**

5. **Use the two-way table to answer each question.**

A **frequency table** shows the frequency of an item, number, or event appearing in a sample space.

a. **Complete the frequency table shown.**

Outcome (Sum of the Number Cubes)	Frequency

b. **What is the sum of the frequencies? Why?**

c. **Which sum appears most often in the frequency table? Why do you think this sum appears the most?**

d. **Using the frequency table, can you determine the probability of rolling a sum of 7? Why or why not?**

e. **What is the probability of rolling an odd sum? Explain your reasoning.**

f. **What is the probability of rolling a sum less than 7? Explain your reasoning.**

ACTIVITY 1.1 Converse of the Multiplication Rule

You have learned that if two events *A* and *B* are independent, the probability of both events occurring, *P*(*A* and *B*), is *P*(*A*) · *P*(*B*).

The converse is also true: If the probability of two events *A* and *B*, *P*(*A* and *B*), occurring together is *P*(*A*) · *P*(*B*), then the two events are independent.

1. **Use the converse of the multiplication rule and the sample space you created in the previous activity to determine whether the events are independent. Explain your reasoning.**

   a. **A result of 3 on the first number cube and a result of 3 on the second number cube**

   b. **A result of two 3s and a sum of 6**

   c. **A result of 6 on the first number cube and a sum less than 7**

   d. **A result of any number on the first number cube and a sum less than 7**

ACTIVITY 1.2

Analyzing Two-Way Tables

A **two-way frequency table**, also called a **contingency table**, shows the number of data points and their frequencies for two variables. One variable is divided into rows, and the other is divided into columns.

A recent study estimates that between 70% to 90% of the world's population is right-handed. Another study suggests that almost 90% of athletes are right-handed. Yet another study shows that left-handed people have a higher percentage of participation in individual sports like wrestling or golf.

Favored hand and sports participation are examples of data sets that can be grouped into categories. These data are called **categorical data**, or **qualitative data**.

Mr. Harris's math class decides to conduct a survey of 63 people to determine which hand is favored and whether the hand favored affects whether a person participates in certain types of sports or no sports at all. The results are shown in the two-way table.

Sports Participation

Favored Hand		Individual	Team	Does Not Play	Total
	Left	3	13	8	
	Right	6	23	4	
	Mixed	1	3	2	
	Total				

1. Name the two variables displayed in the table.

2. Calculate the total for each row and each column in the table.

3. **Use the two-way frequency table to answer each question. Describe how to use the rows and columns to determine each answer.**

   a. **How many of those surveyed are left-handed and do not play sports?**

   b. **How many of those surveyed are right-handed or play team sports?**

   c. **How many of those surveyed play any kind of sport?**

4. **Campbell claims that the figures in the studies are correct because there were more right-handed people who participate in the survey than left-handed and mixed-handed people. Do you agree with Campbell? Explain your reasoning.**

Because there are 3 types of handed people who participated in the surve Mr. Harris's students cannot claim that the studies' figures are correct by simply looking at the frequencies. Instead they must determine the *relative frequencies*. A **relative frequency** is the ratio of occurrences within a category to the total number of occurrences. To determine the ratio for each category, determine the part to the whole for each category.

A **two-way relative frequency table** displays the relative frequencies fo two categories of data.

Use the survey results to calculate the relative frequency of each entry. Record the results in the two-way relative frequency table. Write each result as a fraction and as a percent rounded to the tenths place.

	Individual	Team	Does Not Play	Total
Left	$\frac{3}{63} \approx 4.8\%$			
Right				
Mixed				
Total				

Do your percents add up to 100%? If not, why not?

Suppose a student is randomly selected from the survey. Determine each probability.

a. The student is left-handed.

b. The student is right-handed.

c. The student participates in some kind of sport.

Suppose a student is randomly selected from the survey. Determine each probability. Explain how you calculated your answer.

a. The student is left-handed participating in individual sports.

b. The student is right-handed participating in team sports.

c. The student is left-handed participating in individual sports or right-handed participating in team sports.

8. **Suppose a student is randomly selected from the survey. Determine each probability. Explain how you calculated your answer.**

   a. **The student is left-handed or participates in team sports.**

   b. **The student does not play sports or is mixed-handed.**

How can you use the probability rules you have learned to answer each question?

9. **How do the results of the survey compare with the estimate that between 70% and 90% of the world's population is right-handed?**

10. **How do the results of the survey compare with the estimate that almost 90% of athletes are right-handed?**

    Three students attempted to answer this question. Their work and reasoning are shown.

Danielle

Out of the 63 people surveyed, 6 + 23, or 29, are both right-handed AND play a sport.

$\frac{29}{63} \approx 46\%$

This is much less than the 90% estimate.

Tyler

Out of the 33 people in the survey who are right-handed, 6 + 23, or 29, play a sport.

$\frac{29}{33} \approx 87.9\%$

This is close to the 90% estimate.

Keisha

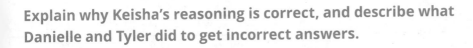

Out of the 10 + 39, or 49, people in the survey who play a sport, 6 + 23, or 29, are right-handed.

$\frac{29}{49} \approx 59.2\%$

This is much less than the 90% estimate.

Explain why Keisha's reasoning is correct, and describe what Danielle and Tyler did to get incorrect answers.

ACTIVITY 1.3 Determining Compound Probabilities from Relative Frequencies

You may prefer to use percents when comparing probabilities. Writing probability in fractional form is helpful because you can see the desired outcomes and the total outcomes.

A survey was conducted in one class about students' favorite after-school activities. The frequencies of male and female responses are shown in the table.

What is your favorite thing to do when you are not in school?

	Male		**Female**		**Total**	
Activity	Freq.	Rel. Freq.	Freq.	Rel. Freq.	Freq.	Rel. Freq.
Listen to music	5		3		8	
Watch TV	5		4		9	
Participate in sports	1		2		3	
Play video games	3		0		3	
Surf the Internet	2		2		4	
Shop	0		1		1	
Read	0		1		1	
Other	1		0		1	
Total	17		13		30	

1. **Calculate the relative frequency of each entry. Record the result in the two-way relative frequency table. Write each result as a fraction and as a percent rounded to the tenths place.**

2. Suppose a student is randomly selected from the class. Determine each probability. Explain how you calculated your answer.

a. The student is male.

b. The student watches TV as their favorite thing to do when not in school.

c. The student is a male who plays video games.

d. The student is a female who listens to music.

e. The student is female and watches TV for her favorite pastime.

f. The student is female or watches TV for his/her favorite pastime.

. Is being male independent of listening to music as a favorite after-school activity? Explain your reasoning.

NOTES

TALK the TALK 

Statistically Speaking

1. Write the term that best completes each statement.

   a. A two-way table is a table that shows the relationship between two data sets, one organized in _________ and one organized in _________.

   b. A _________ table is a table that shows how often each item, number, or event appears in a sample space.

   c. A _________, also called a _________, shows the number of data points and their frequencies for two variables.

   d. Data that can be grouped into categories, such as eye color and gender, are called _________ or _________ data.

   e. A relative frequency is the ratio of occurrences within a category to the _________ of occurrences.

   f. A two-way relative frequency table displays the _________ for two categories of data.

NOTES

2. **Of the students in Molly's homeroom, 11 students have brown hair, 7 have black hair, 5 have auburn hair, 4 have blonde hair, and 3 have red hair. Calculate each relative frequency. Round to the nearest thousandth if necessary.**

   a. **black hair**

   b. **auburn or red hair**

   c. **not brown hair**

   d. **brown and black hair**

NOTES

The two-way frequency table shows the number of students from each grade who plan to attend this year's homecoming football game.

Are you going to the homecoming game?	Grade: Freshmen	Sophomores	Juniors	Seniors	Total
Attending Homecoming Game	31	28	25	32	116
Not Attending Homecoming Game	17	24	11	6	58
Total	48	52	36	38	174

3. Calculate the relative frequency of the entries in the two-way table. Round each relative frequency to the nearest tenth of a percent if necessary.

a. A freshman going to the homecoming game

b. A sophomore not going to the homecoming game

c. Students from all grades going to the homecoming game

d. Students who are not juniors and are not attending the homecoming game

Assignment

Vrite

A __________ is a table that shows the relationship between two data sets, one organized in rows and one organized in columns.

. A __________ is a table that shows the frequency of an item, number, or event appearing in a sample space.

. A __________ or a __________ shows the number of data points and their frequencies for two variables.

. Data that can be grouped into categories is called categorical data or __________.

. A __________ is the ratio of occurrences within a category to the total number of occurrences.

. A table that displays the relative frequencies for two categories of data is called a __________.

Remember

wo-way tables can be used to determine the probabilities of compound events. The converse f the multiplication rule states: "If the probability of two events A and B occurring together is $(A) \cdot P(B)$, then the two events are independent."

Practice

ermaine rolls two number cubes.

. Complete a two-way table to represent all the possible products of the numbers rolled on two number cubes.

2. Create a frequency table with the product of the numbers rolled on the two number cubes and their frequency.

3. Use your two-way table and frequency table to answer each question.

   a. What is the probability of rolling an odd product?

   b. What is the probability of rolling a product less than 10?

4. Use the converse of the multiplication rule to determine whether the events are independent. Explain your reasoning.

   a. Rolling a 2 on the first number cube and rolling a 6 on the second number cube

   b. Rolling a 3 on the first number cube and a product equal to 20

A survey was taken of 24 households on Oak Street to compare the number of cars registered to the household and the number of people who live in the house. The responses are shown in the table.

5. Complete the table. Write each result as a fraction and a percent rounded to the tenths place.

		Number of People in Household								Total	Rel. Freq.
		2		3		4		5			
		Freq.	Rel. Freq.	Freq.	Rel. Freq.	Freq.	Rel. Freq.	Freq.	Rel. Freq.		
Number of Cars	1	1		1		1		0			
	2	4		3		5		3			
	3	0		1		3		1			
Total											

6. Suppose a house on Oak Street is randomly chosen. Determine each probability.

   a. The house has two cars.

   b. The house has 3 people in the household.

   c. The house has 4 people in the household and 3 cars.

   d. The house has 5 people in the household and 2 cars.

Stretch

1. An amusement park randomly surveyed 130 guests about the type of ride they preferred between three types of rides; roller coaster, ferris wheel, and pirate ship. The guests were also asked their ages. The responses and totals are shown in the table.

		Type of Ride			Total
		Roller Coaster	Ferris Wheel	Pirate Ship	
Age	< 30	36	4	1	41
	30–39	25	6	8	39
	40–49	12	12	5	29
	50–59	4	10	7	21
Total		77	32	21	130

a. What is the probability that a randomly chosen guest prefers the ferris wheel?

b. What is the probability that a randomly chosen guest is aged 40–49 and prefers the roller coaster?

c. What number for the probabilities from parts a) and b) denotes the sample space?

d. Suppose a guest is randomly chosen and it is known that they preferred the pirate ship. How many guests would be included in the sample space? Explain your reasoning.

e. What is the probability that out of the guests who preferred the pirate ship, the guest was younger than 30 years old?

Review

1. A game includes a deck of cards with a shape on each card. The table shows the number of each type of card. Suppose each time a card is chosen, the card is replaced before another card is chosen. A player draws three cards. What is the probability the first card will have a square on it and the last card will have a star on it?

Number of Cards	Shape on Card
5	triangle
15	square
4	rectangle
6	circle
12	star

2. A school is giving out prizes at a pep rally to random students whose names are picked out of a hat. The table shows the number of students in each grade. Suppose each time a student's name is chosen, the student's name does not go back into the hat. The principal draws two names. What is the probability that the first student is in twelfth grade or the second student is in tenth grade?

Number of Students	Grade of Student
25	ninth
32	tenth
28	eleventh
25	twelfth

3. A bag contains a red marble, a blue marble, a yellow marble, a green marble, an orange marble, and a purple marble. Jeanine randomly picks a marble from the bag, without replacing it, and then she chooses another marble from the bag. Sketch a tree diagram that represents the sample space.

4. Kamau randomly chooses a card from a deck of eight cards without replacing it. The cards are numbered 1 through 8.

   a. Identify the sample space.

   b. Determine the probability of picking a card that has a number less than 6, *P*(less than 6).

   c. Determine the probability of picking a card that has a number that is a prime number, *P*(prime number).

5. Use a trigonometric ratio to solve for the value of x. Round your answer the nearest tenth.

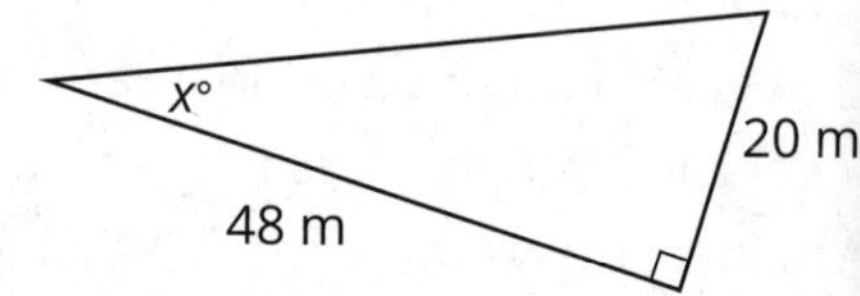

2

It All Depends

Conditional Probability

Warm Up

A teacher administers a random survey to determine the probabilities of a male or female middle school student having their own smartphone. She organizes the data in a two-way frequency table.

1. What could be the variables in her table?
2. What could be the groups within each variable in her table?

Learning Goals

- Use conditional probability to determine the probability of an event given that another event has occurred.
- Use conditional probability to determine whether or not events are independent.

You have calculated probabilities when there was replacement from trial to trial and when there was no replacement. How does the phrase "without replacement" relate to a conditional probability?

Rollin', Rollin', Rollin'

The two-way table represents a situation in which 2 number cubes are rolled, one at a time. The sums of the two rolls are shown.

		Second Roll					
		1	2	3	4	5	6
First Roll	1	2	3	4	5	6	7
	2	3	4	5	6	7	8
	3	4	5	6	7	8	9
	4	5	6	7	8	9	10
	5	6	7	8	9	10	11
	6	7	8	9	10	11	12

Suppose event *A* is rolling a 5 on the first roll, and event *B* is rolling a 4 or less on the second roll.

1. **Determine *P*(*A* and *B*).**

   a. **What is the probability of rolling a 5 on the first roll, *P*(*A*)? On the two-way table, shade the desired outcomes and draw a border around the possible outcomes. Explain your reasoning.**

   b. **What is the probability of rolling a 4 or less on the second roll, *P*(*B*)? On the two-way table, shade the desired outcomes and draw a border around the possible outcomes. Explain your reasoning.**

   c. **What is the probability of rolling a 5 first AND a 4 or less second, *P*(*A* and *B*)? Explain your reasoning.**

ACTIVITY

2.1 Conditional Probability

ecall, a conditional probability is the probability of event *B*, given that vent *A* has already occurred. The probability of rolling a 4 or less on the econd roll of the number cube (*B*), given that a 5 is rolled first (*A*), is an xample of a conditional probability.

The notation for conditional probability is $P(B|A)$, which reads, "the probability of event *B*, given event *A*."

What is the probability of rolling a 4 or less on the second roll, given that a 5 is rolled first, $P(B|A)$? Shade the desired outcomes and draw a border around the possible outcomes. Explain your reasoning.

Second Roll

	1	**2**	**3**	**4**	**5**	**6**
1	2	3	4	5	6	7
2	3	4	5	6	7	8
3	4	5	6	7	8	9
4	5	6	7	8	9	10
5	6	7	8	9	10	11
6	7	8	9	10	11	12

If you know that a 5 is rolled first, does that change the possible outcomes?

. **Compare $P(B|A)$ with $P(B)$.**

a. **What do you notice?**

b. **Do you think event *A* and *B* are independent or dependent events? Explain your reasoning.**

3. **Suppose event *A* is rolling a 5 on the first roll, and event *B* is rolling a sum greater than or equal to 8.**

a. **What is the probability of rolling a 5 on the first roll, *P*(*A*)? Shade the desired outcomes and draw a border around the possible outcomes. Explain your reasoning.**

Second Roll

First Roll		1	2	3	4	5	6
	1	2	3	4	5	6	7
	2	3	4	5	6	7	8
	3	4	5	6	7	8	9
	4	5	6	7	8	9	10
	5	6	7	8	9	10	11
	6	7	8	9	10	11	12

b. **What is the probability of rolling a sum greater than or equal to 8, *P*(*B*)? In the table in part (a), shade the desired outcomes and draw a border around the possible outcomes. Explain your reasoning.**

c. **What is the probability of rolling a 5 first AND a sum greater than or equal to 8, *P*(*A* and *B*)? Explain your reasoning.**

d. What is the probability of rolling a sum greater than or equal to 8, given that a 5 is rolled first, *P*(*B*|*A*)? Shade the desired outcomes and draw a border around the possible outcomes. Explain your reasoning.

Second Roll

	1	**2**	**3**	**4**	**5**	**6**
1	2	3	4	5	6	7
2	3	4	5	6	7	8
3	4	5	6	7	8	9
4	5	6	7	8	9	10
5	6	7	8	9	10	11
6	7	8	9	10	11	12

e. Compare *P*(*B*|*A*) with *P*(*B*). What do you notice?

f. Do you think events *A* and *B* are independent or dependent events? Explain your reasoning.

en two events are independent, $P(B|A) = P(B)$. When two events are pendent, $P(B|A) \neq P(B)$. Thus, two events are independent if and only if $B|A) = P(B)$.

ACTIVITY
2.2

The Conditional Probability Formula

Now you can derive the formula for the conditional probability of two independent events, $P(B|A)$.

1. Let *A* represent the event of rolling a 5 on the first roll. Let *B* represent the event of rolling a number less than or equal to 4 on the second roll.

Second Roll

First Roll	1	2	3	4	5	6
1	2	3	4	5	6	7
2	3	4	5	6	7	8
3	4	5	6	7	8	9
4	5	6	7	8	9	10
5	6	7	8	9	10	11
6	7	8	9	10	11	12

a. Complete the table.

	P(*A*)	*P*(*B*)	*P*(*A* and *B*)	*P*(*B*|*A*)
Desired Outcomes				
Total Outcomes				
Probability				

b. Use the table to verify that Event *A* and Event *B* are independent.

c. What quantity in the table is equivalent to the number of desired outcomes for $P(B|A)$?

d. What quantity in the table is equivalent to the number of total outcomes for $P(B|A)$?

Vorked Example

'he conditional probability, $P(B|A)$, for independent events can be epresented as $\frac{\text{desired outcomes}}{\text{total outcomes}}$.

$$P(B|A) = \frac{\text{desired outcomes}}{\text{total outcomes}}$$

$$= \frac{A \text{ and } B}{A}$$

$$= \frac{A \text{ and } B}{A} \cdot \frac{\frac{1}{\text{total}}}{\frac{1}{\text{total}}}$$

$$= \frac{\frac{A \text{ and } B}{\text{total}}}{\frac{A}{\text{total}}}$$

$$= \frac{P(A \text{ and } B)}{P(A)}$$

Why can you multiply by the second factor?

2. Michael says the probability of rolling a number less than or equal to 4 on the second roll, given a 5 on the first roll, *P*(*B*|*A*), is equal to the probability of rolling a number less than or equal to 4 on the second roll, *P*(*B*), because Events *A* and *B* are independent. Is Michael correct? Explain your reasoning.

How is the formula in the worked example related to Michael's statement in Question 2?

ACTIVITY
2.3

Conditional Probability for Dependent Events

Let's see whether the formula works for actions that affect the outcomes of other actions.

Suppose you have 2 red socks, 1 blue sock, and 1 yellow sock in a drawer. You randomly choose a sock without replacing it, and then randomly choose a second sock.

1. **Write an organized list to represent all of the possible outcomes.**

2. **What is the probability of randomly choosing a red sock first, $P(A)$?**

3. **What is the probability of randomly choosing a red sock second, given that a red sock is randomly chosen first, $P(B|A)$?**

What is the probability of randomly choosing a red sock first and a red sock second, $P(A \text{ and } B)$?

Are Events A and B independent or dependent events? Explain your reasoning.

Is the probability of randomly choosing a red sock second, given that a red sock is randomly chosen first, $P(B|A)$, equal to the probability of $\frac{P(A \text{ and } B)}{P(A)}$? Explain why or why not.

NOTES

TALK the TALK

Flaunt That Formula!

Use the conditional probability formula to answer each question.

1. **A biology teacher gave her students two tests. The probability that a student received a score of 90% or above on both tests is $\frac{1}{10}$. The probability that a student received a score of 90% or above on the first test is $\frac{1}{5}$, and the probability that a student received a score of 90% or above on the second test is $\frac{1}{2}$.**

   a. **What is the probability that a student who received a score of 90% or above on the first test also received a score of 90% or above on the second test?**

   b. **Are "scoring 90% or above on the first test" and "scoring 90% or above on the second test" independent or dependent events? Explain your reasoning.**

2. **The probability of a positive test for a disease and actually having the disease is $\frac{1}{4000}$. The probability of a positive test is $\frac{1}{3000}$. Seventy out of 100 people have the disease.**

   a. **What is the probability of actually having the disease given a positive test?**

NOTES

b. Are testing positive for the disease and having the disease independent events? Explain your reasoning.

A basketball player makes two out of two free throws 49% of the time. She makes 70% of her free throws.

a. What is the probability that she will make the second free throw after making the first?

b. Are making the first free throw and making the second free throw independent or dependent events? Explain your reasoning.

Assignment

Vrite

escribe a conditional probability your own words. Distinguish etween independent and ependent events.

Remember

Conditional probabilities are used to determine the probability of an event given that another event has already occurred and to determine whether or not events are independent. The conditional probability formula is $P(B|A) = \frac{P(A \text{ and } B)}{P(A)}$.

ractice

Suppose you have 3 nickels, 1 quarter, and 1 penny in your pocket. You choose a coin, do not replace it, and then choose a second coin.

a. Write an organized list to represent all of the possible outcomes.

b. What is the probability of randomly picking a penny first, P(penny 1st)?

c. What is the probability of picking a quarter first and a nickel second?

d. What is the probability of picking a nickel second, given that a quarter is picked first?

Walt is selling candy outside the supermarket to raise money for new uniforms for the gymnastics team. The probability of a customer stopping to talk to Walt and buying some candy is $\frac{2}{9}$. The probability of a customer just stopping to talk to Walt is $\frac{5}{12}$. Fifty out of the 120 customers at the supermarket bought candy from Walt.

a. What is the probability of a customer buying candy from Walt given that they stopped to talk to him?

b. Are "a customer talking to Walt" and "a customer buying candy from Walt" independent or dependent events? Explain your reasoning.

. A survey was taken to determine the number of students that own a dog and a cat as a pet. When a student from the survey is chosen at random, the probability that the student owns both a dog and a cat is $\frac{1}{12}$. When a student is chosen at random, the probability that the student owns a dog is $\frac{1}{4}$ and the probability the student owns a cat is $\frac{1}{3}$.

a. What is the probability that a student chosen at random who owns a dog also owns a cat?

b. Are "owning a dog" and "owning a cat" independent or dependent events? Explain your reasoning.

tretch

. A random sample of 100 females are surveyed about their shopping habits. Sixty reported using credit cards, and out of those females, 22 of them are less than thirty years old. Out of the females who do not use credit cards, 15 are thirty years old or older. Suppose a female is randomly chosen. Use the conditional probability formula to determine the probability that the female chosen uses a credit card, given that the female is older than thirty years old.

Review

1. A survey was taken of 60 customers in a pet store to compare the number of pets owned by the shopper and the age of the shopper. The responses are shown in the table.

		Number of Pets			
		1	2	3	4
Age	20–39	6	7	4	2
	40–59	7	11	4	3
	60–79	8	5	2	1

Calculate each probability.

a. A randomly chosen customer has 3 pets.

b. A randomly chosen customer has 2 pets and is aged 60–79.

2. A board game includes a spinner and a deck of cards. A player chooses a card from the deck and then chooses another card from the deck without replacing the first card. What is the probability that the first card chosen is "Go Ahead 1 Space" and the second card is "Pick a Card"?

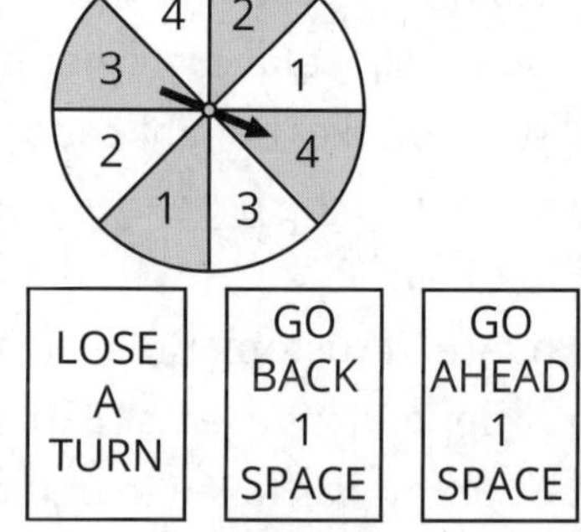

3. Consider the spinner shown in the figure. A player spins the spinner two times. What is the probability that the spinner will land on the letter A the first time or on the letter C the second time?

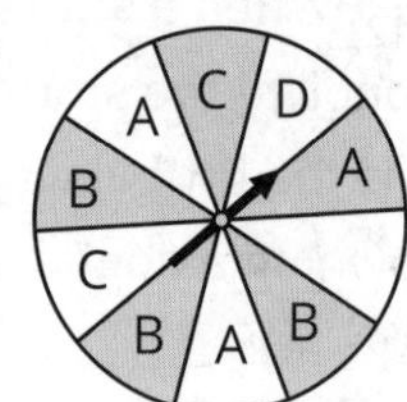

4. Use a trigonometric ratio to solve for the value of *x*. Round your answer to the nearest tenth.

a.

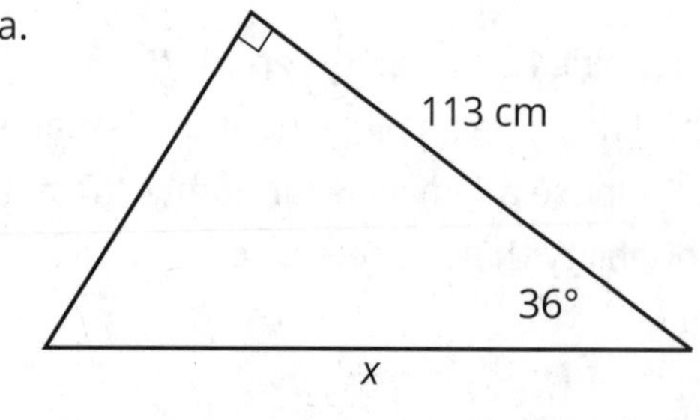

b.

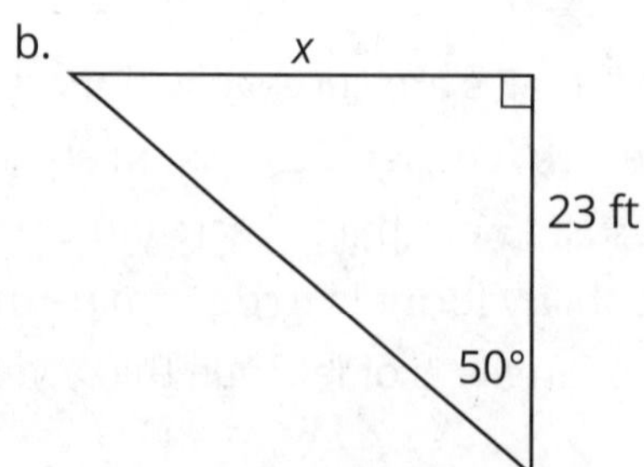

3

Give Me 5!

Permutations and Combinations

Varm Up

etermine the value of each xpression.

$5 \cdot 4 \cdot 3 \cdot 2 \cdot 1$

$\frac{8 \cdot 7 \cdot 6}{4 \cdot 3 \cdot 2 \cdot 1}$

$\frac{6 \cdot 5 \cdot 4 \cdot 3 \cdot 2 \cdot 1}{(3 \cdot 2 \cdot 1)(3 \cdot 2 \cdot 1)}$

Learning Goals

- Use permutations to calculate the size of sample spaces.
- Use combinations to calculate the size of sample spaces.
- Use permutations to calculate probabilities.
- Use combinations to calculate probabilities.
- Calculate permutations with repeated elements.
- Calculate circular permutations.

Key Terms

- factorial
- permutation
- circular permutation
- combination

ou have been drawing tree diagrams and making organized lists to determine the total number f arrangements that can occur when arranging elements of a set. How can you determine the umber of arrangements if the number of elements is too large to create a list?

GETTING STARTED

No Strings Attached

Calculating large sample spaces can present several challenges because it can be too time consuming or impractical to list all of the possible outcomes. Even for a relatively small number of options, listing the sample space can be challenging.

1. **Using the first four letters of the alphabet, list all of the three-letter strings, such as DBA, that can be formed without using the same letter twice in one string.**

2. **How many different strings are possible?**

3. **For each string, how many possible letters could be first? Second? Third?**

4. **How can your answer to Question 3 help you to calculate the number of possible three-letter strings?**

5. **How many different four-letter strings can be made using the first four letters of the alphabet? Explain your reasoning.**

If you were able to use the letters more than once, how many three-letter strings could you list? How many four-letter strings? Explain your reasoning.

If each letter could be used only once, how many 10-letter strings could you list using the first 10 letters of the alphabet? Explain your reasoning.

If you use the entire alphabet, how many three-letter strings can be made if each letter was used only once in each string? Explain your reasoning.

Calculate the number of 26-letter strings possible without replacement.

In general, if there are *n* letters, how many three-letter strings are possible without repetition?

In general, if there are *n* letters, how many three-letter strings are possible with repetition?

ACTIVITY

3.1 Factorials

In 1808, Christian Kramp introduced the *factorial*, which could help you to perform some of the calculations in the previous activity. The **factorial** of *n* which is written with an exclamation mark as *n*!, is the product of all non-negative integers less than or equal to *n*. For example, $3! = 3 \cdot 2 \cdot 1 = 6$.

1. Calculate each factorial.

a. $5! =$

b. $7! =$

c. $10! =$

2. Kalise says that $\frac{10!}{5!}$ is 2! because $10 \div 5 = 2$. Is Kalise correct? If so, explain Kalise's reasoning. If not, show how to calculate the correct quotient.

3. Write each expression as a ratio of two factorials.

a. $(5)(4)(3) =$

b. $7 \cdot 6 \cdot 5 \cdot 4 =$

Vorked Example

'ou can rewrite fractions involving actorials by dividing out common factors. For example:

$$\frac{8!}{6!} = \frac{8 \cdot 7 \cdot \cancel{6!}^{1}}{\cancel{6!}_{1}}$$
$$= 8 \cdot 7$$
$$= 56$$

Determine the value of each expression.

a. $\frac{8!}{6!} =$

b. $\frac{11!}{9!} =$

c. $\frac{7!}{4!} =$

d. $\frac{7!5!}{8!3!} =$

Using factorials, rewrite your answers to the following questions from the Getting Started.

a. How many different four-letter strings can be made using the first four letters of the alphabet?

b. If each letter could be used only once, how many 10-letter strings could you list using the first 10 letters of the alphabet?

c. If you use the entire alphabet, how many three-letter strings can be made if each letter was used only once in each string?

d. In general, if there are *n* letters, how many three-letter strings are possible without repetition?

ACTIVITY

3.2 Permutations

An ordered arrangement of items without repetition is called a **permutation**.

In Questions 1 through 4 of the Getting Started, the different 3-letter strings formed from the first 4 letters of the alphabet are permutations. There are different notations that are used for the permutations of r elements taken from a collection of n items:

$${}_nP_r = P(n, r) = P_r^n$$

1. Suppose you form 2-letter strings from the first 4 letters of the alphabet.

a. How many choices are there for the first letter? The second letter?

b. How many different permutations are there of 2 letters from the first 4 letters of the alphabet, ${}_4P_2$?

c. Write the number of permutations as a ratio of factorials.

2. Suppose you form 3-letter strings from any 5 letters of the alphabet. Write the number of permutations as a ratio of factorials.

How many 4-letter strings can be formed from the first 10 letters of the alphabet? Write the number of permutations as a ratio of factorials.

Analyze the ratios of factorials you wrote in Questions 1 through 3. Let r be the number of letters in a permutation. Let n be the number of letters to choose from.

Write a formula to describe the number of permutations, P, of r letters chosen from n letters.

Graphing calculators have a permutations key: ${}_nP_r$.

Calculate each permutation using the formula ${}_nP_r = \frac{n!}{(n-r)!}$.

a. ${}_6P_3 =$

b. ${}_{10}P_1 =$

c. ${}_5P_2 =$

6. **A sundae shop sells yogurt sundaes with 2 layers, 4 layers, or 5 layers of yogurt flavors. The shop carries 65 flavors in all.**

   a. **How many different 4-layer sundaes could you create without repeating flavors?**

   b. **Which type of sundae would give you the greatest number of choices if you do not repeat flavors?**

7. **A briefcase lock has 3 dials, each with the digits 0–9. The 3-digit code that unlocks the briefcase has no digits repeating.**

   a. **If you tried one code every 5 seconds, what is the greatest amount of time it could take you to open the briefcase?**

   b. **Suppose the briefcase has 10 dials, each with the digits 0–9. How many different 10-digit codes are possible with no repeated digits?**

   c. **What conclusion can you make about the value of 0!? Explain your reasoning.**

ACTIVITY

3.3

Permutations with Repeated Elements

ofie has 4 books on her shelf—2 novels (N_1 and N_2), 1 science book (S), nd 1 reference book (R).

. **How many permutations of all 4 books are there? Write an organized list to verify your answer.**

. **Suppose that Sofie wants to arrange her books by type. The order of the 2 novels doesn't matter to her.**

a. **Does this change the number of permutations? Explain your reasoning.**

b. **If necessary, modify the organized list in Question 1 to show the new number of permutations.**

. **Suppose Sofie has 3 novels (N_1, N_2, N_3) and 1 reference book (R) on her shelf.**

a. **How many permutations of all 4 books are there?**

b. **How many permutations are there if the order of the novels doesn't matter? Write an organized list to determine your answer.**

4. Suppose all 4 of Sophie's books are novels (N_1, N_2, N_3, N_4).

a. How many permutations of all 4 books are there?

b. How many permutations are there if the order of the novel doesn't matter? Write an organized list to determine your answer.

When the order of all of the elements in an arrangement matters, the arrangement contains 1 copy of each element. For example, the arrangement of Sofie's books N_1N_2RS contains 1 copy of each element.

When the order of some or all of the elements in an arrangement does n matter, the arrangement contains 2 or more copies of one or more of the elements. For example, the arrangement NNRS of Sofie's 4 books contair 2 copies of the element N (2 novels).

5. Use your answers from Questions 1 through 4 to complete the first three rows of the table.

List of Elements	Number of Permutations (order of novels matters)	Repeated Elements	Factorial of Number of Repeated Elements	Number of Permutation (order of novels doesr matter)
N_1, N_2, S, R	24			
N_1, N_2, N_3, R	24			
N_1, N_2, N_3, N_4	24			

6. Refer to the table in Question 5 to describe how to calculate the number of permutations when the order of the novels doesn't matter.

Write a formula to describe the number of permutations of *n* elements with *k* copies of an element.

Suppose Sofie has 2 novels and 2 science books. The order of each type of book doesn't matter. Write an organized list of all the different permutations of Sofie's books.

How many repeated elements are there now?

Suppose Sofie has 3 reference books and 2 science books. The order of each type of book doesn't matter. Write an organized list of all the different permutations of Sofie's books.

. Use your answers from Questions 8 and 9 to complete the table.

List of ements	Number of Permutations (order of repeated elements matters)	First Repeated Element	Factorial of First Number of Repeated Elements	Second Repeated Element	Factorial of Second Number of Repeated Elements	Product of Factorials	Number of Permutations (order of repeated elements does not matter)
N_1, N_2, S_1, S_2							
$_1, R_2, R_3, S_1, S_2$							

. Compare the value that you divided by each time to the number of copies. What do you notice?

12. **Write a formula to describe the number of permutations of *n* elements with *k* copies of one element and *h* copies of another element.**

13. **Suppose Sofie has 3 novels, a science book, and a reference book She chooses 2 books. The order of the novels doesn't matter. How many different permutations of 2 books are possible?**

Gary and Denise tried to solve this problem. Explain why Gary is correct and Denise is incorrect.

Denise

There are 5 elements in the collection, and Sofie chooses 2 with 3 elements repeating, so I think the number of permutations is

$${}_nP_r = \frac{n!}{(n-r)!(r!)} = \frac{5!}{(5-2)!(3!)}$$
$$= \frac{120}{36} \approx 3.3 \ldots$$

There are approximately 3.3 permutations.

Gary

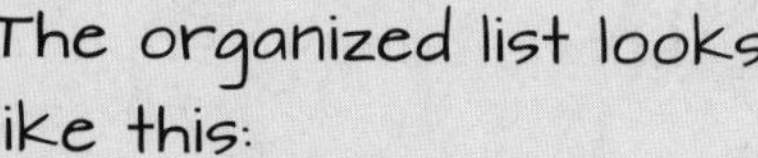

The organized list looks like this:

NN NS NR

SN SR

RN RS

There are 7 permutations.

14. **Does $\frac{n!}{k!}$ describe the correct number of permutations in the situation in Question 13? Explain your reasoning.**

15. **Calculate the number of 6-letter strings that can be formed from the word *cannon*.**

16. **Calculate the number of seven-letter strings that can be forme from the word *Alabama*.**

ACTIVITY
3.4

Circular Permutations

club consists of four officers: a President (P), a Vice President (VP), a ecretary (S), and a Treasurer (T).

. List the different ways that the four officers could be seated at a round table.

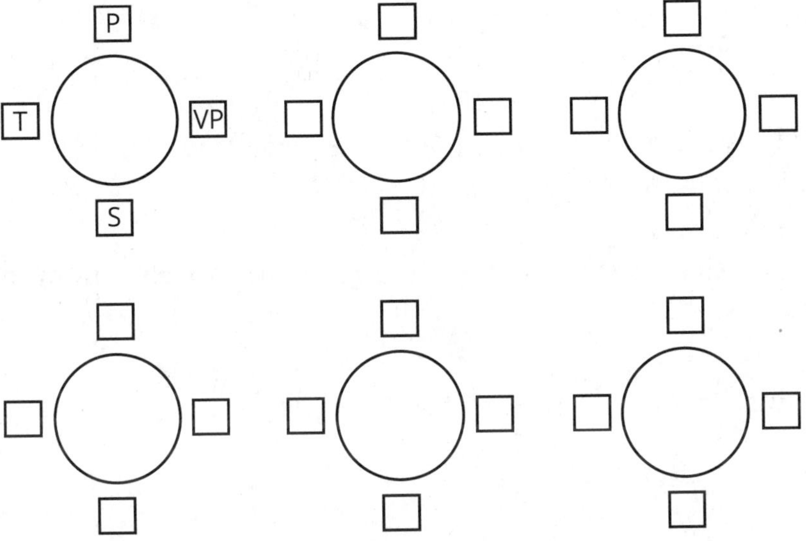

2. List the different ways that the officers could be arranged in a line.

3. Which elements from Question 2 are equivalent to the table seating of President, Vice President, Secretary, Treasurer?

4. Which elements from Question 2 are equivalent to the table seating of President, Secretary, Vice President, Treasurer?

5. **Which elements from Question 2 are equivalent to the table seating of President, Treasurer, Secretary, Vice President?**

6. **Based on Questions 3 through 5, how many equivalent elements are included for each seating arrangement? How does this number appear in the original problem?**

A **circular permutation** is a permutation in which there is no starting point and no ending point.

The seating arrangement problem is a *circular permutation*. The circular permutation of n objects is $(n - 1)!$.

7. **Calculate the number of table arrangements for each number of officers.**

   a. **Five officers**

   b. **Six officers**

   c. **Ten officers**

ACTIVITY

3.5

Combinations

ne 3-letter permutations of DEFG are shown.

$_4P_3 = \frac{4!}{(4-3)!} = 24$ permutations

DEF	EDF	FDE	GDE
DEG	EDG	FDG	GDF
DFE	EFD	FED	GED
DFG	EFG	FEG	GEF
DGE	EGD	FGD	GFD
DGF	EGF	FGE	GFE

1. Consider the list.

a. Start at the top left (DEF). Cross out all the outcomes that contain the exact same elements as DEF, but in a different order. One example is DFE.

b. Move to the next outcome in the first column that is not crossed out, DEG, and repeat the process. Continue until you cannot cross out any outcomes.

he arrangements that you did not cross off are all the *combinations* of letters from the collection of 4 letters. A **combination** is an unordered ollection of items. Different notations can be used for the combinations f *r* elements taken from a collection of *n* elements:

Permutations involve ordered items and combinations involve unordered items.

$$\binom{n}{r} = {}_nC_r = C(n, r) = C_r^n$$

2. Consider the 3-letter permutation list of DEFG.

a. How many combinations of 3-letter strings are there, $_4C_3$?

b. The notation $_4C_3$ represents the number of combinations of 3-letter strings formed from the 4 letters DEFG. Write a value in factorial notation to make the equation true.

$$_4C_3 = \frac{_4P_3}{\square}$$

3. The 2-letter permutations of DEFG are shown.

DE	ED	FD	GD
DF	EF	FE	GE
DG	EG	FG	GF

$_4P_2 = \frac{4!}{(4-2)!} = \frac{24}{2}$

= 12 permutations

a. How many combinations of 2-letter strings are there, $_4C_2$?

b. Write a value in factorial notation to make the equation true.

$_4C_2 = \frac{_4P_2}{\square}$

4. The 3-letter permutations of WXY are shown.

WXY	XWY	YWX
WYX	XYW	YXW

$_3P_3 = \frac{3!}{(3-3)!} = \frac{6}{1}$

= 6 permutations

a. How many combinations of 3-letter strings are there, $_3C_3$?

b. Write a value in factorial notation to make the equation true.

$_3C_3 = \frac{_3P_3}{\square}$

5. The 2-letter permutations of RSTVX are shown.

RS	SR	TR	VR	XR
RT	ST	TS	VS	XS
RV	SV	TV	VT	XT
RX	SX	TX	VX	XV

$_5P_2 = \frac{5!}{(5-2)!} = \frac{120}{6}$

= 20 permutations

a. How many combinations of 2-letter strings are there, $_5C_2$?

b. Write a value in factorial notation to make the equation true

$_5C_2 = \frac{_5P_2}{\square}$

Jse your answers in Questions 1 through 4 to complete :he table.

	n	r	${}_nP_r$	Divided by	${}_nC_r$
Question 1	4				
Question 2	4				
Question 3	3				
Question 4	5				

Compare the value that you divided by each time to the value of r. What do you notice?

Study the table. Write a value in factorial notation to make this general statement true.

$${}_nC_r = \frac{{}_nP_r}{\square}$$

Graphing calculators also have a combinations key: ${}_nC_r$.

9. **Calculate each combination using the formula $_nC_r = \frac{_nP_r}{r!}$ or $_nC_r = \frac{n!}{(n-r)!r!}$.**

   a. $_6C_3$

   b. $_{10}C_1$

   c. $\binom{7}{3}$

10. **Use an organization of 10 members and the formula for combinations to answer each question.**

    a. **How many four-member committees can be chosen?**

    b. **How many six-member committees can be chosen?**

    c. **How many ten-member committees can be chosen?**

NOTES

ALK the TALK 

lever Comb a Perm

State whether each question uses permutations or combinations. Then calculate the answer.

a. Using a standard deck of playing cards, how many different five-card hands can be dealt without replacement?

b. How many different numbers can be made using any three digits of 12,378?

c. How many different ways can you arrange 10 CDs on a shelf?

d. A professional basketball team has 12 members, but only five can play at any one time. How many different groups of players can be on the court at one time?

NOTES

2. Calculate each probability.

   a. Using a standard deck of playing cards, what is the probability that a person is randomly dealt a five-card hand containing an ace, a king, a queen, a jack, and a ten?

   b. Consider the number 12,378. Using any three digits, what is the probability of making a three-digit number whose value is greater than 700?

3. Explain the usefulness of each formula.

   a. ${}_{n}C_{r} = \frac{n!}{(n-r)!r!}$

   b. $\frac{n!}{k!h!}$

   c. ${}_{n}P_{r} = \frac{n!}{(n-r)!}$

   d. $\frac{n!}{k!}$

   e. $(n - 1)!$

   f. $n(n - 1)(n - 2) \ldots$

Assignment

Write

A ______ is an ordered arrangement of items without repetition.

The ______ of n, written as $n!$, is the product of all non-negative integers less than or equal to n.

A ______ is an unordered collection of items.

The ______ of n objects is $(n - 1)!$

Remember

If the order in which the items in a set matters, then each arrangement is called a permutation. If the order of the items in a set does not matter, then each arrangement is called a combination.

Practice

1. State whether each question uses permutations or combinations. Then calculate the answer.
   a. The Debate Club contains 13 members. They need to elect 3 members to the executive board: a president, vice president, and secretary. How many different executive boards are possible?
   b. Quentin used 7 websites during research for a report. How many different ways can he list the websites in his bibliography?
   c. Tyler has 28 songs on his computer. He is transferring 8 songs to his MP3 player. How many different ways can the songs be chosen?
   d. Josy is making a pattern with 2 squares, one triangle, and one circle. How many different patterns can Josy make?
   e. Sydney works at a kennel. She takes the 8 dogs at the kennel out for a walk in groups of 2. How many different groups of dogs can Sydney take?
2. Calculate each probability.
   a. A field hockey team has 10 members and the coach randomly selects 2 players as captains for each game. What is the probability that coach chooses you and your best friend as captains?
   b. Germaine has 2 quarters, a nickel, and a penny that he is randomly placing on the table in a line. What is the probability that the order of the coins will be quarter, nickel, penny, quarter?
3. Calculate the number of arrangements.
   a. How many different 7-digit numbers can be written using the digits 1, 1, 2, 7, 7, 7, 8, and 9?
   b. How many different ways can the letters in the word GEOMETRY be arranged?
4. Mrs. Rynearson is a kindergarten teacher. She asks her students to sit in a circle. Calculate the number of arrangements for each number of students.
   a. Four students
   b. Six students

Stretch

A student is taking a three question true/false quiz. The student only studied a little bit, so she will make educated guesses for each question. The probability she gets each question correct is $\frac{2}{3}$. List all the possible ways the student can answer the questions as well as the probabilities for each. Use *C* for correct and *I* for incorrect.

Review

1. Giorgio is stopping at a coffee shop on the way to work. The probability that Giorgio has to wait in line and buys a doughnut is $\frac{5}{8}$. The probability that Giorgio has to wait in line is $\frac{7}{10}$. Giorgio buys a doughnut every 40 out of 55 times he goes to the coffee shop.
   a. What is the probability Giorgio buys a doughnut given that he waited in line?
   b. Are waiting in line and buying a doughnut independent or dependent events? Explain your reasoning.
2. In a school, when a student is chosen at random the probability that the student takes physics and chemistry is $\frac{3}{25}$. The probability that the student takes just chemistry is $\frac{3}{5}$, and the probability that the student takes just physics is $\frac{1}{5}$.
   a. What is the probability a randomly chosen student takes physics given that they are taking chemistry?
   b. Are taking physics and taking chemistry independent or dependent events? Explain your reasoning.
3. A game includes a deck of cards with a shape on each card. The table shows the numbers of each type of card. Suppose each time a card is chosen, the card is replaced before another card is chosen. A player draws four cards. What is the probability they will all have a different shape on them?

Number of Cards	Shape on Card
5	triangle
15	square
4	rectangle
6	circle
12	star

4. A sphere has a volume of 6,367.4 cubic centimeters. Determine the radius of the sphere. Use 3.14 for π and round your answer to the nearest tenth.
5. A cone that is 5.5 inches high has a volume of 87.56 cubic inches. Determine the radius of the cone. Use 3.14 for π and round your answer to the nearest tenth.

4

A Different Kind of Court Trial

Independent Trials

Warm Up

Describe the probability of each event occurring as *impossible, unlikely, even chance, likely,* or *certain.*

1. The probability of flipping a coin that results in heads.
2. The probability of flipping a coin that results in heads or tails.
3. The probability of rolling a 3 on a six-sided number cube.
4. The probability of not rolling a 3 on a six-sided number cube.

Learning Goals

- Calculate the probability of two trials of two independent events.
- Calculate the probability of multiple trials of two independent events.
- Determine the formula for calculating the probability of multiple trials of independent events.

You have calculated the probability of two independent events both occurring. What would you do if those independent events could happen in more than one way?

GETTING STARTED

Make or Miss?

Walter is a basketball player who is constantly working at improving his free throw shooting. He's worked his way up to consistently making 2 out of 3 free throws.

1. **Walter shoots 2 free throws. Michael, Julie, and Erica determined the probability of Walter making 1 out of 2 free throws.**

Michael

The probability of Walter making 1 out of 2 free throws is $\frac{2}{4}$, or $\frac{1}{2}$ because 2 out of the 4 outcomes in the sample space show one made free throw.

make-make　　miss-miss

(make-miss)　　(miss-make)

Julie

The probability of Walter making 1 out of 2 free throws is $\frac{2}{9}$.

I calculated the probability by multiplying the probability of a make and the probability of a miss.

$$P(1 \text{ make and } 1 \text{ miss}) = P(1 \text{ make}) \cdot P(1 \text{ miss}) = \frac{2}{3} \cdot \frac{1}{3} = \frac{2}{9}$$

Erica

The probability of Walter making 1 out of 2 free throws is $\frac{4}{9}$.

I answered the question by multiplying the probability of a make and the probability of a miss. Then, I multiplied that result by 2 because Walter can make 1 out of 2 in two different ways. He could make the first and miss the second, or miss the first and make the second.

$$P(1 \text{ make and } 1 \text{ miss}) = 2[P(1 \text{ make}) \cdot P(1 \text{ miss})] = 2\left[\frac{2}{3} \cdot \frac{1}{3}\right] = 2\left[\frac{2}{9}\right] = \frac{4}{9}$$

a. Why is Michael's response incorrect? Explain your reasoning.

b. Why is Julie's response incorrect? Explain your reasoning.

c. Explain why Erica's method is correct and Julie's is incorrect.

Calculate each probability.

a. What is the probability of Walter making 2 out of 2 free throws?

b. How many different outcomes result in Walter making 0 out of 2 free throws? What is the probability of Walter making 0 out of 2 free throws?

ACTIVITY 4.1 Calculating Probability Using Combinations

Recall that Walter consistently makes 2 out of 3 free throws.

1. **Walter shoots 3 free throws. Determine the probability of the following events.**

   a. **What is the probability of Walter making 0 out of 3 free throws?**

   b. **What is the probability of Walter making 1 out of 3 free throws?**

   c. **What is the probability of Walter making 2 out of 3 free throws?**

   d. **What is the probability of Walter making 3 out of 3 free throws?**

2. **Susan claims that she can calculate the probability of Walter making free throws more efficiently, using combinations.**

For determining the "3 ways" Walter can make 1 out of 3 free throws, I multiplied $_3C_1$ and P(1 make).

$$
\begin{aligned}
P(1 \text{ make and } 2 \text{ misses}) &= {}_3C_1 \cdot [P(\text{make}) \cdot P(\text{miss}) \cdot P(\text{miss})] \\
&= 3 \cdot [P(\text{make}) \cdot P(\text{miss}) \cdot P(\text{miss})] \\
&= 3 \cdot [\tfrac{2}{3} \cdot \tfrac{1}{3} \cdot \tfrac{1}{3}] \\
&= 3 \cdot [\tfrac{2}{27}] \\
&= \tfrac{6}{27} \\
&= \tfrac{2}{9}
\end{aligned}
$$

Verify that Susan's method works for the calculations in Question 1 by using combinations to calculate each probability.

a. **Walter making 0 out of 3 free throws**

b. **Walter making 1 out of 3 free throws**

c. **Walter making 2 out of 3 free throws**

d. **Walter making 3 out of 3 free throws**

3. **Walter shoots 4 free throws. Use combinations to determine the probability of each event.**

   a. **Walter making 0 out of 4 free throws**

   b. **Walter making 1 out of 4 free throws**

   c. **Walter making 2 out of 4 free throws**

   d. **Walter making 3 out of 4 free throws**

   e. **Walter making 4 out of 4 free throws**

4. Complete the table to summarize the combination calculation that determines the number of ways each outcome can occur.

Number of Free Throws Attempted	Outcome 1	Outcome 2	Outcome 3	Outcome 4	Outcome 5	Outcome 6
1	0 makes, 1 miss occurs **1** way $_1C_0$ = **1**	1 make, 0 misses occur **1** way $_1C_1$ = **1**				
2	0 makes, 2 misses occur **1** way $_2C_0$ = **1**	1 make, 1 miss occurs **2** ways $_2C_1$ = **2**	2 makes, 0 misses occur **1** way $_2C_2$ = **1**			
3						
4						
5						

5. The following is a different way to organize the number of ways each outcome may occur. Analyze any patterns you see. Describe these patterns and use them to write the next two rows.

The triangle of numbers is Pascals' Triangle, named after Blaise Pascal, a 17th century mathematician. In the free throw shooting scenario, the numbers in Pascal's triangle represent the number of ways an outcome can occur.

6. **Summarize the probability of Walter making each number of free throws.**

Number of Free Throws Walter Attempts	Number of Free Throws Walter Makes	Probability of Walter Making Each Free Throw	Probability of Walter Missing Each Free Throw	Probability of Walter Making *r* out of *n* Free Throw Attempts
n	*r*	*P*(*A*)	*P*(~*A*)	
1	0	$\frac{2}{3}$	$\frac{1}{3}$	${}_{1}C_{0}\left(\frac{2}{3}\right)^{0}\left(\frac{1}{3}\right)^{1}$
	1	$\frac{2}{3}$	$\frac{1}{3}$	
2	0	$\frac{2}{3}$	$\frac{1}{3}$	
	1	$\frac{2}{3}$	$\frac{1}{3}$	
	2	$\frac{2}{3}$	$\frac{1}{3}$	
3	0	$\frac{2}{3}$	$\frac{1}{3}$	
	1	$\frac{2}{3}$	$\frac{1}{3}$	
	2	$\frac{2}{3}$	$\frac{1}{3}$	
	3	$\frac{2}{3}$	$\frac{1}{3}$	

a. The probability of Walter making 0 out of 1 free throw is provided. Complete the table to show the additional probabilities.

b. Describe how to calculate the probability of Walter making *r* free throws out of *n* free throw attempts.

c. Write an expression to calculate the probability of Walter making *r* free throws out of *n* free throw attempts.

. Walter's free throw shooting was not as good in the past. He used to make 2 out of every 5 free throws. What was the probability of Walter making 8 out of 10 free throws?

Walter is working to improve his free throw shooting. His goal is to consistently make 9 out of every 10 free throws. What is the probability of Walter making 8 out of 10 free throws?

ACTIVITY

4.2

Using a Formula for Multiple Trials

Suppose you roll a number cube with 4 red faces and 2 blue faces.

1. Calculate each probability.

a. Rolling 4 reds and 1 blue when the number cube is rolled five times.

b. Rolling 3 reds and 3 blues when the number cube is rolled six times.

c. Rolling 1 red and 6 blues when the number cube is rolled seven times.

2. Calculate each probability.

a. Rolling 3 reds and 7 blues when the number cube is rolled ter times.

b. Rolling 3 reds and 4 blues when the number cube is rolled seven times.

egular tetrahedron is a four-sided solid with each face an equilateral ngle. A regular tetrahedron has three sides painted blue (*B*) and one e painted red (*R*).

Calculate each probability.

a. What is *P*(*R*), the probability of rolling a tetrahedron that lands on a red face?

b. What is *P*(*B*), the probability of rolling a tetrahedron that lands on a blue face?

c. What is *P*(5*B* and 2*R*), the probability of rolling a tetrahedron that lands on five blues and two reds in seven rolls?

d. What is *P*(4*B* and 1*R*), the probability of rolling a tetrahedron that lands on four blues and one red in five rolls?

e. What is *P*(5*B* and 5*B*), the probability of rolling a tetrahedron that lands on five blues and five reds in ten rolls?

NOTES

TALK the TALK

It's a D8!

A regular octahedron is an eight-sided solid with each face an equilateral triangle. A regular octahedron has six sides painted yellow and two sides painted green.

1. **What is the probability of rolling a yellow?**

2. **What is the probability of rolling a green?**

3. **What is the probability of rolling seven yellows and one green in eight rolls?**

4. **What is the probability of rolling six yellows and two greens in eight rolls?**

5. **What is the probability of rolling five yellows and two greens in seven rolls?**

Assignment

/rite

escribe a scenario that might use the formula $_r (p)^r (1 - p)^{n-r}$. What do each of the variables present in the formula?

Remember

The arrangements represented by $_nC_r$ can also be computed using Pascal's Triangle.

ractice

A number cube has 5 green sides and 1 orange side.

a. What is the probability of 4 green outcomes and 1 orange outcome when the number cube is rolled 5 times?

b. What is the probability of 2 green outcomes and 2 orange outcomes when the number cube is rolled 4 times?

c. What is the probability of 3 green outcomes and 4 orange outcomes when the number cube is rolled 7 times?

A bag contains 3 nickels and 1 penny. Coins are replaced in the bag after every choice.

a. What is the probability of randomly choosing 4 nickels and one penny in 5 trials?

b. What is the probability of randomly choosing 2 nickels and 3 pennies in 5 trials?

c. What is the probability of randomly choosing 1 nickel and 5 pennies in 6 trials?

d. What is the probability of randomly choosing 4 nickels and 3 pennies in 7 trials?

Stretch

. A student is taking a multiple choice quiz. There are 10 questions on the quiz, and each question has 5 possible responses. The student has to guess on each question because he did not study for the quiz.

a. What is the probability that the student gets at least a 70% on the quiz? Show your work.

b. Is there a good chance the student will pass the quiz by guessing? Explain your reasoning.

Review

1. Sylvia is at an ice cream parlor that has 20 different flavors of ice cream. She is going to have a bowl of ice cream with two scoops. How many different ways can the scoops be chosen? State whether the question uses permutations or combinations. Then calculate the answer.

2. How many different ways can the letters in the word MATHEMATICS be arranged?

3. A school is giving out prizes at a pep rally to random students whose names are picked out of a hat. The table shows the numbers of students in each grade. Suppose each time a student's name is chosen, the student's name does not go back into the hat. The principal draws three names. What is the probability that the first student is in eleventh grade and the third student is in eleventh grade?

Number of Students	Grade of Student
25	ninth
32	tenth
28	eleventh
25	twelfth

4. Two bags of marbles are used for a game with the given content.

   Bag A: 6 red, 5 blue, 4 white

   Bag B: 6 green, 5 orange, 4 purple, 3 black

   A player chooses two marbles from Bag A. What is the probability that the player will choose a red marble first or a white marble second?

5. Consider the graph shown. Identify the key characteristics.
   a. Intervals where the function is increasing or decreasing
   b. Minimum and/or maximum values of the function
   c. x- and y-intercept(s)

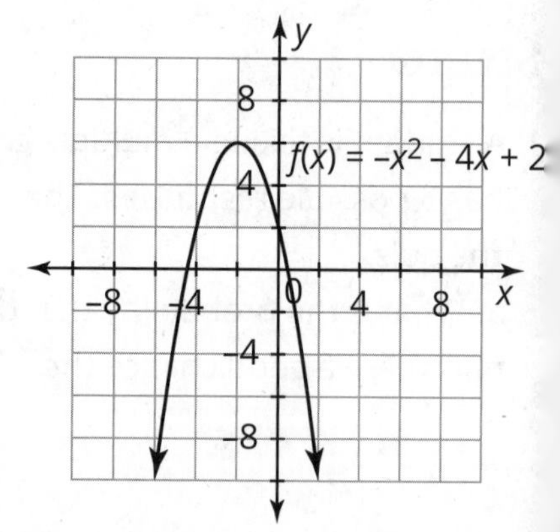

5

What Do You Expect?

Expected Value

Varm Up

etermine the area of each
nshaded section.

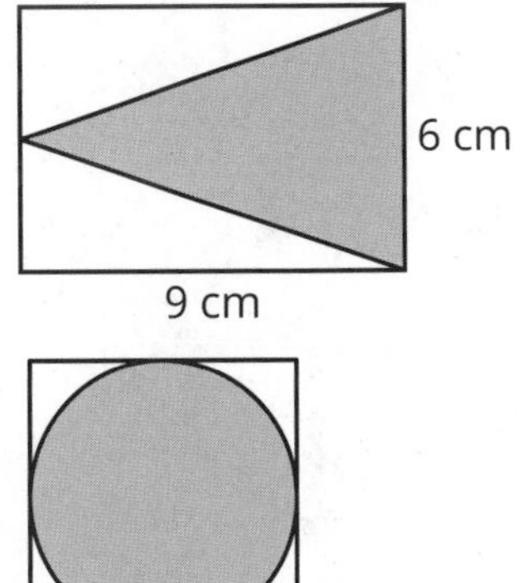

10 ft

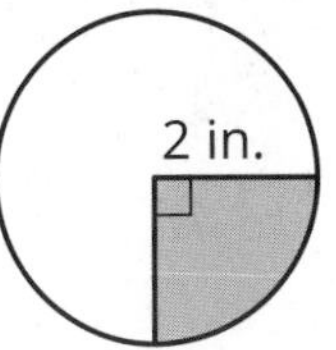

Learning Goals

- Determine geometric probability.
- Calculate the expected value of an event.

Key Terms

- geometric probability
- expected value

ou have worked with the formulas for permutations and combinations. How can these formulas e used to calculate the total number of ways that outcomes can occur, especially if they can ccur many times?

GETTING STARTED

Let's Make a Deal

Suppose you are a contestant on a game show. The host shows you 10 doors and tells you there is a car behind one of the doors and the remaining 9 doors have zonks. You choose door number 3 because it's your lucky number. The host decides to open 8 doors that he knows will all reveal zonks.

The host asks you one more time, do you want to keep your door or switch with the remaining closed door.

1. **Should you keep your door or switch doors? Use probabilities to defend your decision.**

ACTIVITY

5.1 Geometric Probability

class is hosting a dart competition to raise money. Three different esigns under consideration are shown. All of the dartboards are squares at measure 50 cm by 50 cm. For this situation, you have to assume at a dart is thrown randomly at a dart board and that the dart will land omewhere on the dart board.

Big Bullseye

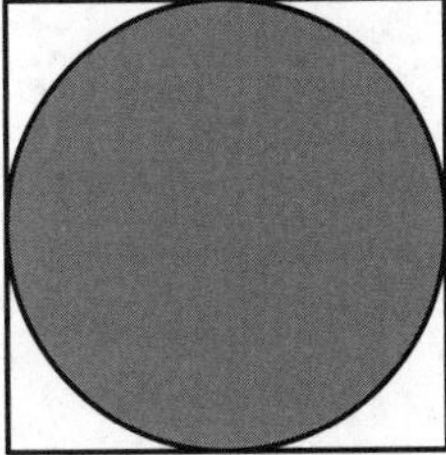

1 shaded circle

Four Circles

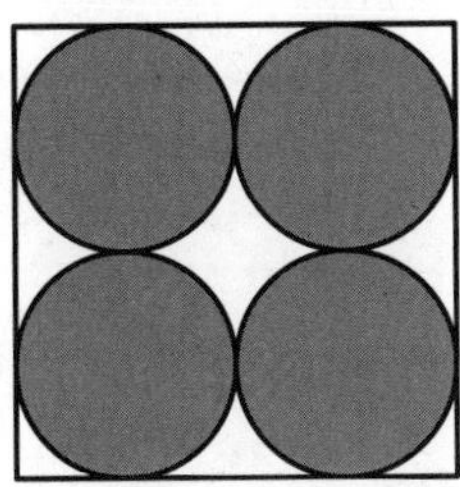

4 congruent shaded circles

Tricky Triangles

6 congruent shaded triangles

. **Which dart board will give the player the greatest chance of hitting a shaded section? Why?**

. **You can use what you know about probability to determine the chance a person has of hitting a shaded section on a dart board.**

a. What value would you use to represent the number of possible outcomes?

b. What value would you use to represent the number of desired outcomes?

3. Devin says that the number of desired outcomes for Big Bullseye is 1 because there is 1 shaded section. That means that Four Circles has 4 desired outcomes, and Tricky Triangles has 6 desired outcomes.
Is Devin's reasoning correct? Explain why or why not.

4. Determine the probability that a dart lands in a shaded section of each dartboard.

Big Bullseye

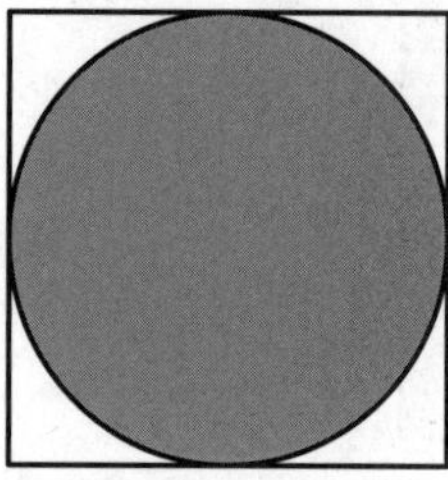

1 shaded circle

a. Big Bullseye

b. Four Circles

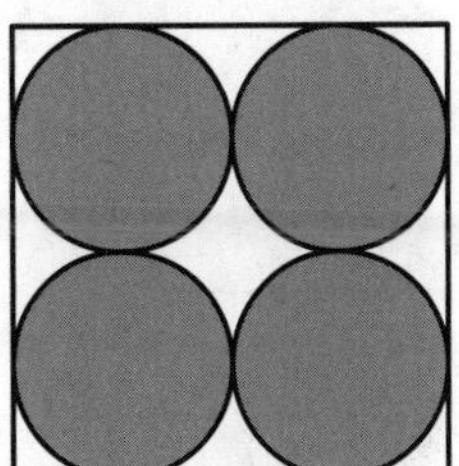

4 congruent shaded circles

c. Tricky Triangles

6 congruent shaded triangles

Which dart board should the class use to make the competition the most difficult? Explain your reasoning.

To determine the probability of hitting a shaded section on a dart board, you used *geometric probability*. **Geometric probability** is probability that involves a geometric measure, such as length, area, volume, and so on.

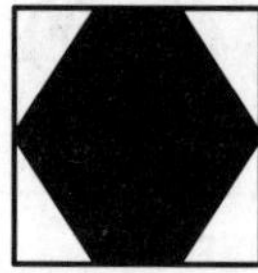

6. The dart board shown is a hexagon inscribed in a square. Two of the vertices of the hexagon bisect two of the sides of the square. The remaining 4 vertices trisect the other two sides of the square. What is the probability that a dart will hit the shaded area of the dart board? Show your work.

ACTIVITY

5.2 Exploring Expected Value

You are a contestant on a game show. In the first round, the host gives you $200. You can choose to keep the money or give the money back and spin the wheel to determine your winnings. All the sections on the wheel are equal in size.

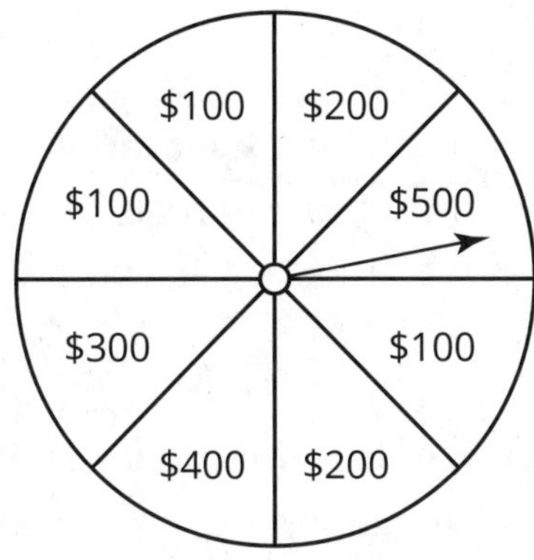

1. Would you choose to keep the $200 or spin the wheel? Why?

2. If you spin the wheel, what is the probability that you will win each amount?

a. $100 **b. $200** **c. $300** **d. $400** **e. $500**

3. If you spin the wheel, how often would you expect to win each amount?

a. $100 **b. $200** **c. $300** **d. $400** **e. $500**

4. Let's calculate the expected value for the game.

a. Multiply each amount by the probability of winning that amount.

b. Calculate the sum of the values from part (a)

The sum in Question 4 part (b) is the **expected value**. The expected value is the average value when the number of trials is large. In this problem, the expected value represents the amount that you could expect to receive from a single spin.

5. Based on the expected value, should you keep the $200 or spin the wheel? Explain your reasoning.

ACTIVITY
5.3 Calculating Expected Value

In the second round of the game show, you are offered another choice. The host gives you $300. You can choose to keep the money or give the money back and spin the wheel shown to determine your winnings. All the sections on the wheel are equal in size.

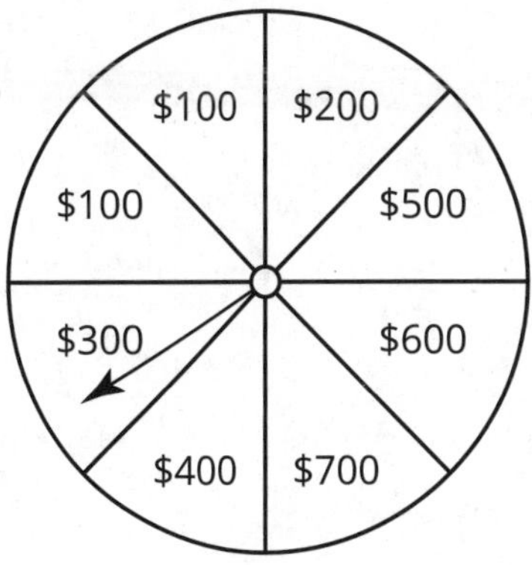

1. Calculate the expected value for one spin of the wheel.

2. Should you keep the $300 or spin the wheel? Explain your reasoning.

ACTIVITY 5.4 Using Geometric Probability to Determine Expected Value

The dart board shown has a diameter of 17.75 inches and 20 congruent sections in a circular scoring area. Players score points by throwing darts inside the scoring area. A dart that lands outside the scoring area scores no points.

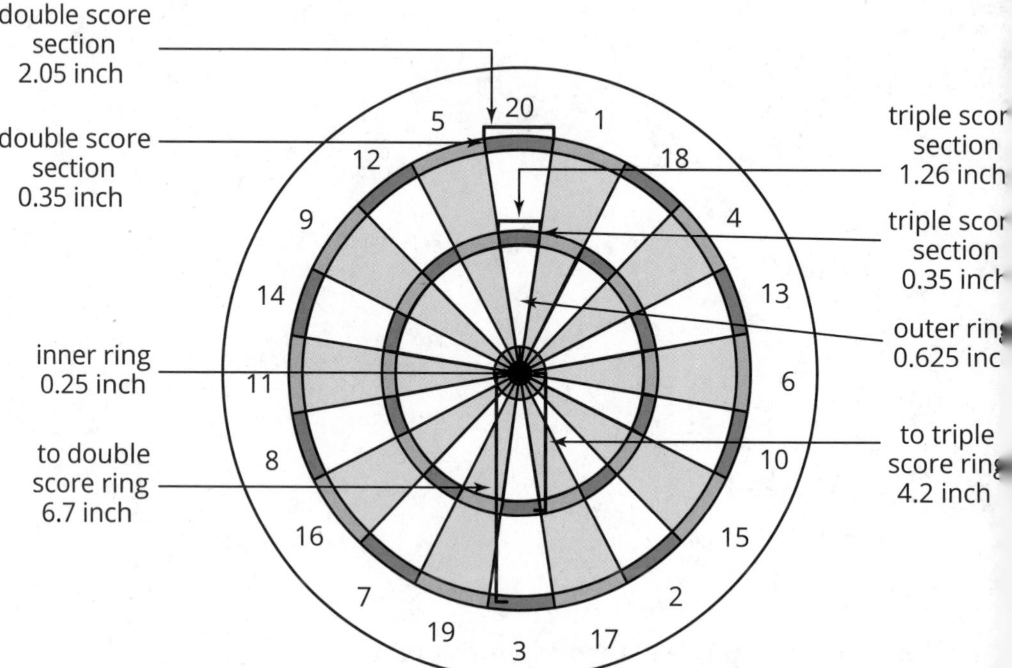

1. **Determine each of the approximate probabilities, assuming that 1 dart is thrown at random at the board. Explain your reasoning and show your work. Round values to the nearest ten-thousandth.**

   a. **Probability of getting any score**

b. **Probability of landing anywhere on the section labeled 20**

c. **Probability of landing within the outer ring but not the inner ring of the bullseye**

d. **Probability of landing within the inner ring of the bullseye**

e. **Probability of getting a triple 20**

f. Probability of getting a double 20

g. Probability of landing on 20 without a double or triple score

2. Suppose the inner bullseye is worth 50 points and the outer bullseye is worth 25 points. What is the expected value for 1 da throw? Show your work.

NOTES

ALK the TALK 

he Birthday Problem

nce there are at most 366 birthdays in a year, if you have a group 367 people, it is guaranteed that 2 people in that group share a rthday. Let's consider how many randomly selected people for it to be ely that there are two people who share a birthday.

How many randomly chosen people are needed before the probability is greater than 50% that at least two of them have the same birthday?

Assignment

Write

1. ________ is the likelihood of an event occurring based on geometric relationships such as length, area, or volume.
2. ________ is the sum of the values of a random variable with each value multiplied by its probability of occurrence.

Remember

It is often valuable to be able to determine the financial risk/reward involved when making a decision that is based upon unknowns. Using the known probabilities can help you make better decisions.

Practice

1. A dart is thrown and lands on random spot on each target. Determine the probability of hitting the shaded region. Write your answers as a percent rounded to the nearest tenth.
   a. The board shown is two circles inscribed inside a rectangle.

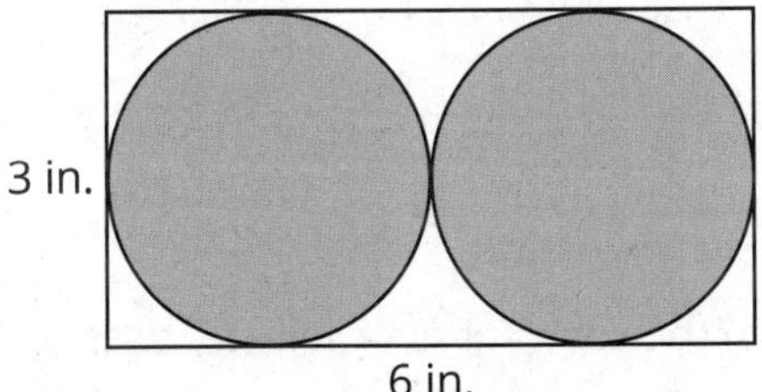

   b. The board shown is a triangle and a trapezoid inside of a rectangle.

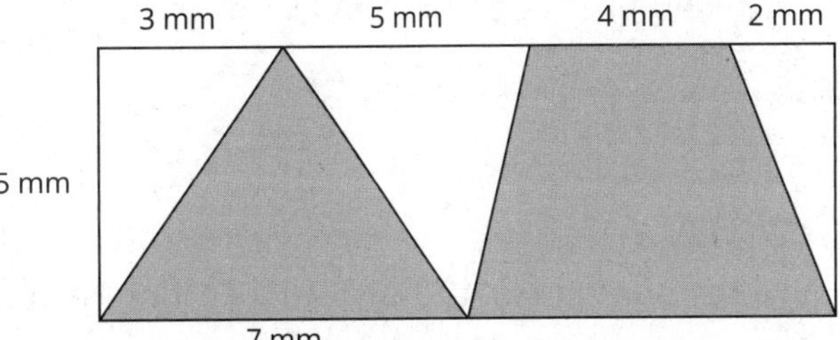

2. At a carnival, Jasmine is playing a game with the dartboard below. The dartboard has a rectangular shaped top and a semicircle along the bottom. She throws a dart that lands randomly on the dartboard, and wins the number of tickets shown in each region.

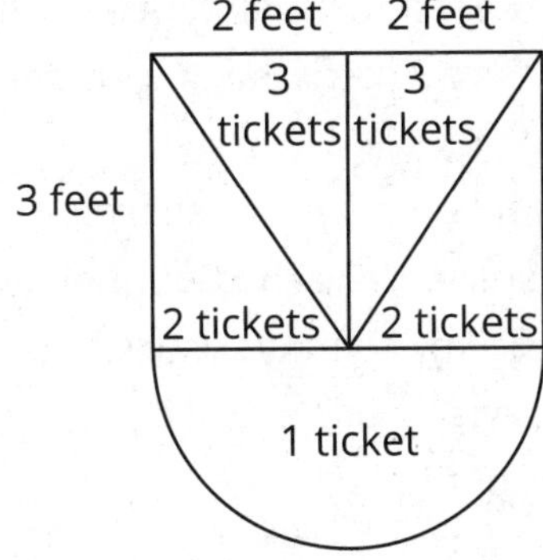

   a. Determine the areas you will need to know to calculate the expected value for the number of tickets Jasmine will win.
   b. Determine the probabilities you will need to know to calculate the expected value for the number of tickets Jasmine will win.
   c. What is the expected value for the number of tickets Jasmine will win?

Stretch

1. The board shown is a square inside a circle that is inside another square. The radius of the circle is $\sqrt{3}$ meters.

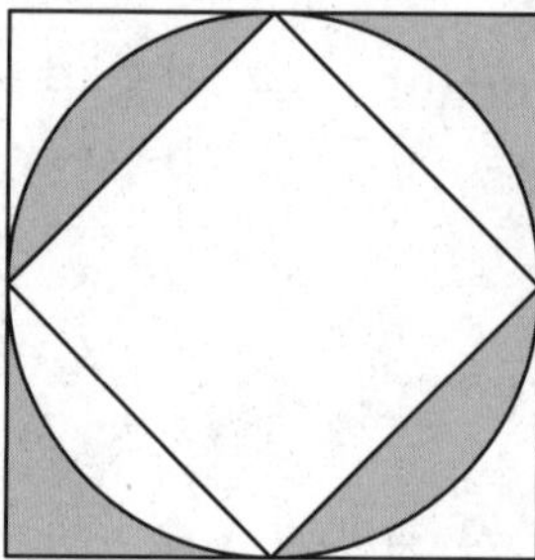

   a. A dart is thrown and lands on a random spot on the board. Determine the probability of hitting the shaded region. Write your answer as a percent rounded to the nearest tenth.

   b. If the dart lands on a shaded area inside the circle, the player is given 10 points. If the dart lands on a shaded area outside the circle, the player is given 20 points. What is the expected value for the number of points a player will get?

Review

1. In a restaurant, $\frac{3}{5}$ of the customers order meat dishes and $\frac{2}{5}$ of the customers order meatless dishes. If eight people sit down for a meal, what is the probability that three of them order meat dishes and five of them order meatless dishes?
2. A spinner has 4 blue spaces and 2 yellow spaces. What is the probability of 3 blue outcomes and 1 yellow outcome when the spinner is spun 4 times?
3. While playing a board game, a player rolls a number cube once and then picks a card. The number cube is numbered 1 through 6. There are 3 cards, each with one animal on them including a pig, a goat, and a cow.
   a. Write an organized list that represents the sample space.
   b. Determine the size of the sample space using the Counting Principle. Show your calculation.
4. Consider the graph shown. Identify the key characteristics.
   a. Intervals where the function is increasing or decreasing
   b. Minimum and/or maximum values of the function
   c. x- and y-intercept(s)

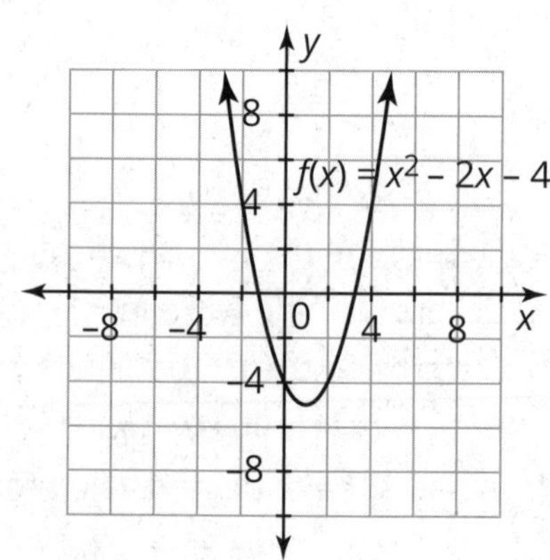

Computing Probabilities Summary

KEY TERMS

- two-way table
- frequency table
- two-way frequency table
- contingency table
- categorical data
- qualitative data
- relative frequency
- two-way relative frequency table
- factorial
- permutation
- circular permutation
- combination
- geometric probability
- expected value

Table Talk

A **two-way table** shows the relationship between two data sets; one data set is organized in rows and the other data set is organized in columns.

For example, the two-way table below represents all of the possible sums that will result from rolling two number cubes one time.

2nd Number Cube

1st Number Cube	1	2	3	4	5	6
1	2	3	4	5	6	7
2	3	4	5	6	7	8
3	4	5	6	7	8	9
4	5	6	7	8	9	10
5	6	7	8	9	10	11
6	7	8	9	10	11	12

A **frequency table** shows the frequency of an item, number, or event appearing in a sample space.

Outcome (sum of number cubes)	Frequency
2	1
3	2
4	3
5	4
6	5
7	6
8	5
9	4
10	3
11	2
12	1

You have learned that if two events *A* and *B* are independent, the probability of both events occurring, *P*(*A* and *B*), is *P*(*A*) · *P*(*B*). The converse is also true: If the probability of two events *A* and *B*, *P*(*A* and *B*), occurring together is *P*(*A*) · *P*(*B*), then the two events are independent.

A **two-way frequency table**, also called a **contingency table**, shows the number of data points and their frequencies for two variables. One variable is divided into rows, and the other is divided into columns.

Categorical data, or **qualitative data**, are data that each fit into exactly one of several different groups, or categories.

For example, consider a survey which asks participants about their favored hand and whether the participant plays in certain types of sport or no sports at all. The results are shown in the two-way table.

Sports Participation

Favored Hand		Individual	Team	Does Not Play	Total
	Left	3	13	8	24
	Right	6	23	4	33
	Mixed	1	3	2	6
	Total	10	39	14	63

relative frequency is the ratio of occurrences within a category to the total number of ccurrences. To determine the ratio for each category, determine the part to the whole for each ategory. A **two-way relative frequency table** displays the relative frequencies for two categories data.

	Individual	**Team**	**Does Not Play**	**Total**
Left	$\frac{3}{63} \approx 4.8\%$	$\frac{13}{63} \approx 25.4\%$	$\frac{8}{63} \approx 12.7\%$	$\frac{24}{63} \approx 38.1\%$
Right	$\frac{6}{63} \approx 9.5\%$	$\frac{23}{63} \approx 36.5\%$	$\frac{4}{63} \approx 6.3\%$	$\frac{33}{63} \approx 52.4\%$
Mixed	$\frac{1}{63} \approx 1.6\%$	$\frac{3}{63} \approx 4.8\%$	$\frac{2}{63} \approx 3.2\%$	$\frac{6}{63} \approx 9.5\%$
Total	$\frac{10}{63} \approx 15.9\%$	$\frac{39}{63} \approx 61.9\%$	$\frac{14}{63} \approx 22.2\%$	$\frac{63}{63} = 100\%$

ou can use a two-way relative frequency table to calculate the probability of events occuring.

or example, P(left handed) $= \frac{24}{63} \approx 38.1\%$, P(right handed in a team sport) $= \frac{23}{63} \approx 36.5\%$, or P(mixed anded or does not play) $= P$(mixed handed) $+ P$(does not play) $- P$(mixed handed and does not lay) $= \frac{6}{63} + \frac{14}{63} - \frac{2}{63} = \frac{18}{63} \approx 28.6\%$.

LESSON 2

It All Depends

conditional probability is the probability of event B, given that event A has already occurred. onsider a number cube that is rolled. The probability of rolling a 4 or less on the second roll of the umber cube (B), given that a 5 is rolled first (A), is an example of a conditional probability.

he notation for conditional probability is $P(B|A)$, which reads, "the probability of event B, given vent A."

Vhen two events are independent, $P(B|A) = P(B)$. When two events are dependent, $P(B|A) \neq P(B)$. hus, two events are independent if and only if $P(B|A) = P(B)$.

he conditional probability, $P(B|A)$, for independent events can be represented as $\frac{\text{desired outcomes}}{\text{total outcomes}}$.

$$P(B|A) = \frac{\text{desired outcomes}}{\text{total outcomes}}$$

$$= \frac{A \text{ and } B}{A}$$

$$= \frac{A \text{ and } B}{A} \cdot \frac{\frac{1}{\text{total}}}{\frac{1}{\text{total}}}$$

$$= \frac{\frac{A \text{ and } B}{\text{total}}}{\frac{A}{\text{total}}}$$

$$= \frac{P(A \text{ and } B)}{P(A)}$$

For example, consider the possible sums when rolling two number cubes.

Let A = rolling a 5

Let B = rolling a sum of 10

$$P(B|A) = \frac{\frac{1}{72}}{\frac{1}{6}} = \frac{1}{12}$$

You can check if these two events are independent by also calculating $P(B) = \frac{3}{36} = \frac{1}{12}$, thus they ar
independent events.

Let A = rolling a 6

Let B = rolling a sum of 12

LESSON

3 Give Me 5!

The **factorial** of n, which is written with an exclamation mark as $n!$, is the product of all non-negat integers less than or equal to n. For example, $3! = 3 \cdot 2 \cdot 1 = 6$.

You can simplify fractions involving factorials by dividing out common factors.

For example: $\frac{8!}{6!} = \frac{8 \cdot 7 \cdot 6 \cdot 5 \cdot 4 \cdot 3 \cdot 2 \cdot 1}{6 \cdot 5 \cdot 4 \cdot 3 \cdot 2 \cdot 1} = 8 \cdot 7 = 56$

An ordered arrangement of items without repetition is called a **permutation**. Being able to determine the different arrangement of 3 letters from the first 4 letters of the alphabet is an example of a permutation. There are different notations that are used for the permutations of r elements taken from a collection of n items:

$$_nP_r = P(n, r) = P^n_r$$

You can calculate permutations using the formula $_nP_r = \frac{n!}{(n - r)!}$.

For example, consider the number of permutations of 2 letters from the first 4 letters of the alphabet.

$$_4P_2 = \frac{4!}{(4 - 2)!} = \frac{4!}{2!} = 4 \cdot 3 = 12$$

There are 12 different combinations of 2 letters using only the first 4 letters of the alphabet.

You must also consider permutations where there are repeated elements in the sample space.

To determine the number of permutations of something with repeated elements you can use the formula, $\frac{n!}{k!}$ where n is the number of elements in the set and k is the number of copies of an element.

For example, Sofie has 4 books on her shelf — 2 novels (N_1 and N_2), 1 science book (S), and 1 reference book (R).

The possible combinations of the four books with the two novels grouped together is $\frac{4!}{2!} = 4 \cdot 3 = 12$.

Another type of permutation is called a circular permutation. A **circular permutation** is a permutation in which there is no starting point and no ending point. The circular permutation of n objects is $(n - 1)!$. A common example of circular permutations are seating arrangements for a group of people.

A **combination** is an unordered collection of items. Different notations can be used for the combinations of r elements taken from a collection of n elements:

$$_nC_r = C(n, r) = C^n_r$$

In permutations the order that the objects are put into is relevant, but in a combination the order is not relevant. For example, all of the 3-letter permutations from the letters DEFG is $_4P_3 = \frac{4!}{(4 - 3)!} = 24$ outcomes. To eliminate any outcomes that repeated the same 3 letters that were just in a different order is to determine the combination of 3-letter strings from the letters DEFG.

You can calculate combinations using the formula $_nC_r = \frac{n!}{(n - r)!r!}$.

For example, the possible combinations of 3-letter strings from the letters DEFG is $_4C_3 = \frac{4!}{(4 - 3)!3!} = \frac{4!}{1!3!} = 4$.

A Different Kind of Court Trial

Independent events can happen in more than one way when performing multiple trials. The probability of the events happening is multiplied by the different ways the events can happen.

For example, the chart below summarizes the probability of a basketball player making each number of free throws using combinations.

Number of Free Throws	Number of Free Throws	Probability of Making	Probability of Missing	Probability of Making r
Attempts	Makes	Each Free Throw	Each Free Throw	out of n Attempts
n	r	$P(A)$	$P(\sim A)$	${}_nC_r\left(\frac{2}{3}\right)^n\left(\frac{1}{3}\right)^r$
1	0	$\frac{2}{3}$	$\frac{1}{3}$	${}_1C_0\left(\frac{2}{3}\right)^0\left(\frac{1}{3}\right)^1$
	1	$\frac{2}{3}$	$\frac{1}{3}$	${}_1C_1\left(\frac{2}{3}\right)^1\left(\frac{1}{3}\right)^0$
2	0	$\frac{2}{3}$	$\frac{1}{3}$	${}_2C_0\left(\frac{2}{3}\right)^0\left(\frac{1}{3}\right)^2$
	1	$\frac{2}{3}$	$\frac{1}{3}$	${}_2C_1\left(\frac{2}{3}\right)^1\left(\frac{1}{3}\right)^1$
	2	$\frac{2}{3}$	$\frac{1}{3}$	${}_2C_2\left(\frac{2}{3}\right)^2\left(\frac{1}{3}\right)^0$
3	0	$\frac{2}{3}$	$\frac{1}{3}$	${}_3C_0\left(\frac{2}{3}\right)^0\left(\frac{1}{3}\right)^3$
	1	$\frac{2}{3}$	$\frac{1}{3}$	${}_3C_1\left(\frac{2}{3}\right)^1\left(\frac{1}{3}\right)^2$
	2	$\frac{2}{3}$	$\frac{1}{3}$	${}_3C_2\left(\frac{2}{3}\right)^2\left(\frac{1}{3}\right)^1$
	3	$\frac{2}{3}$	$\frac{1}{3}$	${}_3C_3\left(\frac{2}{3}\right)^3\left(\frac{1}{3}\right)^0$

LESSON 5

What Do You Expect?

o determine the probability of hitting a shaded section on a dart board, you used geometric robability. **Geometric probability** is probability that involves a geometric measure, such as ength, area, volume, and so on.

or example, consider the dart board shown which is a square that measures 50 cm by 50 cm.

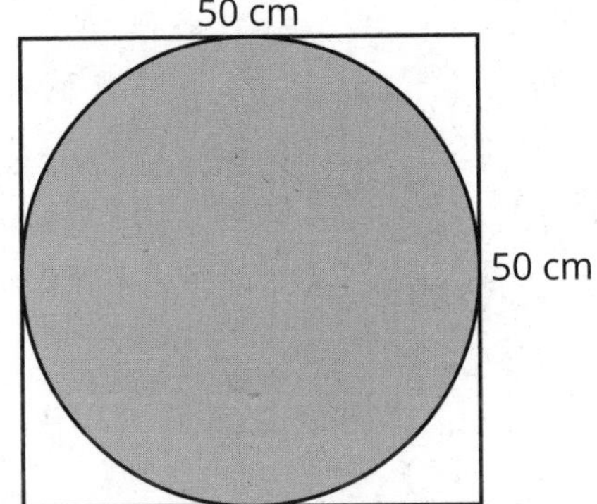

he probability of a dart hitting the shaded region of the dart board is $\frac{\text{area of shaded region}}{\text{area of dart board}}$.

$$\frac{\text{area of shaded region}}{\text{area of dart board}} = \frac{\pi(25)^2}{50 \cdot 50} \approx \frac{1962.5}{2500}$$

he probability that the dart hits the shaded region is $\frac{1962.5}{2500}$, or about 78.5%.

n **expected value** is the average value when the number of trials is large.

or example, suppose you are a contestant on a game show. In the first round, the host gives you $200. ou can choose to keep the money or give the money back and spin the wheel to determine your winnings.

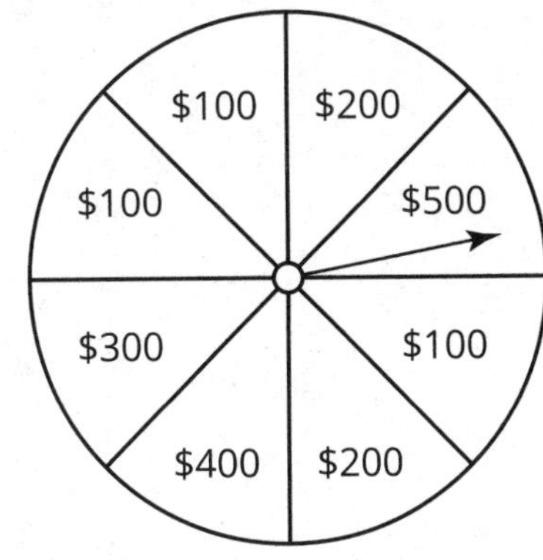

n this problem, the expected value represents the amount that you could expect to receive from a single spin or $\frac{3}{8}(100) + \frac{2}{8}(200) + \frac{1}{8}(300) + \frac{1}{8}(400) + \frac{1}{8}(500) = \$237.50$.

Glossary

A

solute value

absolute value of a number is its distance
n zero on the number line.

mple

= 5 because 5 is 5 units from 0 on the
nber line. $|-3| = 3$ because -3 is 3 units
n 0 on the number line.

dition Property of Equality

addition property of equality states: "If
b, then $a + c = b + c$."

mple

= 2, then $x + 5 = 2 + 5$, or $x + 5 = 7$ is an
mple of the Addition Property of Equality.

Addition Rule for Probability

The Addition Rule for Probability states: "The probability that Event *A* occurs or Event *B* occurs is the probability that Event *A* occurs plus the probability that Event *B* occurs minus the probability that both *A* and *B* occur."

$$P(A \text{ or } B) = P(A) + P(B) = P(A \text{ and } B)$$

Example

You flip a coin two times. Calculate the probability of flipping a heads on the first flip or flipping a heads on the second flip.

Let *A* represent the event of flipping a heads on the first flip. Let *B* represent the event of flipping a heads on the second flip.

$P(A \text{ or } B) = P(A) + P(B) - P(A \text{ and } B)$

$P(A \text{ or } B) = \frac{1}{2} + \frac{1}{2} - \frac{1}{4}$

$P(A \text{ or } B) = \frac{3}{4}$

So, the probability of flipping a heads on the first flip or flipping a heads on the second flip is $\frac{3}{4}$.

adjacent arcs

Adjacent arcs are two arcs of the same circle sharing a common endpoint.

Example

Arcs *ZA* and *AB* are adjacent arcs.

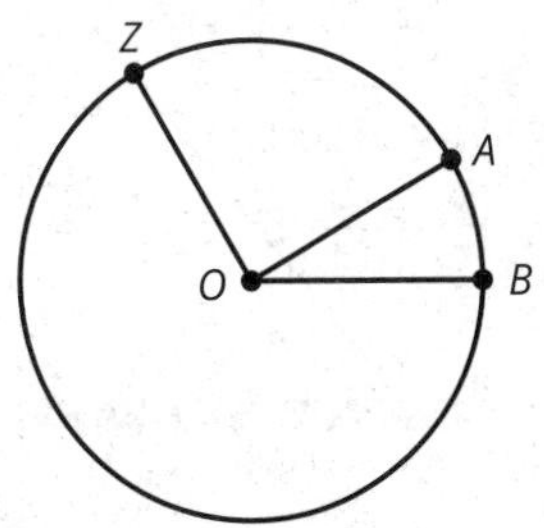

adjacent side

The adjacent side of a triangle is the side adjacent to the reference angle that is not the hypotenuse.

Example

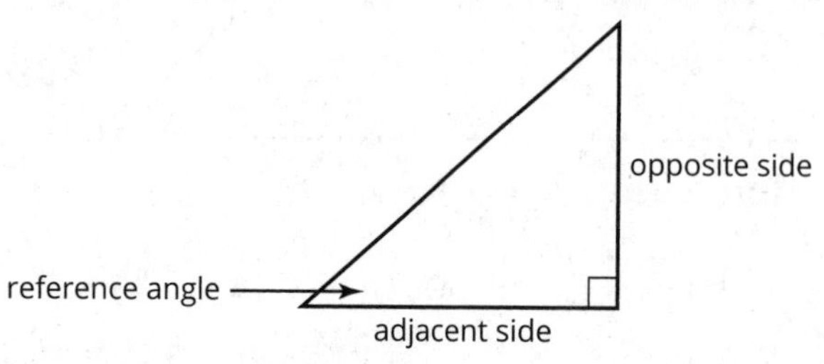

altitude

An altitude is a line segment drawn from a vertex of a triangle perpendicular to the line containing the opposite side.

Example

Segment *EG* is an altitude of $\triangle FED$.

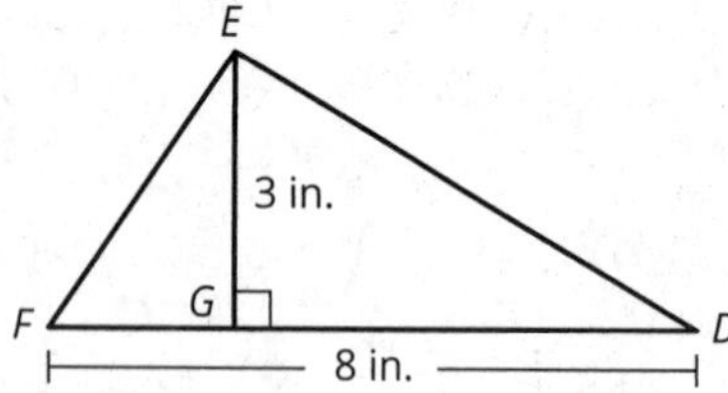

angle of incidence

The angle of incidence is the angle formed by the incidence ray and a line perpendicular to the surface of a mirror.

Example

The angle of incidence measures 40°.

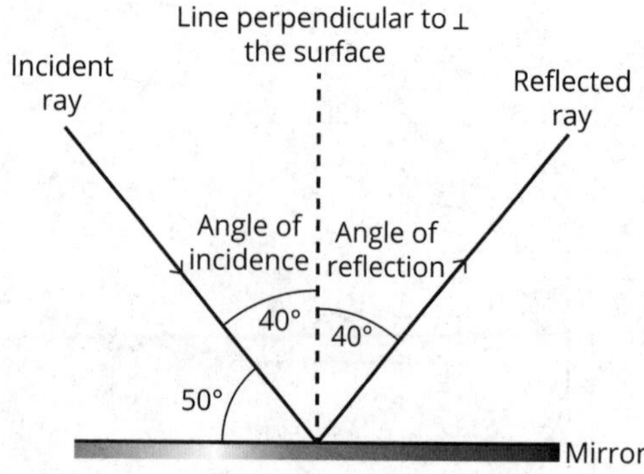

angle of reflection

The angle of reflection is the angle formed by the reflected ray and a line perpendicular to t surface of a mirror.

Example

The angle of reflection measures 40°.

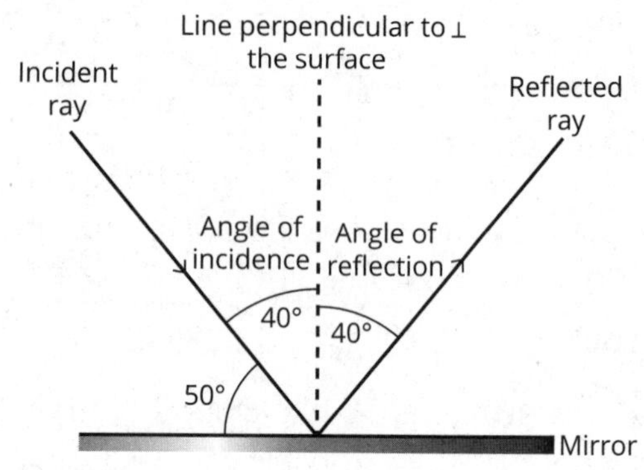

angular velocity

Angular velocity is a type of circular velocity described as an amount of angle movement ir radians over a specified amount of time. Angu velocity can be expressed as $\omega = \frac{\theta}{t}$, where ω = angular velocity, θ = angular measuremer in radians, and t = time.

arc length

An arc length is a portion of the circumference of a circle. The length of an arc of a circle can be calculated by multiplying the circumference of the circle by the ratio of the measure of the arc to 36(

$$\text{arc length} = 2\pi r \cdot \frac{x°}{360°}$$

Example

In circle *A*, the radius $\overline{AB}$ is 3 centimeters and t measure of $\widehat{BC}$ is 83 degrees.

$$(2\pi r)\left(\frac{m\widehat{BC}}{360°}\right) = 2\pi(3)\left(\frac{83}{360°}\right)$$
$$\approx 4.35$$

So, the length of $\widehat{BC}$ is approximately 4.35 centimeters.

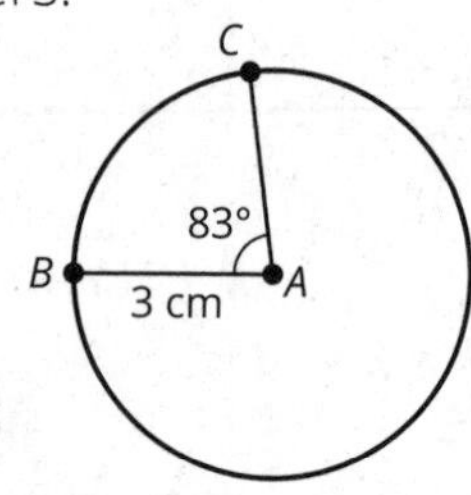

gument of a function

argument of a function is the variable on ch the function operates.

mple

he function $f(x + 5) = 32$, the argument + 5.

xiliary line

auxiliary line is a line that is drawn to help nplete a geometric proof.

ample

auxiliary line is drawn parallel to $\overleftrightarrow{AB}$ through nt C.

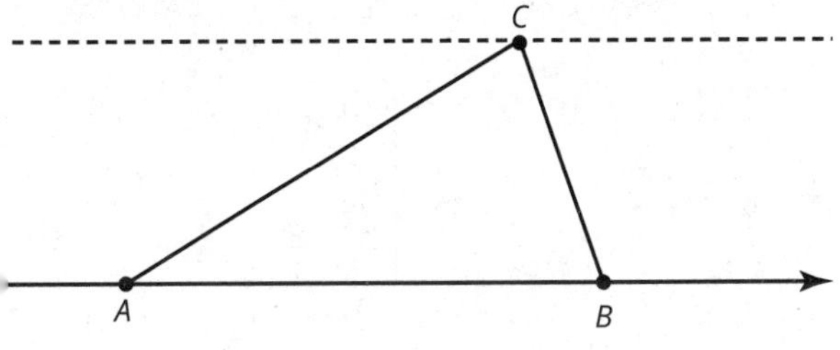

is of symmetry of a parabola

axis of symmetry of a parabola is a line t passes through the vertex and divides the abola into two mirror images.

ample

e k is the axis of symmetry of the parabola.

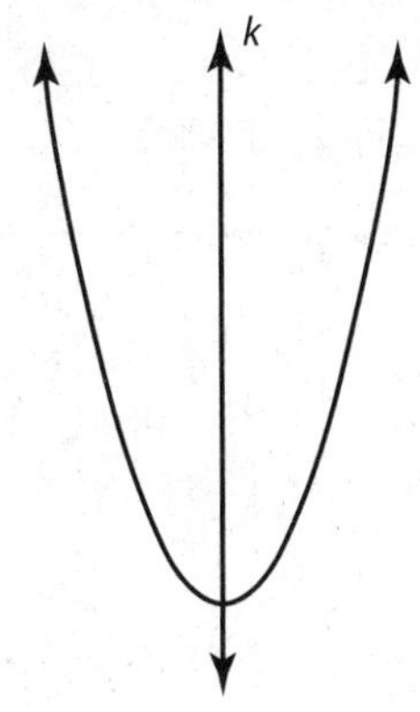

B

base angles of an isosceles triangle

The base angles of an isosceles triangle are the angles between the base and the congruent sides of the triangle.

Example

Angles A and C are the base angles of isosceles triangle ABC.

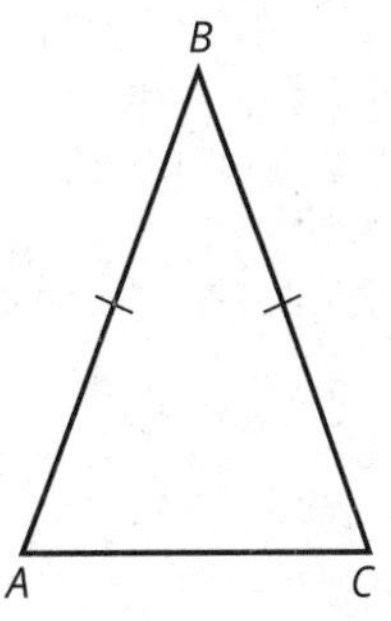

base angles of a trapezoid

The base angles of a trapezoid are either pair of angles that share a base as a common side.

Example

Angle T and angle R are one pair of base angles of trapezoid $PART$. Angle P and angle A are another pair of base angles.

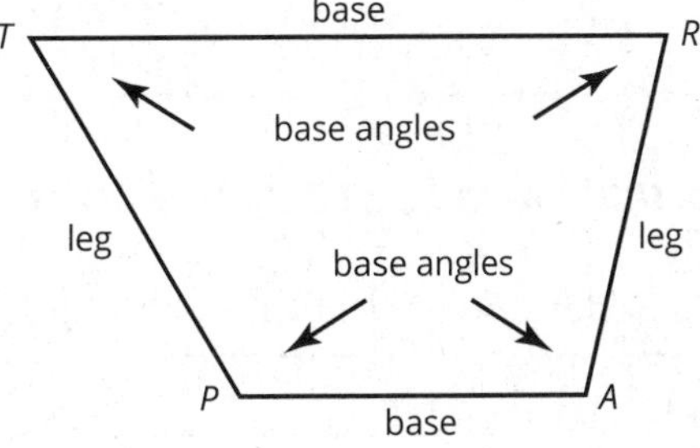

biconditional statement

A biconditional statement is a statement written in the form "if and only if p, then q." It is a combination of both a conditional statement and the converse of that conditional statement. A biconditional statement is true only when the conditional statement and the converse of the statement are both true.

Example

Consider the property of an isosceles trapezoid: "The diagonals of an isosceles trapezoid are congruent." The property states that if a trapezoid is isosceles, then the diagonals are congruent. The converse of this statement is true: "If the diagonals of a trapezoid are congruent, then the trapezoid is an isosceles trapezoid." So, this property can be written as a biconditional statement: "A trapezoid is isosceles if and only if its diagonals are congruent."

binomial

Polynomials with exactly two terms are binomials.

Example

The polynomial $3x + 5$ is a binomial.

C

categorical data (qualitative data)

Categorical data are data that each fit into exactly one of several different groups, or categories. Categorical data are also called "qualitative data."

Example

Animals: lions, tigers, bears, etc.
U.S. Cities: Los Angeles, Atlanta, New York City, Dodge City, etc.

The set of animals and the set of U.S. cities are two examples of categorical data sets.

Cavalieri's Principle

Cavalieri's principle states that if all one-dimensio slices of two-dimensional figures have the same lengths, then the two-dimensional figures have the same area. The principle also states that give two solid figures included between parallel plane if every plane cross section parallel to the given planes has the same area in both solids, then the volumes of the solids are equal.

centroid

The centroid of a triangle is the point at which the medians of the triangle intersect.

Example

Point X is the centroid of triangle $\triangle ABC$.

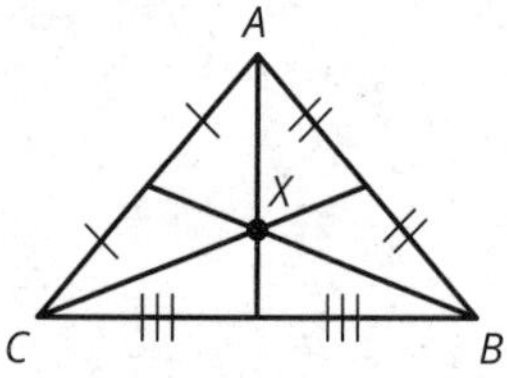

circular permutation

A circular permutation is a permutation in whi there is no starting point and no ending point The circular permutation of n objects is $(n - 1$

Example

A club consists of four officers: a president (P), a vicepresident (VP), a secretary (S), and a treasurer (T). There are $(4 - 1)!$, or 6 ways for t officers to sit around a round table.

circumcenter

The circumcenter of a triangle is the point at which the perpendicular bisectors intersect.

Example

Point X is the circumcenter of $\triangle ABC$.

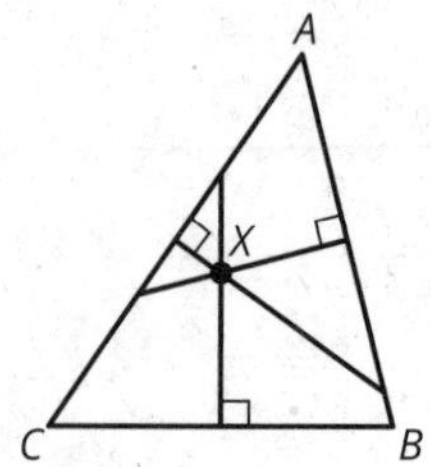

:umscribed angle

·cumscribed angle has its two sides tangent circle.

ımple

le ABC is circumscribed in circle O.

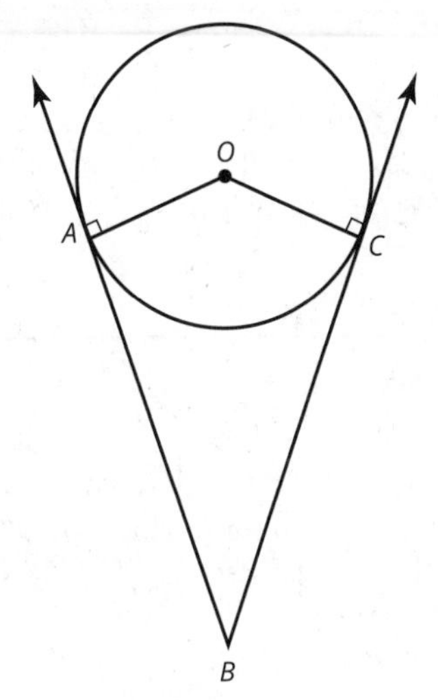

cumscribed circle

rcumscribed circle is a circle that passes ɔugh all the vertices of a polygon.

ımple

:le Q is circumscribed around $\triangle ABC$.

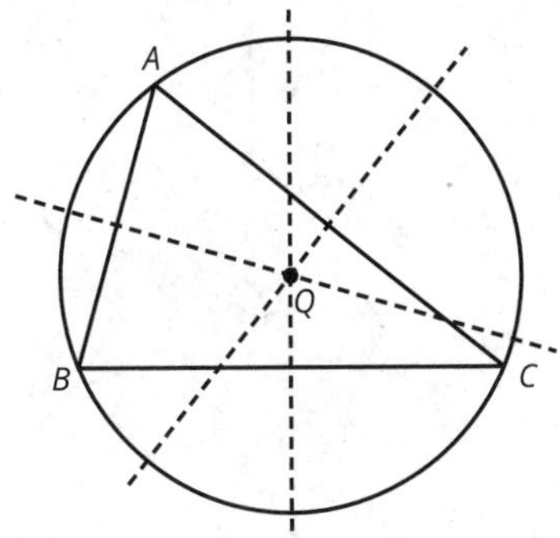

›sed (closure)

ıen an operation is performed on any of the nbers in a set and the result is a number ıt is also in the same set, the set is said to be sed (or to have closure) under that operation.

ample

ᴇ set of whole numbers is closed under dition. The sum of any two whole numbers is ᴠays another whole number.

coincident

Two line segments are coincident if they lie exactly on top of each other.

combination

A combination is an unordered collection of items. One notation for the combinations of r elements taken from a collection of n elements is:

$$_{n}C_{r} = C(n, r) = C^{n}{}_{r}$$

Example

The two-letter combinations of the letters A, B, and C are: AB, AC, BC.

complement of an event

The complement of an event is an event that contains all the outcomes in the sample space that are not outcomes in the event. In mathematical notation, if E is an event, then the complement of E is often denoted as $\overline{E}$ or E^c.

Example

A number cube contains the numbers 1 though 6. Let E represent the event of rolling an even number. The complement of Event E is rolling an odd number.

completing the square

Completing the square is a process for writing a quadratic expression in vertex form which then allows you to solve for the zeros.

complex numbers

The set of complex numbers is the set of all numbers written in the form $a + bi$, where a and b are real numbers.

compound event

A compound event combines two or more events, using the word "and" or the word "or."

Example

You roll a number cube twice. Rolling a six on the first roll and rolling an odd number on the second roll are compound events.

concavity

The concavity of a parabola describes the orientation of the curvature of the parabola.

Example

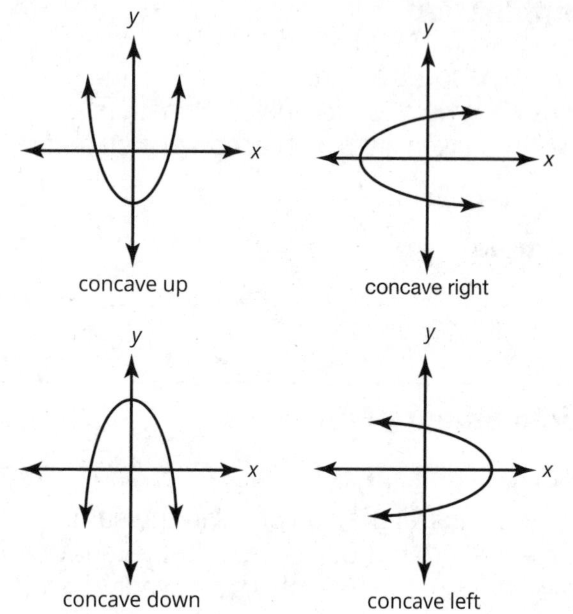

conclusion

A conclusion is the "then" part of an "if-then" statement.

Example

In the statement "If two positive numbers are added, then the sum is positive," the conclusion is "the sum is positive."

concurrent

Concurrent lines, rays, or line segments are three or more lines, rays, or line segments intersecting at a single point.

Example

Lines ℓ, m, and n are concurrent lines.

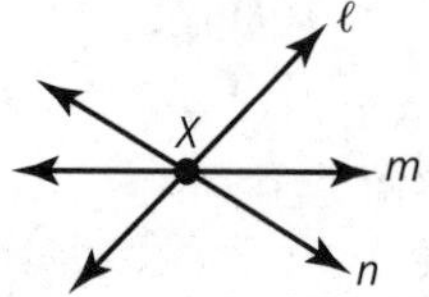

conditional probability

A conditional probability is the probability of event B, given that event A has already occurr The notation for conditional probability is $P(B$ which reads, "the probability of event B, given event A."

Example

The probability of rolling a 4 or less on the second roll of a number cube, given that a 5 is rolled first, is an example of a conditional probability.

conic section

A conic section is a curve obtained as the intersection of the surface of a double-nappe cone with a plane.

Example

A parabola is a conic section that results from the intersection of a plane with one nappe of the double-napped cone, parallel to the edge of the cone.

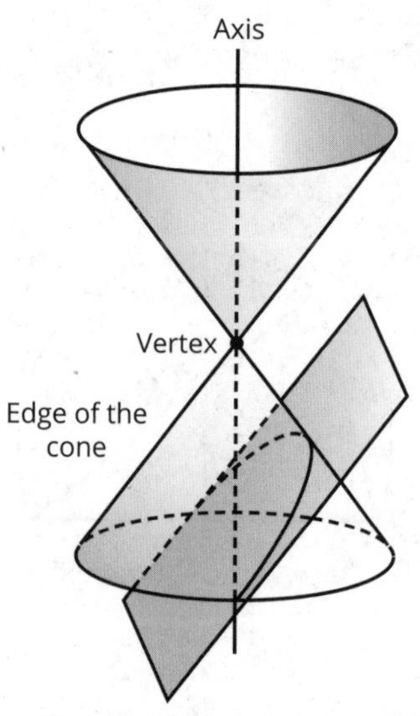

conjecture

A conjecture is a hypothesis that something is true. The hypothesis can later be proved or disproved.

converse

To state the converse of a conditional statement, nterchange the hypothesis and the conclusion.

Conditional Statement: If p, then q.

Converse: If q, then p.

Example

Conditional Statement: If $a = 0$ or $b = 0$, hen $ab = 0$.

Converse: If $ab = 0$, then $a = 0$ or $b = 0$.

corresponding parts of congruent riangles are congruent (CPCTC)

PCTC states that if two triangles are congruent, hen each part of one triangle is congruent to he corresponding part of the other triangle.

xample

n the triangles shown, $\triangle XYZ \cong \triangle LMN$. Because orresponding parts of congruent triangles are ongruent (CPCTC), the following corresponding arts are congruent.

$\angle X \cong \angle L$

$\angle Y \cong \angle M$

$\angle Z \cong \angle N$

$\overline{XY} \cong \overline{LM}$

$\overline{YZ} \cong \overline{MN}$

$\overline{XZ} \cong \overline{LN}$

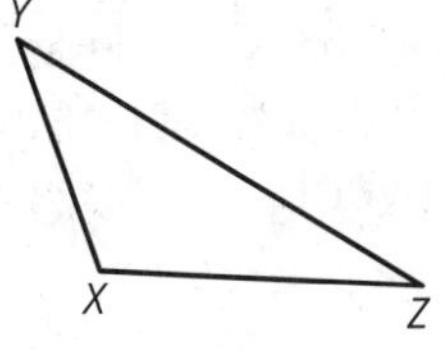

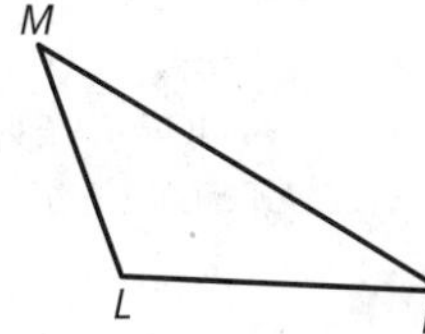

cosecant (csc)

The cosecant (csc) of an acute angle in a right triangle is the ratio of the length of the hypotenuse to the length of the side opposite the angle.

Example

In $\triangle ABC$, the cosecant of $\angle A$ is:

$$\csc A = \frac{\text{length of hypotenuse}}{\text{length of side opposite } \angle A} = \frac{AB}{BC}$$

The expression "csc A" means "the cosecant of angle A."

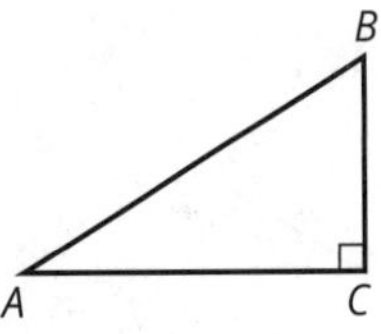

cosine (cos)

The cosine (cos) of an acute angle in a right triangle is the ratio of the length of the side adjacent to the angle to the length of the hypotenuse.

Example

In $\triangle ABC$, the cosine of $\angle A$ is:

$$\cos A = \frac{\text{length of side adjacent to } \angle A}{\text{length of hypotenuse}} = \frac{AC}{AB}$$

The expression "cos A" means "the cosine of angle A."

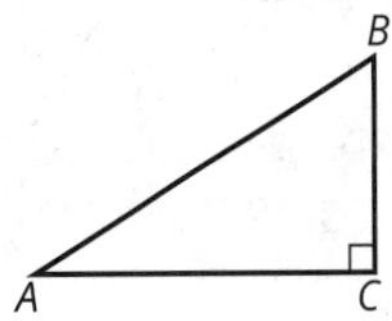

cotangent (cot)

The cotangent (cot) of an acute angle in a right triangle is the ratio of the length of the side adjacent to the angle to the length of the side opposite the angle.

Example

In $\triangle ABC$, the cotangent of $\angle A$ is:

$$\cot A = \frac{\text{length of side adjacent to } \angle A}{\text{length of side opposite } \angle A} = \frac{AC}{BC}$$

The expression "cot *A*" means "the cotangent of angle *A*."

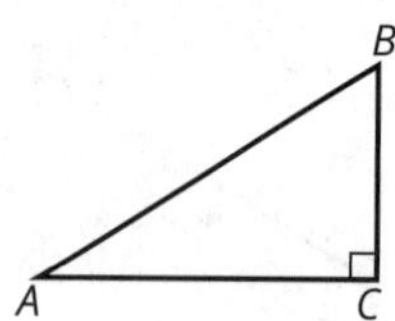

Counting Principle

The Counting Principle states that if action *A* can occur in *m* ways and for each of these *m* ways action *B* can occur in *n* ways, then actions *A* and *B* can occur in $m \cdot n$ ways.

Example

In the school cafeteria, there are 3 different main entrées and 4 different sides. So, there are $3 \cdot 4$, or 12 different lunches that can be created.

cyclic quadrilateral

A cyclic quadrilateral is a quadrilateral whose vertices all lie on a single circle.

Example

Quadrilateral *MATH* is a cyclic quadrilateral whose vertices all lie on circle *O*.

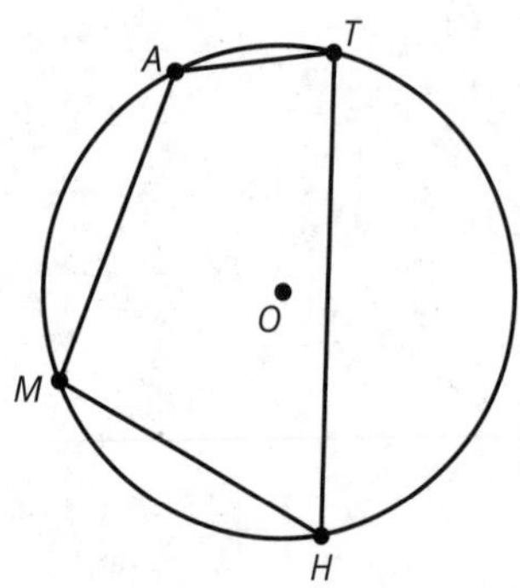

D

degree measure of an arc

The degree measure of a minor arc is equal to the degree measure of its central angle. The degree measure of a major arc is determined by subtracting the degree measure of the minor arc from 360°.

Example

The measure of minor arc *AB* is 30°. The measure of major arc *BZA* is $360° - 30° = 330°$.

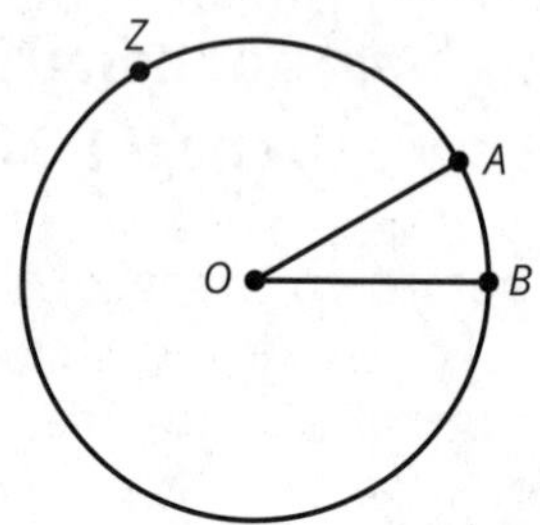

degree of a polynomial

The greatest exponent in a polynomial determines the degree of the polynomial.

Example

The polynomial $2x^3 + 5x^2 - 6x + 1$ has a degree of 3.

dependent events

Dependent events are events for which the occurrence of one event has an impact on the occurrence of subsequent events.

Example

A jar contains 1 blue marble, 1 green marble, and 2 yellow marbles. You randomly choose a yellow marble without replacing the marble in the jar, and then randomly choose a yellow marble again. The events of randomly choosing a yellow marble first and randomly choosing a yellow marble second are dependent events because the 1st yellow marble was not replace in the jar.

diagonal

A diagonal is a line segment joining two vertices of a polygon but is not a side of the polygon.

diameter of a sphere

The diameter of a sphere is a line segment with each endpoint on the sphere that passes through the center of the sphere.

Example

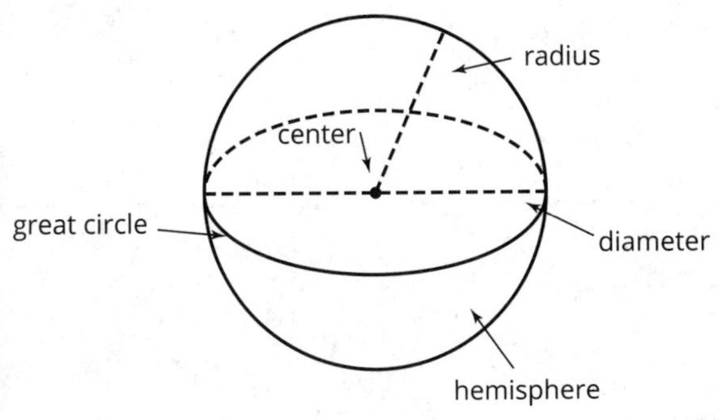

difference of two squares

The difference of two squares is an expression in the form $a^2 - b^2$ that can be factored as $(a + b)(a - b)$.

Example

The expression $x^2 - 4$ is a difference of two squares because it can be written in the form $x^2 - 2^2$. The expression can be factored as $(x + 2)(x - 2)$.

dilation

A dilation is a transformation of the figure in which the figure stretches or shrinks with respect to a fixed point, or center of dilation.

Example

Triangle *DEF* is a dilation of $\triangle ABC$. The center of dilation is point *Y*.

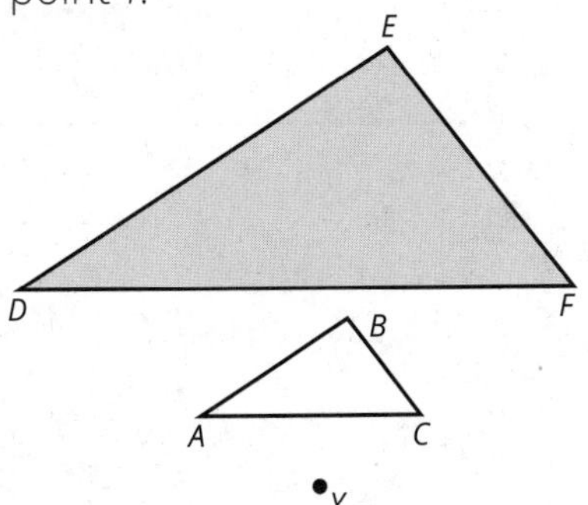

directed line segment

A directed line segment is assigned a direction from one endpoint to the other.

Example

Directed line segment *AB* is mathematically different from directed line segment *BA*.

directrix

The directrix of a parabola is a line such that all points on the parabola are equidistant from the focus and the directrix.

Example

The focus of the parabola shown is the point (0, 2). The directrix of the parabola shown is the line $y = -2$. All points on the parabola are equidistant from the focus and the directrix.

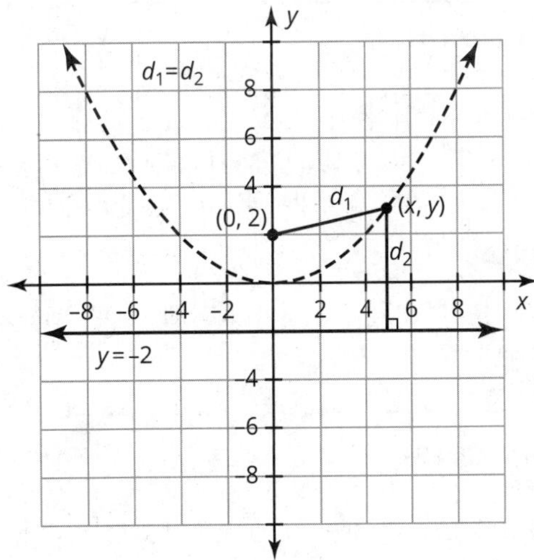

discontinuous graph

A discontinuous graph is a graph that is continuous for some values of the domain with at least one disjoint area between consecutive x-values.

Example

The graph shown is a discontinuous graph.

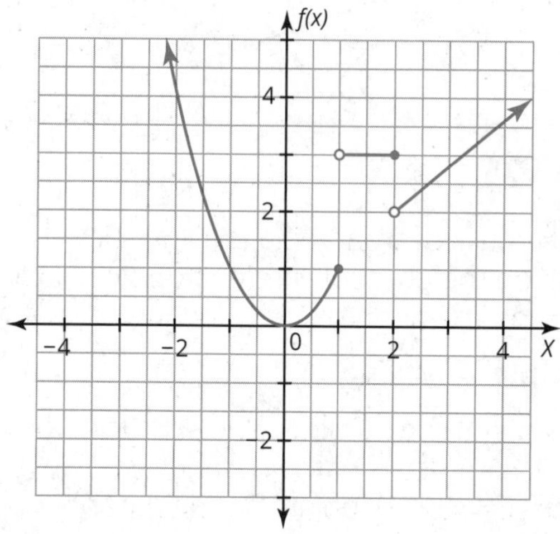

discriminant

The discriminant is the radicand expression in the Quadratic Formula which "discriminates" the number of roots of a quadratic equation.

Example

The discriminant in the Quadratic Formula is the expression $b^2 - 4ac$.

disjoint sets

Two or more sets are disjoint sets if they do not have any common elements.

Example

Let N represent the set of 9th grade students. Let T represent the set of 10th grade students. The sets N and T are disjoint sets because the two sets do not have any common elements. Any student can be in one grade only.

double root

A double root of an equation is a root that appears twice. A double root occurs when the graph just touches the x-axis but does not cross it.

Example

The equation $x^2 + 2x + 1 = 0$ has a double root at $x = -1$.

$x^2 + 2x + 1 = 0$

$(x + 1)(x + 1) = 0$

$x + 1 = 0$ or $x + 1 = 0$

$x = -1$ or $x = -1$

E

element

A member of a set is called an element of that set.

Example

Set B contains the elements a, b, and c.

$B = \{a, b, c\}$

equivalent compound inequality

A compound inequality that is the equivalent of an absolute value inequality.

Example

Absolute Value Inequality	Equivalent Compound Inequality
$\lvert ax + b\rvert < c$	$-c < ax + b < c$
$\lvert ax + b\rvert \leq c$	$-c \leq ax + b \leq c$
$\lvert ax + b\rvert > c$	$ax + b < -c$ or $ax + b > c$
$\lvert ax + b\rvert \geq c$	$ax + b \leq -c$ or $ax + b \geq c$

event

An event is an outcome or a set of outcomes in a sample space.

xample

A number cube contains the numbers 1 through 6. Rolling a 6 is one event. Rolling an even number is another event.

expected value

The expected value is the average value when the number of trials in a probability experiment is large.

exterior angle of a polygon

An exterior angle of a polygon is an angle that is adjacent to an interior angle of a polygon.

xample

ngle *JHI* is an exterior angle of quadrilateral *GHI*. Angle *EDA* is an exterior angle of uadrilateral *ABCD*.

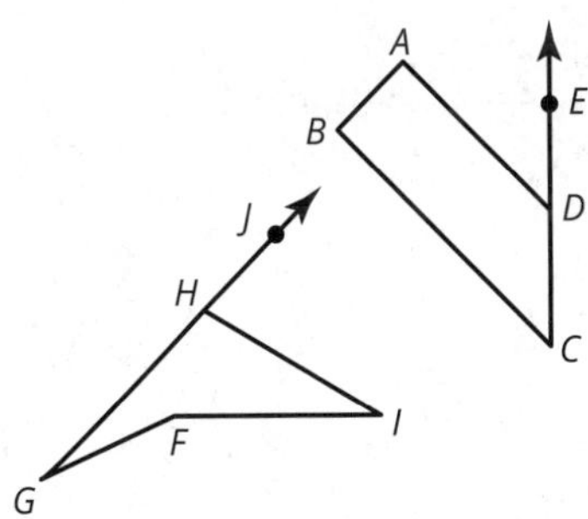

extract the roots

To extract a root is the process of removing all perfect square numbers from under the radical symbol.

Example

To extract the root for $\sqrt{18}$, remove all perfect square numbers that are factors of 18.

$$\begin{aligned}\sqrt{18} &= \sqrt{9} \cdot 2 \\ &= \sqrt{3^2} \cdot 2 \\ &= 3\sqrt{2}\end{aligned}$$

F

factored form

A quadratic function written in factored form is in the form $f(x) = a(x - r_1)(x - r_2)$, where $a \neq 0$.

Example

The function $h(x) = x^2 - 8x + 12$ written in factored form is $(x - 6)(x - 2)$.

factorial

The factorial of n, written as $n!$, is the product of all non-negative integers less than or equal to n.

Example

$3! = 3 \times 2 \times 1 = 6$

flow chart proof

A flow chart proof is a proof in which the steps and corresponding reasons are written in boxes. Arrows connect the boxes and indicate how each step and reason is generated from one or more other steps and reasons.

Example

A flow chart proof is shown for the conditional statement: If $\overline{AB} \cong \overline{CD}$, then $\overline{AC} \cong \overline{BD}$.

Given: $\overline{AB} \cong \overline{CD}$

Prove: $\overline{AC} \cong \overline{BD}$

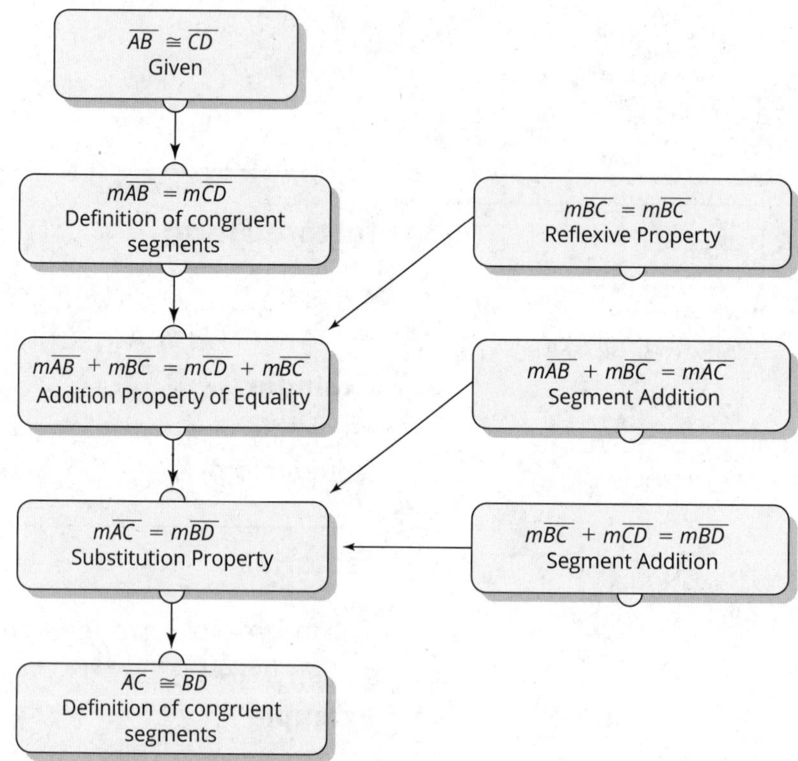

focus

The focus of a parabola is a point such that all points on the parabola are equidistant from the focus and the directrix.

Example

The focus of the parabola shown is the point (0, 2). The directrix of the parabola shown is the line $y = -2$. All points on the parabola are equidistant from the focus and the directrix.

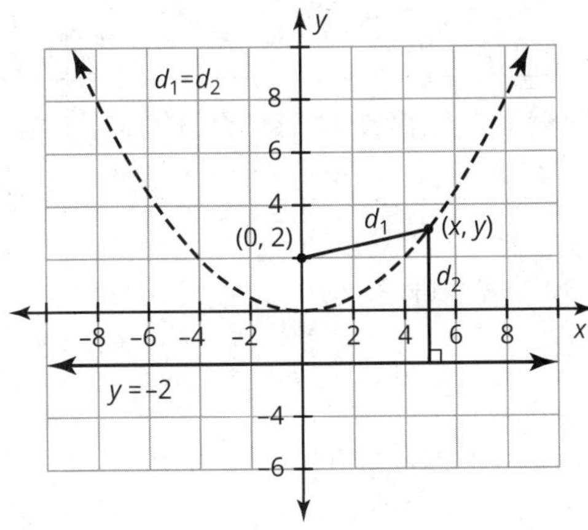

requency table

frequency table shows the frequency of an item, umber, or event appearing in a sample space.

xample

ne frequency table shows the number of times sum of two number cubes occurred.

Sum of Two Number Cubes	Frequency
2	1
3	2
4	3
5	4
6	5
7	6
8	5
9	4
10	3
11	2
12	1

Fundamental Theorem of Algebra

The Fundamental Theorem of Algebra states that any polynomial equation of degree n must have exactly n complex roots or solutions; also, every polynomial function of degree n must have exactly n complex zeros. However, any root or zero may be a multiple root or zero.

Example

The polynomial equation $x^5 + x^2 - 6 = 0$ has 5 complex roots because the polynomial $x^5 + x^2 - 6$ has a degree of 5.

G

general form of a parabola

The general form of a parabola centered at the origin is an equation of the form $Ax^2 + Dy = 0$ or $By^2 + Cx = 0$.

Example

The equation for the parabola shown can be written in general form as $x^2 - 2y = 0$.

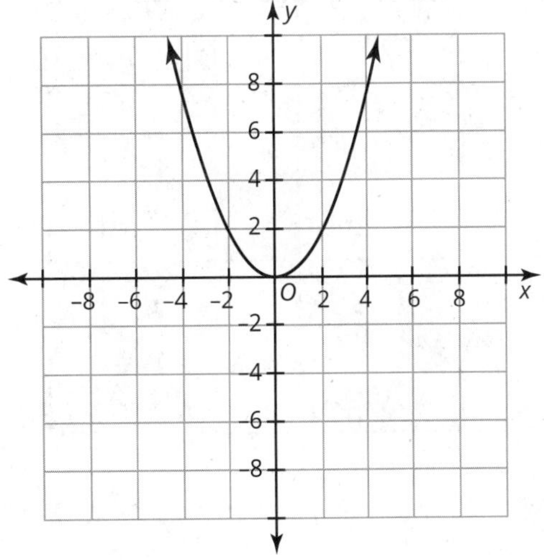

general form (standard form) of a quadratic function

A quadratic function written in the form $f(x) = ax^2 + bx + c$, where $a \neq 0$, is in standard form, or general form.

Example

The function $f(x) = -5x^2 - 10x + 1$ is written in general, or standard, form.

geometric mean

The geometric mean of two positive numbers a and b is the positive number x such that $\frac{a}{x} = \frac{x}{b}$.

Example

The geometric mean of 3 and 12 is 6.

$\frac{3}{x} = \frac{x}{12}$

$x^2 = 36$

$x = 6$

geometric probability

Geometric probability is probability that involves a geometric measure, such as length, area, volume, and so on.

Example

A dartboard has the size and shape shown. The gray shaded area represents a scoring section of the dartboard. Calculate the probability that a dart that lands on a random part of the target will land in a gray scoring section.

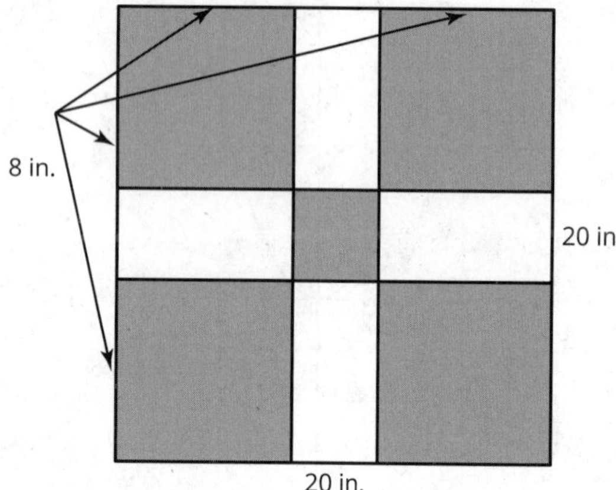

Calculate the area of the dartboard: 20(20) = 400 in.^{2}

There are 4 gray scoring squares with 8-in. sides and a gray scoring square with 20 − 8 − 8 = 4-in. sides. Calculate the area of the gray scoring sections: 4(8)(8) + 4(4) = 272 in.^{2}

Calculate the probability that a dart will hit a gray scoring section: $\frac{272}{400} = 0.68 = 68\%$.

great circle of a sphere

The great circle of a sphere is a cross section of a sphere when a plane passes through the center of the sphere.

Example

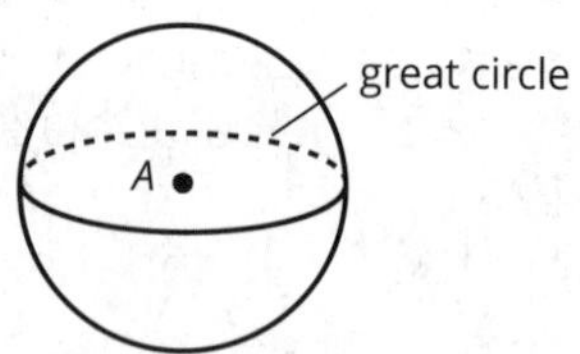

greatest integer function (floor function)

The greatest integer function, also known as a floor function, is defined as the greatest integer less than or equal to x.

Example

The greatest integer function is defined as $G(x) = \lfloor x \rfloor$. If $x = 3.75$ then $G(x) = 3$.

H

hemisphere

A hemisphere is half of a sphere bounded by a great circle.

Example

A hemisphere is shown.

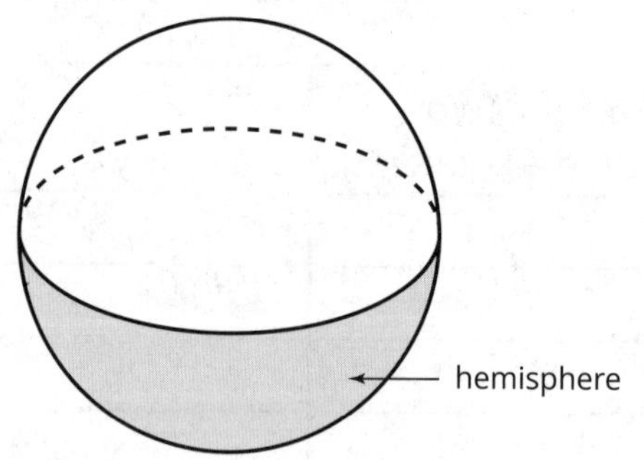

hypothesis

A hypothesis is the "if" part of an "if-then" statement.

Example

In the statement, "If the last digit of a number is a 5, then the number is divisible by 5," the hypothesis is "If the last digit of a number is a 5

I

the imaginary number *i*

The number *i* is a number such that $i^2 = -1$.

imaginary numbers

The set of imaginary numbers is the set of all numbers written in the form $a + bi$, where a and b are real numbers and b is not equal to 0.

imaginary part of a complex number

In a complex number of the form $a + bi$, the term bi is called the imaginary part of a complex number.

Example

The imaginary part of the complex number $3 + 2i$ is $2i$.

imaginary roots/imaginary zeros

Imaginary roots are imaginary solutions to equations.

Example

The quadratic equation $x^2 - 2x + 2$ has two imaginary roots: $1 + i$ and $1 - i$.

incenter

The incenter of a triangle is the point at which the angle bisectors of the triangle intersect.

Example

Point X is the incenter of $\triangle ABC$.

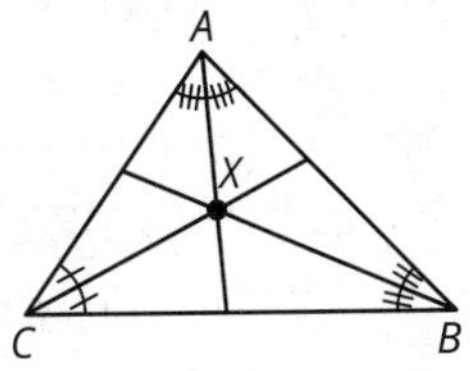

included angle

An included angle is an angle formed by two consecutive sides of a figure.

Example

In $\triangle ABC$, $\angle A$ is the included angle formed by consecutive sides $\overline{AB}$ and $\overline{AC}$.

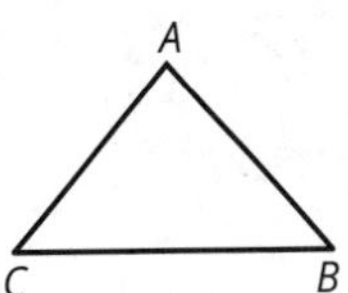

included side

An included side is a line segment between two consecutive angles of a figure.

Example

In $\triangle ABC$, $\overline{AB}$ is the included side formed by consecutive angles A and B.

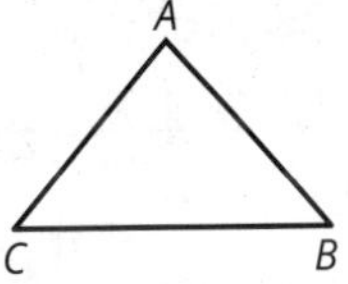

independent events

Independent events are events for which the occurrence of one event has no impact on the occurrence of the other event.

Example

You randomly choose a yellow marble, replace the marble in the jar, and then randomly choose a yellow marble again. The events of randomly choosing a yellow marble first and randomly choosing a yellow marble second are independent events because the 1st yellow marble was replaced in the jar.

indirect measurement

Indirect measurement is a technique that uses proportions to determine a measurement when direct measurement is not possible.

Example

You can use a proportion to solve for the height *x* of the flagpole.

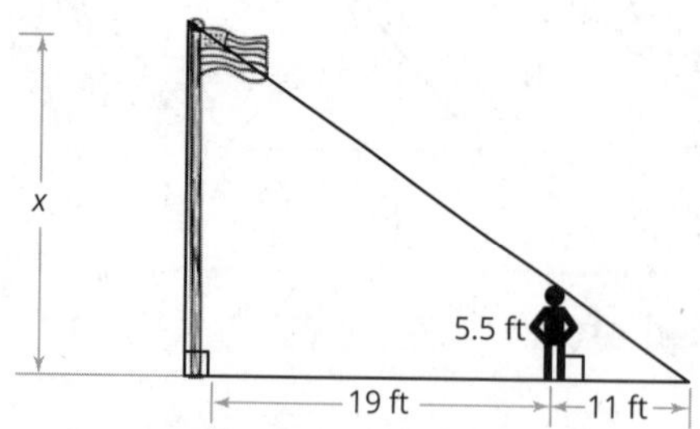

$\frac{x}{5.5} = \frac{19 + 11}{11}$

$\frac{x}{5.5} = \frac{30}{11}$

$11x = 165$

$x = 15$

The flagpole is 15 feet tall.

inscribed angle

An inscribed angle is an angle whose vertex is on a circle and whose sides contain chords of the circle.

Example

Angle *BAC* is an inscribed angle. The vertex of angle *BAC* is on the circle and the sides of angle *BAC* contain the chords $\overline{AB}$ and $\overline{AC}$.

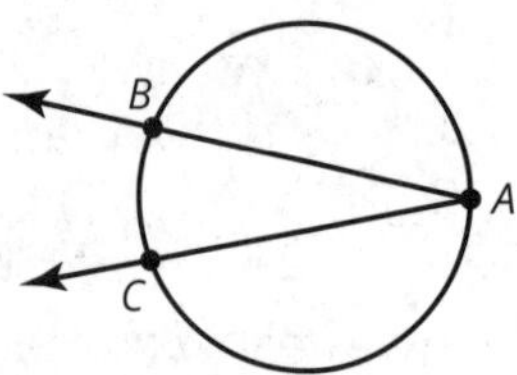

intercepted arc

An intercepted arc is formed by the intersections of the sides of an inscribed angle with a circle.

Example

$\overset{\frown}{PR}$ is an intercepted arc of inscribed angle *PSR*.

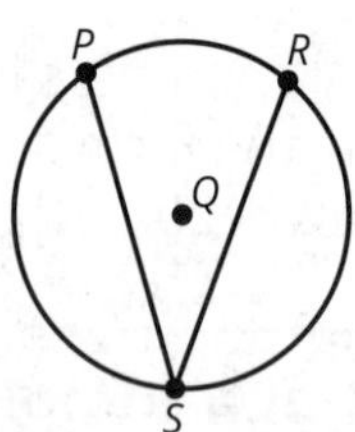

interior angle of a polygon

An interior angle of a polygon is an angle which is formed by consecutive sides of the polygon or shape.

Example

The interior angles of $\triangle ABC$ are $\angle ABC$, $\angle BCA$, and $\angle CAB$.

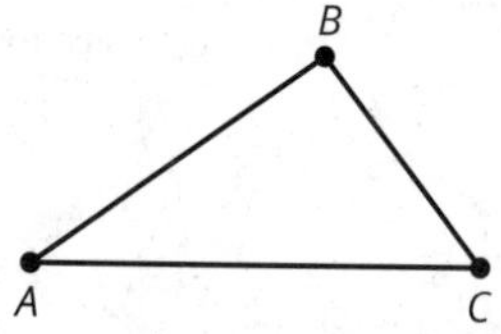

intersecting sets

Two or more sets are intersecting sets if they have common elements.

Example

Let *V* represent the set of students who are on the girls' volleyball team. Let *M* represent the set of students who are in the math club. Julia is on the volleyball team and belongs to the math club. The sets *V* and *M* are intersecting sets because the two sets have at least one common element, Julia.

inverse cosine

The inverse cosine, or arccosine, of x is the measure of an acute angle whose cosine is x.

Example

n right triangle ABC, if $\cos A = x$, then $\cos^{-1} x = m\angle A$.

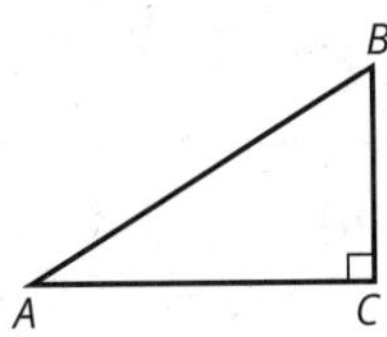

nverse of a function

n inverse of a function takes the output value, erforms some operation(s) on this value, and rrives back at the original function's input value.

xample

he inverse of the function $y = 2x$ is the function $= 2y$, or $y = \frac{x}{2}$.

nverse sine

he inverse sine, or arcsine, of x is the measure f an acute angle whose sine is x.

xample

 right triangle ABC, if $\sin A = x$, then $\sin^{-1} x = m\angle A$.

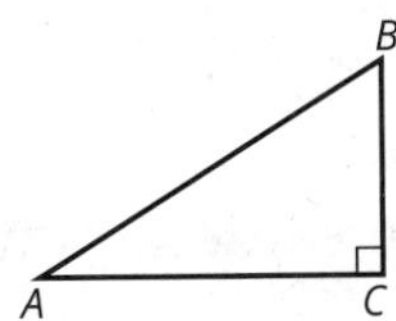

verse tangent

e inverse tangent (or arctangent) of x is the easure of an acute angle whose tangent is x.

xample

right triangle ABC, if $\tan A = x$, then $n^{-1} x = m\angle A$.

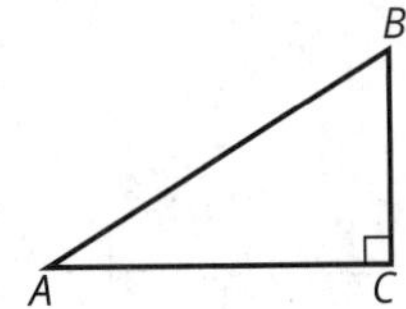

isometric paper

Isometric paper is often used by artists and engineers to create three-dimensional views of objects in two dimensions.

Example

The rectangular prism is shown on isometric paper.

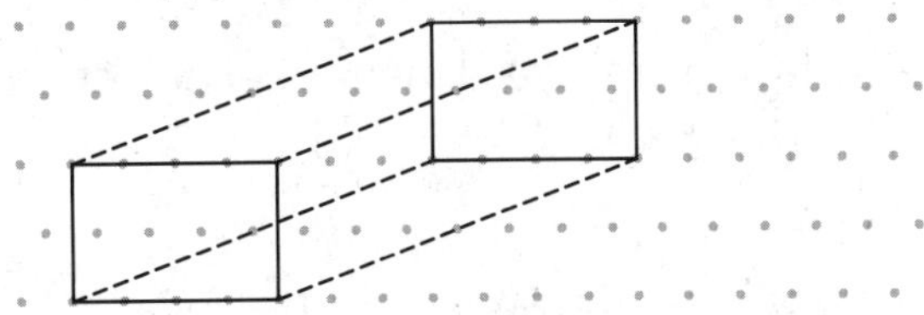

isosceles trapezoid

An isosceles trapezoid is a trapezoid whose nonparallel sides are congruent.

Example

In trapezoid $JKLM$, side $\overline{KL}$ is parallel to side $\overline{JM}$, and the length of side $\overline{JK}$ is equal to the length of side $\overline{LM}$, so trapezoid $JKLM$ is an isosceles trapezoid.

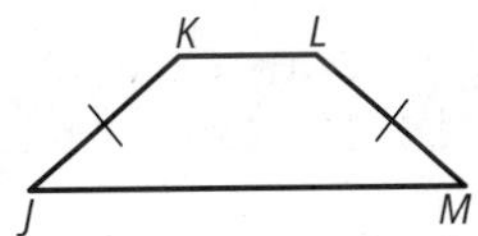

kite

A kite is a quadrilateral with two pairs of equal adjacent sides. If the diagonals of a quadrilateral are perpendicular, non-congruent, and only one bisects the other, it can only be classified as a kite.

Example

Quadrilateral $ABCD$ is a kite.

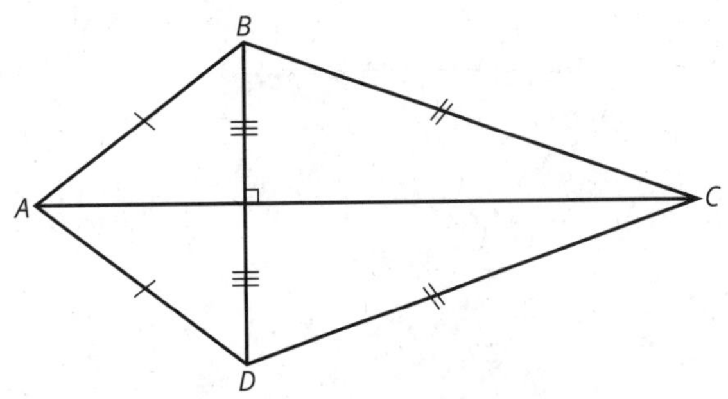

L

Law of Reflection

The Law of Reflection states that the measure of the angle of incidence equals the measure of the angle of reflection.

lateral face

A lateral face of a three-dimensional object is a face that is not a base.

Example

Each lateral face of a right triangular prism is a rectangle.

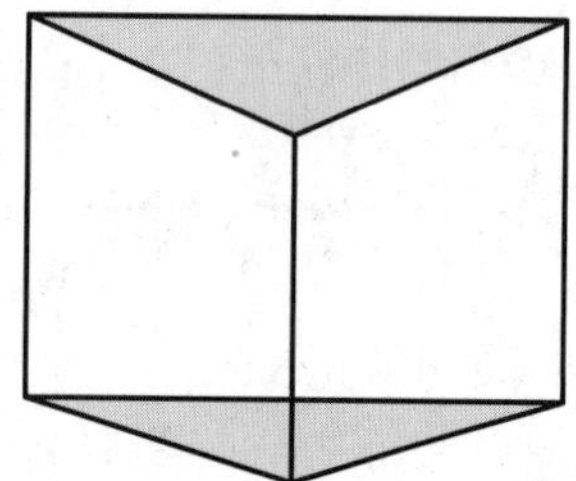

lateral surface area

The lateral surface area of a three-dimensional figure is the sum of the areas of its lateral faces.

Example

The lateral surface area of the right triangular prism is 108 square centimeters.

$$\text{Lateral surface area} = (5 \times 6) + (5 \times 6) + (8 \times 6)$$
$$= 30 + 30 + 48$$
$$= 108$$

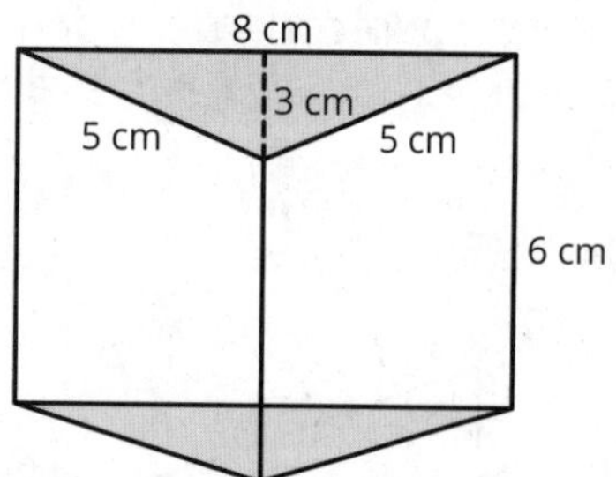

least integer function (ceiling function)

The least integer function, also known as the ceiling function, is defined as the least integer greater than or equal to x.

Example

The least integer function is defined as $L(x) = \lceil x \rceil$. If $x = 3.75$ then $L(x) = 4$.

line of reflection

A line of reflection is the line that the graph is reflected across.

Example

The graph of $y = |x| + 2$ was reflected across the line of reflection, $y = 0$.

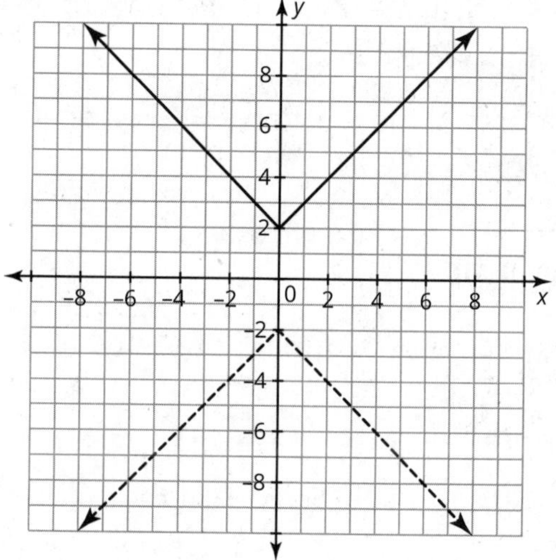

linear absolute value equation

An equation in the form $|x + a| = c$ is a linear absolute value equation.

Example

The equation $|x - 1| = 6$ is a linear absolute value equation.

linear absolute value inequality

An inequality in the form $|x + a| < c$ is a linear absolute value inequality.

Example

The inequality $|w - 145.045| \leq 3.295$ is a linea absolute value inequality.

linear piecewise functions

_inear piecewise functions include linear 'unctions that have equation changes for different parts, or pieces, of the domain.

:xample

'he function $f(x)$ is a linear piecewise function.

$$f(x) = \begin{cases} x + 5, & x \leq -2 \\ -2x + 1, & -2 < x \leq 2 \\ 2x - 9, & x > 2 \end{cases}$$

inear velocity

.inear velocity is a type of circular velocity lescribed as an amount of distance over a pecified amount of time. Linear velocity can be xpressed as $v = \frac{s}{t}$, where v = velocity, s = arc ength, and t = time.

ocus of points

locus of points is a set of points that satisfy ne or more conditions.

xample

circle is defined as a locus of points that are fixed distance, called the radius, from a given oint, called the center.

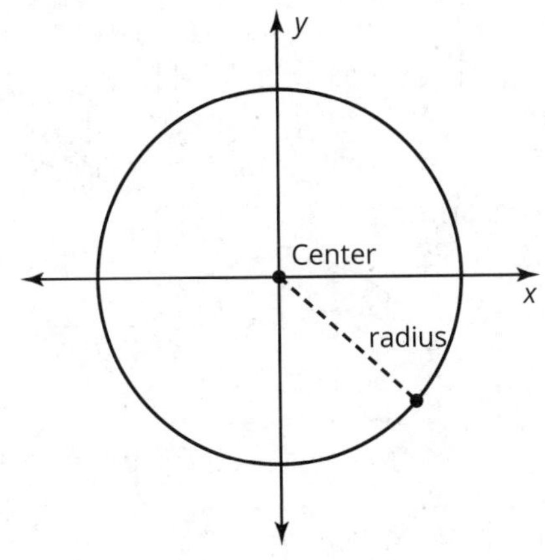

— M —

major arc

Two points on a circle determine a major arc and a minor arc. The arc with the greater measure is the major arc. The other arc is the minor arc.

Example

Circle Q is divided by points A and B into two arcs, arc ACB and arc AB. Arc ACB has the greater measure, so it is the major arc. Arc AB has the lesser measure, so it is the minor arc.

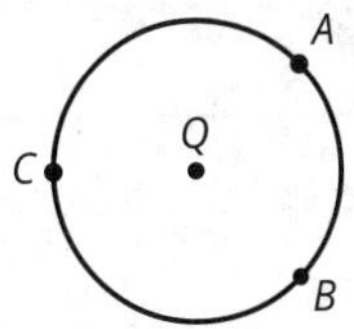

median

The median of a triangle is a line segment drawn from a vertex to the midpoint of the opposite side.

Example

The 3 medians are drawn on the triangle shown.

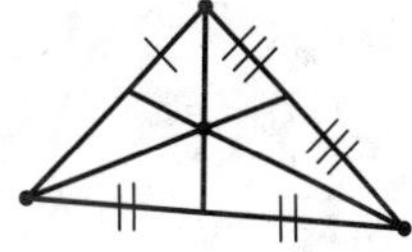

midsegment

A midsegment of a polygon is any line segment that connects two midpoints of the sides of the polygon.

Example

Segment XY is a midsegment of trapezoid $ABCD$.

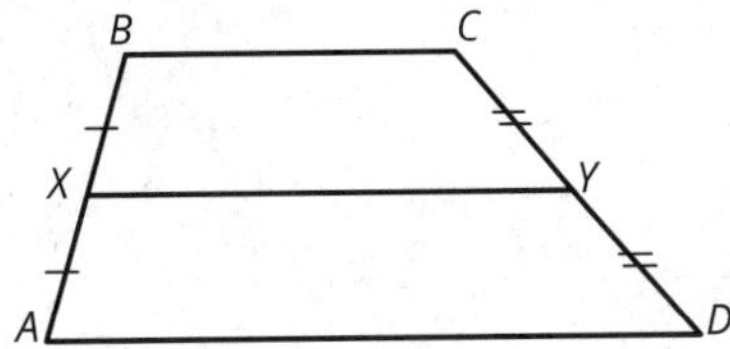

midsegment of a triangle

A midsegment of a triangle is a line segment formed by connecting the midpoints of two sides of a triangle.

Example

Segment *AB* is a midsegment.

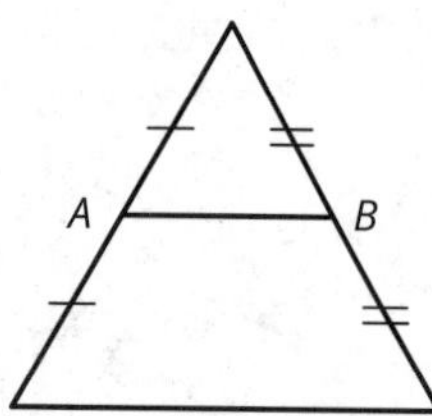

minor arc

Two points on a circle determine a minor arc and a major arc. The arc with the lesser measure is the minor arc. The other arc is the major arc.

Example

Circle *Q* is divided by points *A* and *B* into two arcs, arc *ACB* and arc *AB*. Arc *AB* has the lesser measure, so it is the minor arc. Arc *ACB* has the greater measure, so it is the major arc.

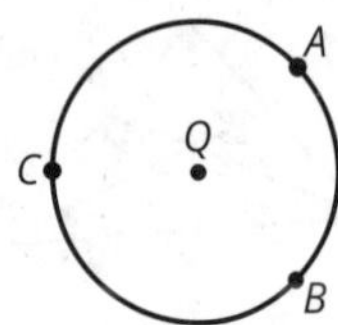

monomial

Polynomials with only one term are monomials.

Example

The expressions $5x$, 7, $-2xy$, and $13x^3$ are monomials.

N

nappes

Nappes are two congruent cones that touch at the vertex with an axis of symmetry that passes through the center of each base.

Example

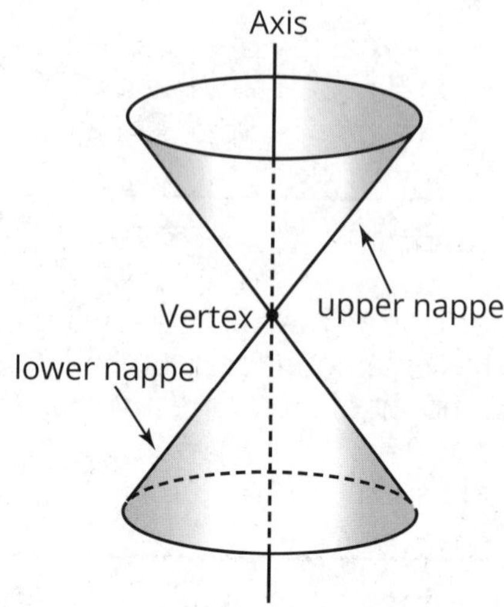

non-uniform probability model

When all probabilities in a probability model are not equivalent to each other, it is called a non-uniform probability model.

Example

Spinning the spinner shown represents a non-uniform probability model because the probability of landing on a shaded space is not equal to the probability of landing on a non-shaded space.

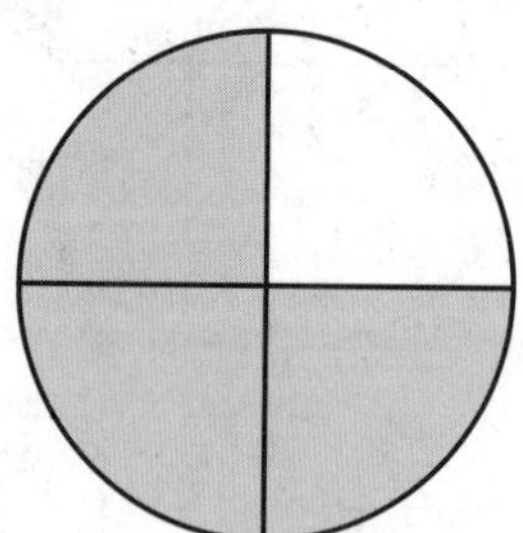

O

oblique cylinder

When a circle is translated through space in a direction that is not perpendicular to the plane containing the circle, the solid formed is an oblique cylinder.

Example

The prism shown is an oblique cylinder.

oblique rectangular prism

When a rectangle is translated through space in direction that is not perpendicular to the plane containing the rectangle, the solid formed is an oblique rectangular prism.

Example

The prism shown is an oblique rectangular prism.

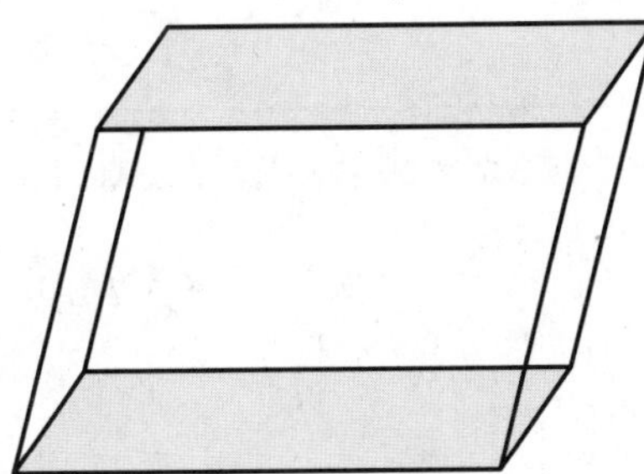

oblique triangular prism

When a triangle is translated through space in a direction that is not perpendicular to the plane containing the triangle, the solid formed is an oblique triangular prism.

Example

The prism shown is an oblique triangular prism.

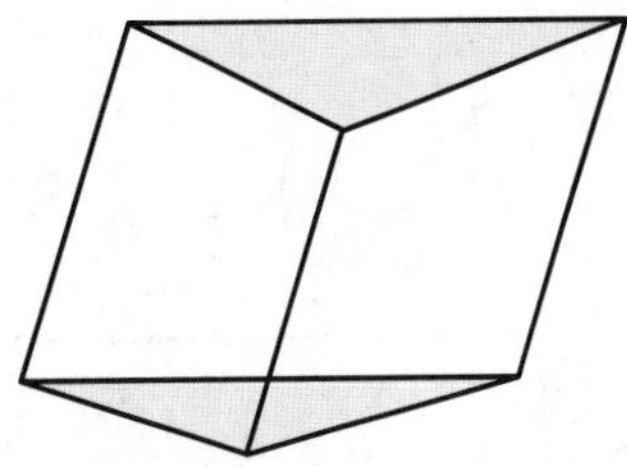

one-to-one function

A function is a one-to-one function if both the function and its inverse are functions.

Example

The equation $y = x^3$ is a one-to-one function because its inverse, $\sqrt[3]{x} = y$, is a function. The equation $y = x^2$ is not a one-to-one function because its inverse, $\pm\sqrt{x} = y$, is not a function.

opposite side

The opposite side of a triangle is the side opposite the reference angle.

Example

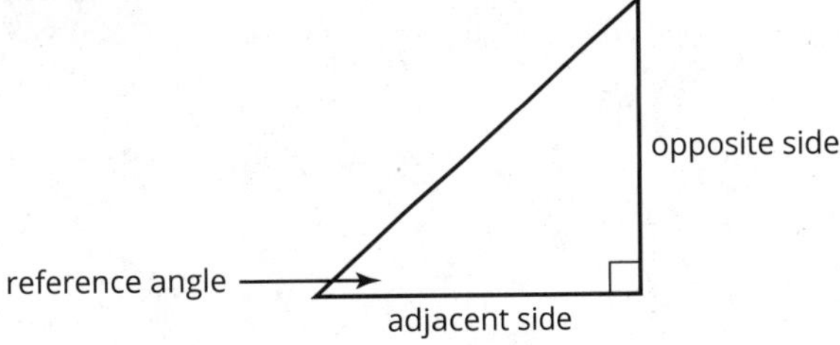

organized list

An organized list is a visual model for determining the sample space of events.

Example

The sample space for flipping a coin 3 times can be represented as an organized list.

HHH THH
HHT THT
HTH TTH
HTT TTT

orthocenter

The orthocenter of a triangle is the point at which the altitudes of the triangle intersect.

Example

Point X is the orthocenter of $\triangle ABC$.

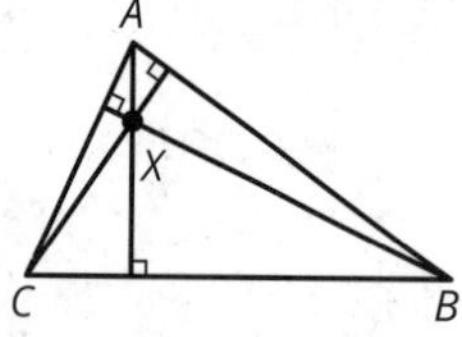

outcome

An outcome is the result of a single trial of an experiment.

Example

Flipping a coin has two outcomes: heads or tails.

P

parabola (conic section)

When a plane intersects one nappe of the double-napped cone parallel to the edge of the cone, the curve that results is a parabola. A parabola is the set of all points in a plane that are equidistant from a fixed point called the focus and a fixed line called the directrix.

Example

The focus of the parabola shown is the point (0, 2). The directrix of the parabola shown is the line $y = -2$. All points on the parabola are equidistant from the focus and the directrix.

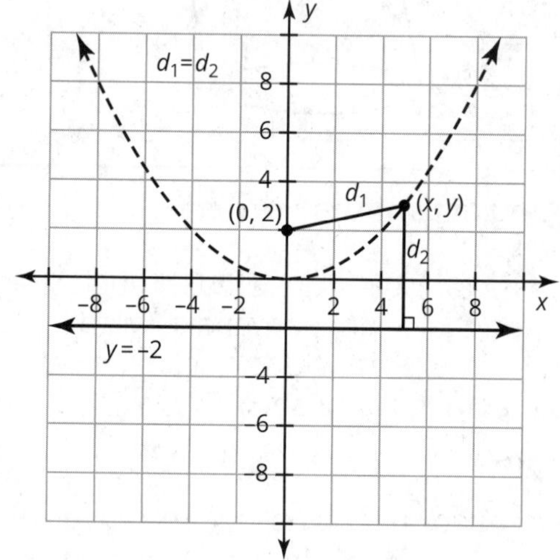

parabola (graph of a quadratic)

The shape that a quadratic function forms whe graphed is called a parabola.

Example

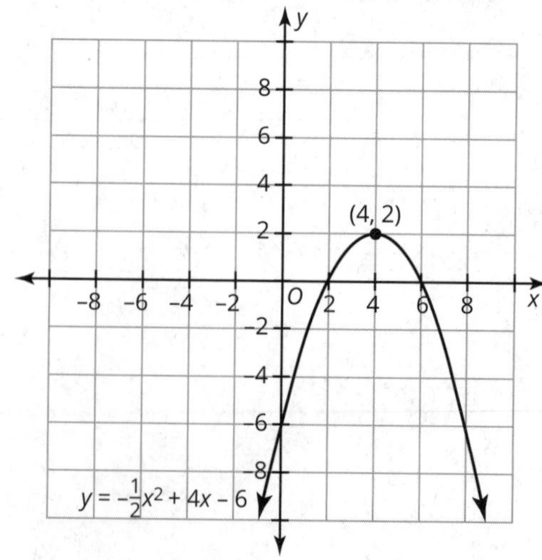

paragraph proof

A paragraph proof is a proof that is written in paragraph form. Each sentence includes mathematical statements that are organized in logical steps with reasons.

Example

The proof shown is a paragraph proof that vertical angles 1 and 3 are congruent.

Angle 1 and angle 3 are vertical angles. By the definition of linear pair, angle 1 and angle 2 form a linear pair. Angle 2 and angle 3 also form a linear pair. By the Linear Pair Postulate, angle 1 and angle 2 are supplementary. Angle 2 and angle 3 are also supplementary. Angle 1 is congruent to angle 3 by the Congruent Supplement Theorem.

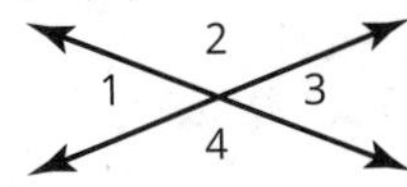

perfect square trinomial

A perfect square trinomial is an expression in the form $a^2 + 2ab + b^2$ or in the form $a^2 - 2ab + b^2$.

Example

The trinomial $x^2 + 6x + 9$ is a perfect square trinomial because it can be written as $x^2 + 2(3)x + 32$.

permutation

A permutation is an ordered arrangement of items without repetition.

Example

The permutations of the letters *A*, *B*, and *C* are:

ABC *ACB*

BAC *BCA*

CAB *CBA*

piecewise function

A piecewise function is a function that can be represented by more than one function, each which corresponds to a part of the domain.

Example

The graph represents a piecewise function.

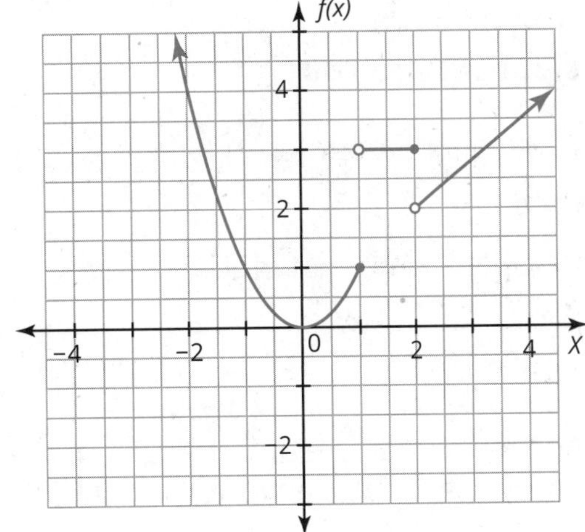

point of concurrency

A point of concurrency is the point at which three or more lines intersect.

Example

Point *X* is the point of concurrency for lines ℓ, *m*, and *n*.

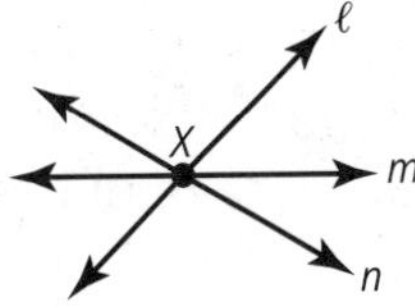

polynomial

A polynomial is a mathematical expression involving the sum of powers in one or more variables multiplied by coefficients.

Example

The expression $3x^3 + 5x - 6x + 1$ is a polynomial.

postulate

A postulate is a statement that is accepted to be true without proof.

Example

The following statement is a postulate: A straight line may be drawn between any two points.

principal square root

A positive square root of a number.

Example

The principal square root of 9 is 3.

probability

The probability of an event is the ratio of the number of desired outcomes to the total number of possible outcomes, $P(A) = \frac{\text{desired outcomes}}{\text{possible outcomes}}$.

Example

When flipping a coin, there are 2 possible outcomes: heads or tails. The probability of flipping a heads is $\frac{1}{2}$.

probability model

A probability model lists the possible outcomes and the probability for each outcome. In a probability model, the sum of the probabilities must equal 1.

Example

The table shows a probability model for flipping a fair coin once.

Outcomes	Head (H)	Tails (H)
Probability	$\frac{1}{2}$	$\frac{1}{2}$

proof

A proof is a series of statements and corresponding reasons forming a valid argument that starts with a hypothesis and arrives at a conclusion.

pure imaginary number

A pure imaginary number is a number of the form bi, where b is not equal to 0.

Example

The imaginary numbers $24i$ and $15i$ are pure imaginary numbers.

Pythagorean identity

A Pythagorean identity is a trigonometric identity that expresses the Pythagorean Theorem in terms of trigonometric ratios.

Example

The basic relationship between the sine and cosine is given by the Pythagorean identity $(\sin \theta)^2 + (\cos \theta)^2 = (1)^2$.

Quadratic Formula

The Quadratic Formula is $x = \frac{-b \pm \sqrt{b^2 - 4ac}}{2a}$.

R

radian

One radian is defined as the measure of a central angle whose arc length is the same as the radius of the circle.

radius of a sphere

The radius of a sphere is a line segment with one endpoint on the sphere and one endpoint at the center.

Example

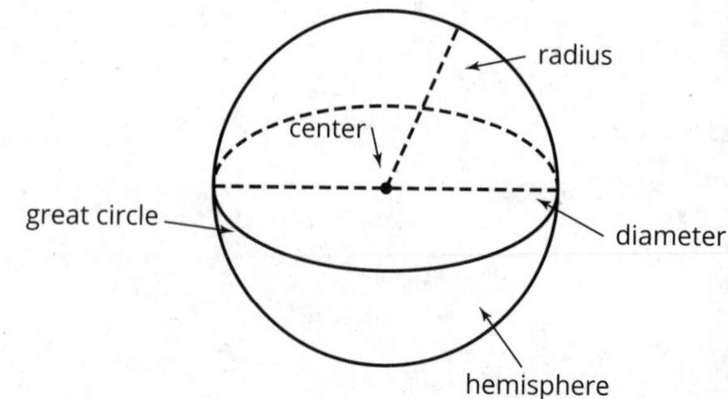

rationalize the denominator

To rationalize the denominator is the process of eliminating a radical from the denominator of an expression. To rationalize the denominator, multiply by a form of one so that the radicand of the radical in the denominator is a perfect square.

Example

Rationalize the denominator of the expression $\frac{5}{\sqrt{3}}$.

$$\frac{5}{\sqrt{3}} = \frac{5}{\sqrt{3}} \cdot \frac{\sqrt{3}}{\sqrt{3}}$$
$$= \frac{5\sqrt{3}}{\sqrt{9}}$$
$$= \frac{5\sqrt{3}}{3}$$

real part of a complex number

In a complex number of the form $a + bi$, the term a is called the real part of a complex number.

Example

The real part of the complex number $3 + 2i$ is 3.

reference angle

A reference angle is the angle of the right triangle being considered. The opposite side and adjacent side are named based on the reference angle.

Example

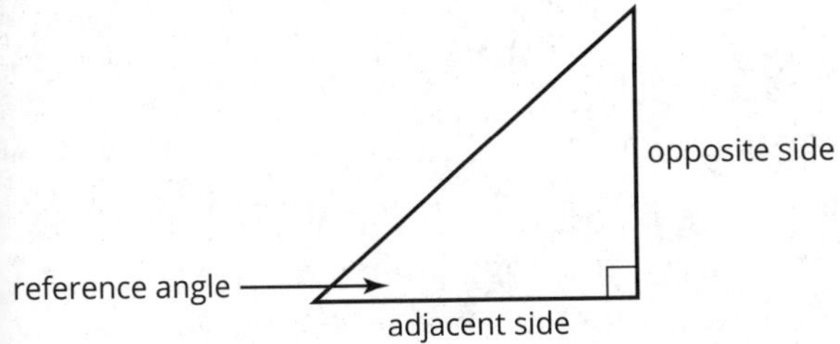

reflection

A reflection of a graph is a mirror image of the graph about a line of reflection.

Example

The triangle on the right is a reflection of the triangle on the left.

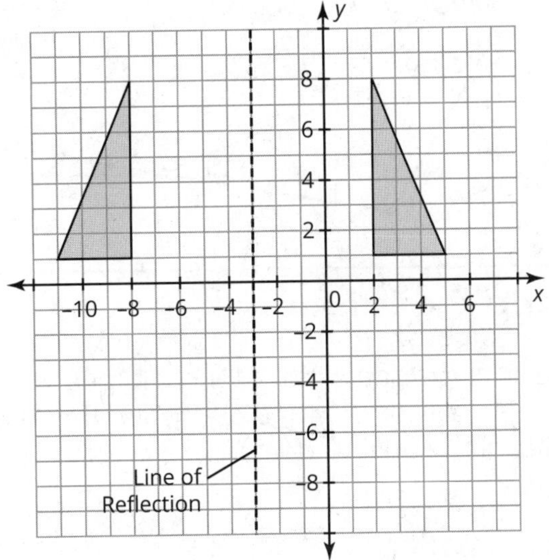

Reflexive Property

The reflexive property states that $a = a$.

Example

The statement $2 = 2$ is an example of the Reflexive Property.

relative frequency

A relative frequency is the ratio or percent of occurrences within a category to the total of the category.

Example

John surveys 100 students in his school about their favorite school subject. Of the 100 students, 37 chose math as their favorite subject. The relative frequency of students show selected math as their favorite subject is $\frac{37}{100}$, or 37%.

remote interior angles of a triangle

The remote interior angles of a triangle are the two angles that are not adjacent to the specified exterior angles.

Example

The remote interior angles with respect to exterior angles 4 are angles 1 and 2.

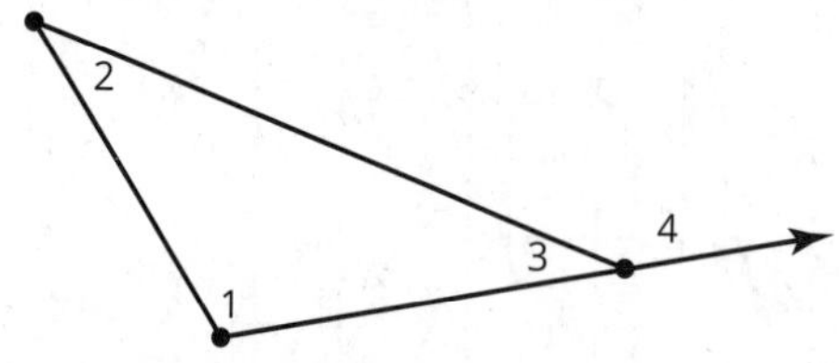

restrict the domain

To restrict the domain of a function means to define a new domain for the function that is a subset of the original domain.

right cylinder

A disc translated through space in a direction perpendicular to the plane containing the disc forms a right cylinder.

Example

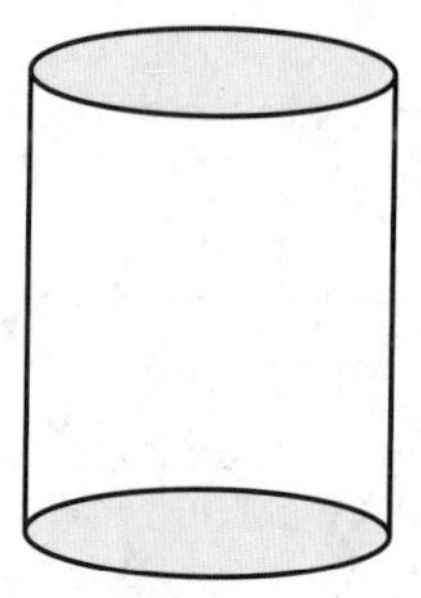

right rectangular prism

A rectangle translated through space in a direction perpendicular to the plane containing the rectangle forms a right rectangular prism.

Example

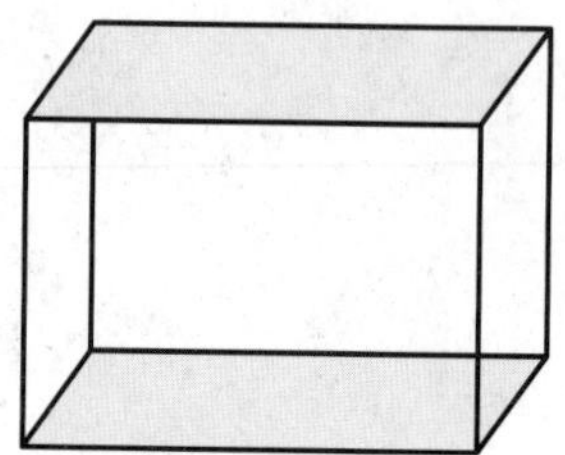

right triangular prism

A triangle translated through space in a directior perpendicular to the plane containing the triangle forms a right triangular prism.

Example

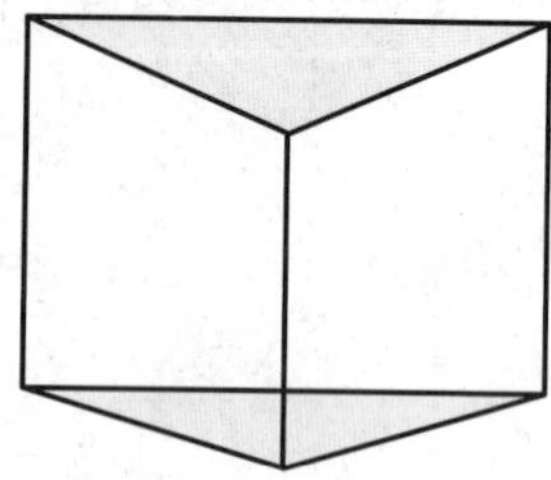

roots

The roots of a quadratic equation indicate wher the graph of the equation crosses the *x*-axis.

Example

The roots of the quadratic equation $x^2 - 4x = -$ are $x = 3$ and $x = 1$.

Rule of Compound Probability involving *and*

The Rule of Compound Probability involving *and* states: "If Event *A* and Event *B* are independent, then the probability that Event *A* happens and Event *B* happens is the product of the probability that Event *A* happens and the probability that Event *B* happens, given that Event *A* has happened."

$$P(A \text{ and } B) = P(A) \cdot P(B)$$

Example

You flip a coin two times. Calculate the probability of flipping a heads on the first flip and flipping a heads on the second flip.

Let *A* represent the event of flipping a heads on the first flip. Let *B* represent the event of flippin a heads on the second flip.

$P(A \text{ and } B) = P(A) \cdot P(B)$

$P(A \text{ and } B) = \frac{1}{2} \cdot \frac{1}{2}$

$P(A \text{ or } B) = \frac{1}{4}$

So, the probability of flipping a heads on the fir flip and flipping a heads on the second flip is $\frac{1}{4}$.

S

sample space

A list of all possible outcomes of an experiment s called a sample space.

Example

Flipping a coin two times consists of four outcomes: HH, HT, TH, and TT.

secant (sec)

The secant (sec) of an acute angle in a right riangle is the ratio of the length of the hypotenuse o the length of the side adjacent to the angle.

Example

n $\triangle ABC$, the secant of $\angle A$ is:

$$\sec A = \frac{\text{length of hypotenuse}}{\text{length of side adjacent to } \angle A} = \frac{AB}{AC}$$

The expression "sec A" means "the secant of ngle A."

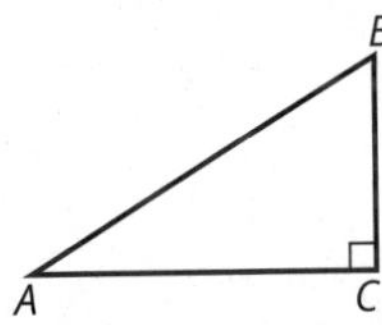

ecant of a circle

secant of a circle is a line that intersects the ircle at two points.

xample

ne line intersecting the circle through points A nd B is a secant.

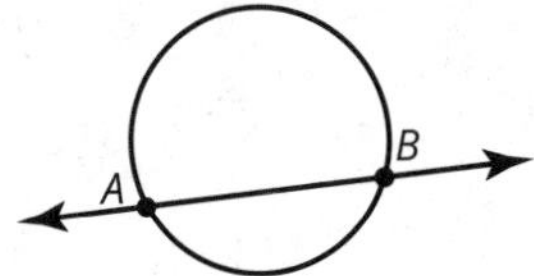

second differences

Second differences are the differences between consecutive values of the first differences.

Example

x	y	First Differences	Second Differences
−3	−5		
		5	
−2	0		−2
		3	
−1	3		−2
		1	
0	4		−2
		−1	
1	3		−2
		−3	
2	0		−2
		−5	
3	−5		

sector of a circle

A sector of a circle is a region of the circle bounded by two radii and the included arc.

Example

In circle Y, $\widehat{XZ}$, radius $\overline{XY}$, and radius $\overline{YZ}$ form a sector.

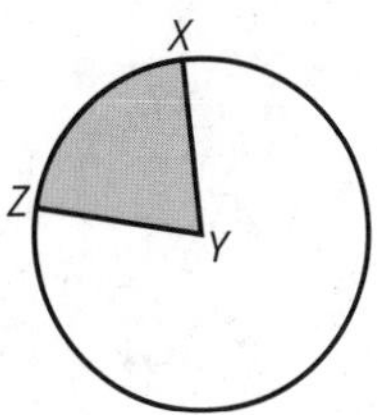

segment of a circle

A segment of a circle is a region bounded by a chord and the included arc.

Example

In circle A, chord $\overline{BC}$ and $\widehat{BC}$ are the boundaries of a segment of the circle.

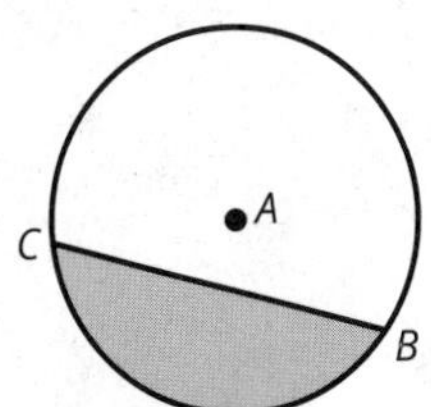

set

A set is a collection of items. If x is a member of set B, then x is an element of set B.

Example

Let E represent the set of even whole numbers.
$E = \{2, 4, 6, 8, \ldots\}$

similar figures

Similar figures are geometric figures where all pairs of corresponding angles are congruent and the lengths of all corresponding sides are proportional. Dilations produce similar figures.

Example

Figures E and X are similar figures.

similar triangles

Similar triangles are triangles that have all pairs of corresponding angles congruent and all corresponding sides are proportional.

Example

$\triangle ABC \sim \triangle DEF$

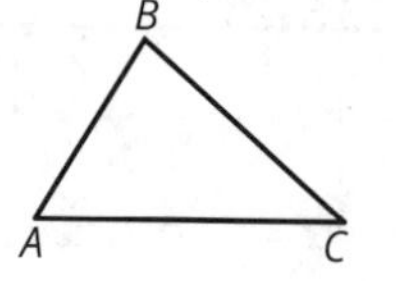

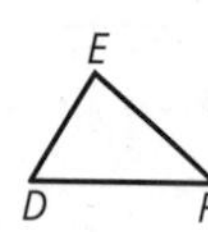

sine (sin)

The sine (sin) of an acute angle in a right triangle is the ratio of the length of the side opposite the angle to the length of the hypotenuse.

Example

In $\triangle ABC$, the sine of $\angle A$ is:

$$\sin A = \frac{\text{length of side opposite } \angle A}{\text{length of hypotenuse}} = \frac{BC}{AB}$$

The expression "sin A" means "the sine of angle A."

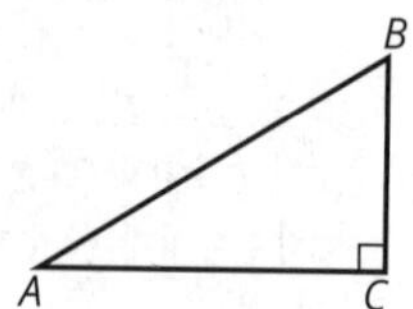

sphere

A sphere is the set of all points in space that are a given distance from a fixed point called the center of the sphere.

Example

A sphere is shown.

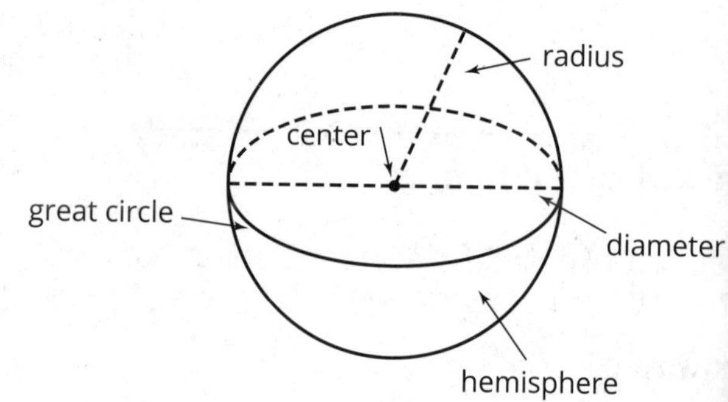

standard form of a parabola

The standard form of a parabola centered at the origin is an equation of the form $x^2 = 4py$ or $y^2 = 4px$, where p represents the distance from the vertex to the focus.

Example

The equation for the parabola shown can be written in standard form as $x^2 = 2y$.

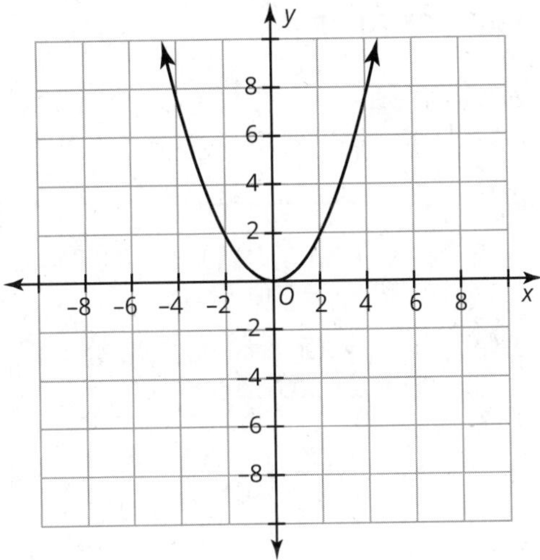

step function

A step function is a piecewise function on a given interval whose pieces are disjoint constant functions.

Example

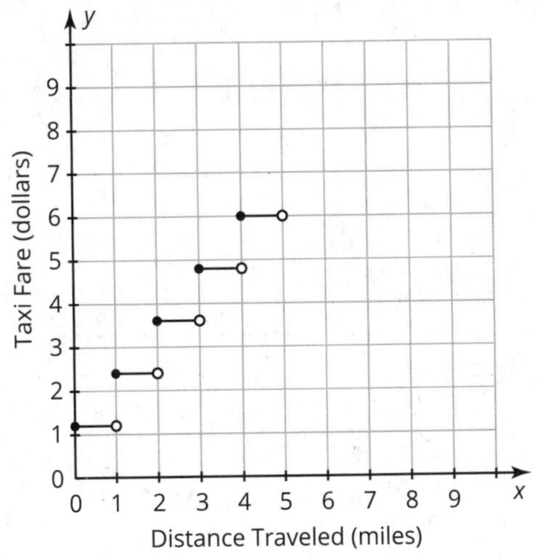

Substitution Property

The Substitution Property of Equality states: "If a and b are real numbers and $a = b$, then a can be substituted for b."

Example

If $AB = 12$ ft and $CD = 12$ ft, then $AB = CD$.

Subtraction Property of Equality

The Subtraction Property of Equality states: "If $a = b$, then $a - c = b - c$."

Example

If $x + 5 = 7$, then $x + 5 - 5 = 7 - 5$, or $x = 2$ is an example of the Subtraction Property of Equality.

T

tangent (tan)

The tangent (tan) of an acute angle in a right triangle is the ratio of the length of the side opposite the angle to the length of the side adjacent to the angle.

Example

In $\triangle ABC$, the tangent of $\angle A$ is:

$$\tan A = \frac{\text{length of side opposite } \angle A}{\text{length of side adjacent to } \angle A} = \frac{BC}{AC}$$

The expression "tan A" means "the tangent of angle A."

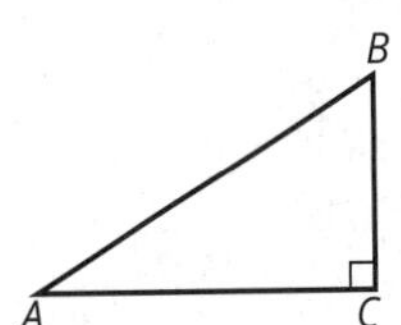

tangent circles

Tangent circles are circles that lie in the same plane and intersect at exactly one point.

Example

Circles *O* and *B* are tangent circles.

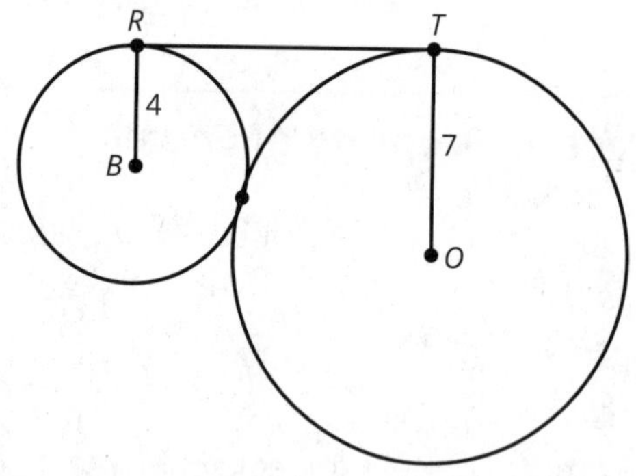

tangent of a circle

A tangent of a circle is a line that intersects the circle at exactly one point, called the point of tangency.

Example

Line *RQ* is tangent to circle *P* at point *Q*.

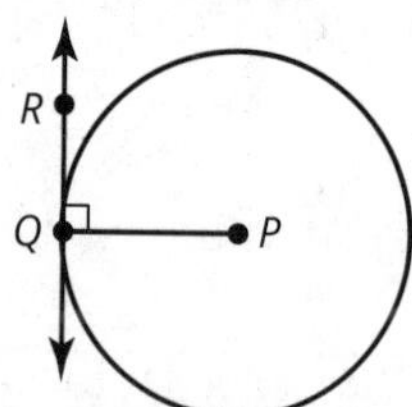

tangent segment

A tangent segment is a line segment formed by connecting a point outside of the circle to a point of tangency.

Example

Line segment *AB* and line segment *AC* are tangent segments.

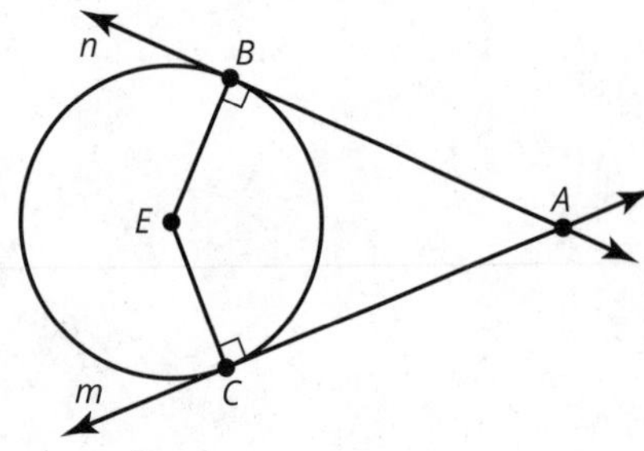

theorem

A theorem is a statement that has been proven to be true.

Example

The Pythagorean Theorem states that if a right triangle has legs of lengths a and b and hypotenuse of length c, then $a^2 + b^2 = c^2$.

total surface area

The total surface area of a three-dimensional figure is the sum of the areas of its bases and lateral faces.

Example

The total surface area of the right triangular prism is 132 square centimeters.

$$\begin{aligned}\text{Total surface area} &= (5 \times 6) + (5 \times 6) + (8 \times 6) \\ &\quad + \tfrac{1}{2}(8 \times 3) + \tfrac{1}{2}(8 \times 3) \\ &= 30 + 30 + 48 + 12 + 12 \\ &= 132\end{aligned}$$

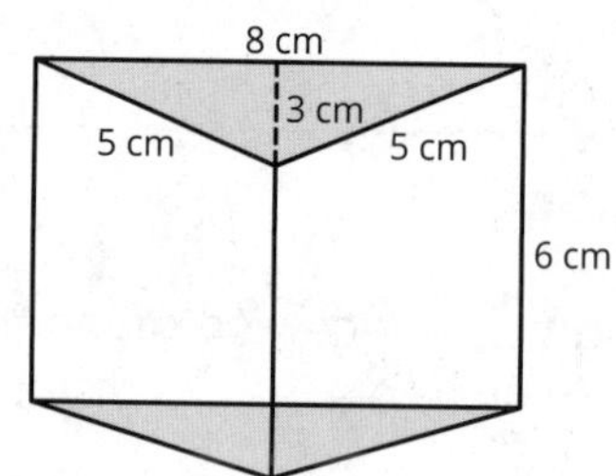

Transitive Property

The Transitive Property states: "If $a = b$ and $b = c$, then $a = c$."

Example

If $x = y$ and $y = 2$, then $x = 2$ is an example of the Transitive Property.

tree diagram

A tree diagram is a diagram that illustrates sequentially the possible outcomes of a given situation.

Example

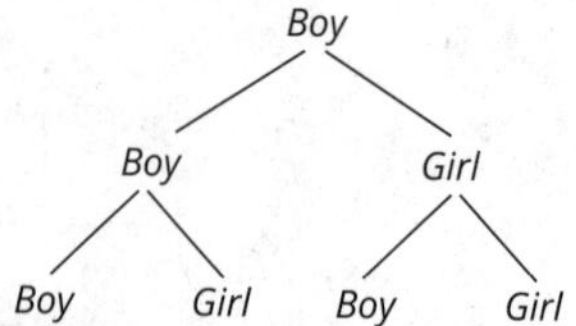

trinomial

Polynomials with exactly three terms are trinomials.

Example

The polynomial $5x^2 - 6x + 9$ is a trinomial.

two-column proof

A two-column proof is a proof consisting of two columns. In the left column are mathematical statements that are organized in logical steps. In the right column are the reasons for each mathematical statement.

Example

The proof shown is a two-column proof.

Statements	Reasons
1. $\angle 1$ and $\angle 3$ are vertical angles.	**1.** Given
2. $\angle 1$ and $\angle 2$ form a linear pair. $\angle 2$ and $\angle 3$ form a linear pair.	**2.** Definition of linear pair
3. $\angle 1$ and $\angle 2$ are supplementary. $\angle 2$ and $\angle 3$ are supplementary.	**3.** Linear Pair Postulate
4. $\angle 1 \cong \angle 3$	**4.** Congruent Supplement Theorem

two-way frequency table (contingency table)

A two-way frequency table, also called a contingency table, shows the number of data points and their frequencies for two variables. One variable is divided into rows, and the other is divided into columns.

Example

The two-way frequency table shows the hand(s) favored by people who do and do not participate in individual or team sports.

Sports Participation

Favored Hand	Individual	Team	Does Not Play	Total
Left	3	13	8	24
Right	6	23	4	33
Mixed	1	3	2	6
Total	10	39	14	63

two-way relative frequency table

A two-way relative frequency table displays the relative frequencies for two categories of data.

Example

The two-way relative frequency table shows the hand(s) favored by people who do and do not participate in individual or team sports.

	Individual	Team	Does Not Play	Total
Left	$\frac{3}{63} \approx 4.8\%$	$\frac{13}{63} \approx 20.6\%$	$\frac{8}{63} \approx 12.7\%$	$\frac{24}{63} \approx 38.1\%$
Right	$\frac{6}{63} \approx 9.5\%$	$\frac{23}{63} \approx 36.5\%$	$\frac{4}{63} \approx 6.3\%$	$\frac{33}{63} \approx 52.4\%$
Mixed	$\frac{1}{63} \approx 1.6\%$	$\frac{3}{63} \approx 4.8\%$	$\frac{2}{63} \approx 3.2\%$	$\frac{6}{63} \approx 9.5\%$
Total	$\frac{10}{63} \approx 15.9\%$	$\frac{39}{63} \approx 61.9\%$	$\frac{14}{63} \approx 22.2\%$	$\frac{63}{63} = 100\%$

two-way table

A two-way table shows the relationship between two data sets, one data set is organized in rows and the other data set is organized in columns.

Example

The two-way table shows all the possible sums that result from rolling two number cubes once.

1st Number Cube \ 2nd Number Cube	1	2	3	4	5	6
1	2	3	4	5	6	7
2	3	4	5	6	7	8
3	4	5	6	7	8	9
4	5	6	7	8	9	10
5	6	7	8	9	10	11
6	7	8	9	10	11	12

U

uniform probability model

A uniform probability model occurs when all the probabilities in a probability model are equally likely to occur.

Example

Rolling a number cube represents a uniform probability model because the probability of rolling eac number is equal.

ınion of sets

 union of sets is a set formed by combining ıll the members of the sets. A member may be 'sted only once.

:xample

.et B represent the set of students in the 11th :rade band. Let C represent the set of students ı the 11th grade chorus. The union of these two ets would be all the students in the 11th grade ›and or the 11th grade chorus. A student in ›oth would be listed only once.

'ertex form

. quadratic function written in vertex form is in ıe form $f(x) = a(x - h)^2 + k$, where $a \neq 0$.

xample

ıe quadratic equation $y = 2(x - 5)^2 + 10$ is 'ritten in vertex form. The vertex of the graph is ıe point (5, 10).

ertex of a parabola (conic section)

ıe vertex of a parabola is the point on the axis f symmetry which is exactly midway between ıe focus and the directrix. It is also the point here the parabola changes direction.

xample

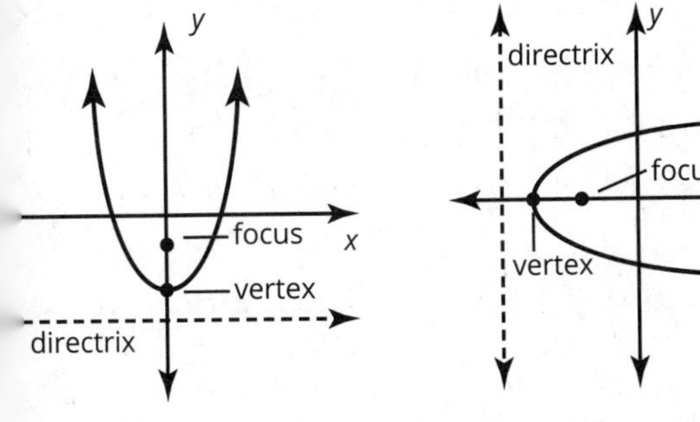

vertex of a parabola (graph of a quadratic)

The vertex of a parabola is the lowest or highest point on the graph of the quadratic function.

Example

The vertex of the graph of $y = x^2 - 2x - 3$ is the point (1, −4), the absolute minimum of the parabola.

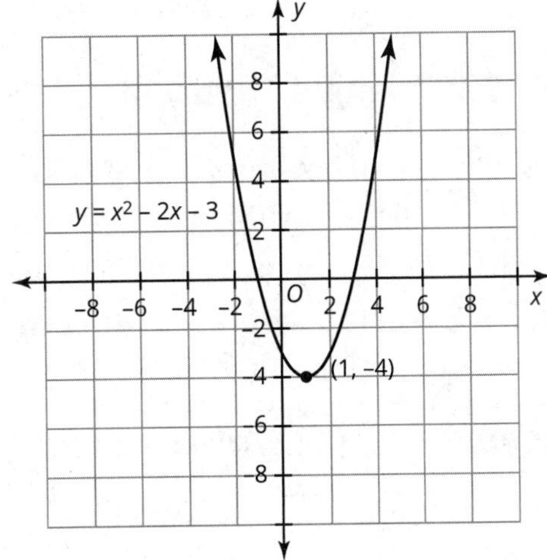

vertical motion model

A vertical motion model is a quadratic equation that models the height of an object at a given time. The equation is of the form $g(t) = -16t^2 + v_0t + h_0$, where $g(t)$ represents the height of the object in feet, t represents the time in seconds that the object has been moving, v_0 represents the initial velocity (speed) of the object in feet per second, and h_0 represents the initial height of the object in feet.

Example

A rock is thrown in the air at a velocity of 10 feet per second from a cliff that is 100 feet high. The height of the rock is modeled by the equation $y = -16t^2 + 10t + 100$.

Zero Product Property

The Zero Product Property states that if the product of two or more factors is equal to zero, then at least one factor must be equal to zero. This is also called the Converse of Multiplication Property of Zero.

Example

If $(x - 2)(x + 3) = 0$, then $x - 2 = 0$ or $x + 3 = 0$.

Postulates and Theorems

30°-60°-90° Triangle Theorem

The length of the hypotenuse in a 30°-60°-90° triangle is 2 times the length of the shorter leg, and the length of the longer leg is $\sqrt{3}$ times the length of the shorter leg.

45°-45°-90° Triangle Theorem

The length of the hypotenuse in a 45°-45°-90° triangle is $\sqrt{2}$ times the length of a leg.

Alternate Exterior Angles Theorem

If two parallel lines are intersected by a transversal, then the alternate exterior angles are congruent.

Alternate Exterior Angles Converse Theorem

If two lines intersected by a transversal form congruent alternate exterior angles, then the lines are parallel.

Alternate Interior Angles Theorem

If two parallel lines are intersected by a transversal, then the alternate interior angles are congruent.

Alternate Interior Angles Converse Theorem

If two lines intersected by a transversal form congruent alternate interior angles, then the lines are parallel.

Angle-Angle Side Congruence Theorem

If two angles and the non-included side of one triangle are congruent to two angles and the non-included side of another triangle, then the two triangles are congruent.

Angle-Angle Similarity Theorem

If two angles of one triangle are congruent to two angles of another triangle, then the triangles are similar.

Angle Bisector/Proportional Side Theorem

A bisector of an angle in a triangle divides the opposite side into two segments whose lengths are in the same ratio as the lengths of the sides adjacent to the angle.

Arc Addition Postulate

The measure of an arc formed by two adjacent arcs is the sum of the measures of the two arcs.

Congruent Chord-Congruent Arc Theorem

If two chords of the same circle or congruent circles are congruent, then their corresponding arcs are congruent.

Congruent Chord-Congruent Converse Arc Theorem

If arcs of the same circle or congruent circles are congruent, then their corresponding chords are congruent.

Congruent Supplement Theorem

If two angles are supplements of the same angle or of congruent angles, then the angles are congruent.

Converse of the Triangle Proportionality Theorem

If a line divides two sides of a triangle proportionally, then it is parallel to the third side.

Corresponding Angles Theorem

f two parallel lines are intersected by a transversal, :hen corresponding angles are congruent.

:orresponding Angles Converse Theorem

f two lines intersected by a transversal form :ongruent corresponding angles, then the lines ıre parallel.

)iameter-Chord Theorem

a circle's diameter is perpendicular to a chord, hen the diameter bisects the chord and bisects he arc determined by the chord.

:quidistant Chord Theorem

two chords of the same circle or congruent ircles are congruent, then they are equidistant om the center of the circle.

quidistant Chord Converse Theorem

two chords of the same circle or congruent rcles are equidistant from the center of the rcle, then the chords are congruent.

xterior Angle Theorem

ıe measure of an exterior angle of a triangle equal to the sum of the measures of the two emote interior angles.

xterior Angles of a Circle Theorem

an angle is formed by two intersecting chords secants of a circle such that the vertex of the ıgle is in the exterior of the circle, then the easure of the angle is half of the difference of e measures of the arcs intercepted by the angle.

ypotenuse-Angle (HA) ongruence Theorem

:he hypotenuse and an acute angle of one ;ht triangle are congruent to the hypotenuse d an acute angle of another right triangle, en the two triangles are congruent.

Hypotenuse-Leg (HL) Congruence Theorem

If the hypotenuse and leg of one right triangle are congruent to the hypotenuse and leg of another right triangle, then the triangles are congruent.

Inscribed Angle Theorem

The measure of an inscribed angle is half the measure of its intercepted arc.

Inscribed Right Triangle-Diameter Theorem

If a triangle is inscribed in a circle such that one side of the triangle is a diameter of the circle, then the triangle is a right triangle.

Inscribed Quadrilateral-Opposite Angles Theorem

If a quadrilateral is inscribed in a circle, then the opposite angles are supplementary.

Interior Angles of a Circle Theorem

If an angle is formed by two intersecting chords or secants of a circle such that the vertex of the angle is in the interior of the circle, then the measure of the angle is half of the sum of the measures of the arcs intercepted by the angle and its vertical angle.

Isosceles Triangle Base Angles Theorem

If two sides of a triangle are congruent, then the angles opposite these sides are congruent.

Isosceles Triangle Base Angles Converse Theorem

If two angles of a triangle are congruent, then the sides opposite these angles are congruent.

Leg-Angle (LA) Congruence Theorem

If the leg and an acute angle of one right triangle are congruent to the corresponding leg and acute angle of another right triangle, then the triangles are congruent.

Leg-Leg (LL) Congruence Theorem

If the two corresponding shorter legs of two right triangles are congruent, then the two triangles are congruent.

Parallelogram/Congruent-Parallel Side Theorem

If one pair of opposite sides of a quadrilateral is both congruent and parallel, then the quadrilateral is a parallelogram.

Perpendicular Bisector Theorem

Points on a perpendicular bisector of a line segment are equidistant from the segment's endpoints.

Perpendicular Bisector Converse Theorem

If a point is equidistant from the endpoints of a line segment, then the point lies on the perpendicular bisector of the segment.

Perpendicular/Parallel Line Theorem

If two lines are perpendicular to the same line, then the two lines are parallel to each other.

Proportional Segments Theorem

If three parallel lines intersect two transversals, then they divide the transversals proportionally.

Right Angle Congruence Postulate

All right angles are congruent.

Right Triangle/Altitude Similarity Theorem

If an altitude is drawn to the hypotenuse of a right triangle, then the two triangles formed are similar to the original triangle and to each other.

Right Triangle Altitude/Hypotenuse Theorem

The measure of the altitude drawn from the vertex of the right angle of a right triangle to its hypotenuse is the geometric mean between the measures of the two segments of the hypotenuse.

Right Triangle Altitude/Leg Theorem

If the altitude is drawn to the hypotenuse of a right triangle, each leg of the right triangle is the geometric mean of the hypotenuse and the segment of the hypotenuse adjacent to the leg.

Same-Side Exterior Angles Theorem

If two parallel lines are intersected by a transversal, then the same-side exterior angles are supplementary.

Same-Side Exterior Angles Converse Theorem

If two lines intersected by a transversal form supplementary same-side exterior angles, then the lines are parallel.

Same-Side Interior Angles Theorem

If two parallel lines are intersected by a transversal, then the interior angles on the same side of the transversal are supplementary.

Same-Side Interior Angles Converse Theorem

If two lines intersected by a transversal form supplementary same-side interior angles, then the lines are parallel.

Side-Angle-Side Similarity Theorem

f two of the corresponding sides of two triangles are proportional and the included angles are congruent, then the triangles are similar.

Side-Side-Side Similarity Theorem

f all three corresponding sides of two triangles are proportional, then the triangles are similar.

Tangent Segment Theorem

f two tangent segments are drawn from the ame point on the exterior of a circle, then the angent segments are congruent.

Tangent to a Circle Theorem

line drawn tangent to a circle is perpendicular o a radius of the circle drawn to the point f tangency.

rapezoid Midsegment Theorem

he midsegment that connects the legs of the apezoid is parallel to each of the bases and s length is one half the sum of the lengths of he bases.

Triangle Midsegment Theorem

The midsegment of a triangle is parallel to the third side of the triangle and is half the measure of the third side of the triangle.

Triangle Proportionality Theorem

If a line parallel to one side of a triangle intersects the other two sides, then it divides the two sides proportionally.

Triangle Sum Theorem

The sum of the measures of the interior angles of a triangle is equal to 180°.

Vertical Angle Theorem

Vertical angles are congruent.

Index

H

I

M

N

O

R

S

T